Photoperiodism and Related Phenomena in Plants and Animals

Proceedings of the Conference on Photoperiodism, October 29-November 2, 1957, sponsored by the Committee on Photobiology of the National Academy of Sciences—National Research Council and supported by the National Science Foundation

◯ ◯ ◯ ◯

Edited by

ROBERT B. WITHROW

SMITHSONIAN INSTITUTION

With the cooperation of

ARTHUR C. GIESE	N. E. TOLBERT
CHARLES E. JENNER	C. S. PITTENDRIGH
ALEXANDER HOLLAENDER	STERLING B. HENDRICKS

Publication No. 55 of the

AMERICAN ASSOCIATION FOR THE ADVANCEMENT OF SCIENCE

Washington, D. C.

1959

Copyright © 1959 by

Printed in the United States of America

DEDICATION

The Committee on Photobiology of the Division of Biology and Agriculture of the National Research Council, dedicates this volume to the memory of Dr. Robert Withrow, whose untimely death occurred when he had practically completed the editing.

Dr. Withrow's death is a great loss to all of us who are interested in the field of photobiology. His broad interests in physics and biology contributed significantly to the development of photobiology, and his devotion to this field is largely responsible for the success of this symposium and the preparation of the manuscripts for publication.

PREFACE

An international symposium was held in Gatlinburg, Tennessee, October 29 to November 2, 1957, to discuss and correlate theories, observations, and hypotheses on photoperiodism and related phenomena in both plants and animals. The present volume is a record of the proceedings of this meeting, which was held under the auspices of the Committee on Photobiology of the National Academy of Sciences–National Research Council and was supported financially by the National Science Foundation.

The principal objective in organizing the symposium was to present a discussion of both plant and animal facets of photoperiodism in order that questions, problems, and observations unique and common to both areas be considered in a unified manner. It was felt that a great mutual advantage could be derived from such an exchange of views. The diversity of approaches in the study of photoperiodic phenomena in such a wide range of organisms and the scope of the field to be covered necessitated the scheduling of a large number of papers. Both current and previously unpublished research, as well as more inclusive review papers, were considered important in giving a panoramic view of the field of photoperiodism. After deliberation, it was decided not to record all extemporaneous remarks, but to encourage those who wished to have their ideas published to submit them in written form. Several short articles are included as a result of this procedure.

The first section of the volume deals with a photochemical analysis of the problems involved and discussion concerning the initial photoreaction. The second group of discussions is concerned with photoperiodic and related phenomena in plants, including seed germination, photomorphogenesis of seedlings and changes in vegetative structures, flowering, kinetics, and possible biochemical pathways resulting in the observed growth. The third division deals chiefly with

v

biological rhythms, both in plants and animals. The final portion of the book presents research in the various phyla of animals on the interrelation of light and temperature with periodic function, particularly with reference to mating behavior and reproduction.

A great deal of appreciation is expressed to all the participants of the symposium who have given wonderful assistance in the editing of the book. The prompt and efficient cooperation of the authors in the reading and return of their proof and the patient and painstaking assistance of Webster True and Mrs. Vivienne Mitchell in the indexing are gratefully acknowledged.

ALICE P. WITHROW

CONTRIBUTORS

CYRUS P. BARNUM, Department of Physiological Chemistry, University of Minnesota, Minneapolis, Minnesota

GEORGE A. BARTHOLOMEW, Department of Zoology, University of California, Los Angeles, California

LELA V. BARTON, Boyce Thompson Institute for Plant Research, Inc., Yonkers, New York

J. BENSINK, Laboratory of Plant Physiological Research, Agricultural University, Wageningen, The Netherlands

JOHN J. BITTNER, The Medical School, University of Minnesota, Minneapolis, Minnesota

LAWRENCE BOGORAD, Department of Botany, University of Chicago, Chicago, Illinois

JAMES BONNER, Division of Biology, California Institute of Technology, Pasadena, California

H. A. BORTHWICK, Crops Research Division, Agricultural Research Service, United States Department of Agriculture, Beltsville, Maryland.

FREDERICK S. BRACKETT, National Institute of Arthritis and Metabolic Diseases, National Institutes of Health, Bethesda, Maryland

VICTOR G. BRUCE, Biology Department, Princeton University, Princeton, New Jersey

M. J. BUKOVAC, Department of Horticulture, Michigan State University, East Lansing, Michigan

WILLIAM S. BULLOUGH, Department of Zoology, Birkbeck College, University of London, London, England

BOB BULLWINKEL, Department of Biology, Princeton University, Princeton, New Jersey

ERWIN BÜNNING, Botanical Institute, University of Tübingen, Tübingen, Germany

MELVIN CALVIN, Radiation Laboratory and Department of Chemistry, University of California, Berkeley, California

HENRY M. CATHEY, Crops Research Division, Agricultural Research Service, United States Department of Agriculture, Beltsville, Maryland

CLYDE CHANDLER, Boyce Thompson Institute for Plant Research, Inc., Yonkers, New York

ROBERT V. DAVIS, JR., Department of Biology, Princeton University, Princeton, New Jersey

P. J. A. L. DE LINT, Laboratory of Plant Physiological Research, Agricultural University, Wageningen, The Netherlands

R. J. DOWNS, Agricultural Research Service, United States Department of Agriculture, Beltsville, Maryland

CHARLES F. EHRET, Division of Biological and Medical Research, Argonne National Laboratory, Lemont, Illinois

WILLIAM L. ENGELS, Department of Zoology, University of North Carolina, Chapel Hill, North Carolina

DONALD S. FARNER, Laboratories of Zoophysiology, State College of Washington, Pullman, Washington

R. M. FRAPS, Agricultural Research Service, United States Department of Agriculture, Beltsville, Maryland

C. S. FRENCH, Department of Plant Biology, Carnegie Institution of Washington, Stanford, California

ARTHUR W. GALSTON, Department of Botany, Josiah Willard Gibbs Research Laboratory, Yale University, New Haven, Connecticut

ARTHUR C. GIESE, Hopkins Marine Station of Stanford University, Pacific Grove, California

ERNEST M. GIFFORD, JR., Department of Botany, University of California, Davis, California

MARGARET CORNETT GREEN, Radcliffe College, Cambridge, Massachusetts

VICTOR A. GREULACH, Department of Botany, University of North Carolina, Chapel Hill, North Carolina

ALAN H. HABER, Biology Division, Oak Ridge National Laboratory, Oak Ridge, Tennessee

JOHN G. HAESLOOP, Department of Botany, University of North Carolina, Chapel Hill, North Carolina

ERNA HALBERG, The Medical School, University of Minnesota, Minneapolis, Minnesota

FRANZ HALBERG, The Medical School, University of Minnesota, Minneapolis, Minnesota

ROBERT WHITING HARRINGTON, JR., Entomological Research Center, Florida State Board of Health, Vero Beach, Florida

J. WOODLAND HASTINGS, Division of Biochemistry, Noyes Laboratory of Chemistry, University of Illinois, Urbana, Illinois

STERLING B. HENDRICKS, Soil and Water Conservation Research Division, Agricultural Research Service, United States Department of Agriculture, Beltsville, Maryland

WILLIAM S. HILLMAN, Department of Botany, Josiah Willard Gibbs Laboratory, Yale University, New Haven, Connecticut

ALEXANDER HOLLAENDER, Biology Division, Oak Ridge National Laboratory, Oak Ridge, Tennessee

WILLIAM P. JACOBS, Department of Biology, Princeton University, Princeton, New Jersey

CHARLES E. JENNER, Department of Zoology, University of North Carolina, Chapel Hill, North Carolina

CHARLES M. KIRKPATRICK, Agricultural Experiment Station, Purdue University, Lafayette, Indiana

WILLIAM H. KLEIN, Division of Radiation and Organisms, Smithsonian Institution, Washington, D. C.

ANTON LANG, Department of Botany, University of California, Los Angeles, California

A. D. LEES, Univ. of Insect Physiology, Agricultural Research Council, Cambridge, England

JAMES L. LIVERMAN, Division of Biology and Medicine, U. S. Atomic Energy Commission, Washington, D. C.[1]

JAMES A. LOCKHART, Kerckhoff Biological Laboratory, California Institute of Technology, Pasadena, California

FAUSTO LONA, Istituto Ed Orto Botanico, Universita degli Studi di Parma, Parma, Italy

WAYNE J. MCILRATH, Department of Botany, The University of Chicago, Chicago, Illinois

[1] On leave from Texas Agricultural Experiment Station, College Station, Texas.

G. MEIJER, Philips Research Laboratories, Eindhoven, The Netherlands

COLETTE NITSCH, Laboratoire du Phytotron, Gif-sur-Yvette (S. et O.), France

J. P. NITSCH, Laboratoire du Phytotron, Gif-sur-Yvette (S. et O.), France

GERALD OSTER, Department of Chemistry, Polytechnic Institute of Brooklyn, Brooklyn, New York

OSCAR H. PARIS, JR., Department of Zoology, University of California, Berkeley, California

COLIN S. PITTENDRIGH, Biology Department, Princeton University, Princeton, New Jersey

KENNETH S. RAWSON, Zoology Department, University of Wisconsin, Madison, Wisconsin

ROY M. SACHS, Department of Floriculture, University of California, Los Angeles, California

FRANK B. SALISBURY, Department of Botany and Plant Pathology, Colorado State University, Fort Collins, Colorado

POWER B. SOGO, Radiation Laboratory, University of California, Berkeley, California

IRWIN SPEAR, Department of Botany, University of Texas, Austin,, Texas

BEATRICE M. SWEENEY, Division of Marine Biology, Scripps Institution of Oceanography, La Jolla, California

N. E. TOLBERT, Department of Agricultural Chemistry, Michigan State University, East Lansing, Michigan

GORDON TOLLIN, Radiation Laboratory, University of California, Berkeley, California

E. H. TOOLE, Agricultural Research Service, United States Department of Agriculture, Beltsville, Maryland

P. F. WAREING, Department of Botany, University College of Wales, Aberystwyth, Great Britain

E. C. WASSINK, Laboratory of Plant Physiological Research, Agricultural University, Wageningen, The Netherlands

LEMEN J. WELLS, Department of Anatomy, University of Minnesota, Minneapolis, Minnesota

FRITS W. WENT, Missouri Botanical Garden, St. Louis, Missouri

RALPH B. WETMORE, Biological Laboratories, Harvard University, Cambridge, Massachusetts

W. O. WILSON, Poultry and Husbandry Department, College of Agriculture, University of California, Davis, California

R. B. WITHROW, Division of Radiation and Organisms, Smithsonian Institution, Washington, D. C.

S. H. WITTWER, Department of Horticulture, Michigan State University, East Lansing, Michigan

FREDERICK T. WOLF, Department of Biology, Vanderbilt University, Nashville, Tennessee

ALBERT WOLFSON, Department of Biological Sciences, Northwestern University, Evanston, Illinois

A. E. WOODARD, Poultry and Husbandry Department, College of Agriculture, University of California, Davis, California

CONTENTS

Section XI   Control of Periodic Functions in Mammals by Light

Photochemical Principles

REVERSIBLE PHOTOCHEMICAL
PROPERTIES OF DYES

GERALD OSTER
Polytechnic Institute of Brooklyn, Brooklyn, New York

Photoperiodic phenomena in plants appear to be confined to the neighborhood of 650 mμ (red) and to be reversed by longer wavelengths in the neighborhood of 730 mμ (far red). Light of these wavelengths is more penetrating in plant tissues than, say, blue light, yet it is sufficiently energetic to affect chemical transformations that require 40 kcal per mole.

The impression I gather from the majority of papers presented at this symposium is that despite the variety of phenomena manifested by organisms exhibiting photoperiodism, there is a common photochemical reaction that triggers the reaction and this reaction is reversed by the far red. Obviously two pigments are involved, yet they have eluded detection by ordinary spectrophotometric techniques. It would perhaps be presumptuous to propose a mechanism for the phenomena on the basis of such meager information. As a chemist who has had some experience with the photochemistry of dyes, the most that I dare do is to acquaint you with certain systems that exhibit reversible photochemistry. By reversible, in this context, I mean photochemical changes obtained with one wavelength of light and reversed by another wavelength of light. First of all, however, I should like to consider the possible nature of what Dr. French calls "this pigment of the imagination."

LIGHT RECEPTORS

In order for the pigments to be absorbing in the red region of the spectrum they should be highly conjugated. If they were carotenes (which, by the way, I doubt because of their photochemical inertness), they would have to consist of 14 or 15 conjugated double bonds. The

3

introduction of electron-donating substituents (such as methyl ammonium groups as in, for example, the triphenyl methane dyes or nitrogen groups in the conjugated chain as in the porphyrins, in the bile colors, and in the cyanine dyes) would shift the maximum to longer wavelengths.

The introduction of sulfur into the conjugated system alters the spectrum profoundly. Thus, replacing the oxygen atom in benzophenone (absorption maximum at 255 mμ) by a sulfur atom results in a blue substance, thiobenzophenone (absorption maximum at 620 mμ)—a shift of 365 mμ! Sulfur compounds exhibit unexpected spectral properties owing to the easily polarizable nature of the π electrons of the sulfur bonds (Rosenthal and Oster, 1954). We have found that alkaline thiobenzophenone is readily bleached by red light (Oster and Citarel, to be published). It is quite likely that the chromophoric material of visual purple (absorption maximum at 500 mμ) is thio vitamin A aldehyde (perhaps in the bound state) and is bleached by light to give vitamin A aldehyde (absorption maximum at 387 mμ) (compare Wald and Brown, 1952, and Dartnall, 1957, Chap. 4, with Oster, 1958).

Most dyes exhibit a shift to longer wavelengths when they are bound to high polymeric substrates (for review, see Oster, 1955). For example, a solution of malachite green in the free state appears blue. When a small amount of polymer to which the dye will bind is added to the solution, the absorption spectrum is shifted to longer wavelengths, and the solution appears green. The bound dye resists reduction by strong reducing agents which readily reduce the free dye (Oster and Bellin, 1957). Those dyes, such as the triphenylmethanes and stilbene derivatives, which are capable of internal rotation, exhibit a much greater fluorescence when bound than when free (Oster and Nishijima, 1956). The same enhancement of fluorescence is observed if the viscosity of the medium is increased. Apparently planarity of the dye molecule is a necessary condition for fluorescence.

The profound changes in properties which a dye may undergo when it is separated from its substrate indicate the problems that might be encountered in attempts to isolate the pigments of photoperiodic systems. In fact, discrepancies between action spectra and absorption spectra of isolated pigments of a photochemical system are not of significance without some knowledge of the state of binding of the pigments in their natural state.

SPECTRAL SHIFTS IN METASTABLE SYSTEMS

It has been known for more than 50 years that certain dyes in very rigid media (e.g., glycerol at −80°C or boric acid glass at room temperature) exhibit a phosphorescence. The phosphorescence may be of the same color as the normal fluorescence or, more usually, of longer wavelength; these are referred to as alpha and beta phosphorescence, respectively (for review, see Pringsheim, 1949). It is generally agreed that a metastable state of the dye is involved which lies intermediate between the first excited singlet state and the ground state, and that alpha phosphorescence arises from thermal excitation of the molecules in the metastable state to the ground state via the singlet excited state (Jablonski, 1935). On the other hand, passage directly from the metastable state to the ground state is accompanied by beta phosphorescence. This latter transition is "forbidden" by ordinary spectroscopic rules, and the metastable state is long-lived. In fact, G. N. Lewis and his co-workers have shown that the metastable state is the triplet excitation state (for review, see Kasha, 1947).

Since the triplet state for an excited dye in very rapid media may have a lifetime of several seconds, it is possible to populate this state with high-intensity illumination (such as is obtainable from a super-high-pressure mercury lamp of the AH-6 type, for example). If then the absorption spectra of the dye are determined under intense cross-illumination, the spectra of the metastable species are obtained. Thus, it was found that fluorescein in boric acid glass which normally absorbs maximally at 490 mμ exhibits its maximum absorption at 660 mμ when cross-illuminated (Lewis *et al.*, 1941).

It is unlikely, however, that light-induced spectral shifts of this kind are of direct importance in photoperiodism. The probability of transition to the triplet state is generally low, and the lifetime of this state under normal viscosity conditions is only about one-tenth of a millisecond (Adelman and Oster, 1956). Of more relevance, perhaps, is the fact that many aromatic substances form dimers under the action of light. In most cases ultraviolet light is required, and the dimer is reasonably stable (for review, see Mustafa, 1952). In some cases the dimer may be decomposed by heat to give monomers. Thus, anthracene in solution readily forms dimers when illuminated with ultraviolet light; the dimer is insoluble in hydrocarbons and is converted to the monomeric form by heating. We have found that acridine dyes form dimers on illumination with blue light; the photodimer absorbs at longer wavelengths than does the monomer but it is unstable and reverts to the monomer as soon as the illumination ceases (Oster and Millich, to be published).

Many dyes capable of cis-trans isomerization are capable of conversion to one or the other form by suitably chosen incident light (for review, see Wyman, 1955). Thus, cis-thioindigo (absorption maximum at 490 mμ) is converted by blue light into the trans isomer (absorption maximum at 560 mμ), and the latter is converted back to the cis form by irradiation with yellow light (Brode and Wyman, 1951). Heating also favors the trans form. Isomerization may also be operative in some cases of reversible photoeffects of complicated organic molecules at very low temperatures (Hirshberg, 1956). My own feeling is that at least with bianthone derivatives the blue substance formed by irradiation with ultraviolet which is destroyed by yellow light is a semiquinone form of the bianthrone. If so, it should exhibit a paramagnetic resonance spectrum. Semiquinones are usually quite unstable unless kept at low temperatures. They are highly colored and are paramagnetic (for review, see Michaelis, 1940). It is possible that far-red-absorbing semiquinones are produced by red light in photoperiodism, but the required stability of hours or even of days is not in their favor. Semiquinones are generally unstable in the presence of atmospheric oxygen, especially at room temperature. The possibility of stable semiquinones of the anthocyanidines being the far-red pigment should not be overlooked, however.

A curious case of a light-induced spectral shift is that of methylene blue when bound to polymethacrylic acid (Wotherspoon and Oster, 1957). Only with this polymeric substrate and no other polymeric acid is the dye converted with red light to a purple dye. The reaction involves the conversion of methyl ammonium groups on methylene blue to amino groups by some unknown process. Although this reaction of itself has no relevance to photoperiodism, I mention it only to indicate the possible role of specific high polymeric substrates to which the pigments of the photoperiodic system may be bound.

PHOTOREDUCTION

In none of the photoreactions described above is a chemical change in the surrounding medium indicated. If the mystery of photoperiodism is ever to be solved, it must be determined what chemical transformations have taken place in the cell as a result of the illumination with red or with far-red light. Lacking this essential information, I venture to suggest that the photochemical act involves an oxidation-reduction reaction. If that is the case, then some of the photochemical reactions studied by me and my students may provide suggestive models for photoperiodic reactions. First let us consider the photoreduction of dyes.

Many colored substances (azo dyes and carotenes seem to be notable exceptions) undergo photoreduction when irradiated in the presence of mild reducing agents. Such mild reducing agents include, among other things, ascorbic acid and glutathione, two naturally occurring reducing agents. Riboflavin is an exceptional dye in that it has its own reducing agent built in, so to speak. Ethylenediaminetetraacetic acid and other chelating agents containing secondary and tertiary nitrogens serve as electron donors for the light-excited dyes (Oster and Wotherspoon, 1957). These chelating agents are not reducing agents in the ordinary sense since they are not oxidized by oxygen even when flushed with the gas for 24 hours.

The photoreduction of dyes generally results in colorless species, since the conjugation and hence color-imparting structure is interrupted by addition of hydrogens. With the porphyrins, however, photoreduction can take place in stages. The red form of chlorophyll obtained by photoreduction of the pigment in pyridine in the presence of ascorbic acid (Krasnovsky, 1948) is, in my opinion, only one of the many reduction states of chlorophyll, and intermediate colored forms of photoreduced porphyrins are obtainable. It is possible that chlorophyll in the plant is photoreduced in stages, each stage being a colored species. If three or four such stages could take place successively and if the energy thus accumulated could be used for chemical reaction, the required energy of 120 kcal would be accounted for (cf. Chap. 8 of Hill and Whittingham, 1955).

Although some dyes such as the acridines are difficult to reduce by ordinary chemical means, they are readily photoreduced in the presence of suitable electron donors. The reduced dye is a powerful reducing agent, its extra energy having been obtained from the light. For example, reduced acriflavin will reduce nitrobenzene to aniline. All photoreducible dyes in their reduced form will convert tetrazolium salts to their corresponding reduced formazans (highly colored water-insoluble species). I somehow feel that reactivation by blue light of organisms which had been inactivated with far ultraviolet light (Kellner, 1949) involves a flavin-sensitized photoreduction of nucleotides which had been photooxidized (although no O_2 is involved) by far (254 mμ) ultraviolet light.

The reduced form of a dye will react with oxygen to regenerate the normal dye. This dark reaction is accompanied by the production of free radicals (probably hydroxyl radicals). Hence, if a vinyl monomer is present, considerable polymerization ensues via a chain reaction (Oster, 1954). Overall quantum yields as high as one billion are possible by this technique (Oster, Oster, and Prati, 1957).

In the total absence of oxygen the dye may not be regenerated in the dark if the reduced dye is too feeble a reducing agent. This appears to be the case for leuco methylene blue, for example, which was made by photoreduction. With acriflavin, on the other hand, the leuco dye can reduce the oxidized reducing agent (e.g., dehydroascorbic acid) so that the system is regenerated in the dark (Oster and Millich, to be published). Even with weak leuco dyes, however, the dye can be regenerated if near ultraviolet light is employed (Oster and Wotherspoon, 1954). Thus we have the completely reversible system

$$D + AH_2 \underset{UV}{\overset{red}{\rightleftharpoons}} DH_2 + A$$

where D and DH_2 are the dye and reduced (leuco) dye, respectively, and AH_2 and A are the reducing agent and its oxidized form, respectively. This reaction, which proceeds best below pH 7 (Oster and Wotherspoon, 1957), has been proposed as a model for photoperiodic reactions (Hendricks and Borthwick, 1954). To press this analogy farther, I should like to hypothesize that the red-absorbing pigment in photoperiodic systems is a reduced form of a highly conjugated molecule which, on absorbing red light, results in the production of a far-red-absorbing species (having lost its labile hydrogens and therefore absorbing at longer wavelengths) and reduction of its substrate. This picture requires that the reduced substrate (AH_2) be a promoter of the eventual physiological responses, whereas the oxidized substrate (A) produced with far red is an inhibitor of the first stages of a chain of reactions leading to these responses.

In a series of papers dealing with the kinetics of photoreduction of dyes we have ascertained that it is not the initially light-excited dye (to its first electronically excited state, lifetime about 10^{-9} sec) that is chemically reactive, but rather its metastable state (triplet state, lifetime in water about 10^{-4} sec) that reacts with the reducing agent (see, for example, Oster and Adelman, 1956; Adelman and Oster, 1956). Trace amounts of substances such as nitrobenzene will retard, i.e., slow down the photoreduction. This is one indication that long-lived excited states are involved since diffusion calculations show that, in order for the retarding molecules (at low concentrations) to encounter a dye molecule while it is in an excited state, the reactive state must be of long life. It was further found that the quantum yield of photoreduction decreases with increasing dye concentration. Apparently dye molecules in the ground state quench the triplet state of the excited dye molecules.

In highly viscous media the number of collisions between excited dye and reducing agent is decreased and the photoreduction (and photorecovery) is suppressed (Oster and Wotherspoon, 1954). We have recently found, however, that dyes in a rigid glucose glass are readily photoreduced with visible light and reformed with ultraviolet light (Oster and Broyde, to be published). Apparently the medium itself acts as the hydrogen transfer agent so that reactions take place with the dye and its immediate surroundings, and no diffusion is required. Incidentally, by this method we have been able to trap certain intermediate reduction states (semiquinones) of the dyes.

At dye concentrations above about $10^{-3}M$, photoreduction practically ceases because of the concentration quenching of the triplet state, which I mentioned earlier. One might wonder how any photochemical reaction can take place with chlorophyll in the plant since the chlorophyll concentration in chloroplasts may be as high as $0.2M$ (see for example, Hill and Whittingham, 1955, p. 27). The answer to this apparent anomaly, I feel, lies in the fact that in nature the chlorophyll molecules are bound to the substrate. I have already indicated some changes in properties that dyes undergo when bound to high polymers. Most striking are the differences between the photochemical properties of free and of bound dyes. In the bound state the quantum yield of photoreduction increases with increasing dye concentration (Bellin and Oster, 1957), in marked contrast to the behavior of the free dye. Even certain dyes which do not undergo photoreduction in the free state will do so in the bound state (Oster and Bellin, 1957). Another characteristic of bound dyes, at least in the limited number of cases that we have studied, is that certain impurities (e.g., nitrobenzene) in trace amounts inhibit rather than merely retard the photoreduction. The induction period is proportional to the concentration of the inhibitor. One inhibitor molecule can affect many dye molecules in analogy with the concept of the photosynthetic unit which has been postulated for plants (see, for example, Hill and Whittingham, 1955, pp. 60–62). Our kinetic analysis indicates that an excited bound dye exchanges its energy with a neighboring ground state bound dye to give the chemically reactive triplet state species. The inhibitor molecules react with some intermediate reduction species of the dye and are thereby destroyed. It is amusing to note that although triphenylmethane dyes are more difficult to reduce in the dark when bound, the opposite is true for photoreduction of these dyes (Oster and Bellin, 1957).

PHOTOOXIDATION

It has been known since 1900 that organisms containing certain dyes are killed if exposed to visible light (Raab, 1900; for reviews, see Blum, 1941, and Clare, 1956). This phenomenon, referred to as "photodynamic action," requires oxygen and is clearly a dye-sensitized autoxidation of some constituents of the organism. We have been able to duplicate this reaction with synthetic systems by using p-phenylene-diamine as the substrate. This substance (or its tolyl analog) is a convenient substrate since it becomes highly colored when oxidized, and hence the course of the oxidation can be followed colorimetrically. Kinetic analysis of our data (Schrader, 1955) shows that the dye in the triplet state reacts with oxygen to form a photoperoxide, which in turn attacks the substrate to give oxidized substrate and regenerated dye. Thus the dye can be used over and over again, and oxidized substrate is continually being formed as long as the system is illuminated and oxygen is being continually supplied.

We have further established that there is a one-to-one correspondence between the photodynamic action for living organisms and the dye-sensitized photauxidation of p-phenylenediamine (Oster and Kimball, to be published). Retarders (e.g., certain reducing agents) for one process are retarders for the other. Still further, we have shown that the dyes which are effective for these two processes are also the dyes which are capable of being photoreduced in the presence of suitable electron donors. The connection between the ability of certain dyes to be photoreduced and their ability to be sensitizers for photooxidation lies in the fact that these particular dyes are readily converted to the triplet excited state.

I doubt that dye-sensitized photauxidation is a factor in photoperiodism simply because of the presence in plants of reducing agents which would prevent such a process. For example, chlorophyll in vitro is a powerful sensitizer for the photodynamic action. Obviously, chlorophyll does not function in this manner in the natural state; otherwise any plant would be destroyed in a few minutes with exposure to full sunlight. The in vitro sensitizing action of chlorophyll can be stopped by adding a small amount of ascorbic acid or glutathione to the system. The presence of reducing agents together with the fact that chlorophyll is bound in the plant precludes any appreciable photodynamic action in vivo. Photooxidation in recovery of leuco dyes is another matter, of course. Here oxidation of substrate takes place with light but, unlike photauxidation, no oxygen is involved and complete reversibility is possible.

SUGGESTIONS FOR FURTHER EXPERIMENTS

With the small amount of information available at the present time, it is not easy to propose a mechanism of photoperiodism. I would like to suggest certain experiments to help in choosing between the various hypotheses that I have set forth.

If the phenomenon is a photauxidation, then illuminating a plant that has been treated with p-phenylenediamine should be revealing. Soaking a leaf in a solution of this substance (at about pH 7) and illuminating with red or with far red would yield a purple substance (autoxidized phenylenediamine) at a rate greater than that obtained in the absence of light.

If the process involves photoreduction, then light-induced production of formazan from its tetrazolium salt should take place. Dr. Hendricks reminds me that seedling viability tests with tetrazolium salts are dependent on the presence of light. This seems to me to be extraordinarily interesting, and an action spectra for the formation of the formazan should be determined. Ascorbic acid and glutathione do not convert tetrazolium salts at pH 7 or lower, and if this is the pH of the plant cells, it would appear that the viability test is really a test for photoreduction in which naturally occurring reducing agents not available in dead cells participate as the electron donors for the light-excited pigments.

It would be interesting to see whether photoperiodism involves the production of free radicals. Calcium acrylate, a divinyl monomer which is water soluble is converted into a voluminous precipitate in the presence of free radicals. Illumination of leaves or seeds soaked with this monomer under the spectral requirements of photoperiodism would reveal the presence of free radicals in the photoreaction.

The reagents which I have proposed may well inhibit the subsequent growth, germination, or flowering processes associated with photoperiodism. This may not be of consequence, however, since these processes are assumed to be initiated by the photoreaction, the chemical nature of which one wishes to reveal in its earliest phases.

REFERENCES

Adelman, A. H., and G. Oster. 1956. Long-lived states in photochemical reactions. II. Photoreduction of fluorescein and its halogenated derivatives. *J. Am. Chem. Soc., 78,* 3977–80.

Bellin, J. S., and G. Oster. 1957. Photoreduction of eosin in the bound state. *J. Am. Chem. Soc., 79,* 2461–64.

Blum, H. F. 1941. *Photodynamic Action and Diseases Caused by Light.* Reinhold, New York.

Brode, W. R., and G. M. Wyman. 1951. Absorption spectra of thioindigo dyes in benzene and chloroform. *J. Research Natl. Bur. Standards, 47,* 170–78.

Clare, N. T. 1956. Photodynamic action and its pathological effects. *Radiation Biology,* Vol. III. A. Hollaender, Editor. McGraw-Hill, New York.

Dartnall, H. J. A. 1957. *The Visual Pigments.* Wiley, New York.

Hendricks, S. B., and H. A. Borthwick. 1954. Photoperiodism in plants. *Proc. 1st Intern. Photobiol. Congr., Amsterdam,* 23–35.

Hill, R., and C. P. Whittingham. 1955. *Photosynthesis.* Methuen, London.

Hirshberg, Y. 1956. Reversible formation and eradication of colors by irradiation at low temperatures. *J. Am. Chem. Soc., 78,* 2304–12.

Jablonski, A. 1935. Weitere Versuche über die negative Polarization der Phosphoreszenz. *Acta Phys. Polon., 4,* 311–24.

Kasha, M. 1947. Phosphorescence and the role of the triplet state in the electronic excitation of complex molecules. *Chem. Revs., 41,* 401–19.

Kellner, A. 1949. Effect of visible light on the photorecovery of *Streptomyces griseus* conidia from ultraviolet light injury. *Proc. Natl. Acad. Sci. U. S., 35,* 73–79.

Krasnovsky, A. A. 1948. Reversible photoreduction of chlorophyll. *Doklady Akad. Nauk S.S.S.R., 60,* 421–28.

Lewis, G. N., D. Lipkin, and T. T. Magel. 1941. Reversible photochemical processes in rigid media. A study of the phosphorescent state. *J. Am. Chem. Soc., 63,* 3005–18.

Michaelis, M. 1940. Occurrence and significance of semiquinone radicals. *Ann. N. Y. Acad. Sci., 40,* 39–76.

Mustafa, A. 1952. Dimerization reactions in sunlight. *Chem. Revs., 51,* 1–23.

Oster, G. 1954. Dye-sensitized photopolymerization. *Nature, 173,* 300.

Oster, G. 1955. Dye binding to high polymers. *J. Polymer Sci., 16,* 235–44.

Oster, G. 1958. Models of the visual process. *Ann. N. Y. Acad. Sci., 74,* 305–09.

Oster, G., and A. H. Adelman. 1956. Long-lived states in photochemical reactions I. Photoreduction of eosin. *J. Am. Chem. Soc., 78,* 913–16.

Oster, G., and J. S. Bellin. 1957. Photoreduction of triphenylmethane dyes in the bound state. *J. Am. Chem. Soc., 79,* 294–98.

Oster, G., and B. Broyde. Photobleaching and photorecovery of dyes in glucose glass. (To be published.)

Oster, G., and L. Citarel. Visible light photochemistry of sulfur compounds. (To be published.)

Oster, G., and R. Kimball. Relation between photodynamic action and photauxidation of synthetic substrates. (To be published.)

Oster, G., and F. Millich. Photochemistry of the acridines. (To be published.)

Oster, G., and Y. Nishijima. 1956. Fluorescence and internal rotation: their dependence on viscosity of the medium. *J. Am. Chem. Soc., 78,* 1581–84.

Oster, G. K., G. Oster, and G. Prati. 1957. Dye-sensitized photopolymerization of acrylamide. *J. Am. Chem. Soc., 79,* 595–98.

Oster, G., and N. Wotherspoon. 1954. Photobleaching and photorecovery of dyes. *J. Chem. Phys. 22,* 157–58.

Oster, G., and N. Wotherspoon. 1957. Photoreduction of methylene blue by ethylenediaminetetraacetic acid. *J. Am. Chem. Soc., 79,* 4836–38.

Pringsheim, P. 1949. *Fluorescence and Phosphorescence.* Interscience, New York.

Raab, O. 1900. Ueber die Wirkung fluoresierender Stoffe auf Infusorien. *Z. Biol., 39,* 524.

Rosenthal, N., and G. Oster. 1954. Recent progress in the chemistry of disulfides. *J. Soc. Cosmetic Chemists, 5,* 286–307.

Schrader, M. E. 1956. Photochemical autoxidation of aromatic diamines. Ph.D. thesis, Polytechnic Institute of Brooklyn, Brooklyn, New York.

Wald, G., and P. K. Brown. 1952. The role of sulfhydryl groups in the bleaching and synthesis of rhodopsin. *J. Gen. Physiol. 35,* 797–821.

Wotherspoon, N., and G. Oster. 1957. Light induced spectral shift of the thiazine dyes in the bound state. *J. Am. Chem. Soc., 79,* 3992–95.

Wyman, G. 1955. The cis-trans isomerization of conjugated compounds. *Chem. Revs., 55,* 625–57.

INCIPLES
Euglena in water with the
of the pigments from the
of Shibata, Benson, and
our purposes because,

ιington,

d line)
hibata,

co the participation of
major reason for wanting
,emical and photobiological
ive pigment. The active pigment
olved in the process caused by the
a photochemical reaction is the plot of
a wavelengths in causing the reaction to
tain favorable conditions it may be an exact
ion spectrum of the active pigment. In some

al in
rect
nd
s

a difference between the actually measured action
ne true absorption spectrum of the pigment itself. An-
cal value in knowing the action spectrum, of course, is
ils us the most suitable color of the light to use for producing
red effect.

It will clarify the problems of measuring and understanding action spectra to consider first some of the peculiar optical properties of living cells. For pigment identification it is necessary to be aware of the difference between the absorption spectra of pigments in living cells and in pure solutions. These differences are equally relevant to the consideration of action spectra since action and *in vivo* absorption spectra are usually plotted together to substantiate the identification of the active pigment.

ABSORPTION OF LIGHT BY LIVING CELLS

Since this conference represents both zoologists and botanists, I have chosen *Euglena* to illustrate our first topic. Figure 1 compares the

absorption spectrum of a suspension of
absorption spectrum of an alcohol extract
same quantity of cells. These measurements
Calvin (1954) are particularly useful for

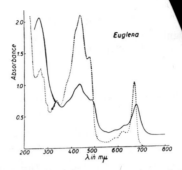

FIG. 1.   The absorption spectra of a suspension of *Euglena* (so
and of an alcoholic extract from the same volume of cells (dots) (S
Benson, and Calvin, 1954).

throughout the visible part of the spectrum, all the colored mater
the cells is soluble in alcohol. The two curves therefore give a d
comparison of absorption of the pigments themselves in solution a
in their natural state. The two curves are very different, for reason
that we will consider in some detail.

The dotted line, representing the absorption by the alcohol extract,
is higher at some wavelengths and lower at other wavelengths than
the solid line representing the absorption by the cell suspension.
Furthermore, the positions of the peaks of the two curves are at
different wavelengths, a fact that is most clearly seen at the red
absorption peak of chlorophyll *a*. The red peak is at about 662 mμ in
alcohol and at about 675 mμ in the cells. This shift of wavelength
position is probably due to real chemical differences of the pigment
in the two cases. In solution the pigments are actually combined with
the solvent, as is evident from the fact that the peak position depends
on the type of solvent. In the cells many pigments, and presumably
also chlorophyll, are combined with proteins. In fact, much of the
evidence for the chemical nature of pigments in cells comes from
absorption spectroscopy. There are, however, other groups of pig-

ments, such as cytochromes and anthocyanins, the spectra of which are much the same in pure solution and in the living cells.

In living cells the absorption peaks are lower and broader. The lowering of the peak absorption and the broadening of the curves is known as the flattening effect, some aspects of which have been described mathematically by Duysens (1956). In brief, a part of this effect is caused by the occurrence of the pigments in living cells as small solid particles. In the spaces between these particles the light can come through without being absorbed; hence the lower value of the absorption maxima. These particles are highly enough colored that the absorption may be practically complete within a single particle. Therefore another particle behind it cannot greatly influence the spectrum at the height of the peak, but only in regions of greater transparency.

The spectra of pigments in intact living cells, with all their complicated structures, might well be different from those in alcohol extracts

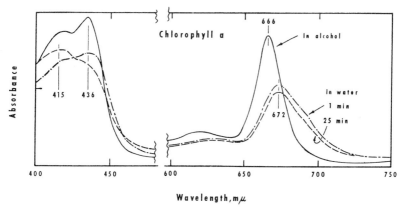

FIG. 2.   The absorption spectra of the same amount of chlorophyll *a* in alcohol and in water 1 and 25 min. after dilution. Opal glass was used with all three samples to reduce scattering effects from the colloidal water solution and to make the slit widths identical.

for several reasons. Comparable flattening, however, may be seen in a much simpler system, as shown in Fig. 2. Here the absorption of a dilute solution of chlorophyll *a* in alcohol is shown by the upper curve. The same amount of chlorophyll in a small volume of alcohol was added to a large volume of water, which does not dissolve chlorophyll. The chlorophyll precipitated as small colloidal particles that gave the curve shown below that of the alcohol extract. This curve was measured 1 min after the alcoholic solution of chlorophyll had been added to water. The flattening effect can be seen by comparing the curve of the colloidal particles with that for the solution. The bottom curve, measured 25 min later, shows the further aggregation of the chlorophyll into larger colloidal particles. Such solutions when first prepared are clear for a few minutes, then become cloudy as the aggregates grow. Another part of the flattening effect in the solid state comes from the fact that molecules tangle with each other, thus cramping each other's freedom to vibrate at their own characteristic frequencies. Thus, internal interaction between molecules, as well as the purely optical shading of one particle by another, may result in a broadening of the absorption spectrum.

An interesting effect shows up in the blue part of the spectrum of the two colloidal chlorophyll solutions. The 436-mμ peak of the freshly precipitated material is at first higher than the 415-mμ peak. However, after 25 min the 415-mμ peak has risen while that at 436 mμ has lowered. The exact explanation for this effect is not obvious, but there is evidently a slowly occurring combination of chlorophyll molecules with each other which differently influences their relative freedom to vibrate at the two frequencies. Similar shifts of peak position and broadening of chlorophyll bands of chlorophyll adsorbed on filter paper have been studied by Smith, Shibata, and Hart (1957). Here again the 415-mμ peak is much more prominent than that at 436 mμ.

So far we have talked about chlorophyll in the amorphous, non-crystalline state. The work of Jacobs, Vatter, and Holt (1954) has shown the appearance of another absorption band at about 740 mμ characteristic of chlorophyll crystals. The height of this band increases with the size of the crystal. There is much interest in the possibility of such microcrystalline chlorophyll units occurring in living cells, but absorption of light in this region has not yet been detected by chlorophyll *in vivo*.

We have seen the spectral changes that occur when a single pure substance changes from a solution to a solid. Let us turn to the more complicated system of pigments inside living cells. The major complication in cells is the scattering of light by more or less colorless cellular components. This scattering by colorless particles is caused by the difference in the refractive index of the particles and that of the water in which they are suspended. The refractive index changes slowly with wavelength through the spectrum, the difference from that of water being greater at shorter wavelengths. Very small particles, about the size of a wavelength of light, scatter light in proportion to the fourth power of the wavelength. Larger particles scatter with a smaller value of the exponent, but blue is always scattered more than red.

In addition to this scattering of particles which do not themselves absorb light, there is a particular kind of scattering by colored particles. This effect is more important than has been widely realized. Latimer and Rabinowitch (1956) made measurements of the intensity of light scattered at right angles to an incident beam from a suspension of *Chlorella* cells. Their results are shown by the middle curve of Fig. 3 (Latimer, 1957). The scattering is much greater on the long-wavelength side of the pigments' absorption bands. This wavelength selective scattering is due to the sharp change of refractive index of the pigment itself at wavelengths near an absorption band, the so-called anomalous dispersion effect.

A beam of light passing through a suspension of cells is attenuated in two different ways: first by actual absorption and secondly by scattering of both types. The scattering changes the direction in which the beam emerges from the sample being measured, so that the light may be only partially detected by the photocell as ordinarily placed in a spectrophotometer. The top curve in Fig. 3 (Latimer, 1957) shows a measurement of the attenuation of light by a suspension of *Chlorella* measured with a recording Beckman spectrophotometer. This instrument has its light receptor at a considerable distance from the vessel containing the experimental material. Therefore, the instrument records only the light coming from the suspension in a direction nearly parallel to the incident light. In this narrow beam the attenuation by scattering is far greater than the attenuation by actual absorption. The large relative contribution of scattering to the total attenua-

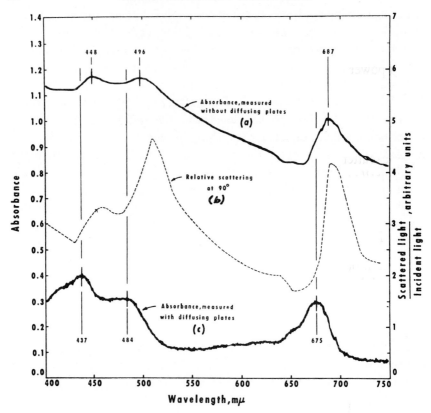

FIG. 3.   Bottom curve, absorption spectrum of a *Chlorella* suspension measured with the Beckman DK2 recording spectrophotometer using opal glass plates. Top curve, the same without opal glass. Middle curve, light scattering at 90° from another *Chlorella* suspension (Latimer, 1957).

tion is seen by comparing the top curve with that for the middle 90° scattering curve, and for the absorption alone given by the bottom curve.

Dr. Latimer also investigated the effect of the angle of light gathered by the photocell in a spectrophotometer on the apparent absorption spectra of cellular suspensions. With his apparatus it was possible to measure the absorption spectrum of a cellular suspension for a highly collimated narrow beam and to compare this measurement with the spectra measured through annular rings subtending different angles. The results of a series of such measurements are shown in Fig. 4. In

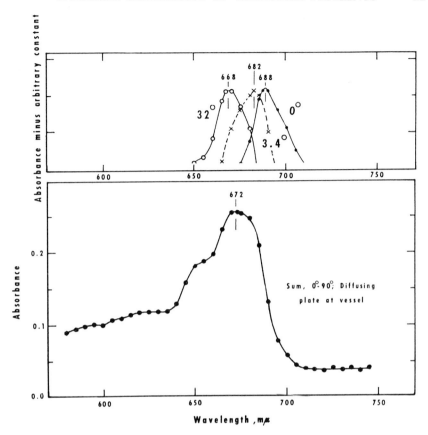

FIG. 4. Top set of curves, apparent absorption spectra of the same *Chlorella* suspension measured with a special spectrophotometer arranged to gather light from the suspension at various angles. The peak position varies greatly with the angle at which the light is collected. Bottom curve, the same suspension measured with an opal glass plate averaging all angles (Latimer, 1957).

the upper part a line with solid black points shows the apparent absorption spectrum of a *Chlorella* suspension when measured with a narrow beam. The position of the maximum is 688 mμ. The shape of this curve is primarily determined by wavelength-selective scattering of the pigment particles, and the curve has very little relation to the actual absorption spectrum. By measuring at an angle of about 3.4° ± 0.2°, the apparent peak position is shifted to 682 mμ. In taking a larger angle of $32 \pm 2°$, the peak position is shifted to 668 mμ. This range of 20 mμ for the peak position shows the extreme differences that may be given by various types of spectrophotometers. The implications of this experiment by Latimer are that small differences reported from different laboratories for the absorption peaks of biological materials should be disregarded, and even large differences should be interpreted with much caution.

If we want to compare action spectra with absorption spectra of the same material we are at once faced with the problem of how an absorption spectrum really can be measured without any such distortion being introduced by the peculiarities of a particular measuring apparatus. For pigment identification or for comparing the absorption spectra of living cells with action spectra it is usually not worth while to worry about the reflection of light from the front surface of the sample. The measurement of absorption for purposes of calculating quantum yields, however, requires this further refinement.

MEASUREMENT OF ABSORPTION SPECTRA OF LIVE CELLS

Light entering a suspension of cells or a whole organ is to various degrees reflected, transmitted, scattered, and absorbed. Since the light from the sample comes out in various directions, it is difficult to measure. Probably the soundest procedure theoretically, and in many cases the simplest for practical problems, is to put the sample inside a white sphere having a photocell in its wall. The photocell is supposed to catch light coming out from the sample with equal effectiveness in all directions. Such Ulbricht spheres have been used for years to measure the total output of electric lamps. The spectrophotometer designed by Hardy and made by the General Electric Company is built around such a sphere. Some integrating sphere attachments are available for other types of recording spectrophotometers. However, it is quite simple to make a perfectly adequate laboratory setup from a good monochromator and an appropriate photocell or photomultiplier. The home-made devices have the virtue of flexibility and adaptability to specific problems that may be very difficult to attain with well-made commercial instruments. Some of the theory of integrating spheres has recently been worked out in detail and usable conclusions have been presented by Jacquez and Kuppenheim (1955). Several arrangements of integrating spheres as used for photosynthetic organisms are discussed by French and Young (1956). The sphere does not, however, correct the measurements for the variation of the average path length of the light within the sample. Owing to scattering, this path length varies with wavelength and so may distort the shape of the absorption spectrum.

While a sphere is probably the best method of finding out how much light is actually absorbed by a suspension for such purposes as quantum yield measurements, there are simple procedures that give just as good results for many purposes. A large spherical mirror with a monochromator and photocell has been used to measure diffuse reflection spectra of leaves. Reversing the photocell and placing the mirror on the other side of the sample from the light beam makes a reasonably good absorbance spectrophotometer with a gathering angle of about 90°. Another good procedure for laboratory setups used by Emerson and Lewis (1943) and by Haxo and Blinks (1950) is to put the sample in direct contact with a barrier layer photocell of large area.

Methods summarized by Shibata (1956) depend on the diffusing properties of opal glass. The great value of Shibata's methods is that they may be applied easily with common recording spectrophotometers, and the cost of the extra equipment is negligible. The principle of the opal glass method for measuring absorption spectra of suspensions and other translucent biological materials is illustrated by Shibata, Benson, and Calvin (1954). The opal glass mixes the light that comes out of the suspension at various angles. Therefore the light reaching the photocell is a more or less representative sample of all the light from the vessel, regardless of its angular distribution. A simple holder for measuring leaves or other translucent sheets of material with opal glass in the recording Beckman spectrophotometer is described by Smith, Shibata, and Hart (1957).

An opal glass device has been developed by Shibata (1957a) for the absolute measurement of reflection spectra with a recording spectrophotometer. Details of the various ways in which opal glass may be used to measure absorption and reflection, and the absorption spectra corrected for reflection as needed for quantum yield experiments are described by Shibata (1958). Barer (1955) has reduced the scattering from cell walls by suspending cells in concentrated protein solutions to measure their absorption spectra. Bateman and Monk (1955) have used a glass flask packed in white powder as an integrating sphere. The flask is filled with water for the incident intensity reading, then with the highly diluted sample.

We have seen how light scattering can greatly distort absorption spectra of live cells and how some of this trouble can be avoided. If the absorption of tissues or cells are correctly measured by these or similar procedures, the absorption can be compared directly with action spectra.

ACTION SPECTRA

One of the basic principles of photochemistry is that only light that is absorbed has a chemical effect. For this reason, the effectiveness of different wavelengths in causing chemical action is proportional to the absorption by the active pigment concerned. An action spectrum, when determined with appropriate precautions, thus gives the absorption spectrum and hence identifies the light-absorbing pigment.

When no inactive pigments are present, the action spectrum may be practically identical with the absorption spectrum of the whole system. At the other extreme the action spectrum may have bands that are not identifiable in the absorption spectrum and may show no effectiveness whatever for some pigments the absorption of which is evident. The basic requirement that should be met in determining precise action spectra is to use a sufficiently thin layer of lightly pigmented material. It is necessary to make sure in this way that all parts of the sample receive equal intensities of light. In addition to this basic optical requirement, the chemical requirement of not saturating the system with light must be met. This means that intensities should be used in the range where the effectiveness of the light is proportional to its intensity. Even if these two requirements are satisfied, the resulting action spectra may be distorted if the system contains a high concentration of other pigments which are inactive but which may act as an internal screen for some colors. Fortunately, internal scattering is no particular problem in action spectra measurements, since all parts of the sample are supposed to be equally illuminated.

Each photobiological process requires special consideration of the means of measuring the response used to determine an action spectrum. Such things as a chemical change, a mechanical motion, or a color change may be the final result. As a general principle, however, it is far better to work with the intensity of light of various wavelengths needed to give the same amount of response than to use constant intensity and measure the variable response. In this way nonlinearity of response causes no difficulty.

In the 1880's Englemann observed action spectra for photosynthesis in filamentous algae by projecting a microspectrum directly on a single filament. The liquid surrounding the filament was a suspension of motile bacteria. These bacteria congregated where oxygen was evolved. The bacteria showed activity at the red end of the spectrum near the chlorophyll absorption band and also near the blue absorption band of chlorophyll. More recent work on the action spectra of photosynthesis in various organisms has confirmed Englemann's qualitative conclusions. Emerson and Lewis (1943) measured the action spectrum for photosynthesis of *Chlorella* and compared the action with the absorption by the whole cells. The approximate agreement of these curves shows that most of the pigments present were active in photosynthesis. The yield, however, was somewhat lower, around 480 mμ, where carotenoid absorption is very strong.

A very different situation was found by Haxo and Blinks (1950). Their data for a red alga are given in Fig. 5 as plotted by French and Young to show the spectrum of the inactive as well as of the active components. The absorption from 475 to 625 mμ is due to phycobilin pigments, and the activity in this region is high. The striking fact about this set of measurements is the relative inactivity of the chlorophyll which is evident both in red and blue. If red algae were more widely distributed in nature, we would probably think of chlorophyll as a second-rate photosynthetic pigment.

One of the most spectacular uses of action spectrum measurements was the determination of the chemical nature of the cellular respiratory enzyme which combines directly with oxygen. Warburg's respiratory enzyme, which the British prefer to call cytochrome oxidase,

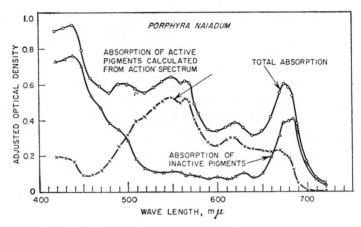

FIG. 5. The absorption and photosynthesis action spectra of a red alga replotted from Haxo and Blinks (1950) to show also the spectrum of the inactive absorption (French and Young, 1956).

combines with carbon monoxide as well as with oxygen. The carbon monoxide complex is inactive, but the carbon monoxide may be dissociated by exposing the cells to light. Therefore the inhibition caused by adding carbon monoxide to a suspension of cells is lessened when the cells are illuminated. Warburg and Negelein (1928) measured the action spectrum for the decrease of carbon monoxide inhibition of the respiratory activity in several microorganisms. These spectra led to the identification of the active group of the respiratory enzyme as a porphyrin, an achievement for which Warburg was awarded the Nobel Prize in 1931. This investigation was a most remarkable accomplishment because the spectrum of the active material was entirely obscured by other colored components of the cells, and the enzyme could not be isolated. Many other action spectra have led to equally definitive results, but the use of this technique has not always proved equally rewarding.

Let us consider the action spectrum for chlorophyll formation. No chlorophyll is formed in leaves grown in the dark. A colored precursor, protochlorophyll, does, however, accumulate in trace amounts. Upon illumination of dark-grown leaves protochlorophyll is transformed immediately into chlorophyll *a*. This transformation, reviewed by Smith and Young (1956), may be measured by direct spectrophotometry of the intact leaves, as was done by Shibata (1957b). The absorption peak of protochlorophyll consists of two components with maxima at about 635 and 650 mμ. Upon illumination the maximum at 650 decreases and chlorophyll a is formed with an absorption peak at 682 mμ. After standing in the dark for about 30 min the chlorophyll changes over to another form absorbing at about 670 mμ. The first change from protochlorophyll to C682 is a purely photochemical action which will take place even at the temperature of solid carbon dioxide.

Light is not necessary for the transformation of C682 to C670. The action spectrum for the photochemical change was determined in corn seedlings by Koski, French, and Smith (1951) with the apparatus shown in Fig. 6. The light from a high-pressure mercury lamp was sent through a monochromator, and an image of the grating was

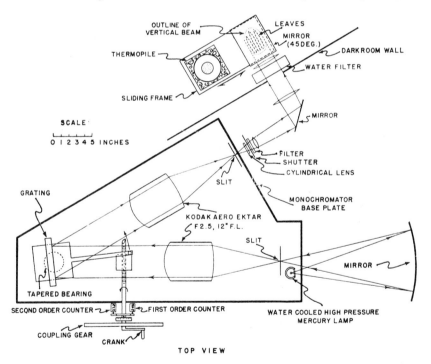

FIG. 6.   The monochromator and optical systems used to measure the action spectrum of chlorophyll formation in etiolated corn leaves (Koski, French, and Smith, 1951).

focused on a platform holding the leaves. The intensity was measured by a thermopile. After exposures of various times at each wavelength the leaves were removed, the pigments extracted, and the amounts of chlorophyll and protochlorophyll determined spectrophotometrically in solution. The intensity of light necessary to transform 20% of the protochlorophyll into chlorophyll was plotted against wavelength.

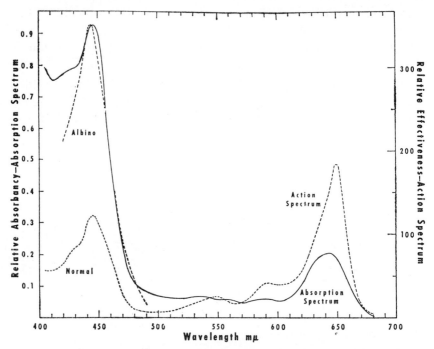

FIG. 7. The action spectra for chlorophyll formation in normal and in a carotenoid-free corn mutant as compared with the absorption spectrum of another carotenoid-free corn leaf (Smith, 1957).

The resulting action spectrum for an albino corn mutant lacking carotenoids is shown as the upper dotted curve of Fig. 7 (Smith, 1957). A corresponding set of measurements for normal corn containing carotenoids is indicated by the lower curve showing reduction of the blue light effectiveness by internal screening. The carotenoids, however, do not absorb in the red part of the spectrum, so that the two curves are identical there. The red action peak comes at 650 mμ, where the absorption peak for one form of protochlorophyll is located. It is clear from the comparison of action and absorption in this figure that direct absorption of light by protochlorophyll itself is necessary for its transformation to chlorophyll. In another experiment a leaf already containing both chlorophyll and protochlorophyll was illuminated with light of 670 mμ, which was absorbed by chlorophyll but not by protochlorophyll. This wavelength did not cause any further transformation. This action spectrum was measured with the usual point-by-point procedure, each point requiring a 2-hr chemical analysis.

When Dr. Halldal was working at this laboratory, he wanted to measure the action spectrum for the phototaxis of dinoflagellates. A method was devised for measuring the complete action spectrum in a single experiment, much like the microprojection procedure of Englemann. The procedure (Halldal, 1958b), however, was modified so that quantitative results could be obtained and the data presented as curves. The motile algae were put in a small lucite box. This box was illuminated uniformly by a reference beam from the left, as shown in Fig. 8. On the right side of the box he projected a spectrum with a

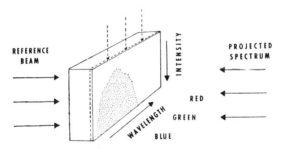

FIG. 8.   A simple method for making motile algae plot their own action spectra for phototaxis (Halldal, 1956).

vertical intensity gradient. The spectrum was bright at the bottom and weak at the top. The spectrum was produced by a grating, and the gradient of the light intensity came from a wedge-shaped slit. The gradient was further sharpened by a photographic density wedge attached to the slit. These motile algae will swim in the direction of the light which is most effective in phototaxis. Without the projected spectrum they all swim to the side of the vessel facing the reference beam and stick on the wall. However, in the parts of the spectrum that are more effective than the reference beam they swim to the spectrum side. At each wavelength there is an intensity at which that wavelength is just as effective as the reference beam. Below that point the algae all swim to the spectrum side; above it they swim to the reference beam. By exposing a suspension of algae to these opposing beams for a few minutes a complete set of response data for an action spectrum can be obtained. The intensity and wavelengths had previously been measured for the whole surface of the projected spectrum. All that remains to make the resulting automatic plot truly quantitative is to take a picture of the response pattern, or to mark the dividing line on the front of the vessel, and carry through the calculations.

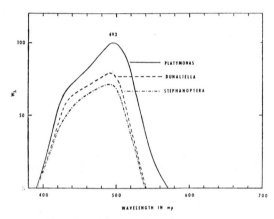

FIG. 9.   Phototaxis action spectra.

Figure 9 for the phototaxis action spectra of some motile algae so measured looks very much like most phototaxis and phototropism action spectra. Their shape could very well be attributed to light absorption by carotenoids with some lowering in the blue through internal screening by chlorophyll. In Fig. 10, however, the action spectrum for phototaxis of *Prorocentrum* shows a narrow peak at 570. This is a highly unusual discovery. The absorption curve for this organism does not show anything particular at this wavelength, and the nature of the pigment responsible for phototaxis in this organism is not yet known. The fact that the absorbing substance for the action in this species cannot be found in the absorption spectrum shows the

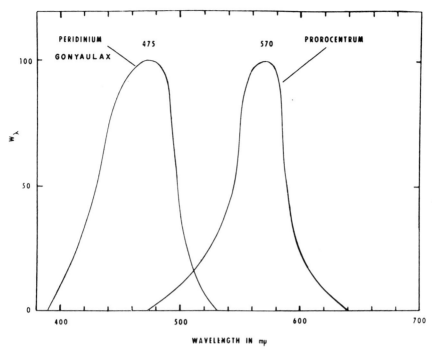

Fig. 10.   Phototaxis action spectra.

need for better methods of detecting minor pigment components in absorption spectra.

DERIVATIVE SPECTROPHOTOMETRY

We have recently completed a device for recording the slope of an absorption curve rather than its height. This machine plots the first derivative of optical density against wavelength. The method is expected to be useful for detecting minor bands which are obscured by more strongly absorbing pigments (Giese and French, 1955). The type of measurement given by this device is shown in Fig. 11 from French (1957). On the left is plotted the absorption of chlorophyll *a* in ether solution as measured by the Beckman recording spectrophotometer. On the upper right we see the first derivative of optical density, $d\mathrm{E}/d\lambda$, plotted against wavelength λ, by the new machine. The integral of this plot is drawn as the full line on the upper left for

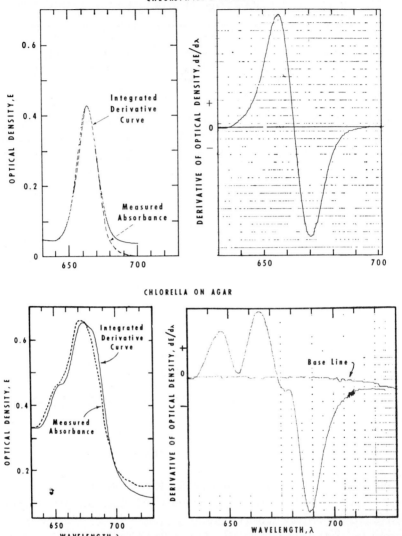

FIG. 11. Top, the red absorption band of chlorophyll *a* in ether, as measured with the recording Beckman spectrophotometer (dotted line). The first derivative of the absorbance of the same sample with respect to wavelength plotted by the derivative spectrophotometer. The integral of this curve (solid line) is compared with the directly measured absorbance curve on the left. Bottom, the same type of data for live *Chlorella* cells showing chlorophyll *b* more clearly in the derivative curve. The shoulder of the derivative curve at 675–680 mμ indicates that this peak consists of two components.

32

comparison with the directly measured curve. On the lower right is the absorbance curve measured with the recording Beckman spectrophotometer for a culture of *Chlorella*. The lower right shows the derivative spectrum of the same *Chlorella* sample. The notch and the extra peak in the neighborhood of 650 mμ is due to chlorophyll *b*, which shows only as a small shoulder on the absorbance curve. The most interesting part of the *Chlorella* absorption curve is, however, the shoulder of 675 to 680 mμ. This shoulder means that the chlorophyll *a* band in *Chlorella* is made up of two components having absorption peaks at slightly different wavelengths. The shape of this shoulder is dependent on temperature. At 5°C a separate peak, rather than a shoulder, shows on the derivative curve.

With the derivative spectrophotometer we can easily study the shape of the chlorophyll *c* band in brown algae. In *Ulva* the chlorophyll *b* band was found to consist of two components.

This machine is showing fascinating and previously undetectable details in absorption spectra of common objects. Work with it is much like applying a microscope for the first time to the study of objects well known macroscopically. The major question of immediate concern is the shape of the red chlorophyll *a* band in green plants. Does its variation in shape mean that there are many different kinds of *in vivo* chlorophyll *a*? Are the observed differences due to only two forms of chlorophyll *a* occurring in various proportions? Is the variation merely a secondary result of the flattening effect being dependent on size of particles? Are the different spectroscopic forms of chlorophyll *a* correlated with differences in photosynthetic function? Many of these questions have arisen from the work of the Krasnovskii group (translations by Rabinowitch and by Milner). To answer them completely we may have to wait for the development of methods for measuring action spectra with resolving power equal to that of absorption spectroscopy.

The absorption of pigments in trace amounts in living cells can be measured with great accuracy by another means known as difference spectrophotometry. Difference, or differential spectrophotometry, as it is also known, is extremely useful in comparing two samples which differ only by the presence or the reduction state of the significant pigments. A modification of this procedure is to compare, for a single sample, the absorption for various wavelengths with that for a fixed wavelength. Difference spectrophotometry has been used by Duysens, Chance, Kok, Witt, Lundegardh, and Rabinowitch (reviewed by French, 1959) for studies of changes in the absorption of photosynthetic organisms when they are illuminated.

FLUORESCENCE SPECTROPHOTOMETRY OF *in vivo* PIGMENTS

By measuring the spectral energy distribution of fluorescent light from living material, it is possible to identify pigments that happen to be fluorescent. A very pale leaf containing extremely small amounts of chlorophyll gives a spectrum similar in shape to that of chlorophyll *a* in solution but shifted in wavelength, as are the corresponding absorption spectra. However, chlorophyll has a very strong absorption band which overlaps its fluorescence peak. Therefore, if the fluorescent light generated in a sample containing chlorophyll has to pass through an appreciable amount of this pigment before emerging, those wavelengths strongly absorbed by chlorophyll will be weak or lacking in the observed fluorescence spectrum. A green leaf containing many air spaces scatters the light around within the leaf thus increasing the chances of reabsorption of the fluorescent wavelengths that fall within the absorption band. Illuminating such a leaf with blue light at 436 mμ produces a two-peaked spectrum recognizable as that of chlorophyll but greatly distorted by reabsorption of light in the neighborhood of the main peak (French, 1955). In this leaf the far-red chlorophyll *a* fluorescence peak at 725 mμ is higher than the characteristic 685-mμ chlorophyll peak. Blue light is very strongly absorbed by chlorophyll. Green light, on the other hand, is absorbed weakly by chlorophyll so that a large amount of the fluorescence excited by green, 546 mμ, comes from deep within the leaf. On its way out the fluorescent light is absorbed strongly at wavelengths where the chlorophyll *a* absorption band is high. For green incident light the 685-mμ peak, characteristic of chlorophyll *a* fluorescence, disappears almost completely in a dark leaf, leaving only the long-wavelength secondary maximum of fluorescence. Virgin (1954) has found the distortion to be greatly reduced by infiltrating the leaves with water to decrease the internal scattering. It would be very easy to consider a distorted curve of this type as the discovery of a new fluorescent pigment. Nevertheless, when the danger of making such mistakes by improper interpretation of fluorescence spectra is realized, it is possible to use fluorescence spectroscopy for difficult problems of pigment identification.

Goodwin, Koski, and Owens (1951) discovered an orange-fluorescing pigment in the cells surrounding the guard cells of the epidermis of vetch leaves. By comparing its fluorescence spectrum with those of known porphyrins, they established that this pigment, insoluble both in water and in alcohol, is similar to or identical with uroporphyrin I methyl ester. In view of its very specific distribution, the function of this pigment may eventually be found to have some connection with the action of guard cells.

If several fluorescent pigments occur together in living cells, it is possible to excite fluorescence of one or another by using incident wavelengths which are absorbed by the different pigments. Only chlorophyll fluorescence appears in a red alga illuminated by blue light (French and Young, 1952). However, green light, which is absorbed almost entirely by phycoerythrin, shows phycoerythrin, phycocyanin, and also chlorophyll fluorescence. The action spectrum was determined for the excitation of chlorophyll fluorescence in the red alga *Porphyridium cruentum*. The action spectrum matched the absorption spectrum of the red phycoerythrin. Therefore, it is presumed that the accessory phycobilin pigments are arranged within the chloroplasts in such a way that they can transfer energy to chlorophyll. Experiments like this have led to the conclusion that the participation of these accessory pigments in photosynthesis is simply by extra light absorption. Chlorophyll seems to have some peculiar chemical property necessary for the photosynthetic reaction in addition to its ability to absorb light.

INVESTIGATION OF PHOTOBIOLOGICAL EFFECTS WITH CROSSED GRADIENTS

We have already seen that it is possible to measure the action spectrum of certain photobiological effects by exposing the material to a field in which the intensity of light varies along one axis and wave-

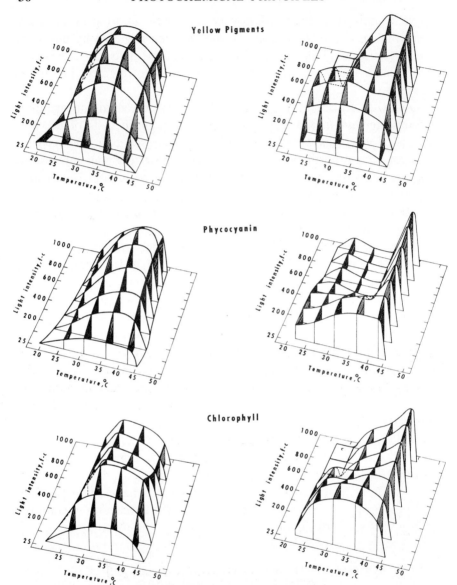

FIG. 12.   The relative content of three pigments in *Anacystis* after 1 and after 2 days growth on a plate having crossed gradients of temperature and light intensity (Halldal, 1958a).

length on the other axis. The same principle of crossed gradients may be applied to such processes as growth and pigment formation. Since the temperature and light intensity which influence a biological process must often be investigated in some detail before it is practical to make action spectrum measurements under the right conditions, it may be worth while to make a preliminary study of the interrelation of such variables as temperature and light intensity.

A large petri dish made of a thick aluminum plate is used for these crossed gradient experiments. One edge of this aluminum plate is kept cold by flowing water through a long hole just inside its left edge. The opposite edge is similarly kept warm. There is therefore a flow of heat across the plate giving a stable temperature gradient from left to right. A thin layer of agar on the surface of the plate is inoculated with algae. Now at right angles to the temperature gradient there is a light-intensity gradient established by diffuse illumination from above. Thus, at each temperature we have a complete series of intensities. Therefore, the growth of the algae on a plate of this type will automatically plot out their survival limits and will also indicate their intensity and temperature requirements for optimum growth. Halldal (1958b) has taken samples of algae from different parts of the plate to see the effects of temperature and light intensity on the formation of different pigments as shown in Fig. 12. It is possible that experiments of this type may be useful in establishing relations between intensity of light and temperature for other photobiological processes. The device has been described by Halldal and French (1958).

REFERENCES

Barer, R. 1955. Spectrophotometry of clarified cell suspensions. *Science, 121,* 709–15.

Bateman, J. B., and G. W. Monk. 1955. Spectral absorption of turbid systems using diffuse light. *Science, 121,* 441–42.

Duysens, L. N. M. 1956. The flattening of the absorption spectrum of suspensions, as compared to that of solutions. *Biochim. et Biophys. Acta, 19,* 1–12.

Emerson, R., and C. M. Lewis. 1943. The dependence of the quantum yield of *Chlorella* photosynthesis on wavelength of light. *Am. J. Botany, 30,* 165–78.

French, C. S. 1955. Fluorescence spectrophotometry of photosynthetic pigments. *The Luminescence of Biological Systems,* pp. 51–74. F. H. Johnson, Editor. American Association for the Advancement of Science, Washington, D. C.

French, C. S. 1957. Derivative spectrophotometry, *Proc. I.S.A.,* pp. 83–94.

Paper given at Instrumentation 2nd Central Symposium sponsored by Northern California section, Instrument Society of America, Berkeley, Calif., May 14, 1957.

French, C. S. 1959. The chlorophylls *in vivo* and *in vitro*. *Encyclopedia of Plant Physiology.* W. Ruhland, Editor.

French, C. S., J. H. C. Smith, H. I. Virgin, and R. L. Airth. 1956. Fluorescence-spectrum curves of chlorophylls, pheophytins, phycoerythrins, phycocyanins, and hypericin. *Plant Physiol., 31,* 369–74.

French, C. S., and V. K. Young. 1952. The fluorescence spectra of red algae and the transfer of energy from phycoerythrin to phycocyanin and chlorophyll. *J. Gen. Physiol., 35,* 873–90.

French, C. S., and V. K. Young. 1956. The absorption, action and fluorescence spectra of photosynthetic pigments in living cells and in solutions. *Radiation Biology, 3,* 343–91. McGraw-Hill, New York.

Giese, A. T., and C. S. French. 1955. The analysis of overlapping spectral absorption bands by derivative spectrophotometry. *Appl. Spectroscopy, 9,* 78–96.

Goodwin, R. H., V. M. Koski, and O. v.H. Owens. 1951. The distribution and properties of a porphyrin from the epidermis of Vicia shoots. *Am. J. Botany, 38,* 629–35.

Halldal, P. 1958a. Action spectra of phototaxis and related problems in volvocales, ulva gametes and dinophyceae. *Physiol. Plantarum, 11,* 118–53.

Halldal, P. 1958b. Pigment formation and growth in blue-green algae in crossed gradients of light intensity and temperature. *Physiol. Plantarum, 11,* 401–20.

Halldal, P., and C. S. French. 1956. The growth of algae in crossed gradients of light intensity and temperature. *Carnegie Inst. Wash. Year Book, 55,* 261–65.

Halldal, P., and C. S. French. 1958. Algae growth in crossed gradients of light intensity and temperature. *Plant Physiol., 33,* 249–52.

Haxo, F. T., and L. R. Blinks. 1950. Photosynthetic action spectra of marine algae. *J. Gen. Physiol., 33,* 389–422.

Jacobs, E. E., A. E. Vatter, and A. S. Holt. 1954. Crystalline chlorophyll and bacteriochlorophyll. *Arch. Biochem. Biophys., 53,* 228–38.

Jacquez, J. A., and H. F. Kuppenheim. 1955. Theory of the integrating sphere. *J. Opt. Soc. Am., 45,* 460–70.

Koski, V. M., C. S. French, and J. H. C. Smith. 1951. The action spectrum for the transformation of protochlorophyll to chlorophyll a in normal and albino corn seedlings. *Arch. Biochem. Biophys., 31,* 1–17.

Krasnovskiĭ, A. A., *et al.* (See Milner and Rabinowitch.)

Latimer, P. 1957. Apparent shifts of absorption bands of cell suspensions caused by optical effects. *Carnegie Inst. Wash. Year Book, 56,*

Latimer, P., and E. Rabinowitch. 1956. Selective scattering of light by pigment containing plant cells. *J. Chem. Phys., 24,* 480.

Milner, H. W. Translator, Russian papers on photochemistry and photosynthesis. 3 vols., 818 pages. (Available from Crerar Library, Chicago.)

Rabinowitch, E. I. 1956. Translator, Fluorescence and photochemistry of chlorophyll, papers of A. A. Krasnovskiĭ, V. B. Evstigneev, and co-workers. U. S. Atomic Energy Comm. Tech. Inf. Extension, Oak Ridge, Tennessee.

Available from Office of Technical Services, Department of Commerce, Washington 25, D. C.

Shibata, K. 1956. Spectral measurements of true absorption and reflection of translucent materials. *Carnegie Inst. Wash. Year Book, 55,* 252–56.

Shibata, K. 1957a. Simple absolute method for measuring diffuse reflectance spectra. *J. Opt. Soc. Am., 47,* 172–75.

Shibata, K. 1957b. Spectroscopic studies on chlorophyll formation in intact leaves. *J. Biochem. Japan, 44,* 147–73.

Shibata, K. 1958. Spectrophotometry of intact biological materials: Absolute and relative measurements of their transmission, reflection, and absorption spectra. *J. Biochem. Japan, 45,* 599–623.

Shibata, K., A. A. Benson, and M. Calvin. 1954. The absorption spectra of suspensions of living microorganisms. *Biochim. et Biophys. Acta, 15,* 461–70.

Smith, J. H. C. 1957. Protochlorophyll, photoreceptor in the accumulation of chlorophyll. *Proc. Second Intern. Congr. Photobiology, Turin,* pp. 333–42.

Smith, J. H. C., K. Shibata, and R. W. Hart. 1957. A spectrophotometer accessory for measuring absorption spectra of light scattering samples: Spectra of dark-grown albino leaves and of adsorbed chlorophylls. *Arch. Biochem. Biophys., 72,* 457–64.

Smith, J. H. C., and V. M. K. Young. 1956. Chlorophyll formation and accumulation in plants. *Radiation Biology,* Vol. III, pp. 393–442. A. Hollaender, Editor. McGraw-Hill, New York.

Virgin, I. 1954. The distortion of fluorescence spectra in leaves by light scattering and its reduction by infiltration. *Physiol. Plantarum, 7,* 560–70.

Warburg, O., and E. Negelein. 1928. Ueber den Einfluss der Wellenlänge auf die Verteilung des Atmungsferments (Absorptionsspektrum des Atmungsferments). *Biochem. Z., 193,* 339–46.

REMARKS ON THE SIGNIFICANCE
OF ACTION SPECTRA

FREDERICK S. BRACKETT and ALEXANDER HOLLAENDER [1]

National Institute of Arthritis and Metabolic Diseases, National Institutes of Health, Bethesda, Maryland

Action spectra are often obtained as an aid in identifying the molecules initiating an action through comparison with known absorption spectra. Unfortunately, other factors besides absorption may contribute to the form of the action spectrum. These factors include: (1) quantum efficiency, (2) screening by overlying layers, and (3) competition with other absorbing molecules.

Most dramatic is the case where the quantum threshold lies within that portion of the spectrum where absorption exists. At the threshold the action rises sharply from zero on the long wavelength side to a value controlled by the quantum efficiency on the short wavelength side. The quantum efficiency may be a fraction, often near 1, but sometimes a large value as in case of a chain reaction.

Let us consider a case where n quanta are required to produce a unit action (molecule transformed, cell killed 50% of time, etc.), $1/n$ being the quantum efficiency. Then Nn quanta are required to transform N units per unit volume. With I_0 radiant power incident per unit area acting for time t with a fraction A absorbed, in x thickness, the energy absorbed per unit volume in time t is $I_0 t A / x$ in customary units. Owing to screening and competition only a fraction ϕ may be available, so

$$Nn = \phi \frac{I_0 t A}{x h \nu} \qquad (1)$$

In an action spectrum one usually plots $N/I_0 t$ for the chosen end point, so

$$\frac{N}{I_0 t} = \frac{\phi}{n h \nu} \frac{A}{x} \qquad (2)$$

It would of course be preferable to express the action in terms of quanta

---

[1] Present Address: Oak Ridge National Laboratory, Oak Ridge, Tennessee.

for each wavelength. Then one computes the number of quanta incident during the required exposure as $q_\lambda = I_0 t / h v$, so

$$\frac{N}{q_\lambda} = \frac{\phi}{nx} A \qquad (3)$$

If the thickness is concealed one may prefer to observe the number of units transformed per unit area instead of per unit volume, say $N_s = Nx$, and we have

$$\frac{N_s}{q_\lambda} = \frac{\phi}{n} A \qquad (4)$$

As Dr. French has pointed out in the preceding paper, a weak absorption or "thin sample" may be desirable and will enable us to further analyze A/x. In a homogeneous system

$$A = 1 - T = 1 - e^{-(\alpha_1 c_1 + \alpha_2 c_2 + \cdots + \alpha_n c_n)x}$$

If the exponent is small because of the thinness of the sample (x or c small)

$$\frac{A}{x} = \alpha_1 c_1 + \alpha_2 c_2 + \cdots \alpha_n c_n$$

where α_n is the molecular extinction coefficient and c_n the concentration of the type n molecule, the sum being extended to all absorbing molecules.

Under these conditions $\alpha_1 c_1$ may be the portion initiating our reaction and

$$\phi = \frac{\alpha_1 c_1}{\alpha_1 c_1 + \alpha_2 c_2 + \cdots \alpha_n c_n}$$

in the case of competition without screening. Thus in an ideal case of a thin homogeneous sample, equation (2) may be written

$$\frac{N}{q_\lambda} = \frac{Nhv}{I_0 t} = \frac{1}{n} \alpha_1 c_1 \qquad (5)$$

In the actual case of a biological system one deals not only with organized structure but often screening layers such as skin and cell wall. Here ϕ is further reduced and may be characteristically wavelength dependent.

Where one can manipulate the concentration and thickness, it may be possible to gain information on both efficiency (ϕ/n) and absorption A as in the following case from experiments published only in abstract.[2]

Yeast cells were exposed in suspension to a suitable range of ultraviolet energies at representative wavelengths. These were plated out and colonies were counted. Thus a family of log survival curves could be constructed for different suspension densities as well as wavelengths. From each curve a 50% survival point is obtained and used as our *action end point*. These end point values of I_0t/N are plotted in Fig. 1 for different choices of cell suspension density. At the left near

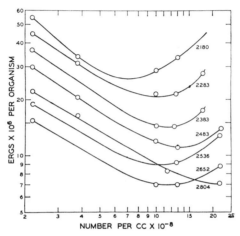

FIG. 1.   Energy of ultraviolet incident for 50% survival of a rapidly stirred cell suspension plotted against the population density.   Each point is found from a survival curve not shown.

2×10^8 cells/cc we have the points for a typical "thin sample" action spectrum. Plotting the reciprocal, N/I_0t, against wavelength, we have curve B, Fig. 2. Here the greater part of the energy is lost through the cuvette, i.e., the transmission T is large. Again from Fig. 1, as the density of cell suspension is increased, this loss diminishes and a minimum value is reached. To some extent, treated cells screen untreated cells so that further increase in density reduces the efficiency. The

[2] F. S. Brackett and A. Hollaender, Physical factors governing biological action of radiation. *Phys. Rev.*, 55 (1939). Abstract.

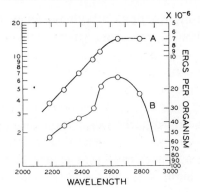

FIG. 2. Action spectra. Curve *A*, minimum energy values found for optimal population density—log scale on right and inverse on left. This is a close approach to an efficiency spectrum. Curve *B*, Values for small population density (points at left of Fig. 1). This shows influence of both absorption and efficiency.

optimal value of cell density depends upon the total absorption per cell and upon the stirring. Hence it occurs at a different cell density for each wavelength. Thus, if we plot $1/N$ for the energy minimums, we obtain a curve (Fig. 3) strongly resembling the total absorption. If we plot the minimum energy against each wavelength, we obtain an action spectrum (curve *A*, Fig. 2). All evidence of absorption has disap-

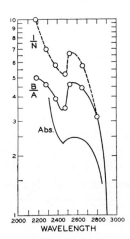

FIG. 3. Comparison of observed total absorption with the implied effective absorption B/A and reciprocal of optimal density $1/N$.

peared from this spectrum, and instead we find an approximation to a typical efficiency trend—maximum for the longest wavelength and falling off as the quantum becomes unnecessarily large and there is less close resonance.

Assuming that curve A is proportional to $\phi/nh\nu$ we divide B by A and obtain a curve B/A (Fig. 3), which now approximates the absorption which contributes to the lethality, as seen from equation (2). Note the similarity between the observed absorption, the indirectly deduced total absorption $1/N$, and the action spectrum corrected for efficiency shown by curve B/A.

One is not often so fortunate in the control of optical density as in the case cited. Reducing the population density often fails to produce a typically "weak" absorption. While the transmission can be made high, this may be the result of radiation which has not passed through an organism, and hence only dilutes the transmitted radiation. Nevertheless, each cell may absorb heavily from the radiation which passes through its volume, exhibiting the typical "thick sample" properties— augmenting weak absorption and penalizing strong bands. This is typical of spectra for unicellular organisms such as *Euglena* and *Chlorella* as to chlorophyll absorption because of the great concentration in the chloroplasts. In extreme cases strong bands may "saturate" and exhibit reduced efficiency or reversal, owing to self screening.

ENERGY TRANSFER IN ORDERED AND UNORDERED PHOTOCHEMICAL SYSTEMS [1]

GORDON TOLLIN, POWER B. SOGO, and MELVIN CALVIN
Radiation Laboratory and Department of Chemistry, University of
California, Berkeley, California

The phenomenon of energy transfer has been receiving an ever increasing amount of attention from physicists, physical chemists, and biochemists alike since the pioneering work of Franck (Cairo and Franck, 1922, 1923; Franck and Teller, 1938) and Vavilov (1925). This concept has proved to be of fundamental importance for an understanding of many of the photoinduced phenomena of molecules, both in solution and in the solid state, and is proving to be of increasing significance to biology.

Our concern here will be mainly with a qualitative discussion of the theoretical aspects of energy migration, with some of the experimental criteria of this phenomenon, and, finally, with its possible role in the primary quantum conversion act in photosynthesis.

GENERAL CONSIDERATIONS OF ENERGY TRANSFER IN UNORDERED SYSTEMS

Spectroscopic Properties of Molecules in Solution

Some of the main qualitative features of the effects of visible and UV radiation on molecules in solution may be understood by a consideration of the diagram in Fig. 1. Process *a* represents the absorption of a quantum of light by the molecule resulting in a change in its electronic state. Molecules in the lowest excited singlet state may then undergo one of four processes: they may emit a quantum of light as fluorescence (process *b*); the electronic excitation energy may be degraded into heat (process *c*); a small portion of the electronic energy

---

[1] The work described in this paper was sponsored by the U. S. Atomic Energy Commission.

may be degraded into heat, concomitant with an unpairing of electron spins, resulting in an intersystem crossing into the lowest excited triplet state (process *d*); the quantum of excitation energy may be transferred to another molecule. Molecules in the lowest excited triplet state may,

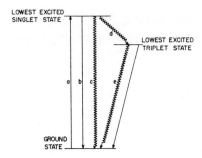

FIG. 1. Lowest electronic energy levels of an isolated molecule. Straight lines represent radiative processes; zigzag lines represent radiationless (thermal) processes. *a*, absorption of light; *b*, fluorescence; *c*, thermal degradation; *d*, intersystem crossing; *e*, thermal degradation; *f*, phosphorescence.

similarly, undergo one of three processes: phosphorescence (process *f*), thermal degradation (process *e*), or energy transfer to another molecule.

Theoretical Aspects of Energy Transfer

There are three mechanisms by which electronic excitation energy may be transferred from one molecule to another in unordered systems. These are:

1. The emission of a quantum of radiation by the excited molecule followed by the reabsorption of this quantum by an unexcited molecule. This may be repeated many times. The probability of this process is determined simply by the Beer-Lambert law and by the geometry of the system. In general, the lifetime of the excited state of a particular molecule will remain the same, but the lifetime of the emission in a finite system may be increased by the "imprisonment of radiation" (Pringsheim, 1949, pp. 60–63). This mechanism has been shown to be of relatively minor importance in energy transfer in solution (Furst and Kallman, 1954; Kallman *et al.*, 1956).

2. The transfer of electronic excitation energy through close col-

lisions between excited and unexcited molecules. The energy levels of the molecules will, in general, be significantly perturbed by such collisions, and thus the absorption and emission spectra of the components may be changed. If, on occasion, only a small amount of the excitation energy is removed, this being transformed into vibrational energy of the acceptor molecule, the excited molecule may be brought into the triplet state (Pringsheim, 1949, pp. 99–100). Such a process may occur with particularly high probability if the acceptor molecule contains an atom of high atomic number or is paramagnetic (Kasha, 1952; Kasha and McGlynn, 1956). The close collision mechanism is believed to be the most important one in the fluorescence of liquid organic solutions induced by high-energy radiation (Furst and Kallman, 1954). It has been shown to be unimportant in some UV-induced energy transfer phenomena (Hardwick, 1957).

3. The transfer of electronic excitation energy through collisions over a distance of several molecular diameters (resonance transfer) (Kallman and London, 1928; Förster, 1948, 1951; Vavilov, 1943). The main quantitative theory of resonance transfer is due to Förster (1951) and is based on a calculation of a mutually induced dipole interaction between donor and acceptor molecules, both of which are capable of being excited to the same energy level. The theory predicts that the probability of transfer is proportional to the extent of the overlap between the emission spectrum of the donor and the absorption spectrum of the acceptor, and also to the intensity of these transitions. This phenomenon may be thought of as being analogous to the property of resonance in organic molecules, inasmuch as, during the actual collision, the interaction between the molecules makes it impossible to consider the excitation energy as belonging to only one of the partners, but rather to both of them simultaneously. Thus, on subsequent separation of the colliding molecules, the energy has a definite calculable probability of being found in the previously unexcited molecule. Förster estimated that, for typical dye molecules (i.e., molecules with intense transitions in the visible region), the probability of energy transfer during an excited state lifetime of 10^{-8} sec will become equal to the probability of fluorescence when the colliding molecules come within about 100 A of each other, i.e., about 10 times their ordinary kinetic collision diameter. The probability of transfer, and thus the

number of molecules over which transfer occurs, is also inversely proportional to the sixth power of the distance between the molecules and thus directly proportional to the square of the concentration. In general, the absorption and emission spectra of the components will not be changed by resonance transfer. This mechanism is generally considered to be the most important one in visible or UV-induced energy transfer phenomena.

Experimental Aspects of Energy Transfer

Efficient energy transfer has been demonstrated thus far only from aromatic compounds, with one exception, 1,4-dioxane (Kallman *et al.*, 1956). Energy transfer from many other types of organic molecules, both saturated and unsaturated, has been observed, but only with lower efficiency. This is probably due to the fact that the excited state lifetimes of these molecules are much shorter than those of the aromatic solvents. Thus, a higher concentration of acceptor molecules is necessary. With such poor solvents it is possible to increase the yield of energy transfer by adding a small amount, say 10%, of an efficient energy acceptor. This acceptor will then mediate the transfer of energy from solvent to solute.

The general types of observable phenomena which can be interpreted in terms of energy transfer are as follows:

1. *Sensitized emission.* In such measurements one dissolves a small amount of an emitting substance in a solvent which absorbs energy at somewhat shorter wavelengths (i.e., higher energy) than does the solute. Upon excitation of such a system with radiation absorbed only by the solvent, the resulting emitted light is that characteristic of the solute. The solvent emission is normally almost completely absent.

2. *Concentration depolarization.* The fluorescence emitted by dilute solutions of organic molecules in viscous solvents is normally partially polarized owing to a limited amount of orientation of the molecules. As the concentration is increased, however, the extent of polarization decreases. This is due to a transfer of excitation energy between molecules in different orientations.

3. *Self-quenching of fluorescence.* The quantum yield of fluorescence of solutions of organic molecules generally decreases with increasing concentration. This phenomenon is made somewhat more

complicated by the possible occurrence of other effects such as the equilibrium formation of relatively stable, nonfluorescent dimers (Rabinowitch and Epstein, 1941). In many cases, the nature of the concentration dependence and also the effects of temperature and viscosity enable one to decide between the mechanisms. If resonance transfer is to lead to self-quenching, some of the molecules must be in a nonfluorescent state and, furthermore, the lifetime of such a state must be comparable to or longer than the average time which the excitation energy spends in any one molecule. Förster (1951) suggests that such a nonfluorescent energy sink is a statistical dimer.

4. *Quenching of fluorescence by solutes.* This phenomenon is essentially similar to self-quenching in that the final energy acceptor must be nonfluorescent, the electronic excitation energy eventually being degraded into the thermal energy of the solvent. Interpretations in terms of resonance transfer may be complicated by the occurrence of intermolecular spin-orbital perturbations (Kasha and McGlynn, 1956) leading to an increased probability of an intersystem crossing into the triplet state.

It would be impossible here to review all of the many systems in which the above phenomena have been observed. However, we will mention a few of the more significant examples. Förster (1949), in a study of the concentration dependence of the quenching of the fluorescence of solutions of tryptaflavine by rhodamine B, demonstrated that nonradiative energy transfer occurs efficiently at distances as great as 70 A, in agreement with the predictions of his theory. Similarly, Lavorel (1957), in a study of alkaline fluorescein solutions, was able to calculate that a resonance transfer of energy occurred over an average of about 300 molecules. Of particular biological significance is the demonstration by Watson and Livingston (1950) and by Duysens (1951) of the sensitization of chlorophyll *a* fluorescence in methanol solution by chlorophyll *b*. In addition, there have been a number of studies of energy transfer in protein-dye conjugates (Shore and Pardee, 1956) whereby energy absorbed in the protein (e.g., lysozyme, bovine, plasma albumin, chymotrypsinogen, and ribonuclease) portion of the conjugate excited the fluorescence of the dye (e.g., 1-dimethylaminonaphthalene-5-sulfonyl chloride).

A series of very interesting experiments by Terenin and Ermolaev

(Terenin and Ermolaev, 1952, 1956; Ermolaev, 1955) has demonstrated sensitized phosphorescence in rigid solutions at −180°C. These workers studied various combinations of naphthalene, benzaldehyde, biphenyl, and benzophenone. The donor molecule was selected to have its lowest excited singlet state below that of the acceptor and its lowest triplet above that of the acceptor. When such mixtures were illuminated with light absorbed only by the donor, the phosphorescence of the acceptor was sensitized and that of the donor was quenched. They interpreted these results in terms of an energy transfer between the triplet states of the molecules involved.

Although the application to biology of the concepts outlined above must at present be reserved mainly for the future, there are a number of examples which one might cite in which energy transfer is of importance. The first, of somewhat trivial significance, is scintillation counting (Birks, 1953), in which solutions of hydrocarbons are used to detect and measure high-energy radiations in tracer work. The second is the well-known demonstration of the transfer of energy from various plant pigments such as phycocyanin and phycoerythrin to chlorophyll in plant material (Wassink, 1948; French and Young, 1952). Finally, we might mention the experiments of Arnold and Meek (1956), who have demonstrated the transfer of energy among chlorophyll molecules in the grana through a study of the polarization of the fluorescence. Rabinowitch (1957) has suggested that this energy migration is a result of resonance transfer and has estimated that, for excited state lifetimes of about 10^{-9} sec and intermolecular distances between chlorophyll molecules of about 10 A, energy transfer chains of the order of 100 or 1000 molecules could easily occur.

GENERAL CONSIDERATIONS OF ENERGY TRANSFER IN ORDERED SYSTEMS

Theoretical Aspects

There are three mechanisms by which energy transfer may proceed in ordered systems. These are:

1. The emission of a quantum of radiation followed by its reabsorption by an unexcited molecule. This is analogous to the mechanism proposed for fluid solutions. The main proponent of this theory has

been Birks (1953). There is some disagreement as to the importance of this mechanism (Bowen and Lawley, 1949; Bowen, 1951), and it has been shown to be of little significance in a number of instances (Ferguson, 1956a,b).

2. Resonance transfer analogous to unordered systems (Franck and Livingston, 1949; Livingston, 1957). According to this theory, the energy is transferred by an overlap of the electronic systems of the excited donor and the unexcited acceptor molecules. In this case, the interaction between molecules is small enough to permit them to be considered as individual electronic systems. The probability of transfer will increase with the magnitude of the interaction.

3. The migration of excitons throughout the crystal (Curran, 1953; Davydov, 1948; French and Teller, 1938; Frenkel, 1931; Kittel, 1956; Leverenz, 1950; Peirls, 1922). The main features of this theory may

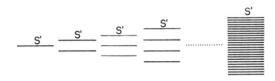

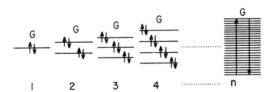

FIG. 2.   Schematic representation of the formation of energy bands in crystals through the interaction of n molecules. The pairs of arrows represent electrons with antiparallel spins. *G*, ground state; *S'*, lowest excited singlet state.

be understood by a consideration of the diagram in Fig. 2. The interactions between the pi-orbitals of the *n* molecules in the crystal are so large as to lead to a splitting of the energy levels, resulting in the formation of *n* closely spaced levels. In general, the lower band of levels will be completely occupied by electrons, whereas the upper bands will be vacant. Absorption of a quantum of light will raise an electron from the lowest, ground state, band into the upper, singlet state, band. Inasmuch as the levels in this upper band are very closely spaced, at most temperatures the thermal energy will be sufficient to allow the electron to move from any one level in the band to any other level. Thus, the excited state cannot be considered as belonging to any one molecule in the crystal, but rather must be considered as belonging to the crystal as a whole. We thus arrive at a concept of an excited state free to migrate throughout an ordered array of molecules. Such an excited state can be visualized as consisting of a negatively charged electron in the upper, or excited, band and a positively charged hole (the vacancy left by the electron when it is raised into the upper band) in the lower, or valence, band. This is shown schematically in Fig. 3.

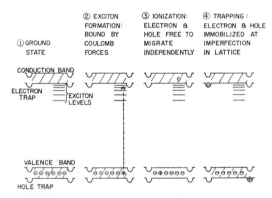

FIG. 3. Schematic representation of conduction bands and trapping levels in an ordered array of molecules.

This electron-hole pair will attract each other through ordinary Coulomb forces and will migrate as a unit throughout the crystal. Such a state of the crystal is called an exciton, inasmuch as it is formally equivalent to a neutral, massless particle with spin zero traveling through the crystal. It is apparent that it is possible to have triplet excitons as well as singlet excitons.

In an ideal crystal, such an exciton would migrate throughout the crystal until either it recombined with the emission of a quantum of radiation or its energy became degraded into the lattice vibrations of the crystal. However, all real crystals contain imperfections in the lattice structure resulting from dislocations, vacancies, impurities, etc. Such imperfections will cause some of the excitons to be ionized, i.e., the electron and the hole will no longer be constrained to migrate as a unit, but rather each will be capable of moving independently of the other. Furthermore, the crystal imperfections will give rise to trapping centers which are capable of immobilizing the electrons or the holes or both. These traps may be considered as energy levels lying somewhat below the lowest level of the conduction band. Ultimately, the electrons and holes will recombine with each other, but it is quite possible for them to have very different histories before recombination, spending various amounts of time trapped in impurities and imperfections in different parts of the crystal. In general, the most mobile entities in organic crystals are the holes (Kallman and Silver, 1956).

There is some controversy in the literature (Birks, 1953) as to whether exciton migration or resonance transfer is the most significant mechanism for energy transfer in ordered systems. The objections of Franck and Livingston (1949) and of Livingston (1957) to the exciton theory, in the case of anthracene crystals, are primarily that one cannot account for the absorption and emission spectra of the pure crystals in terms of it. However, it must be pointed out that an adequate quantum mechanical interpretation of the absorption spectrum of crystalline anthracene has been given by Davydov (1948) and by Craig and Hobbins (1955) on the basis of exciton theory. Furthermore, recent work (Compton et al., 1957) on the photoconductivity (see below) of anthracene crystals and on the sensitized fluorescence of impurities in anthracene crystals suggests that both of these phenomena represent alternative pathways for the degradation of an exciton, which probably takes place at a dislocation in the crystal.

Experimental Aspects

The above discussion, while greatly oversimplified, enables one to obtain insight into many of the electronic properties of organic crystals, some of which include:

1. *Photoconductivity*. The electrons and holes formed as a result of the absorption of light, being free to migrate throughout the crystal, endow the crystal with the property of conducting an electric current.

The exciton itself, being neutral, does not contribute to the photoconductivity.

2. *Semiconductivity.* At room temperature, the thermal energy is normally insufficient to achieve a very large dark population of the conduction band in most crystals. However, as the temperature is raised, more and more electrons are excited into the conduction band in accordance with Boltzmann's law. Thus, many crystals that are insulators at low temperatures exhibit an increasing conductivity as a function of temperature.

3. *Luminescence.* There are, in general, four main mechanisms of luminescence in organic crystalline semiconductors, not all of which need be operative simultaneously. These are: (*a*) direct decay of the exciton (fluorescence or phosphorescence), (*b*) recombination and radiative decay of the electron and hole subsequent to ionization but prior to trapping, (*c*) excitation of the trapped electron and/or hole into the conduction band followed by recombination and radiative decay, and (*d*) transfer of the excitation energy to a fluorescent impurity in the crystalline lattice (sensitized fluorescence).

Luminescence processes *a*, *b*, and *c* will all lead to emissions of the same wavelength but with different time constants and temperature dependencies. Process *a* will be relatively temperature independent; process *b* may or may not exhibit a temperature coefficient depending upon the actual mechanism of ionization; process *c* will have a very definite temperature dependence as a function of the depth of the traps.

4. *Thermoluminescence.* If the trap depths are such that, at a given temperature, the excitation of the trapped electron or hole into the conduction band does not proceed at a measurable rate, irradiation followed by an increase in temperature will lead to luminescence. Under such conditions, the luminescence vs. temperature curve of the crystal will exhibit peaks corresponding to the various trap depths.

A typical example of an energy transfer process in molecular crystals is given by the study of Bowen and co-workers (1949) on anthracene crystals. They found that the presence of 0.1% of naphthacene in anthracene almost completely quenches the blue-violet fluorescence of anthracene and replaces it with the yellow-green emission of naphthacene. The quantum yield of this process is only slightly less than that of the fluorescence of pure anthracene. Similarly, traces of anthracene in naphthalene replaces the UV fluorescence of the naphthalene with the blue-violet anthracene fluorescence. The semiconductivity and photoconductivity of anthracene have been quite extensively studied (Compton *et al.*, 1957) and, of somewhat more biological interest, similar studies have been carried out on the phthalocyanines (Fielding and Gutman, 1957)

A very interesting series of experiments (Borthwick *et al.*, 1952; Evanari and Stein, 1953; Evanari *et al.*, 1953; Stein, 1954) on the germination of seed by Hendricks and co-workers and by Evanari and co-workers has shown that red light (5250–7000 A) stimulates such germination whereas infrared radiation (7000–8200 A) reverses this effect. These effects show a marked resemblance to phenomena exhibited by many crystalline phosphors, and, in fact, the suggestion has been made that these phenomena are the result of the formation of trapped electrons in a semiconducting system by the action of the red light and of the detrapping of the electrons by the infrared light. It will be interesting to see if further experimentation supports this viewpoint.

ENERGY TRANSFER IN GREEN PLANT MATERIALS

Katz, in 1949, and, independently, Bradley and Calvin, in 1955, suggested that aggregates of chlorophyll molecules in the chloroplasts might give rise to conduction bands in which photoproduced electrons and holes could migrate. Such a system would have the advantage of providing for a separation of the oxidizing and reducing entities known to be necessary for photosynthesis.

This concept remained purely speculative until, quite recently, a number of researches have been published which suggest that something of this nature may indeed take place within chloroplasts. In 1956 Commoner and co-workers published evidence for the presence of a light-induced electron spin resonance (ESR) in spinach chloroplasts due to the photoproduction of unpaired electrons. Again, in 1957, these co-workers showed the presence of two kinds of unpaired spins, one of which is transformed into the other. In 1957 Arnold and Sherwood studied dried chloroplast films and found them to exhibit semiconductivity and thermoluminescence. In addition some studies by

Strehler and co-workers (Strehler, 1951; Strehler and Arnold, 1951; Strehler and Lynch, 1957; Arthur and Strehler, 1957) have demonstrated the existence of temperature-dependent long-lived luminescences in algae and in chloroplasts.

Our own experiments in this area began in 1956 with the demonstration by Sogo of a light-induced ESR signal in dried eucalyptus leaves. Inasmuch as these results were rather poorly reproducible, it was decided to study isolated chloroplasts (Sogo et al., 1957). Furthermore, when it became apparent that the spin resonance signals decayed fairly rapidly when the light was turned off, the possibility that at least part of the energy associated with these unpaired spins might appear as luminescence led us to a study of the light emission properties of the chloroplasts (Tollin and Calvin, 1957).

The chloroplasts are prepared (Sogo et al., 1957) by grinding spinach leaves in a blendor and carrying out a series of differential centrifugations. These enable us to obtain what we shall call intact chloroplasts and large and small chloroplast fragments.

Some typical ESR curves for wet, large chloroplast fragments are shown in Fig. 4. These curves are essentially plots of microwave power absorbed in the sample vs. magnetic field strength. It is seen that there

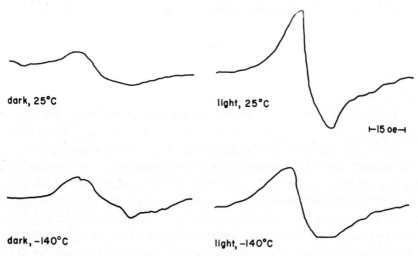

dark, 25°C   light, 25°C   ⊢15 oe⊣

dark, −140°C   light, −140°C

Fɪɢ. 4.   Typical spin resonance spectra from wet, large spinach chloroplast fragments.

is an increase in the number of unpaired spins when the light is turned on both at room temperature and at $-140°C$. These signals represent approximately 10^{16} unpaired spins. The wavelengths of light effective in exciting these signals are between 3500 A and 4500 A and between 6000 A and 7000 A, indicating absorption by chlorophyll. A rough quantum yield measurement indicates a value lying between 0.1 and 1.

Figure 5 shows some results of growth and decay time measure-

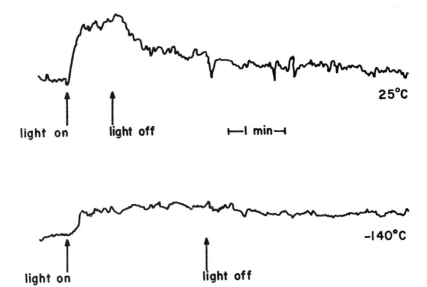

FIG. 5.   Some results of growth and decay time measurements on wet, large spinach chloroplast fragments.

ments on the same samples. In this case, the curves represent power absorption vs. time at constant magnetic field strength. The half-time for the decay at 25°C is of the order of 30 sec. At low light intensities (about 10^{15} quanta per sec), the rise time is about 30 sec, and at higher light intensities (about 10^{16} quanta per sec) the rise time is about 6 sec. There is good reason to believe that even the 6-sec figure is light-limited. At $-140°C$, essentially the same rise times are observed, but the decay time is of the order of hours. This effect of cooling is completely reversible. With dried chloroplasts at 25°C, the rise times are similar, but the decay times are of the order of hours. How-

TABLE I. Comparison of ESR and Luminescence Observations on Chloroplasts

	Rise Time		Decay Time	
t, °C	ESR*	700–900 mμ Luminescence*	ESR[a]	700–900 mμ Luminescence[a]
		Wet Chloroplasts		
25	~sec (light-limited)	<0.1 sec	~30 sec	0.15 sec (6%) 2.15 sec (94%)
−140	~sec (light-limited)	No signal	~hr	No signal
		Dried Chloroplasts		
25	~min	No signal	~hr	No signal
60	~sec	?	~sec	~sec

[a] Excited by wavelengths between 350–450 mμ or 600–700 mμ.

ever, at 60°C, the decay time of the dried material is of the order of seconds. These figures are summarized again in Table I.

Some of the luminescence decay curves for wet, whole spinach chloroplasts are shown in Fig. 6. The apparatus (Tollin and Calvin,

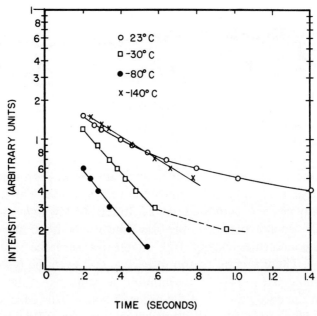

FIG. 6. Luminescence decay curves for wet, whole spinach chloroplasts at four temperatures: log intensity vs. time.

1957) is designed so that we are able to observe continuously the light emitted from the chloroplasts approximately 0.1 sec after excitation by a flash of light. An analysis of these curves and those for intermediate temperatures demonstrates that the room temperature emission consists of at least three components having different temperature dependencies and having half-lives of 0.15, 2, and 15 sec, respectively. Approximately 6% of the total integrated light intensity up to about 7 sec after the flash is due to the 0.15-sec emission. When the chloroplasts are cooled, the slower components diminish in intensity and vanish at about $-35°C$. At this temperature, the decay curve is the same as that obtained by subtracting the slower components from the room temperature curve. When the chloroplasts are cooled still further, the 0.15-sec component diminishes in intensity, its decay constant remaining approximately the same, and it is gone at about $-100°C$. At about $-90°C$, a fourth emission begins to grow in and gradually increases in intensity down to liquid nitrogen temperature. This emission has a half-life of about 0.3 sec. These cooling effects are completely reversible. Both large and small spinach chloroplast fragments behave similarly.

The excitation and emission spectra of the luminescence were measured by using Corning glass filters between the flash and the sample and between the sample and the detector. Such experiments demonstrate that the room temperature and $-40°C$ emissions are excited by the same bands of wavelengths that induce the electron spin resonance, thus again indicating absorption by chlorophyll. These emissions consist of wavelengths lying between 7000 A and 9000 A. The crude measurements indicate that at least 90% of the emitted light is of longer wavelengths than 7000 A. The *in vivo* fluorescence from the chlorophyll singlet lies mainly between 6500 A and 7200 A. This suggests that we are observing the lowest triplet state of chlorophyll rather than the lowest singlet. However, better spectra[2] are needed to

---

[2] Subsequent to this Conference, accurate measurements of the luminescence emission spectra under various conditions were carried out (see Tollin, Fujimori, and Calvin, 1958; Tollin, Sogo, and Calvin, 1958). These measurements demonstrate that the luminescence of spinach chloroplasts does not originate in the triplet state of chlorophyll as is tentatively suggested above but is, rather, the result of the singlet state to ground state transition of chlorophyll. A fuller discussion of the implications of this finding is presented in the above-mentioned references.

clarify this point, and these are in the process of being measured in our laboratory. Similar experiments demonstrate that the low-temperature 0.3-sec emission is excited only by wavelengths between 3500 A and 4500 A (light between 6000 A and 7000 A has no effect) and that this emission consists of wavelengths between 10,000 A and 12,000 A.

Figure 7 shows the effects of allowing freshly prepared chloroplasts

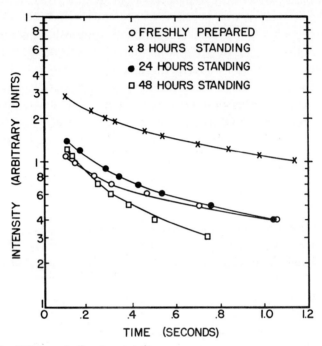

FIG. 7. Effects of allowing freshly prepared wet, whole spinach chloroplasts to stand in the dark at 23°C.

to stand in the dark at 23°C. Up to 8 hr, the luminescence gradually increases in intensity and reaches a maximum intensity of 2.7 times that of freshly prepared material. This larger signal exhibits the same decay curve, wavelength properties, and temperature behavior as does the original signal. Allowing the chloroplasts to stand still longer decreases the luminescence intensity and causes changes in the decay curve. After about 72 hr the luminescence has disappeared entirely, and the chloroplasts will exhibit thermoluminescence similar to that observed by Arnold and Sherwood (1957) for quick-dried chloro-plasts.

While it is not possible to compare quantitatively the ESR results with the luminescence results at this time, there are a number of quali-tative similarities that are significant. These are summarized in Table I.

1. Both phenomena are excited by the same bands of wavelengths and both are due to absorption by chlorophyll.

2. The 25°C decay times for wet chloroplasts are of the same order of magnitude for both phenomena. Inasmuch as the ESR spectrometer had a time constant of 2 sec, the ESR decay corresponding to the shorter luminescence decay times could not have been detected.

3. At −140°C, the ESR decay times are of the order of hours and no luminescence could be detected (a luminescence with a decay time of the order of hours would be undetectable with the apparatus used in the present studies).

4. The decay time of the ESR at 25°C for dried chloroplasts is of the order of hours, and under similar conditions the chloroplasts did not luminesce.

5. At 60°C, the ESR of the dried chloroplasts had a decay time of the order of seconds. At this same temperature, we have observed a peak in the thermoluminescence of the dried chloroplasts.

The above similarities strongly suggest that the 7000–9000 A light emission of chloroplasts is at least in part the result of the decay of the unpaired spins detected by the ESR experiments. A quantitative com-parison of the quantum yields, action spectra, and kinetic constants of these two phenomena is now being carried out. This should lead to a more definitive assessment of the relationships between them.

There are four possible mechanisms for the production of either ESR or delayed light emission in systems of the type we are concerned with here: (1) the production of radicals by the direct photodissocia-tion of a single bond, followed by their recombination in the dark, (2) the excitation and decay of a triplet state, (3) the reversible photo-sensitization of chemical or enzymatic processes leading to the produc-tion of free radicals, and (4) production of trapped electrons in a quasi-ordered lattice.

Mechanism (1) is incompatible with the following considerations. No known stable naturally occurring chemical bond can be dissociated by 6000–7000 A light. Furthermore, decay times of the order of many seconds are not in the range to be expected for radical recombinations at relatively high temperatures. Finally, it is difficult to reconcile such a mechanism with the existence of three separate emissions of the same wavelength.

The excitation and decay of a long-lived triplet state, as in mechanism (2), is incompatible with the observed definite temperature dependence of the chloroplast luminescence, i.e., it is very unlikely that lowering the temperature to $-100°C$ would increase the triplet lifetime to the order of hours. Furthermore, such a mechanism cannot result in three separate emission acts having different time constants but of the same wavelength.

If enzymatic processes were involved here, as in mechanism (3), cooling to $-140°C$ should decrease the rates of these processes to essentially zero. This is not in accord with the fact that the rise time and the concentration of unpaired spins are about the same at this temperature as at $25°C$. Similarly, the presence of the 0.15-sec emission down to as low a temperature as $-100°C$ rules out the participation of enzymatic processes in either the forward or reverse transformations in this case. If, then, only the 2- and 15-sec emissions represent chemical processes, one would expect that cooling, by preventing the reaction leading to radical formation from taking place, would result in a greater amount of energy appearing in the form of the 0.15-sec decay. In fact, the emission at $-80°C$ is less than it is at room temperature. Such a viewpoint is supported by the aging experiments mentioned earlier. Thus, if one assumes that the aging process involves the inactivation of enzymes, the creation of centers (or radicals) for the 2- and 15-sec emission processes by enzymatic means should be reduced. This reduction of competitive processes should then lead to an increase in the 0.15-sec emission intensity together with a concomitant decrease in the 2- and 15-sec emission intensities. In fact, for aging periods up to 8 hr, all three emission intensities are increased by the same amount.

We are thus left with mechanism (4) as the most likely explanation for the phenomena we are reporting here. We shall next see how such a scheme fits the data. Figure 8 shows a schematic representation of the electronic energy bands in chloroplasts. Light is absorbed to pro-

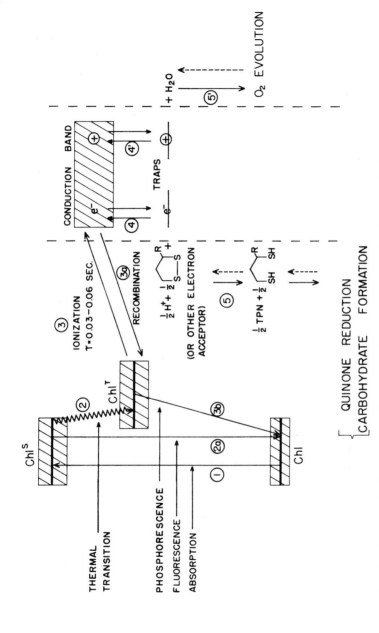

Fig. 8.   Proposed scheme for various photochemical processes in photosynthesis.

duce the transition from the ground state band of an aggregate of chlorophyll molecules to the first excited singlet state band (process 1). From the first excited singlet, the energy is split between conversion to an exciton in the first excited triplet band (process 2) and fluorescence (process 2a). All these processes are well known in ordinary molecular systems, and all will have time constants of the order of 10^{-8} sec or faster.

According to this picture, the triplet state excitons will undergo ionization resulting in electrons and holes in the conduction band (process 3). At the instant the exciting light is turned off, then, a certain fraction of these electrons and holes will be in the traps (processes 4 and 4'). The number of these traps in the chloroplast is probably very small, perhaps of the order of one per several thousand chlorophyll molecules. Thus, this scheme leads directly to the idea of a "photosynthetic unit." (Gaffron and Wohl, 1936.) A small proportion of the remaining electrons and holes will be near enough to each other to recombine (process 3a) and return to the ground state via process 3b. We will identify this recombination process with the rate-limiting step of the 0.15-sec emission. The decay constant of such a process should be relatively temperature independent and the experimental results are in accord with this. The fact that the intensity of this emission decreases with the temperature suggests the existence of a process the rate of which increases with decreasing temperature and which is competitive with the recombination. Whether this is the actual trapping of the electron or hole or is some side process is not known.

Arthur and Strehler (1957) observed a temperature-independent emission in chloroplasts with a half-life of about 0.01 sec. It is possible that this emission represents the direct decay of the exciton via process 3b.

The electrons and holes that are trapped will give rise to a spin resonance signal. The traps will be thermally depopulated and the resultant electrons and holes in the conduction band will recombine and a temperature-dependent luminescence will result. The 2- and 15-sec lifetime emissions may then be identified with the depopulation of traps of different depths. At low temperatures, the thermal energy will be insufficient to excite the electrons and holes out of the traps. This will result in the disappearance of the luminescence and the appearance of a long-lived ESR signal. According to this picture, the thermoluminescence referred to earlier would be the result of a deepening of the traps due to drying.

The electrons and holes in the traps may also be used up by enzymatic processes (processes 5 and 5′). Any reversibility in these enzymatic processes would then lead to a long-lived luminescence which could be classified as a chemiluminescence. It is likely that some of the longer-lived emissions reported by Strehler and co-workers (Strehler, 1951; Strehler and Arnold, 1951) are of this nature and perhaps also the 15-sec emission reported here. The fact that almost three times as much energy is emitted as light in aged chloroplasts as in fresh chloroplasts suggests that these enzymes are easily inactivated and that this enzymatic utilization represents the normal pathway for most of the electrons and holes in the living cell. In this way the light energy could be made available to the photosynthetic mechanism.

REFERENCES

Arnold, W., and E. S. Meek. 1956. The polarization of fluorescence and energy transfer in grana. *Arch. Biochem. Biophys., 60,* 82–90.

Arnold, W., and H. K. Sherwood. 1957. Are chloroplasts semiconductors? *Proc. Natl. Acad. Sci. U. S., 43,* 105–14.

Arthur, W. E., and B. L. Strehler. 1957. Studies on the primary process in photosynthesis. I. Photosynthetic luminescence: Multiple reactants. *Arch. Biochem. Biophys., 70,* 507–26.

Birks, J. B. 1953. *Scintillation Counters.* Pergamon Press, London.

Borthwick, H. A., S. B. Hendricks, M. W. Parker, E. H. Toole, and V. Toole. 1952. Reversible photoreaction controlling seed germination. *Proc. Natl. Acad. Sci. U. S., 38,* 662–66.

Bowen, E. J. 1951. Resonance transfer of energy between molecules. *Symposia Soc. Exptl. Biol.,* No. 5, 152–60.

Bowen, E. J., and P. D. Lawley. 1949. Crystal size and fluorescence intensity. *Nature, 164,* 572–73.

Bowen, E. J., E. Mikiewicz, and F. Smith. 1949. Resonance transfer of electronic energy in organic crystals. *Proc. Phys. Soc. (London), 62,* 26–31.

Bradley, D. F., and M. Calvin. 1955. The effect of thioctic acid on the quantum efficiency of the Hill reaction in intermittent light. *Proc. Natl. Acad. Sci. U. S., 41,* 563–71.

Cario, G., and J. Franck. 1922. The dissociation of hydrogen molecules by means of excited mercury atoms. *Z. Physik, 11,* 161.

———. 1923. Sensitized fluorescence of gases. *Z. Physik, 17,* 202–208.

Commoner, B., J. J. Heise, B. B. Lippincott, R. E. Norberg, J. V. Passoneau, and J. Townsend. 1957. Biological activity of free radicals. *Science, 126,* 57–63.

Commoner, B., J. J. Heise, and J. Townsend. 1956. Light-induced paramagnetism in chloroplasts. *Proc. Natl. Acad. Sci. U. S., 42,* 710–18.

Compton, D. M. J., W. G. Schneider, and T. C. Waddington. 1957. Photoconductivity of anthracene. III. *J. Chem. Phys., 27,* 160–72.

Craig, D. P., and P. C. Hobbins. 1955. The polarized spectrum of anthracene. Part I. The assignment of the intense short wavelength system. *J. Chem. Soc., 1955,* 539–48.

Curran, S. C. 1953. *Luminescence and the Scintillation Counter.* Academic, New York, Chaps. 6, 7.

Davydov, A. S. 1948. Theory of absorption spectra of molecular crystals. *J. Exptl. Theoret. Phys. U.S.S.R., 18,* 210–18.

Duysens, L. 1951. Transfer of light energy within the pigment systems present in photosynthesizing cells. *Nature, 168,* 548–50.

Ermolaev, V. 1955. Sensitized phosphorescence of organic molecules at low temperatures. *Doklady Akad. Nauk S.S.S.R., 102,* 925–30.

Evenari, M., G. Neumann, and G. Stein. 1953. Factors modifying the influence of light on germination. *Nature, 172,* 452–53.

Evenari, M., and G. Stein. 1953. The influence of light upon germination. *Experientia, 9,* 94–95.

Ferguson, J. 1956a. Migration of excitation energy in organic crystals. I. Tetracene included in anthracene. *Australian J. Chem., 9,* 160–71.

――――. 1956b. Migration of excitation energy in organic crystals. II. Solid solution of anthracene and tetracene in naphthalene. *Australian J. Chem.,* 172–79.

Fielding, P. E., and F. Gutman. 1957. Electrical properties of phthalocyanines. *J. Chem. Phys., 26,* 411–19.

Förster, T. 1948. Zwischenmolekulare Energiewanderung und Fluoreszenz. *Ann. Physik, 2,* 55–65.

――――. 1949. Versuche zum zwischenmolekularen Übergang von Elektronenanregungsenergie. *Z. Elektrochem., 53,* 93–99.

――――. (1951) *Fluoreszenz organischer Verbindungen.* Vanderhoeck and Ruprecht, Göttingen.

Franck, J., and R. Livingston. 1949. Intra- and inter-molecular migration of excitation energy. *Revs. Modern Phys., 21,* 505–509.

Franck, J., and E. Teller. 1938. Migration and photochemical action of excitation energy in crystals. *J. Chem. Phys., 6,* 861–72.

French, C. S., and V. K. Young. 1952. The fluorescence spectra of red algae and the transfer of energy from phycoerythrin to phycocyanin and chlorophyll. *J. Gen. Physiol., 35,* 873–90.

Frenkel, J. 1931. On the transformation of light into heat in solids. I. *Phys. Rev., 37,* 17–44.

Furst, M., and H. P. Kallman. 1954. Magnitude of excitation energy and energy transfer by collision. *Phys. Rev., 96,* 902–903.

Gaffron, N., and K. Wohl. 1936. The theory of assimilation. *Naturwissenschaften, 24,* 81–90; 103–107.

Hardwick, R. 1957. Role of collision transfers in fluorescent solutions. *J. Chem. Phys., 26,* 323–24.

Kallman, H. P., M. Furst, and F. H. Brown. 1956. Investigation of energy transfer in liquid organic systems. Paper presented at Symposium on Fluorescence and Semiconductors, Garmisch-Partenkirchen, Germany.

Kallman, K., and F. London. 1928. Über quantenmechanische Energieübertragung zwischen atomaren Systemen. *Z. phys. Chem., B2,* 207–43.

Kallman, H. P., and M. Silver. 1956. Hole motion in anthracene crystals. Paper presented at Symposium on Fluorescence and Semiconductors, Garmisch-Partenkirchen, Germany.

Kasha, M. 1952. Collisional perturbation of spin-orbital coupling and the mechanism of fluorescence quenching. A visual demonstration of the perturbation. *J. Chem. Phys., 20,* 71–74.

Kasha, M., and S. P. McGlynn. 1956. Molecular electronic spectroscopy. Spin intercombinations in molecules. *Ann. Rev. Phys. Chem., 7,* 403–24.

Katz, E. 1949. Chlorophyll fluorescence as an energy flowmeter in photosynthesis. *Photosynthesis in Plants,* W. E. Loomis and J. Franck, Editors. Iowa State College Press, Ames, pp. 291–95.

Kittel, C. 1956. *Introduction to Solid State Physics.* Wiley, New York, Chaps. 13, 17, and 18.

Lavorel, J. 1957. Effect of energy migration on fluorescence of dye solutions. *J. Phys. Chem., 61,* 864–69.

Leverenz, H. W. 1950. *An Introduction to the Luminescence of Solids.* Wiley, New York.

Livingston, R. 1957. Intermolecular transfer of electronic excitation. *J. Phys. Chem., 61,* 860–64.

Peirls, R. 1922. Zur Theorie der absorptionsspektren fester Körper. *Ann. Phys., 13,* 905–15.

Pringsheim, P. 1949. *Fluorescence and Phosphorescence.* Interscience, New York.

Rabinowitch, E. I. 1957. Photosynthesis and energy transfer. *J. Phys. Chem., 61,* 870–78.

Rabinowitch, E. I., and L. Epstein. 1941. Polymerization of dye-stuffs in solution. Thionine and methylene blue. *J. Am. Chem. Soc., 63,* 69–78.

Shore, V. G., and A. B. Pardee. 1956. Energy transfer in conjugated proteins and nucleic acids. *Arch. Biochem. Biophys., 62,* 355–68.

Sogo, P. B., N. G. Pon, and M. Calvin. 1957. Photo spin resonance in chlorophyll-containing plant material. *Proc. Natl. Acad. Sci. U. S., 43,* 387–93.

Stein, G. 1954. Metastable states in irradiated biological systems. *J. chim. phys., 51,* 133–36.

Strehler, B. L. 1951. The luminescence of isolated chloroplasts. *Arch. Biochem. Biophys., 34,* 239–48.

Strehler, B. L., and W. Arnold. 1951. Light production by green plants. *J. Gen. Physiol., 34,* 809–20.

Strehler, B. L., and V. K. Lynch. 1957. Studies on the primary process in photosynthesis. II. Some relationships between light-induced absorption spectrum changes and chemiluminescence during photosynthesis. *Arch. Biochem. Biophys., 70,* 527–46.

Terenin, A., and V. Ermolaev. 1952. Sensitized phosphorescence of organic molecules at low temperatures. Intermolecular transfer of energy through the excited triplet state. *Doklady Akad. Nauk S.S.S.R., 85,* 547–50.

———. 1956. Sensitized phosphorescence in organic solutions at low temperatures. Energy transfer between triplet states. *Trans. Faraday Soc., 52,* 1042–52.

Tollin, G., and M. Calvin. 1957. The luminescence of chlorophyll-containing plant material. *Proc. Natl. Acad. Sci. U. S., 43,* 895–908.

Tollin, G., E. Fujimori, and M. Calvin. 1958. Action and emission spectra of the luminescence of plant materials. *Nature, 181,* 1266.

Tollin, G., P. B. Sogo, and M. Calvin. 1958. Energy transfer in ordered and unordered photochemical systems. *Ann. N. Y. Acad. Sci., 74,* 310.

Vavilov, S. I. 1925. The decrease in the fluorescence of solutions of dyestuffs at high concentrations. *Z. Physik, 31,* 750–55.

———. 1943. The theory of the influence of concentration on the fluorescence of solutions. *J. Phys. U.S.S.R., 7,* 141–48.

Wassink, E. C. 1948. Chromophyllins and the paths of energy transfer in photosynthesis. *Enzymologia, 12,* 362–72.

Watson, W., and R. Livingston. 1950. Self-quenching and sensitization of fluorescence of chlorophyll solutions. *J. Chem. Phys., 18,* 802–809.

SECTION II

Photocontrol of Seed Germination and
Vegetative Growth by Red Light

PHOTOPERIODISM IN SEEDS AND BUDS

P. F. WAREING
Department of Botany, University College of Wales,
Aberystwyth, Wales

Although only a small fraction of the total work on photoperiodism has been devoted to the effects of day length on dormancy, nevertheless it is clear that such effects are very widespread in higher plants, particularly in woody species. The seedlings of many woody species respond to short days by ceasing active extension growth and forming resting buds, whereas under long-day conditions the onset of dormancy is delayed or entirely suppressed (for the relevant literature, see Wareing, 1956). Moreover, in certain species, such as *Fagus sylvatica, Betula pubescens, Larix europaea,* and *Pinus* spp., seedlings that have been rendered dormant by previous short-day treatment can be induced to resume growth by transferring them to long-day conditions or continuous illumination. Even *leafless* dormant seedlings of these last species expand their buds under long days, whereas under short days they remain dormant. There is every indication that this is a real photoperiodic effect (Wareing, 1953). Thus, in these species we have photoperiodic sensitivity even in the very young leaf primordia present in the resting buds. When this fact was first established it seemed very unusual to find photoperiodic sensitivity in embryonic tissue, since it was generally held that, in the photoperiodic control of flowering in herbaceous species, it is only the fully expanded leaves which are sensitive to daylength conditions. More recently, however, it has been shown that, in *Xanthium,* it is the half-expanded leaves which are most sensitive (Khudairi and Hamner, 1954). The difference between woody and herbaceous species with respect to the sensitivity of the immature leaves would thus appear to be one of degree only.

SEED GERMINATION IN VARIOUS SPECTRAL REGIONS

The observation that the buds of birch seedlings show photoperiodic responses led us to investigate whether the seeds of this species show photoperiodic effects, and this was found to be so (Black and Wareing, 1954, 1955). The behavior of the seeds is markedly affected by temperature. At 15°C, the seeds show definite photoperiodic responses, so that a high germination is obtained under long days, whereas under short days germination is low. It is found that 8 long-day cycles are required to give maximum germination. At temperatures of 20–25°C, the response is radically modified and 50% germination will now occur in response to a single light exposure of 8 to 12 hr. At the higher temperature, therefore, the photoperiodic behavior is lost and germination occurs in response to a single light-exposure, as with lettuce seed. It is found that the most effective spectral region for stimulation of germination of birch seed lies in the red, and the effect of a single exposure to red radiation can be completely nullified if it is followed by infrared irradiation.

Photoperiodic effects in seeds have also been reported by Isikawa (1954) and Bünning et al. (1955), who found not only seeds in which germination is promoted by long days, but others which give a higher germination under short days than under long days. We have investigated (Black, 1957; Black and Wareing, 1957) the responses in such a "short-day" seed, as a corollary to our studies in birch seed, and for this purpose the seed of Nemophila insignis was selected, since it has long been known to be a light-inhibited seed (Lehmann, 1909). This seed is also known to be very temperature-sensitive, and germinates equally in light and dark at temperatures of 19°C or lower, whereas it is completely inhibited in both light and darkness at temperatures of 26°C and above. At 21–22°C, however, the germination is affected by the light conditions, and with white fluorescent tubes the response is markedly photoperiodic, a high germination percentage being obtained under short days, whereas germination is strongly inhibited under long days. The response is affected by the duration of both the light and the dark periods, but particularly by the latter. We have investigated the response of this seed to various spectral regions.

Earlier workers reported that the seed of Phacelia tanacetifolia, a species related to Nemophila, is inhibited by both blue and red light (Meischke, 1936; Resühr, 1939). For this purpose we used a set of 10 Schott interference filters (having a band pass of 10–14 mµ at half-maximum transmission) so chosen as to cover the range 405 to 760 mμ, at intervals of approximately 50 mμ between peaks. The source used was a 500-watt tungsten filament lamp. In order to eliminate the possibility of the transmittance of an appreciable quantity of infrared radiation, copper sulfate gelatin filters were used in conjunction with the blue interference filters. It was arranged that the energy level at the position of the seeds was the same (50 or 80 μw/cm^2) for each spectral region. It was found that *Nemophila* seed is inhibited by blue light (i.e., with filters peaking at 452, 483, and 496 mμ), but only slightly inhibited under the filters peaking at 542, 547, 596, and 651 mμ. The inhibition is very strong in the far red, at 710 mμ, and somewhat less at 760 mμ.

The possibility that the blue region was inhibitory because of "stray" far-red radiation seems to be excluded by the observation that similar inhibition could be obtained by using as a source blue fluorescent tubes in conjunction with blue Perspex (B.705) and 1-cm screen of $M/3$ copper chloride. The latter would effectively remove any small component of far-red radiation emitted by the tubes. In spite of this, the seeds were strongly inhibited by light from this source, which covered the band from 400 to 520 mμ. Thus, seed of *Nemophila* is inhibited not only by a far-red region, but also by blue light. These results agree very well with those of Resühr (1939) for *Phacelia tanacetifolia*. The inhibitory effect of far red is considerably greater than that of blue. Thus, a 4-hr daily photoperiod of far red brings about almost complete inhibition of *Nemophila* seed, whereas 16- to 20-hr photoperiods are required with blue radiation even at "saturating" intensities.

In view of the markedly inhibitory effect of blue in *Nemophila* it was decided to reinvestigate the reported effects of blue in lettuce seed. Flint and McAlister (1935) reported inhibitory effects of long periods of irradiation with blue light on lettuce seed. They exposed the seeds first to a short period of red light, sufficient to induce 50% germination, and then exposed them for 48 hr to various spectral regions. They found inhibition in the blue region and published a detailed action spectrum for this effect. Borthwick *et al.* (1954), apparently using short periods of irradiation, also reported both stimulation and inhibition of germination by blue alone, but the effects were not great. They found that maximum sensitivity for the promotive effect occurred at 12–20 hr of imbibition, and maximum sensitivity for inhibition after more than 48 hr from sowing. Also with short periods of irradiation Evenari and Stein (1957) confirmed that the promotive effect of blue light increases progressively during the first 16 hr of imbibition. With one type of filter they obtained inhibition during the first hours of imbibition, and this was followed by a promotive effect with longer periods of imbibition.

We have carried out experiments to determine how the responses of the seeds to blue light vary both with the imbibition period and with the duration of exposure. It was found that although a *short* period of irradiation with blue inhibits during the first 2–3 hr of imbibition, a longer exposure of 1–2 hr during this period is markedly stimulatory. As the period of imbibition increases, short periods of irradiation become promotive, whereas longer periods (1–2 hr) of irradiation become less promotive and ultimately become slightly inhibitory, after about 10 hr of imbibition (Fig. 1). Short periods of irradiation do not become inhibitory, at least up to 20 hr of imbibition.

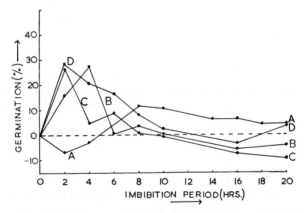

FIG. 1. Effect of irradiation with blue for various periods at different times during the period of imbibition. Blue fluorescent source. Intensity 100 μw/cm^2. The germination percentages represent differences from "dark" control (taken as 0%). Exposure periods (minutes): A, 10; B, 30; C, 60; D, 120.

Having determined the time at which the inhibitory effect becomes predominant, we investigated the interaction between the promotive effects of red light and the inhibitory effects of blue. Borthwick *et al.* (1954) were able to obtain only slight reversal of the promotive effect of red when the latter was followed by blue. The period of blue irradiation was not stated, but was presumably short. When we used 1½ min of red (at 100 μw/cm²), followed by various periods of blue (at 100 μw/cm²) ranging from ½ hr to 4 hr, some reversal was obtained with periods of 1–2 hr, but much more effective reversal was obtained with 4 hr of blue. In a further experiment, in which we used 1½ min of red and 4 hr of blue, the effects of a succession of irradiations with red and blue were investigated. It was found that repeated photoreversal can be obtained (Table I), and that the response of the seed

TABLE I. Lettuce, var. Grand Rapids, Photoreversal of Promotion and Inhibition of Germination by Red and Blue

Irradiation[a]	Germination
R	77.7
R – B	33.0
B – R	75.5
R – B – R	86.1
R – B – R – B	49.0
Dark control	29.0

[a] R, 1½ min red at 100 μw/cm² from fluorescent source; B, 4 hr blue at 100 μw/cm² from fluorescent source. Treatments were commenced 26 hr after sowing.

is determined by the nature of the last irradiation, as in the interaction between red and far red (Borthwick *et al.*, 1954). This would appear to be the first case in which successful reversal of the effects of red by blue have been obtained.

With the series of interference filters, we attempted to determine the effective spectral region for the inhibition of germination by blue, and it was found that the greatest inhibition was obtained with the filter peaking at 452 mμ.

The effects of blue have also been investigated in birch. We have never successfully induced any germination of birch by exposure to blue alone, but there is a marked interaction between blue and red. At a temperature of 21–22°C, birch seed was exposed to 8 hr of red light to induce germination, and this treatment was either preceded or followed by blue at 80 μw/cm², with the blue fluorescent source described above. It was found that 24 hr of blue given after the red markedly inhibited germination (Table II). On the other hand, blue

TABLE II. Seed of *Betula pubescens*, Effect of Various Periods
of Blue Irradiation Before and After Exposure to Red

Treatment	Percentage Germination
1. 8 hr red only	32.6
2. 8 hr red, preceded by blue: (a) 1½ hr	37.8
3. 8 hr red, preceded by blue: (b) 3 hr	52.5
4. 8 hr red, preceded by blue: (c) 12 hr	67.0
5. 8 hr red, preceded by blue: (d) 24 hr	70.6
6. 8 hr red, followed by blue: (a) 12 hr	16.5
7. 8 hr red, followed by blue: (b) 24 hr	13.1
8. 8 hr red, followed by blue: (c) 48 hr	19.2

Source, blue fluorescent tubes with blue Perspex and copper chloride
screen. Intensity, 80 μw/cm^2.

given before the red very strongly promoted germination. Further
experiments indicated that relatively long periods (about 12 hr) of
exposure to blue are necessary to obtain maximum stimulation or inhibition. Experiments with the interference filters indicated that the
most effective spectral region for these effects lies in the region of 452
mμ.

In order to explain the promotive and inhibitory effects of blue in
lettuce seed, Borthwick *et al.* (1954) have postulated that the photoreceptors for the red and far-red responses must have absorption
regions in the blue which overlap. This hypothesis would explain why
the response of the seed is so dependent upon the duration of exposure
and the period of imbibition, since these two variables can be envisaged as affecting the equilibrium between the promotive and inhibitory processes. The Beltsville group was unable to obtain any
appreciable reversal of the effects of red by blue, however. It is now
clear that, in order to obtain photoreversal, the period of irradiation
by blue must be about 4 hr, whereas much shorter periods are effective
with far red.

The greater period of exposure required with blue may result from
the fact that, even at long imbibition periods, there may still be some
promotive effect of blue and that the balance is only decisively toward
inhibition when longer periods of irradiation are used. Further, it is
known that light transmission by the seed coat of lettuce is very much
less for blue than for far red (Evenari, 1956), and it is possible that
shorter periods of irradiation with blue would be more effective at

higher intensities than that used ($100 \mu w/cm^2$) in the present experiments.

There would no longer seem to be any doubt that the inhibitory effects of far red and blue are operating through the same photoreceptor. This conclusion is in full agreement with the fact that blue and far red are frequently found to act similarly in internode elongation and in the flowering of certain species (see Wassink and Stolwijk, 1956). The promotive effects of blue on lettuce seed germination are best explained on the hypothesis that the photoreceptor for red also has an absorption in the blue, as suggested by Borthwick *et al.*

The effects of blue clearly merit further attention not only because of their importance for the study of dormancy, but also because elucidation of the phenomena in seeds may have an important bearing on the interpretation of the effects of blue on flowering.

POSSIBLE ROLE OF INHIBITORS IN DORMANCY

We turn now from a consideration of the photoreactions involved in seed photoperiodism to what would seem to be another important factor in determining the overall response. The first piece of work to be described was carried out on birch seed by Dr. M. Black at Manchester (1957).

Now, the light requirement of birch seed is a property only of the *intact* seed, since embryos from which the pericarp and endosperm have been dissected will germinate equally well in both light and dark and show no apparent photoperiodic effects at all. This indicates that the presence of the pericarp or endosperm must have an inhibitory effect on the growth of the embryo, and that light is necessary to enable the embryo to overcome this inhibitory effect.

Two possible ways in which this inhibitory effect might arise would appear to be that either (1) the pericarp or endosperm contains an inhibitory substance which holds the embryo dormant, or (2) these seed coverings might interfere with gaseous exchange, particularly with oxygen uptake by the embryo. Both these types of mechanism are known to play a role in the dormancy of certain seeds. In order to test the first possibility, birch seeds were extracted with 80% aqueous methanol, the extract was concentrated and then chromatographed on paper, with 80% aqueous isopropanol and 1% ammonia as a running solvent. After drying, the chromatogram was cut up into 10 equal strips, each of which was placed in a small petri dish and moistened with water. Ten isolated birch embryos were then planted on each of the filter paper strips and observations made on the growth inhibitory activity of the different regions of the chromatogram. It was found that there was a powerful growth inhibitor present on the chromatogram in the region Rf 0.7–0.9. The same inhibitory zone was found in a sample of birch achenes which were entirely lacking in the embryos. Thus, it would seem that the inhibitor is located primarily in the pericarp. The presence of a growth inhibitor in the pericarp does not, of course, necessarily imply that it constitutes the sole basis of the inhibitory effect of the pericarp on the embryo, and further experiments were carried out in an endeavor to obtain decisive evidence on this question.

First, it was found that when birch embryos were planted on the inhibitory zone and then exposed to different photoperiodic treatments a high proportion of embryos germinated when maintained under long days, but gave only a low germination percentage under short days. That is to say, whereas the isolated embryos planted on filter paper moistened only with water germinated equally well in both light and dark, when they are planted on filter paper containing the inhibitor their photoperiodic behavior is restored. In a further experiment, intact seeds were slowly leached in water in darkness for 3 weeks. They were then sown and held under long-day or short-day conditions, and their germination was compared with that of unleached seeds. It was found that in the leached seeds germination was high not only under long days but also under short days. The two foregoing experiments thus indicate that (1) the photoperiodic behavior of the intact seeds can be largely restored if isolated embryos are planted on the inhibitor, and (2) if the inhibitor is leached out of intact seeds, their photoperiodic behavior is largely lost. These results are, therefore, consistent with the hypothesis that the inhibitory effect of the pericarp arises primarily from the presence of the growth inhibitor. It was shown that at the low light intensities used, there is very little photodestruction of the inhibitor on the filter paper, and it would seem that the effect of light is primarily on the *embryo,* which is thereby stimulated to overcome the effect of the inhibitor.

On the other hand, it was found that it is not necessary to remove the pericarp from the embryo completely in order to abolish its light requirement. Slitting the pericarp and endosperm on one side, or even simply pricking, is sufficient to bring about an appreciable germination in the dark. This observation is difficult to interpret on the "inhibitor hypothesis" and suggests rather that the inhibitory effect of the pericarp is due to interference with gaseous exchange. Further evidence in support of this view is seen in the fact that pricking the pericarp is even more effective in stimulating germination if the seeds are subsequently maintained in an atmosphere of high oxygen content instead of in air. However, a high oxygen tension is ineffective if the pericarp is maintained intact. These results strongly suggest that interference with oxygen uptake also constitutes an important part of the inhibitory effect of the pericarp. Experiments to determine the minimum oxygen requirements for the growth of birch embryos indicated that they will germinate even in commercial nitrogen which has been passed through alkaline pyrogallol, and which must have had an extremely low oxygen content. Therefore, it seems unlikely that the oxygen requirement would not be met in an intact seed maintained in an atmosphere of 70% oxygen. Thus interference with oxygen uptake by the pericarp does not seem adequate to explain all the phenomena. Now, from a study of dormancy in *Xanthium* seeds it appears that both interference with oxygen uptake by the testa and the occurrence of a growth inhibitor in the embryo play important roles, and that oxygen is necessary for the breakdown of the inhibitor, before germination can occur (Wareing and Foda, 1957). A similar hypothesis would seem to be best adapted to explain the dormancy effects in birch seed. Some evidence in support of this hypothesis is seen from the results of an experiment in which leached and unleached seeds were first scratched and then exposed to various oxygen concentrations. It was found that leached seeds gave an appreciably higher germination at low oxygen tensions than did unleached seeds.

We have found that gibberellic acid is effective in breaking the dormancy of birch seed, as with lettuce seed (Lona, 1956; Kahn *et al.*, 1957). Moreover, the dormancy of birch and *Xanthium* seed has several other features in common with that of lettuce seed. For example, light-requiring lettuce seed may be induced to germinate if maintained in an atmosphere of pure oxygen (Borthwick and Robbins, 1928), or if the pericarp is split or pricked (Evenari and Neumann, 1952); this suggests that oxygen effects are important also in this seed.

These observations raise the question as to whether inhibitors also play a role in the dormancy of lettuce seed. The presence of inhibitors in lettuce seed has been demonstrated (Shuck, 1935; Wareing and Foda, 1957; Poljakoff-Mayber *et al.*, 1956), and one of these is a water-soluble substance occurring at about the same position on chromatograms as the main *Xanthium* inhibitor (Wareing and Foda, 1957). It has not been possible, however, to determine whether the inhibitors play any role in the dormancy of lettuce seed, which is, for this purpose, more difficult material than *Xanthium* seed. Nevertheless, the close parallel between the dormancy phenomena in the seeds of these two species (both members of the family Compositeae) strongly suggests that the underlying mechanism is the same in both cases. It is tempting, therefore, to postulate that the dormancy of lettuce seed involves a growth inhibitor, the effect of which is in some way overcome by light, as in birch seed. One difficulty for this hypothesis is that we have recently found that certain light-requiring varieties of lettuce seed contain no detectable amounts of the water-soluble inhibitor found in Grand Rapids. It must be remembered, however, that the light requirement of lettuce seed is very small, and this may arise from the fact that the level of inhibitor present is also very low.

The responses of birch seeds also have certain features in common with those of birch buds (Wareing, 1957). It seems unlikely that dormancy in the buds is due primarily to interference with oxygen exchange, since frequently it is observed that the terminal bud formed in response to short days is lax and by no means tightly enclosed by bud scales. Moreover, it is clear that interference with oxygen exchange by the bud scales cannot be the primary factor inducing the formation of resting buds, since until such a bud is formed there is no interference with oxygen exchange by the shoot apical region. On the other hand, some evidence that bud dormancy may be due to the presence of growth inhibitors has been put forward by Hemberg (1949) and others. It is possible, therefore, that the formation of resting buds in response to short days may be due to the production of greater amounts of a growth inhibitor under short days than under long days. We have carried out investigations to test this hypothesis using primarily *Acer pseudoplatanus* (Phillips and Wareing, 1958).

Preliminary experiments showed that there is an inhibitor in the leaves and buds of *A. pseudoplatanus* which is completely extractable with 80% aqueous methanol. After extracting the tissues with this solvent, the extracts were partitioned by paper chromatography by using a running solvent consisting of 80 parts isopropanol to 20 parts aqueous ammonia (0.88 S.G. x $\frac{1}{100}$). After development the chromatograms were eluted in water and assayed for growth activity by using primarily the wheat coleoptile section test. The growth inhibitor was found to occur between Rf 0.6 and 0.8. A study was made of the

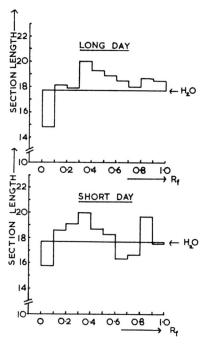

FIG. 2. Assay with wheat coleoptile sections of chromatographed extracts (each equivalent to 0.1 g dry weight of tissue) of mature leaves.

inhibitor contents of the leaves and shoot apices of seedlings grown
under long-day or short-day conditions. Samples of the leaves and
shoot apices were taken from each series after 2, 5, 10, and 33 days
following the commencement of the treatments. It was found that
there was consistently more inhibitor present in the leaves and shoot
apices of short-day seedlings than of long-day seedlings (Fig. 2). A
difference between the two series was detectable even after two short-
day cycles, but this became greater after five cycles (Fig. 3). We have

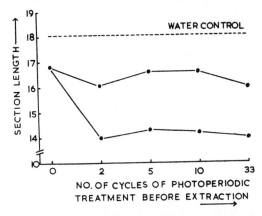

FIG. 3.   Coleoptile section assay of the inhibitory eluates (Rf 0.55–0.88)
from chromatograms of extracts of mature leaves. The extracts were
prepared from plants growing under controlled photoperiodic conditions;
the leaf samples were made at the start of the experiment, and after 2,
5, 10, and 33 cycles of long day or short day. Extract from 1.0 g dry
weight of tissue was chromatographed in each case. Upper curve, long day;
lower curve, short day.

confirmed these results several times. When the chromatograms were
assayed by planting seed of lettuce var. New Market (a non-light-
requiring variety) on the various zones, it was found that germination was markedly inhibited by the same region as were wheat coleoptiles, and that there were very great differences between the short-day
and long-day extracts in this respect. Recent experiments with extracts
of seedlings of birch grown under long and short days have given
similar results.

These results do not, of course, necessarily imply a causal relationship between the production of inhibitor and the induction of dor-

mancy. It is possible that the greater production of inhibitor under short days is the *result* of reduced growth. The observation that differences in inhibitor content can be detected after 2–5 days of treatment, although the short-day plants continued to expand leaves for a further 10 days, would seem to indicate, however, that the inhibitor differences are not primarily due to differences in growth. If the inhibitor hypothesis is substantiated, we shall have made an important step forward in the elucidation of the mechanism of photoperiodism in buds and seeds. It is not suggested that photoperiodic control of flowering necessarily involves growth inhibitors. Considerable evidence suggests that there is much in common between photoperiodism in dormancy phenomena and in the control of flowering (Wareing, 1956), and this would seem to imply that the basic light and dark processes are identical in both types of response. Nevertheless, the induction of dormancy is clearly different from the induction of flowering, and it is possible that the changes in inhibitor content observed in woody plants are secondary effects arising from earlier steps in the basic photoperiodic processes.

SUMMARY

Photoperiodic control of dormancy is well established for both buds and seeds. Among light-sensitive seeds the germination of some species is promoted by long days, whereas in others germination is inhibited by long days and promoted by short days. The seed of *Nemophila insignis* behaves as short-day seed at temperatures of 21–22°C. The seed of this species is inhibited by both far red and by blue.

A reexamination of the effects of blue in Grand Rapids lettuce seed has shown that blue may be promotive or inhibitory to germination depending upon the duration of exposure and the imbibition period. With 4-hr periods of blue, it is possible to reverse the effects of a preceding exposure to red. The photoreceptors for the well-known effects of red and far red in lettuce seed appear to have absorption bands in the blue which overlap. The inhibition of germination by blue and far red appears to involve the same photoreceptor.

Studies of dormancy in birch seed seem to indicate that the inhibitory effect of the pericarp and endosperm involve both the presence of a growth inhibitor and also interference with gaseous exchange. Light is apparently necessary to enable the embryo to overcome this inhibiting effect of the pericarp and endosperm.

A study of the growth inhibitors in *Acer pseudoplatanus* in relation to day length conditions seems to indicate that more inhibitor is produced in the leaves under short days than under long days, suggesting that onset of dormancy of the short apices in response to short days is due to the accumulation of inhibitor in this region under such day length conditions.

REFERENCES

Black, M. 1956. Interrelationships of germination inhibitors and oxygen in the dormancy of seed of *Betula*. *Nature, 178,* 924–25.

————. 1957. Dormancy studies in light-sensitive seeds. Ph.D. thesis, University of Manchester, Manchester, England.

Black, M., and P. F. Wareing. 1954. Photoperiodic control of germination in seed of birch (*Betula pubescens* Ehr.). *Nature, 174,* 705.

————. 1955. Growth studies in woody species. VII. Photoperiodic control of germination in *Betula pubescens* Ehr. *Physiol. Plantarum, 8,* 300–16.

————. 1957. Sensitivity of light-inhibited seeds to certain spectral regions. *Nature, 180,* 395.

Borthwick, H. A., S. B. Hendricks, E. H. Toole, and V. K. Toole. 1954. Action of light on lettuce-seed germination. *Botan. Gaz., 115,* 205–25.

Borthwick, H. A., and W. W. Robbins. 1928. Lettuce seed and its germination. *Hilgardia, 3,* 275–305.

Bünning, E., I. I. Chaudrhi, and Zain ul Abidin. 1955. Der Beziehung von Photo- und Thermoperiodismus bei der Samenkeimung zur endogenen Tagesrhythmik. *Ber. deut. Botan. Ges., 68,* 41–45.

Evenari, M. 1956. Seed germination. *Radiation Biology,* Vol. III, A. Hollaender, Editor. McGraw-Hill, New York.

Evenari, M., and G. Neumann. 1952. The germination of lettuce seed. II. The influence of fruit coat, seed coat and endosperm on germination. *Bull. Research Council Israel, 2,* 15–17.

Evenari, M., G. Neumann, and G. Stein. 1957. Action of blue light on the germination of seeds. *Nature, 180,* 609–10.

Flint, L. H., and E. D. McAlister. 1935. Wavelengths of radiation in the visible spectrum inhibiting the germination of light-sensitive lettuce seed. *Smithsonian Inst. Publs., Misc. Collections, 94,* 1–11.

Hemberg, T. 1949. Growth-inhibiting substances in the terminal buds of *Fraxinus*. *Physiol. Plantarum, 2,* 37–44.

Isikawa, S. 1954. Light sensitivity against germination. I. "Photoperiodism" of seeds. *Botan. Mag. Tokyo, 67,* 51–56.

Kahn, A., J. A. Goss, and D. E. Smith. 1957. Effect of gibberellin on germination of lettuce seed. *Science, 125,* 645–46.

Khudairi, A. K., and K. C. Hamner. 1954. The relative sensitivity of *Xanthium* leaves of different ages to photoperiodic induction. *Plant Physiol., 29,* 251–57.

Lehmann, E. 1909. Zur Keimungs-physiologie und -biologie von *Ranunculus sceleratus* und einiger anderen Samen. *Ber. deut. botan. Ges., 27,* 476.

Lona, F. 1956. L'acido gibberellico determina la germinazione dei semi di *Lactuca scariola* in fase di scoto-inibizione. *Ateneo parmense, 27* (4), 641–44.

Meischke, D. 1936. Über den Einfluss der Strahlung auf Licht- und Dunkelkeimer. *Jahrb. Wiss. Botan., 83,* 359–405.

Mohr, H. 1956. Die Beeinflussung der Keimung von Farnsporen durch Licht und anderen Faktoren. *Planta, 46,* 534–51.

Phillips, D. J., and P. F. Wareing. 1958. Effect of photoperiodic conditions on the level of growth inhibitors in *Acer pseudoplatanus. Naturwissenschaften, 13,* 317.

Poljakoff-Mayber, A., S. Goldschmidt-Blumenthal, and M. Evenari. 1957. The growth substances content of germinating lettuce seeds. *Physiol. Plantarum, 10,* 14–19.

Resühr, B. 1939. Beiträge zur Lichtkeimung von *Amaranthus candatus* L. und *Phacelia tanacetifolia* Benth. *Planta, 30,* 471–506.

Shuck, A. L. 1935. A growth-inhibiting substance in lettuce seed. *Science, 81,* 236.

Wareing. P. F. 1953. Growth studies in woody species. V. Photoperiodism in dormant buds of *Fagus sylvatica* L. *Physiol. Plantarum, 6,* 692–706.

———. 1956. Photoperiodism in woody plants. *Ann. Rev. Plant Physiol., 7,* 191–214.

———. 1957. Photoperiodism in seeds, buds and seedlings of woody species. *Proc. Harvard Forest Symp. Tree Physiol.*

Wareing, P. F., and H. A. Foda. 1956. The possible role of growth inhibitors in the dormancy of seed of *Xanthium* and lettuce. *Nature, 178,* 908.

———. 1957. Growth inhibitors and dormancy in *Xanthium* seed. *Physiol. Plantarum, 10,* 266–80.

Wassink, E. C., and J. A. J. Stolwijk. 1956. Effects of light quality on plant growth. *Ann. Rev. Plant Physiol. 7,* 373–400.

EFFECT OF LIGHT ON THE GERMINATION
OF SEEDS

E. H. TOOLE

**Agricultural Research Service, U. S. Department of Agriculture,
Beltsville, Maryland**

The effect of light on the germination of seeds has been discussed for
nearly a hundred years, but it was the work of Flint and McAlister in
1937 that first demonstrated a clear-cut promotion of germination by
red light and an inhibition by far-red radiation. Reviews of much of
the voluminous literature on the role of light in seed germination have
been given by Crocker (1936), Evenari (1956), and Toole *et al.*
(1956).

The work of our group started with the results of Flint and Mc-
Alister as a background. The two-prism (glass) spectrograph previously described by Parker *et al.* (1946) permitted the determination
of quantitative action spectra for the germination of seeds of Grand
Rapids lettuce (*Lactuca sativa* L.) (Borthwick *et al.*, 1952) and of
Lepidium virginicum L. (Toole *et al.*, 1955a). The results (Fig. 1)
are expressed as relative incident energies at different wavelengths
required to promote or to inhibit germination to half its maximum
value. The regions of the spectrum effective for promotion and for
inhibition are not far separated; in fact, an overlapping of effects
actually occurs at about 7000 A. The activity of the blue end of the
spectrum (4100–5200 A) was tested, but the response in this region
was very low.

A similar response to these two regions of the spectrum has also
been demonstrated in our laboratory for seeds of the following
species: *Barbarea vulgaris* R. Br., *Berteroa incana* (L.) DC., *Brassica
nigra* (L.) Koch., *Camelina microcarpa* Andrz., *Capsella bursa-
pastoris* (L.) Medic., *Lamium amplexicaule* L., *Lepidium densiflorum*
Schrad., *Lycopersicum esculentum* Mill., *Lythrum salicaria* L., *Nicotiana tabacum* L., *Oenothera biennis* L., *Pinus virginiana* Mill., *Sisym-*

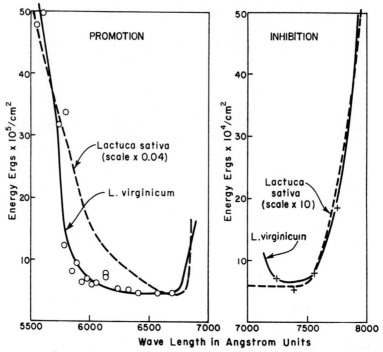

FIG. 1.   Action spectra for promotion and inhibition of germination of seeds of *Lepidium virginicum* and of *Lactuca sativa* to 50% (Toole *et al.*, 1956).

brium altissimum L., *Sisymbrium officinale* (L.). Scop., *Thlaspi arvense* L., and *Ulmus americana* L.

The response of seeds to a given light exposure varies with the time of imbibition preceding the exposure (Borthwick *et al.*, 1954). After lettuce seeds are placed on the moist substratum and imbibition starts, the amount of promotion with a fixed irradiance with red increases for 8 to 10 hr and then remains constant until about 20 hr (Fig. 2). After 20 hr the amount of stimulation decreases rapidly. The amount of inhibition with a fixed irradiance with far red also remains constant for imbibition times of 10 to 20 hr but increases after 20 hr. The fact that as one sensitivity *increases,* the other *decreases* is a strong argument that the photocontrol of seed germination is a coupled reaction.

That the promoting effect of red and the inhibiting effect of far-red radiation are immediately and repeatedly reversible has been shown for seeds of both lettuce (Borthwick *et al.*, 1952) and *Lepidium* (Toole *et al.*, 1955a) (Fig. 3). This repeated reversal was carried out at 27° and 7°C with almost identical results. The possibility of re-

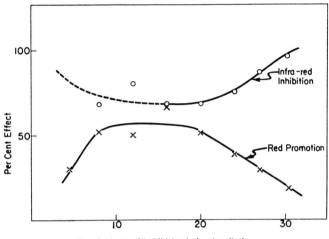

FIG. 2. Variation in germination response of seeds of Grand Rapids lettuce with increased time of imbibition at a fixed irradiance in the red and in the far red (near infrared) (Borthwick *et al.*, 1954).

peated reversal indicates that the pigment is immediately changed without other reactions.

After promotion by red light, the germination process progresses in 12 hr so far that the promotion effect on most of the seeds cannot be reversed by far-red radiation, as shown in Fig. 4 (Toole *et al.*, 1953).

The photocontrol of seed germination is closely interrelated with the temperature of germination (Table I). Light-sensitive lettuce seeds respond differently to light at different temperatures and will not respond to it at high temperatures (Toole *et al.*, 1957). When fully promoted seeds are held at high temperatures, the seeds gradually lose the ability to germinate in darkness at 20°C. A thermal reversal of the pigment occurs, and the seeds revert to the nongerminating condition. The reversal is more rapid at 35° than at 30° (Table II).

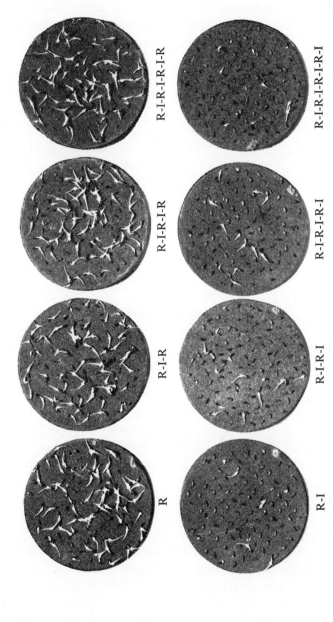

R-I-R-I-R-I-R

R-I-R-I-R

R-I-R

R

R-I-R-I-R-I-R-I

R-I-R-I-R-I

R-I-R-I

R-I

Fig. 3. Germination response of imbibed Grand Rapids lettuce seeds exposed at 7°C alternately to red (R) and far-red (I) radiation and then held at 20° in the dark for 2 days.

92

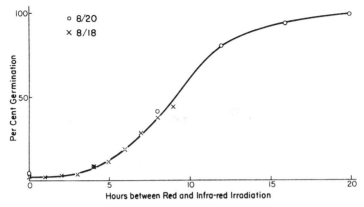

FIG. 4.   The rate of escape of Grand Rapids lettuce seeds from control by far-red radiation. Seeds irradiated 4 min with red after imbibition for 1 hr, and then after varying periods in the dark irradiated 16 min with far red and returned to 20°C in darkness.

With additional light exposure, however, germination takes place in darkness at 20° (Toole *et al.*, 1953). Also, some samples of lettuce seed that originally germinate equally well in red light or darkness are made sensitive to light by holding the imbibed seeds 3 or 4 days at a temperature too high for germination (Table III) (Borthwick *et al.*, 1954).

TABLE I.   Germination of Seeds of Two Varieties of Lettuce at Different Temperatures in Red Light and in Darkness

Variety and Germination Temperature, °C	Seeds Germinating under Indicated Light Condition, %	
	Red	Darkness
White Boston		
10	99	95
15	99	78
20	98	57
25	1	0
Grand Rapids		
15	94	52
20	96	40
25	96	10
30	1	0

TABLE II.   Development of Dormancy in Grand Rapids Lettuce
Seeds Fully Promoted and Then Held at High Temperatures[a]

Period at High Temperature, hr	Per Cent Seeds Germinating at 20°C After Period at	
	30°C	35°C
0	96	94
8	96	85
16	93	55
24	60	20
32	41	6
40	26	—
48	22	—
32[b]	—	95
48[b]	94	—

[a] After being imbibed 1 hr at 20°C in darkness, seeds irradiated 4 min
in red and then transferred to 30° or 35°; after various periods at the
high temperatures, seeds transferred to 20° in darkness for 2 days for
germination.
[b] Seeds given an additional 4 min of red at time of transfer to 20°C.

The interaction of temperature and light response is evident in
Lepidium in a different way (Toole *et al.,* 1955a). At constant
temperatures of 15° or 25°C, seeds of *Lepidium virginicum* show a
definite response to light, but maximum germination is below 50%.'
However, if after imbibition for 48 hr at 15°, followed by a saturating
exposure to red light, the seeds are transferred to 25°, the germination
is markedly increased (Table IV). The photoreaction had been the
same in all sets of tests, but germination of many of the seeds was
blocked when they were maintained at a constant temperature. This

TABLE III.   Germination at 20°C with and without
Irradiation of Great Lakes Lettuce Seeds Previously
Held Imbibed at 35° for 4 Days[a]

Period of Irradiation, min		Seeds Germinating at 20°C, %
Red	Far Red	
0	0	11
1	0	95
1	1	95
1	32	22

[a] Germination 95% at 20° in darkness when not exposed to 35°.

TABLE IV. Germination of Seeds of *Lepidium virginicum* with Different Temperature Treatments[a]

Temperature, °C, First 2 Days	Temperature, °C, After 2 Days	Seeds Germinating, %	
		Irradiated	Not Irradiated
15	15	37	0
25	25	41	0
25	15	32	0
15	25	92	0

[a] Seeds irradiated with red at end of 2 days.

block was removed and more of the seeds could respond to the photo-stimulation if a suitable temperature change was made at the time of irradiation.

Germination of seeds of *Lepidium virginicum* is also increased by a short period at a high temperature (35°C) at or near the time of irradiation (Toole *et al.*, 1955b). When *Lepidium* seeds are imbibed in the dark at 20° for 24 hr, given a saturating irradiation with red light either just before or just after a 2-hr exposure to a temperature of 35° and then returned to 20° for about 4 days, germination is practically complete (Table V). The energy of irradiation required for a germination of 50% is greatly influenced by the timing of the

TABLE V. Germination of Seeds of *Lepidium virginicum* Irradiated Just before or Just after Being Held for 2 hr at 35°C[a]

Duration of Irradiation, sec		Seeds Germinating When Irradiated, %	
Red	Far Red	Before 2-hr Period at 35°C	After 2-hr Period at 35°C
0	0	3	3
10	0	—	56
20	0	26	74
80	0	52	95
320	0	96	98
Saturation[b]	0	98	99
Saturation[b]	20	84	91
Saturation[b]	40	39	46
Saturation[b]	80	8	14

[a] Seeds imbibed in water at 20° for 24 hr before placing at 35°; returned to 20° after treatments.

[b] Duration 64 and 16 min, respectively, for lots irradiated before and after 2-hr period at 35°C. Germination 0, 27, and 55%, respectively, for seeds held continuously at 20°C in the dark or with prior 4 or 64 min of red.

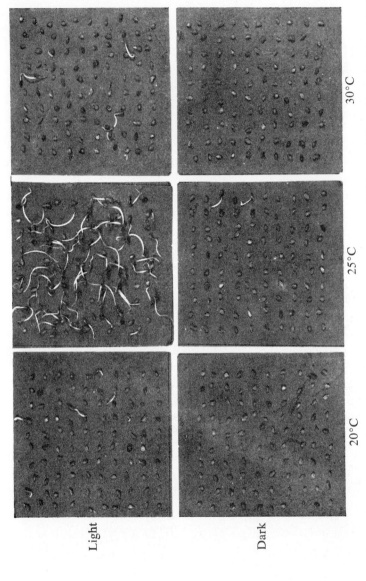

FIG. 5. Germination responses of seeds of *Pinus virginiana* to red light at different constant temperatures.

exposure to the high temperature. If the high temperature comes after the irradiation, 8 times as much energy is required for promotion of 50% germination as is required if the high temperature precedes the irradiation. The short period at the high temperature changes the sensitivity of the photoreaction. For inhibition by far red, the energy requirement was slightly less if the high temperature came after rather than before irradiation. In all instances when the sensitivity to red light increased, the sensitivity to far-red radiation decreased, and the reverse.

Interaction between light and temperature occurs in the germination of other seeds. Seeds of *Pinus virginiana* respond to exposure to red light when held at 25°C, but not when held at 20° or 30° (Toole *et al.*, 1956). Here also some block in the germination process prevents complete response to the photoreaction at 25° (Fig. 5). If

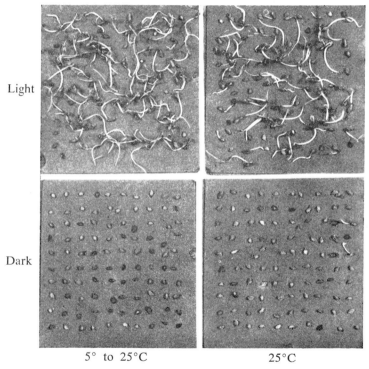

Light

Dark

5° to 25°C   25°C

Fig. 6.   Germination responses of seeds of *Pinus virginiana* to red light as influenced by temperature change.

imbibition for the 24 hr preceding irradiation is at 5° and if the seeds are placed at 25° after irradiation, however, germination is practically complete (Fig. 6).

The light exposures discussed thus far were of only one short duration (measured in seconds or minutes) after a given imbibition time. However, not all seeds respond with full germination after a single short exposure to red light. The seeds of *Puya berteroniana* Mez (Bromeliaceae) respond to daily irradiations.[1] A short (19-min) exposure to red light each day promotes germination of only a portion of the seeds. If the 19-min exposure is divided and 4 min are given at 8 A.M. and 15 min at 4 P.M., germination of the viable seeds is practically complete (Table VI).

TABLE VI.   Germination of Seeds of *Puya berteroniana* with Different Timing of Daily Irradiations[a]

Daily Irradiations, min		Per Cent Seeds Germinating in
8 A.M.	4 P.M.	20 Days
0	0	0
19	0	28
4	0	4
4	4	16
4	8	68
4	15	92

[a] Seeds irradiated in red for first 12 days and kept at 15°C in darkness except during irradiations.

REFERENCES

Borthwick, H. A., S. B. Hendricks, M. W. Parker, E. H. Toole, and Vivian K. Toole. 1952. A reversible photoreaction controlling seed germination. *Proc. Natl. Acad. Sci. U. S. 38*, 662–66.

Borthwick, H. A., S. B. Hendricks, E. H. Toole, and V. K. Toole. 1954. Action of light on lettuce-seed germination. *Botan. Gaz., 115,* 205–25.

Crocker, William. 1936. Effect of the visible spectrum upon the germination of seeds and fruits. *Biological Effects of Radiation,* B. M. Duggar, Editor. McGraw-Hill, New York, pp. 791–828.

Evenari, Michael. 1956. Seed germination. *Radiation Biology,* Vol. III, A. Hollaender, Editor. McGraw-Hill, New York, pp. 518–49.

Flint, Lewis H., and E. D. McAlister. 1937. Wave lengths of radiation in the

[1] R. J. Downs and Toole, V. K., unpublished data.

visible spectrum promoting the germination of light-sensitive lettuce seed. *Smithsonian Inst. Publs. Misc. Collections, 96,* 1–8.

Parker, M. W., S. B. Hendricks, H. A. Borthwick, and N. J. Scully. 1946. Action spectrum for the photoperiodic control of floral initiation of short-day plants. *Botan. Gaz., 108,* 1–26.

Toole, E. H., H. A. Borthwick, S. B. Hendricks, and Vivian K. Toole. 1953. Physiological studies of the effects of light and temperature on seed germination. *Proc. Intern. Seed Testing Assoc., 18* (2), 267–76.

Toole, E. H., S. B. Hendricks, H. A. Borthwick, and Vivian K. Toole. 1956. Physiology of seed germination. *Ann. Rev. Plant Physiol., 7,* 299–324.

Toole, E. H., A. G. Snow, Jr., V. K. Toole, and H. A. Borthwick. 1956. Effects of light and temperature on germination of Virginia pine seeds. *Plant Physiol., 31* (Suppl.), xxxvi (Abstract).

Toole, E. H., V. K. Toole, and S. B. Hendricks. 1955a. Photocontrol of *Lepidium* seed germination. *Plant Physiol., 30,* 15–21.

Toole, E. H., V. K. Toole, H. A. Borthwick, and S. B. Hendricks. 1955b. Interaction of temperature and light in germination of seeds. *Plant Physiol., 30,* 473–78.

Toole, E. H., V. K. Toole, S. B. Hendricks, and H. A. Borthwick. 1957. Effect of temperature on germination of light-sensitive seeds. *Proc. Intern. Seed Testing Assoc., 22* (1), 196–204.

PHOTOMORPHOGENESIS IN DIFFERENT SPECTRAL REGIONS

G. MEIJER

Philips Research Laboratories, N. V. Philips' Gloeilampenfabrieken
Eindhoven, Netherlands

PHOTOPERIODISM

In photoperiodism it is well known that the red part of the visible spectrum has the greatest influence on the flowering of long-day and short-day plants, whether this light is supplied for a number of hours to supplement a short day or used as an interruption of the corresponding long dark period (Withrow and Biebel, 1936; Parker *et al.*, 1950). Moreover, the effect of a night break by red light can be nullified by a near infrared (far red) irradiation (Borthwick *et al.*, 1952). This red-near infrared antagonism has been found to exist also in a great number of other light-controlled processes, e.g., seed germination, elongation, and pigmentation.

By growing plants in light of different spectral regions, it has been shown by Stolwijk and Zeevaart (1955) that the inclusion of a certain amount of violet, blue, or infrared in the long day is necessary to obtain a long-day effect in *Hyoscyamus niger*. A long-day treatment in red light exhibited only a slight long-day effect, i.e., a flower-inducing effect; in green light no flower initiation at all was obtained.

In a number of experiments we have shown that this blue and near infrared influence on the long-day effect is not restricted to *Hyoscyamus niger* (Meijer, 1957; Meijer and van der Veen, 1957). By using a combination of colored fluorescent tubes with suitable filters, high-intensity light of different spectral regions was obtained: red, green, blue, and blue in combination with infrared. The infrared was emitted by the blue fluorescent tubes and transmitted by the blue filter. It was found that *Salvia occidentalis,* an obligate short-day plant, does not flower in a long day in red or in blue light. In a long day in green

101

Fig. 1. The response of *Salvia occidentalis* to a long-day treatment in colored light. From left to right: plants grown in red, green, blue, and blue + infrared light, 16 hr per day, 900 μw/cm², 56 days after the beginning of the treatment.

light, however, no long-day effect was obtained at all, and thus flowering was not prevented (Fig. 1).

In other experiments in which unequal intensities but equal amounts of light quanta were given, it was found that red light was less effective than blue (the flower induction was retarded but not prevented) (Tables I and II).

Table I. Response of *Salvia occidentalis* to a Short-Day and a Long-Day Treatment in Different Spectral Regions (Equal Amounts of Light Quanta) (Duration of treatment, 32 days; day temperature, 22°C; night temperature, 17°C)

Spectral Regions	Intensity, μw/cm²	Day Length, Hr/Day	Condition of Apex	Number of Leaf Pairs Up to Inflorescence
Blue	600	10	Generative	5
Red	370	10	Generative	5
Blue	600	16	Vegetative	>10
Blue + infrared	600	16	Vegetative	>11
Green	500	16	Generative	5
Red	370	16	Generative	8

TABLE II. Flowering Response of *Salvia occidentalis* to Long-Day Treatment with Different Light Intensities (Duration of treatment, 28 days; day temperature, 22°C; night temperature, 17°C)

Spectral Region, 16 hr/day Light Intensity, μw/cm²	Blue	Blue + Infrared	Red
75		Vegetative	
90	Vegetative		
250		Vegetative	
300	Vegetative		
360			Generative
375		Vegetative	
420	Vegetative		
750		Vegetative	
880	Vegetative		
1200			Vegetative
1800			Vegetative
3600			Vegetative

The influence of near infrared on the day-length effect was studied in plants growing in 16 hr of green light per day (900 μw/cm²); near infrared was added simultaneously by means of incandescent light passing through an infrared filter. Under the experimental conditions, it was found that an amount of ±30 μw/cm² of near infrared was still effective in causing a long-day effect (Fig. 2). It is obvious that for *Salvia occidentalis,* a short-day plant, and *Hyoscyamus niger,* a long-day plant, the same blue-infrared necessity exists to obtain a long-day effect. Other plants also show the same dependence on light quality for the long-day effect, e.g., *Petunia, Arabidopsis thaliana, Plantago major, Silene armeria,* and lettuce, all long-day plants.

Certain other plants, however, e.g., *Poinsettia, Kalanchoë,* and *Xanthium,* do not show this spectral dependence, nor does *Larix leptolepis,* in which species a long day in red, green, or blue light always prevents winter dormancy. It is possible that for these plants the light intensity was too high to show the spectral dependence mentioned above.

Growing *Hyoscyamus* and *Salvia* in a short day (10 hr of white fluorescent light per day, 500 μw/cm²), a long-day effect was obtained by interrupting the dark period. In this process, red light was more effective than blue, and a red-near infrared antagonism existed. The influence of light quality of the short day on the flower-inducing or flower-inhibiting action of such a night break was demonstrated in

FIG. 2. The influence of an addition of infrared on the flowering of *Salvia occidentalis*, grown in 16 hr green light per day. From left to right: plants grown in green light (900 μw/cm^2) without infrared and with 25, 40, or 60 μw/cm^2 infrared, 60 days after the beginning of the treatment.

experiments in which a short day was given in colored light and the long dark period was interrupted. As can be seen in Table III, a long-day effect could be obtained only by a combination of a short day in blue light and a night break with red or green light.

For *Larix leptolepis,* it was found also that this spectral dependence existed for the prevention of winter dormancy. Interruptions of the long dark periods were more effective when the plants received blue light instead of red during the preceding short main light period of 10 hr. Whereas *Larix* in this type of experiment shows the spectral dependence for the main light period, it seems justifiable to assume that the negative results in the long-day (16 hr) experiments in colored light mentioned earlier must be due to experimental conditions, e.g., the light intensity. For several plant species such as *Salvia occidentalis, Poinsettia, Kalanchoë,* and *Larix,* no influence of light quality on the short-day effect could be found.

A remarkable and unexpected effect was obtained by growing *Salvia occidentalis* in a short day of 8 hr white fluorescent light per

TABLE III. Influence of Light Quality of a Main Light Period and of a Dark Interruption on Flowering (Duration of treatment, 16 days; condition of growing points 58 days after beginning of treatment)

Main Light Period, 10 hr/day	Dark Control	Night Break, 10 min[a] 10′ Red	10′ Green	10′ Blue
Salvia occidentalis (S.D. plant), 4 plants per treatment				
Red, 900 μw/cm²	++++	−+++	++++	++++
Green, 850 μw/cm²	++++	++++	++++	++++
Blue, 950 μw/cm²	++++	−−−−	−−−−	++++
Hyoscyamus niger (L.D. plant), 3 plants per treatment				
Red, 900 μw/cm²	−−−	−−−	−−−	−−−
Green, 850 μw/cm²	−−−	−−−	−−−	−−−
Blue, 950 μw/cm²	−−−	+++	+++	−−−

[a] Generative +; vegetative −.

day followed by a supplementary irradiation of 8 hr with red, green, or blue. The results of this treatment are given in Table IV. By using this type of treatment to obtain a long-day effect, it is obvious that blue light is more effective than green or red in prolonging a short day. This behavior of *Salvia* is similar to that of the *Cruciferae* (Funke, 1948; Wassink *et al.*, 1956).

In Stolwijk's experiments the filters transmitted not only the blue light but also a small amount of infrared, and for this reason it might appear that the blue light effect in his experiments could be due to

TABLE IV. Influence of Light Quality of a Supplementary Irradiation of 8 hr after a Short Day (8 hr) in White Light (2100 μw/cm²) on Flowering of *Salvia occidentalis* (S.D. plant)[a]

Spectral Region Light intensity, μw/cm²	Red	Green	Blue	Dark Control
0				+
50			−	
65	+			
85		+		
250			−	
325	−			
415		+		
500			−	
650	−			
830		+		

[a] Generative +; vegetative −.

such infrared contamination. This explanation, however, does not hold true, because in our experiments the same effect was obtained in pure blue light.

It is impossible, however, to grow plants in blue light without the influence of light of other spectral regions. Plants growing in blue light look reddish owing to the fluorescence of the chlorophyll. The effect of blue light could therefore be due to such fluorescence. This explanation does not seem to be correct, however, because in some experiments it was shown that low intensities of blue light of about 70 μw/cm^2 were still effective, whereas green light of much higher intensity (900μw/cm^2) was inactive.

Thus, it may be concluded that in photoperiodism, besides the red-infrared photoreaction, still another photoreaction exists which is very sensitive to near infrared and blue light.

STEM ELONGATION

There seem to be many different opinions concerning the influence of colored light on elongation of plants. Several investigators have concluded that the absence of light of short wavelengths causes an increase in stem length (Wassink *et al.,* 1956, 1957). Roodenburg (1940) was probably one of the first to state that the near infrared had a strong elongation effect on many plants. Most of the older experiments were carried out in light which had a predominance of a special spectral region, but which contained light of other wavelengths as well.

Wassink and co-workers (1956) purified the light of different colored fluorescent tubes by means of suitable filters. In their experiments it was shown that elongation occurred in red, yellow, and green light, but not in blue or in violet. However, when these colors were given in low intensities as additional light to a short day of white, the effect was just the opposite. They then obtained strong elongation with weak blue light and no elongation with weak red or yellow light. In addition to this effect, there was a very strong elongating effect by infrared.

Vince and Stoughton (1957) confirmed for tomato plants the inhibitive effect of blue, whereas this part of the spectrum had a promotive effect on the elongation of peas and of *Calendula.* It was concluded by Downs *et al.* (1957) that the principal effects in their experiments made with blue fluorescent light depend on "relative amounts of red and far-red and not of the blue irradiation." In their experiments, elongation is only connected with the red-infrared antagonism and an influence of blue light is ignored. It was therefore assumed that the elongating effect of blue light found by Wassink *et al.* and by Vince might not be caused by the blue light itself, but by the presence of traces of near infrared (Meijer, 1957; Wassink *et al.*, 1957).

In our laboratory we studied the elongation of many different plants in our light chambers. Plants are grown under natural daylight or white fluorescent light before they are subjected to colored light. The first thing we observed was that species react very differently; therefore we were able to classify plants into different groups.

Some plants show a strong elongation of internodes in blue light, whereas they remain short in red and green light or in darkness. Near-infrared irradiation also causes an increase in length. This near-infrared irradiation was given simultaneously with green light which in itself is ineffective in this respect. A strong red ⇌ near-infrared antagonism exists. An addition of near infrared to blue light has hardly any elongating effect. Examples of this group are *Petunia,* gherkin (Table V), and *Calendula.*

TABLE V. Influence of Light (16 hr per day) of Different Spectral Regions on Elongation

(Length in millimeters. Intensity of red, green, and blue light: 475 μw/cm^2)

Plant Species	Duration of Treatment, Days	Red	Red + Infrared	Green	Green + Infrared	Blue	Blue + Infrared
Gherkin hypocotyl	8	23	36	26	101	79	81
Mirabilis jalapa first internode	30	182	179	174	188	128	153
Salvia occidentalis internode	30	42	60	43	82	64	90
Tomato hypocotyl	11	27	29	24	54	28	42
Tomato first internode	15	69	74	62	63	38	38

Other plants, on the contrary, show a strong elongation in red or green light and have short internodes in blue light. An addition of near infrared to blue light causes only a slight increase in internode length over the plants in blue light; an addition to red or green light does not have any effect. Plants of this group are *Mirabilis jalapa* (Table V), *Rivina humilis,* and *Mentha longifolia.*

The older internodes of young tomato plants obtain about the same length in red, green, or blue light. An addition of near infrared to blue and green light has a strong elongating effect. The younger internodes, completely grown out in the colored light behave, however, like plants of the second group (Table V).

As far as blue light has an elongating effect on the internodes of *Salvia occidentalis* (Table V) as compared with plants grown in red or blue light, this species resembles the plants of the first group. An addition of near infrared to blue light, however, enhances the elongation and in this respect *Salvia* resembles tomato.

It may be assumed that the elongation of internodes is controlled by an inhibiting process occurring in red light and another one occurring in blue light. In white light both processes take place. In addition to this inhibiting effect, blue light—and to a much greater extent near infrared irradiation—has also a neutralizing influence on the inhibiting effect of red light. This neutralizing influence is only visible when it is stronger than the inhibiting effect of blue light (plants of group 1 and *Salvia*). In tomato plants and also in plants of the second group, this neutralizing effect of blue light might be completely suppressed because the inhibiting effect of blue light is relatively strong.

REFERENCES

Borthwick, H. A., S. B. Hendricks, and M. W. Parker. 1952. The reaction controlling floral initiation. *Proc. Natl. Acad. Sci. U. S., 38,* 929–34.

Downs, R. J., S. B. Hendricks, and H. A. Borthwick. 1957. Photoreversible control of elongation of Pinto beans and other plants under normal conditions of growth. *Botan. Gaz., 118,* 199–208.

Funke, G. L. 1948. The photoperiodicity of flowering under short day with supplemental light of different wavelengths. *Vernalization and Photoperiodism,* A. E. Murneek and R. O. Whyte, Editors. Chronica Botanica, Waltham, Mass., pp. 79–82.

Meijer, G. 1957. The influence of light quality on the flowering response of *Salvia occidentalis, Acta Botan. Neerl., 6,* 395–406.

Meijer, G., and R. van der Veen. 1957. Wavelength dependence of photo-periodic responses. *Acta Botan. Neerl., 6,* 429–33.

Parker, M. W., S. B. Hendricks, and H. A. Borthwick. 1950. Action spectrum for the photoperiodic control of floral initiation of the long day plant *Hyoscyamus niger. Botan. Gaz., 111,* 242–52.

Roodenburg, J. W. M. 1940. Das Verhalten von Pflanzen in verschieden farbigem Licht. *Rec. trav. botan. néerl., 37,* 303–74.

Stolwijk, J. A. J., and J. A. D. Zeevaart. 1955. Wavelength dependence of different light reactions governing flowering in *Hyoscyamus niger. Proc. Koninkl. Ned. Akad. Wetenschap., C58,* 386–96.

Vince, D., and R. H. Stoughton. 1957. Artificial light in plant experimental work. *Control of the Plant Environment,* J. P. Hudson, Editor. Butterworths, London.

Wassink, E. C., and J. A. J. Stolwijk. 1956. Effects of light quality on plant growth. *Ann. Rev. Plant Physiol., 7,* 373–400.

Wassink, E. C., J. Bensink, and P. J. A. L. de Lint. 1957. Formative effects of light quality and intensity on plants. 2nd Intern. Photobiol. Congr., Turin.

Withrow, R. B., and P. J. Biebel. 1936. Photoperiodic response of certain long and short-day plants to filtered radiation applied as a supplement to day light. *Plant Physiol., 11,* 807–19.

SOME EFFECTS OF HIGH-INTENSITY IRRADIATION OF NARROW SPECTRAL REGIONS[1]

E. C. WASSINK, P. J. A. L. DE LINT, and J. BENSINK

Laboratory of Plant Physiological Research, Agricultural University, Wageningen, Netherlands

TECHNIQUES

This paper reports the results of a study of formative effects of light of narrow spectral regions on plants, when these plants are exposed only to such light during the entire experimental period. In the majority of

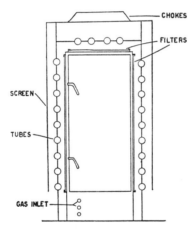

FIG. 1. Schematic diagram of a light cabinet for growing plants exclusively in light of restricted spectral composition. (Wassink and Stolwijk, 1952.)

cases this requires high light intensities over large areas. To meet this requirement, we built cabinets (Wassink and Stolwijk, 1952) about 1 m long, 30 cm wide, 70 cm high, with side walls and top of clear glass, and with metal doors at both ends (Fig. 1). In the top and side

[1] Laboratory of Plant Physiological Research, Agricultural University, Wageningen, 172nd Communication.

111

walls are slits that can accommodate colored glass or plastic filter sheets. Each of the cabinets is placed under a separate metal frame on which the light sources are mounted. As light sources, various types of monophosphor fluorescent tubes, sodium lamps, and incandescent lamps are used, depending on the spectral region required. The filters (one sheet on each side, one on top) provide additional purification of the light, e.g., eliminating the blue, green, and yellow mercury lines from red light. Colored glass sheets of the sizes required are selected from specimens of the ordinary trade glass with the aid of a hand spectroscope. The intensity level aimed at in the cabinets is $\sim$40,000 ergs/cm^2 sec ϕ sphere, as measured with a spherical radiation meter (Wassink and van der Scheer, 1951). This is equivalent more or less to an intensity of 10,000 ergs/cm^2 sec as measured in one direction with a flat light meter.

Apart from high-intensity illumination in separate, relatively very pure spectral regions, various combinations can be achieved. Thus, for example, we used two types of cabinets supplying near-infrared radiation, one with a red glass filter and incandescent lamps only, the other with red fluorescent tubes and red glass on the sides, thus supplying the same amount of the same red light as in the pure red light cabinet, while, in addition, near infrared (mixed with far infrared) is supplied from the top by incandescent lamps filtered by red + blue glass.

Our blue light cabinet has recently been improved. The blue glass filter used previously in combination with blue fluorescent tubes transmits a small amount of near infrared.[2] We now have a blue plastic filter which, according to any measuring instrument as well as to the naked eye, is completely opaque to far red and near-infrared radiation. When this filter is used in combination with red glass, even the direct sun cannot be seen. We have also mounted red glass with a red filter on top of a blue cabinet to study antagonisms in long-term experiments. The adaptability of the equipment to various problems is obvious.

---

[2] We have explained (Wassink and Stolwijk, 1956) why we prefer to keep this term for the radiation next to the visible region instead of using the more recent expression, far red. Hillman and Galston (1957) followed our terminology.

Our green cabinet consists of green fluorescent tubes with a lemon yellow filter (characteristics about equal to GG 11 of Schott). This filter transmits fairly high energies, although the region transmitted extends somewhat too far toward the long wavelengths. We plan soon to remove the red radiation to determine whether this has any effect on some of the results observed.

I will briefly mention that we have three types of equipment for large-surface and long-time spectral irradiation, as follows:

1. Low-intensity spectral series (~ 1000 ergs/cm^2 sec) used for day length extension following a short day in strong white (artificial) light.

2. High-intensity spectral series (level $\sim 40,000$ ergs/cm^2 sec ϕ sphere), described above.

3. Intensity ranges from very high to very low in three spectral regions, blue, yellow, and near infrared, permitting the study of intensity effects in narrow spectral regions.

The experiments reported in this paper were carried out principally with the second and third types of equipment.

STEM ELONGATION AND FLOWERING IN *Hyoscyamus*

The results to be discussed were obtained with *Hyoscyamus,* annual strain, which was also used for studying the effects of gibberellic acid. Stolwijk and Zeevaart (1955), working in our laboratory, had studied flowering of these plants under high-intensity treatment in separate spectral regions. Stem elongation and flowering were very rapid in violet, blue, and red + infrared, namely, red + 300% infrared (obtained by incandescent light + red filters), and also in red + 30% infrared (infrared "top" on red cabinet, see above). Stem elongation and flowering were very much delayed or absent in green, yellow, and red. Curry and Wassink (1956) studied flowering of *Hyoscyamus* under similar conditions in greater detail, in combination with the effect of gibberellic acid. Of special interest were the rapid elongation and flowering in the blue light. Since the blue originally used contained some near infrared, we attempted to decrease this as much as possible by using the blue plastic filter (Plexiglas B27, alt, of Röhm & Haas, Darmstadt, Germany) mentioned above; we used a cabinet

Fig. 2. Formative and flowering effects on *Hyoscyamus niger,* annual strain in various spectral regions of light at different GA concentrations (μg/plant/day). Experiment 2 (Curry and Wassink, 1956), photographed Sept. 3, 1956, after 30 days. (Rearranged from Curry and Wassink, 1956, plate 2c.)

114

with this filter along with one with the earlier mentioned blue glass filter. The red + infrared cabinet had incandescent lamps and red glass. On the whole, the results fully confirmed and extended those obtained earlier by Stolwijk and Zeevaart. Shoot elongation and flowering were rapid in the red + infrared cabinet, and in both blue cabinets. It is of interest and probably of importance that the behavior of the plants does not show any detectable difference in blue light with a small amount of near infrared radiation, and in blue light without detectable traces of near infrared. Elongation and flowering were very much slower in green and red light. Yellow was not used in this series (Fig. 2).

As for the influence of gibberellic acid, plants were given 0, 0.1, 1, and 10 μg/plant/day. These additions promoted shoot growth and flowering, increasingly so with increasing concentration. The difference between zero and the highest concentration was somewhat different in different spectral regions. The smallest difference between concentrations was in the infrared and in the blue cabinets, especially in the one having a slight admixture of infrared. The greatest difference was in the green and red regions, in which, especially after 30 days, the plants receiving the highest GA concentration were the only ones to show conspicuous elongation, and ultimately (after ~60 days) to exhibit flowering.

Unfortunately, it could not be shown whether GA promotes primarily the initiation of flower buds or the elongation, or whether one is a consequence of the other. In all cases examined for this point, the two processes seemed to occur simultaneously.

The lowest number of days to stem appearance, after the beginning of the colored light treatment, was 13 occurring in the two blues and in red + infrared with 10 μg GA/plant/day. The highest number in these colors was 15. In green and red it was 15 with 10 μg GA/plant/day. In green it was 23 with 1.0 μg GA, and over 30 with 0.1 μg GA and without GA. In red it was 23 and 25 with 1.0 and 0.1 μg GA respectively, and >30 without GA. In Fig. 3 are plants given 10 μg GA and green showing greatly delayed flowering (photographed after 68 days).

A subsequent series of experiments (de Lint, unpublished) included the two different near-infrared cabinets, as mentioned previously.

FIG. 3. Two plants from green light with 10 μg GA applied daily, Experiment 2 (Curry and Wassink, 1956), photographed Oct. 11, 1956, after 68 days.

Also, a blue cabinet was introduced with red tubes (+ red filter) on top. After 15 days, the expected changes in appearance were already evident. The plants then were (for technical reasons) transferred to a short day in white fluorescent light, where the phenomena developed further. The plants in blue and in both red + infrared mixtures elongated, the shoots of those in blue + red top remained short like those in red and green. Both types of red + infrared showed no difference, confirming Stolwijk and Zeevaart's experiment. In some of the plants, 2 × 10 μg GA was administered, on the first or on the last long day (colored light). In these plants stems also developed in the red, green, and red + blue series, although they were much shorter than in the infrared and blue series.

The elongation in the red + infrared top cabinet as compared with red (containing only a small amount of infrared) and the suppression of elongation in the blue by the addition of red was also observed in an earlier series (Fig. 4, top).

If GA was given on the first day, elongation in blue and in both

Fig. 4. *Hyoscyamus niger,* cultivated in high-intensity spectral light cabinets. Top figure (earlier experiment), R + I = red + infrared top illumination, R = red pure, B + R = blue + red top illumination, V = "far blue." Bottom figure (more recent experiment, continuous light), G = green, RB⁻ = blue without near infrared + 2 red tubes + red glass on top; RB⁺ = same, but blue + ∼1% near infrared. The "far blue" of the top figure is identical with the blue of the bottom figure. The earlier blue had its maximum more toward the green than that used later on and then designated as blue.

infrared cabinets was speeded up as compared to the control without GA. The difference was especially obvious in the first 2 weeks. Later, the differences were greatest in the "slower" colors: red, green, and blue + red.

Next we compared the effect of red top illumination in both of our blue cabinets, namely, the one with a small amount of near infrared and the one without any detectable near infrared. The same amount of red light (2 tubes plus red glass on top of the cabinet with 26 blue tubes) depressed elongation much more strongly in the blue cabinet without infrared than in that with infrared. The plants in the former were even shorter than those in green light (Fig. 4, bottom).

The explanation of these experiments involves the following considerations. First of all, it seems beyond doubt that in our experiments, near infrared strongly speeds up shooting and flowering in this annual strain of *Hyoscyamus*. Gibberellic acid enhances this influence and induces it in case infrared is absent. The experiments also strongly indicate that blue light has an effect similar to that of near infrared. Furthermore, a red-infrared antagonism and a red-blue antagonism are apparent, in which red suppresses elongation under the conditions of our experiments. It may be asked whether all experiments can be explained by the effectiveness of infrared and a red-infrared antagonism alone. Notwithstanding the fact that this paper is confined to high light intensity effects, it should be mentioned that in recent years some effects of internode elongation formerly obtained with blue supplementary light containing some near infrared (Wassink, Stolwijk, and Beemster, 1951) could be reproduced by using this infrared content alone (Wassink, Bensink, and de Lint, 1957). These effects, however, were not obtained with blue that contained no detectable infrared. The last results with *Hyoscyamus* seem open to two different explanations: (1) Near infrared and blue have similar effects upon elongation in *Hyoscyamus,* which effects are suppressed by red. In the latter respect, red inhibits blue effects much more strongly than it does near-infrared effects (or else blue effects require much higher intensities than infrared effects). (2) All responses, including those in blue, are due to slight contaminations with near infrared, even with the blue plastic filter.

In view of the complete opacity of this filter for near infrared, we feel inclined at present to ascribe the elongation in blue to the blue radiation itself and thus give preference to the first explanation. If, indeed, the effect still were due to near infrared contamination, the infrared would have to be extremely effective—so much so that one might ask whether near infrared generation by chlorophyll fluorescence might not play a part.

We now have experiments under way in which further improvement of the light qualities of our cabinets is envisaged, especially with respect to the removal of traces of red and near infrared in the cabinets in which spectral purity is desired.

HIGH LIGHT INTENSITY FORMATIVE EFFECTS IN LETTUCE

Heading of lettuce is possible only under fairly high light intensities. This phenomenon has been studied in detail in our laboratory by J. Bensink during recent years (Wassink, 1957). The following data appear of interest for the present discussion (cf. also Bensink, 1958a,b).

The shape of successive leaves in young lettuce plants changes gradually. The plant starts with the formation of relatively narrow leaves, with a length-breadth relation >2. Successive leaves gradually become broader, so that under normal conditions of illumination the length-breadth relation approaches 1.0 from about the eighth leaf onward. The latter leaves make heading possible.

The relation outlined is subject to changes due to several factors, both external and internal. Those investigated up to the present are light intensity, night temperature, nitrogen supply, variety of lettuce, and spectral region. Lower light intensities "lift up" the curves, i.e., a certain leaf has a higher length-breadth ratio than it has under higher light intensities. The same holds true for higher night temperatures, for higher nitrogen concentrations, for certain varieties with respect to others, also for yellow light as compared with blue light.

The two varieties investigated were Meikoningin and Wonder van Voorburg; the latter has higher light requirements than the former. At the lowest light intensity used (25,000 ergs cm^2 sec daylight fluorescent tubes), Wonder van Voorburg shows a remarkable phenomenon. Instead of the normal behavior in which successive leaves gradually become relatively broader, successive leaves become relatively narrower. In this case also internode elongation occurs, which is not related to flowering.

This internode elongation, as well as relative elongation of leaves, can also be induced by supplementary near-infrared radiation, as was found earlier (Wassink, Stolwijk, and Beemster, 1951). The effect of supplementary radiation depends upon the intensity of the basic white light period. If the basic light intensity is, for example, 25,000 ergs/cm^2 sec, the effect of supplementary irradiation is much more apparent than if it is in the order of 66,000 ergs/cm^2 sec (Fig. 5).

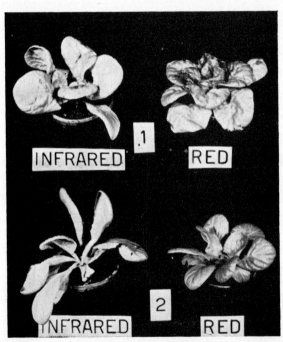

Fig. 5. Lettuce, var. Meikoningin. Influence of 8-hr supplementary irradiation with infrared (1000 egrs/cm^2 sec), after 10 hr light of two different intensities. (1) 66,000 ergs/cm^2 sec; (2) 25,000 ergs/cm^2 sec, photographed Feb. 10, 1953.

As stated above, successive leaves in a young lettuce plant gradually become broader, so that length/breadth decreases. If now, for example, at 12 leaves, the 6 latest ones are removed, the next leaf approaches the shape of the sixth leaf and not that of the twelfth. A few leaves of a relatively high length/breadth relation are then produced, after which decrease of length/breadth again is observed, the curve is fairly parallel to that of the original set of the sixth to the twelfth, and, at about the twenty-fourth leaf, the curve is again more or less on the level of the twelfth leaf. The effect of defoliation indicates the existence of a correlative connection between the various leaves. We will presently see another example of such a correlation.

As stated above, the effects of yellow and of blue light on leaf shape in lettuce are related as are those of lower and higher light intensities. In each spectral region, moreover, a light intensity dependence of leaf shape is clear (Fig. 6). The figure shows that a plant at 11,000 ergs/cm² sec in yellow light is much more elongated than one at 10,000 ergs/cm² sec in blue light (var. Meikoningin).

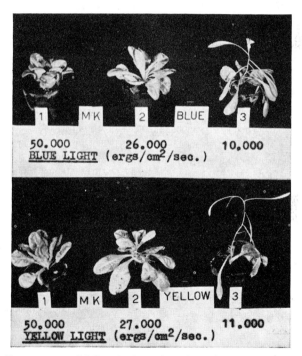

Fig. 6.   Lettuce, var. Meikoningin, grown in either exclusively blue light or exclusively yellow light, both at three different intensities. Photographed July 21, 1955.

It is interesting to compare the illustration of Meikoningin with that of the variety requiring higher intensities, Wonder van Voorburg (Fig 7). The difference between the two varieties is somewhat less obvious in blue light than in yellow. Nevertheless it is clear that Wonder van Voorburg at 26,000 ergs/cm^2 sec in yellow light is much more elongated than the corresponding one in blue light, and also much more elongated than the corresponding Meikoningin plant.

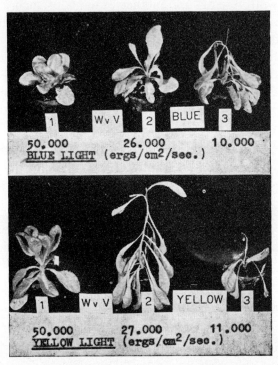

FIG. 7. Lettuce, var. Wonder van Voorburg, grown in either exclusively blue light or exclusively yellow light, both at three different intensities. Photographed July 21, 1955.

Bensink has cultivated a Meikoningin plant in blue light of 10,000 ergs/cm^2 sec which produces narrow leaves and considerable stem elongation. This plant, upon being transferred to blue light of 50,000 ergs/cm^2 sec, produced round leaves at its top, with short internodes. This illustrates the possibility of direct reaction of young leaves to light intensity.

Conversely, other phenomena, like the partial defoliation experiment, also show correlations with the light factor. Under high light intensities, a lettuce plant builds a head consisting of round leaves. The growing point is covered by leaves and doubtless receives a much lower light intensity than the outer leaves. Nevertheless, it produces "high light intensity" leaves. If a plant that has formed a head is placed under low light intensities, the growing point again starts building long and narrow leaves which protrude from the head. The nature of these correlations is still unknown.

An elongated leaf is flat, and the lamina can be cut at either side of the midrib, retaining its original shape. A round ("high light intensity") leaf is strongly folded, and, when cut alongside the midrib, the lamina can easily be stretched to about twice the length of the midrib. Thus, it is mainly the growth inhibition of the midrib that causes the rounded leaves.

Bensink has studied cell shapes and sizes and finds that the cells on the lamina of broad and of narrow leaves do not differ much in shape. In the midrib, however, differences do exist. In a broad, folded leaf, the cells are much shorter at the base of the midrib than at its top. In an elongated, flat leaf, on the contrary, the cells at the top of the midrib do not differ much in size from those at its base.

De Lint has recently studied morphogenetic changes of the leaves of lettuce plants in the colored light cabinets, in combination with gibberellic acid. The effects are reminiscent of those in *Hyoscyamus,* inasmuch as high doses of GA produce strong elongation of leaves and internodes in all colors. The reaction obtained with the different colors in the absence of GA has not yet been sufficiently studied. The effect of differences in intensity in the various spectral regions is still to be analyzed in greater detail. An effect that deserves special attention in view of its difference from that in *Hyoscyamus* is that red with much infrared does not seem to produce more (rather, even less) elongation than pure red, and the effect of GA does not seem very manifest in the red + infrared cabinet (Fig. 8) and the plant with the highest dose probably is not quite representative. It is clear that, in general, GA produces a low light intensity type. This is even more obvious in an experiment in white light, done at equal light intensities and with dif-

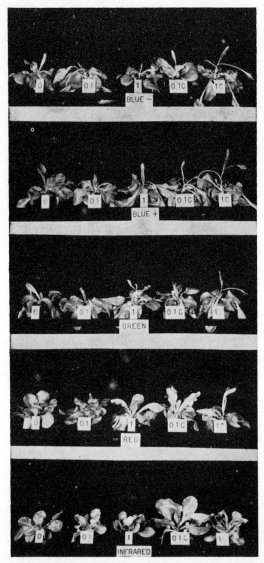

FIG. 8. Lettuce, var. Wonder van Voorburg. Treated with GA: 0, 0.1, and 1 μg on the first day; 0.1 c and 1 c = μg daily. Irradiation during 16-hr day with monochromatic light of high intensity. Photographed on March 16, 1957, after 30 days of treatment.

F<small>IG</small>. 9.   Lettuce, var. Wonder van Voorburg. Irradiation with 30,000 ergs/cm^2 sec. T.L.-daylight fluorescent light. Treatment: 0, 0.1, 1, 2.5, and 10 μg GA/plant. $3\times$ = on the first and every 10th day; $30\times$ = every day. Photographed after 30 days of treatment, on Mar. 16, 1957.

ferent doses and frequencies of GA application. Figure 9 shows a selection of items chosen in this series.

The discussed elongation effects in lettuce have no connection with flower initiation.

ADDITIONAL REMARKS

De Lint has started investigating the elongation of *Avena* coleoptiles in various spectral light regimes. This work is still in a preliminary stage. The plant material permits the running of large series in a short time. The seedlings are allowed to germinate in the dark for 2 days, remain in the dark for 1 day after having been planted, then are irradiated for a few hours, put back into the dark, and are measured after 5 days when the coleoptiles have stopped growing.

Two subsequent 2-hr illuminations in various spectral regions (intensities ~20,000 ergs/cm² sec) show results as indicated in Table I. Also darkness is included as alternative treatment.

TABLE I.   Effect of Two Successive 2-hr Treatments as Indicated on Final Length of *Avena* Coleoptiles Grown in Darkness (De Lint, unpublished)

Second 2-hr Period	First 2-hr Period →	Blue	Yellow	Infrared	Dark
Blue		65	64	68	—
Yellow		57	55	60	—
Infrared		86	82	85	—
Dark		71	69	89	100

Irradiation always decreases the final coleoptile length as compared with darkness. In most cases, two subsequent spectral irradiations yield shorter coleoptiles than one followed by darkness. Also irradiation with near infrared (including longer wavelengths) yields shorter coleoptiles than complete darkness. It is curious, however, that near infrared, following blue or yellow (the only regions tested so far) de-inhibits the elongation process, yielding longer coleoptiles than those obtained if the 2-hr color period were followed directly by darkness. This de-inhibition, however, is not observed when the first irradiation period also is near infrared (see Table I and de Lint, 1957).

De Lint, furthermore, is running extensive light intensity-exposure time series in blue and yellow light. The inhibition in length is fairly proportional with the log *It*. Blue light shows a somewhat stronger inhibition than yellow light, which seems qualitatively concordant with Bensink's results on lettuce leaf shape, discussed earlier in this paper.

Finally, we would like to mention that, in connection with horticultural practice, Wassink and Wassink-van Lummel have started following growth of tomato plants in light of wide spectral regions. In the series run so far, growth has been compared in equal incident intensities with white daylight fluorescent sources, red fluorescent tubes (unfiltered), and incandescent light. In all cases, incandescent light yields a more elongated growth type, accompanied by conspicuously higher dry weight. It has so far not yet been determined whether this is due— as one might be inclined to suppose—to the higher near infrared content of this light source, or to its greater predominance of red over blue. Previous work of this laboratory (Wassink and Stolwijk, 1952) has shown that in tomato, red light produces a more elongated and taller growth than blue light, if given as almost pure spectral regions. The present work is being continued, and several recent findings are still to be elaborated (see also Wassink, 1957).

REFERENCES

Bensink, J. 1958a. Morphogenetic effects of light intensity and night temperature on the growth of lettuce (*Lactuca sativa* L.), with special reference to the process of heading. *Proc. Koninkl. Ned. Akad. Wetenschap., C61,* 89–100.
———. 1958b. Heading of lettuce (*Lactuca sativa* L.) as a morphogenetic effect of leaf growth. *15th Intern. Horticultural Congr.,* Nice, April 1958, in press.
Curry, G. M., and E. C. Wassink. 1956. Photoperiodic and formative effects of various wavelength regions in *Hyoscyamus niger* as influenced by gibberellic acid. *Mededel. Landbouwhogeschool Wageningen, 56* (14), 1–8.
de Lint, P. J. A. L. 1957. Double action of near infrared in length growth of the *Avena* coleoptile. *Mededel. Landbouwhogeschool Wageningen, 57* (10), 1–9.
Hillman, W. S., and A. W. Galston. 1957. Inductive control of indoleacetic acid oxidase activity by red and near infrared light. *Plant Physiol., 32,* 129–35.
Stolwijk, J. A. J., and J. A. D. Zeevaart. 1955. Wave length dependence of different light reactions governing in *Hyoscyamus niger. Proc. Koninkl. Ned. Akad. Wettenschap., C58:* 386–96.
Wassink, E. C. 1957. Interaction of light, other external factors and genetic differences in formative effects in plants. Simposio Internazionale di fotoperiodismo (organizzato sotto gli auspici dell' I.U.B.S.), Parma, giugno 1957.
Wassink, E. C., J. Bensink, and P. J. A. L. de Lint. 1957. Formative effects of light quality and intensity on plants. *Atti 2° Intern. di Photobiologie,* Turin, Italy, June 1957, pp. 343-60.
Wassink, E. C., and J. A. J. Stolwijk. 1952. Effects of light of narrow spectral regions on growth and development of plants. *Proc. Koninkl. Ned. Akad. Wettenschap., C55,* 471–88.
———. 1956. Effects of light quality on plant growth. *Ann. Rev. Plant Physiol., 7,* 373–400.
Wassink, E. C., J. A. J. Stolwijk, and A. B. R. Beemster. 1951. Dependence of formative and photoperiodic reactions in *Brassica rapa* var. *Cosmos* and *Lactuca* on wavelength and time of irradiation. *Proc. Koninkl. Ned. Akad. Wetenschap., C54:* 421–32.
Wassink, E. C., and C. van der Scheer. 1951. A spherical radiation meter. *Mededel. Landbouwhogeschool Wageningen, 51,* 175–83.

PHOTOCONTROL OF VEGETATIVE GROWTH

R. J. DOWNS

Agricultural Research Service, U. S. Department of Agriculture, Beltsville, Maryland

The vegetative growth of many plants is regulated to a remarkable degree by light. This is particularly well illustrated by the growth of a great many woody plants whose preparation for winter is largely light-controlled. Light affects growth in two major ways, and both are expressions of the same basic photoreaction (Borthwick, Hendricks, and Parker, 1952; Borthwick *et al.*, 1952; Downs, 1955; Liverman *et al.*, 1955; Mohr, 1956). The first way, which is photoperiodically controlled, determines whether woody plants shall continue to elongate, and the second, which is photo-controlled, although not truly photoperiodic, determines whether the elongation made under the stimulus of a favorable photoperiod shall be long or short.

The woody plant thus appears to be running two different systems with the same photoregulator. In one system, the photoperiodic one, the regulator seems to operate as an ordinary on-off switch in that long photoperiods allow growth to continue while short photoperiods induce dormancy and cessation of growth (Downs and Borthwick, 1956). In the other case, the photoregulator operates as a modulating device and as such permits very delicate control of the response. This modulator is the ratio of the red-absorbing to the far-red-absorbing form of the pigment. For example, the growth of loblolly pine (*Pinus taeda* L.) on long photoperiods increases when the plants enter the dark period with the red-absorbing form of the pigment predominating (Table I).

The ratio of the red-absorbing to the far-red-absorbing form of the pigment may be controlled by proper choice of the supplemental light source. In spite of the considerable red-radiant energy emitted, the high far-red emittance of the incandescent lamp is apparently adequate to shift the pigment equilibrium in favor of the red-absorbing form and thereby induce additional growth and elongation. The fluorescent

TABLE I.   Effect of Kind of Supplemental Light on Growth of Loblolly Pine

	Incandescent[a]	Fluorescent[a]
Total growth, cm	30.5	14.1
Fresh weight of stem, g	6.77	4.36
Dry weight		
Stem, g	1.84	1.11
Root, g	0.85	0.60
Length of needles, cm	15.0	12.6

[a] Eight hours of the kind of supplemental light indicated.

lamp, with high red and almost no far-red emittance, leaves the pigment system predominantly in the far-red-absorbing form and thereby reduces growth.

Herbaceous plants, many of which are able to make elongative growth over a wider range of photoperiods than many woody plants, nevertheless react much as woody plants do to the modulation of elongative growth by the pigment system. For example, soybean (*Glycine max* (L.) Merr. var. Biloxi and var. Agate) and tomato (*Lycopersicum esculentum* Mill. var. Marglobe) reacted as loblolly pine did, producing longer internodes when the plants entered the dark period with the pigment system predominantly in the red-absorbing form; that is, under incandescent supplemental light (Table II). Thus, the operation of the regulator as a modulating device is readily demonstrated with herbaceous plants as well as with woody ones. However,

TABLE II.   Effect of Photoperiod Length and Kind of Supplemental Light on Growth of Tomato and Soybean

	Photoperiod,[a] 12 hr		Photoperiod,[a] 16 hr	
Plant	Incandescent	Fluorescent	Incandescent	Fluorescent
Marglobe tomato				
Nodes	8	8	9	8
Stem length, cm	29.3	20.2	31.8	18.6
Biloxi soybean				
Nodes	10	10	10	11
Stem length, cm	90.6	72.2	100.0	68.8
Agate soybean				
Nodes	6	5	5	5
Stem length, cm	44.8	22.0	61.9	26.4

[a] Eight hours of natural light plus the duration of supplemental light necessary to obtain these photoperiods.

for some reason the second operation of the regulator, the photo-periodic on-off switch, is less sharply defined in control of growth of herbaceous plants than it is in woody ones.

Flowering of a rosette type plant typically involves two phenomena: the production of the flower primordia and flowers and the promotion of stem and branch development. The two phenomena are so inter-woven and interdependent that we seldom think of them as separable. Although they are usually not separable, they can, to a degree, be independently controlled by light. Thus, one is able to influence stem elongation by appropriate light treatment and thereby indirectly influence flowering.

Flowering of millet (*Setaria italica* (L.) Beauv.), which occurs slowly on 16-hr photoperiods, is accelerated by use of incandescent supplemental light rather than fluorescent (Table III). This promotion

TABLE III. Effect of Photoperiod Length and Kind of Supplemental Light on Stem and Spike Lengths of Millet

	Photoperiod,[a] 12 hr		Photoperiod,[a] 16 hr	
	Incandescent	Fluorescent	Incandescent	Fluorescent
Stem length, mm	420	308	222	82
Spike length,[b] mm	21.6	16.9	1.4	0.6

[a] Eight hours of natural light plus the duration of supplemental light necessary to obtain these photoperiods.

[b] A measure of the rate of flowering.

is apparently due to an increased rate of stem elongation resulting from the plant's entering the dark period with the pigment system predominantly in the red-absorbing form. If the red-radiant energy from the incandescent lamp is prevented from reaching the plant so that only relatively pure far red is available, a more efficient method is obtained for converting the pigment system into the red-absorbing form. As little as a 5-min exposure to far-red radiant energy at the close of each 16-hr period of high-intensity light was adequate to in-crease the rate of stem elongation and consequently the rate of flower-ing of millet (Fig. 1). The high-intensity light period was obtained by means of fluorescent lamps, and the control plants, therefore, entered the dark period with the pigment predominantly in the far-red-absorb-ing form. The potential effect of the far-red irradiation could be re-

FIG. 1.   Millet plants received no additional radiant energy, 5 min of far red, or 5 min of far red followed by 5 min of red at the end of each 16-hr photoperiod (left to right).

versed by shifting the pigment equilibrium back to a predominance of the far-red-absorbing form. This conversion of the red-absorbing to the far-red-absorbing form was accomplished by following the far-red irradiation by a brief exposure to red radiant energy.

In order to study some of the details of operation of the modulating control of growth, we thought it advantageous to study elongation independent of flowering. Pinto beans were selected as the test plant although other bean varieties or other species of plants would have been equally suitable (Fig. 2). In general, a brief exposure to far red at the beginning of the dark period induced internode elongation. This potential elongation was reversed when the far-red irradiation was followed by a brief exposure to red radiant energy (Downs *et al.*, 1957; Hendricks *et al.*, 1956). The responsiveness of the plants depended upon the number of hours of darkness during which the pigment remained in the red-absorbing form (Fig. 3). This dependence probably does not arise from differences in the amount of pigment present or from differences in the relative sensitivity of the pigment system to red

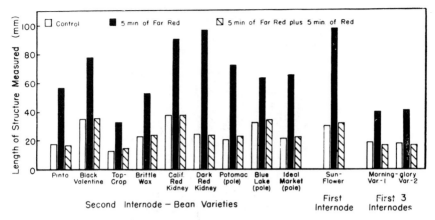

Fig. 2.   Effect of 5 min of far red or far red followed by 5 min of red on internode lengths of beans, sunflower, and morning-glory when the irradiations are made at the end of an 8-hr photoperiod of high-intensity fluorescent light.

and far red. It seems to be caused by differences in subsequent reactions initiated by the active form of the pigment. The linear relation between response and duration of darkness fails for dark periods in excess of 20 hr, indicating a dependence upon some other factor, possibly some function of photosynthesis.

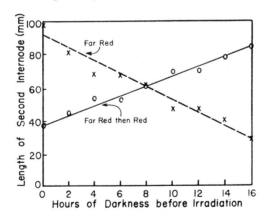

Fig. 3.   Length of second internodes of Pinto bean plants in relation to time within a 16-hr dark period at which length-promoting or length-inhibiting treatments with radiant energy are given. Solid line, 5 min of far red at 0 time followed by 5 min of red at hour shown. Broken line, 5 min of far red at hour shown.

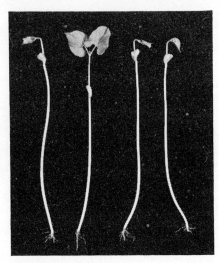

FIG. 4. Dark-grown Red Kidney bean seedlings after 10 days in continuous darkness and after being given 2 min of red radiation, 2 min of red and 5 min of far red, or 5 min of far red only (left to right).

Dark-grown bean plants also respond to red and far red (Fig. 4) (Downs, 1955; Liverman *et al.*, 1955). Unlike light-grown plants, however, the dark-grown ones must first be irradiated with red. Then, the far red reverses the potential effect of the red irradiation. This apparent difference in the responses of light-grown and dark-grown beans are in reality fundamental ones that arise from the form of the pigment at the beginning of treatment. Dark-grown material contains the pigment system predominantly in the red-absorbing form prior to treatment, whereas the light-grown material contains the pigment largely in the far-red-absorbing form. Control of internode lengthening thus illustrates that the pigment system is not destroyed by light but is present and functional in the plant at any time whether it is in light or in darkness.

REFERENCES

Borthwick, H. A., S. B. Hendricks, and M. W. Parker. 1952. The reaction controlling floral initiation. *Proc. Natl. Acad. Sci. U. S., 38,* 929–34.

Borthwick, H. A., S. B. Hendricks, M. W. Parker, E. H. Toole, and V. K. Toole. 1952. A reversible photoreaction controlling seed germination. *Proc. Natl. Acad. Sci. U. S., 38,* 662–66.

Downs, R. J. 1955. Photoreversibility of leaf and hypocotyl elongation of dark-grown Red Kidney bean seedlings. *Plant Physiol. 30,* 468–72.

Downs, R. J., and H. A. Borthwick. 1956. Effects of photoperiod on the growth of trees. *Botan. Gaz., 117,* 310-26.

Downs, R. J., S. B. Hendricks, and H. A. Borthwick. 1957. Photoreversible control of elongation of Pinto beans and other plants under normal conditions of growth. *Botan. Gaz., 118,* 199–208.

Hendricks, S. B., H. A. Borthwick, and R. J. Downs. 1956. Pigment conversion in the formative responses of plants to radiation. *Proc. Natl. Acad. Sci. U. S., 42,* 19–26.

Liverman, J. L., M. P. Johnson, and L. Starr. 1955. Reversible photoreaction in controlling expansion of etiolated bean leaf discs. *Science, 121,* 440–41.

Mohr, H. 1956. Die Beeinflussung der Keimung von Farnsporen durch Licht und andere Factoren. *Planta, 46,* 534–51.

STUDIES ON INDOLEACETIC ACID OXIDASE INHIBITOR AND ITS RELATION TO PHOTOMORPHOGENESIS

ARTHUR W. GALSTON
Department of Botany, Josiah Willard Gibbs Research Laboratory, Yale University, New Haven, Connecticut

The experimenter attempting to understand the biochemistry of the reversible photoreaction controlling many aspects of plant growth and development has available essentially three possible avenues of approach:

1. He may attempt to isolate or otherwise obtain exact information about the photoreceptor pigment which represents the starting point of the chain of reactions culminating in some biological response. Presumably, exact knowledge of the photoreceptor could lead to additional information about the subsequent reactants in the chain.

2. Going to the other end of the reaction chain, he can choose some measurable biological effect of the irradiation, such as seed germination, bean hook opening, or floral initiation, and study such subjects as the kinetics of the forward and back reactions, the relation of these reactions to various growth-regulating substances, and effects of other environmental variables on the course of the reaction. Presumably, this type of study, being pursued by so many people, will give some indication of the kind of growth regulatory system through which the initial photoreaction exerts its ultimate effects.

3. Finally, if he knows of some precise chemical change produced directly by the reversible photoreaction, he can try to understand the mechanism by which this change has resulted from the irradiation

[1] These investigations have been supported for several years by a series of grants from the National Science Foundation. Certain of the experiments were performed with the technical assistance of Suzanne L. Fried and Hava Warburg. The work on the inhibitor and cofactor for indoleacetic acid oxidase has been performed by Dr. Z. Rose and Dr. H. Sharpensteen, respectively, under partial support furnished by the American Cancer Society.

137

treatment, and further, the path by which it is linked, if at all, to the eventual growth reaction.

Each of these approaches has certain advantages, and each, in the hands of competent investigators, has yielded some useful information about the physiology of photomorphogenesis. For a variety of reasons, some carefully conceived and others entirely accidental or without reason, we have concentrated on the third approach. As it happens, this is the approach that has been least followed in the past, owing undoubtedly to the fact that very few specific chemical changes can as yet be directly related to the reversible photoreaction. However, theoretically at least, this approach should be quite rewarding, in that very specific chemical questions can be asked of the organism in relation to photomorphogenesis.

To the best of our knowledge, only four specific chemical changes have thus far been fairly directly linked with the red-far red photoreceptor system:

1. The production of a yellow pigment in the cuticle of Rutgers tomato fruits is controlled by light (Piringer and Heinze, 1954). This pigment, presumably a flavonoid, is synthesized by a fruit given an inductive red light treatment. The red light effect, which has an action spectrum very similar to that for the inhibition of flowering in *Xanthium,* is negated by subsequently applied far-red light.

2. Anthocyanin synthesis in cabbage and turnip seedlings and in apple hypodermis is enhanced by preirradiation with red light, this enhancement also being reversible by subsequently applied far red (Siegelman and Hendricks, 1956, 1957; Mohr, 1957).

3. The lag phase in chlorophyll synthesis in dark-grown bean leaves is eliminated by pretreatment with red light, the effect again being reversible by far red (Withrow *et al.,* 1956). The same photoreaction apparently also controls protochlorophyll synthesis (Wolff *et al.,* 1957).

4. The activity of the enzyme indoleacetic acid oxidase found in etiolated pea buds is sharply decreased several hours after an exposure of the plant to low irradiances of red light (Hillman and Galston, 1957). This effect, which is also readily reversible by subsequently applied far-red irradiation, is due to an increased level in the bud of a substance which inhibits the enzyme (Hillman and Galston, 1957)

This IAA oxidase inhibitor is water soluble, heat stable, and dialyzable, and, on the basis of yet incomplete evidence, is considered to be a phenol.

From the heterogeneous nature of these effects, it is clear that any attempt to generalize is at present ill-advised. Investigation of any one of the effects could be expected to yield interesting information on the biochemistry of photomorphogenesis. For several years, we have been concerned with the relation between the photomorphogenic reaction and auxin metabolism. It is for this reason that we have concentrated on the last-described phenomenon. We have currently in progress investigations of the chemical nature of the inhibitor, its distribution in the plant, and the effect of environmental and chemical treatments on its level. In all these experiments, we assay for this substance by its inhibition of indoleacetic acid destruction. However, we wish to make it clear that we are in no sense committed to the thesis that the action of this substance *in vivo* is, in fact, connected with auxin destruction. So far as we are now concerned, the inhibitor has great intrinsic interest because its production seems so directly connected with the red-far red reaction, and the IAA-oxidase system is merely a handy tool for the assay of this unknown substance. By the same token, we in no way wish to rule out the possibility that the inhibitor does, in fact, affect growth by sparing auxin from destruction.

It is thus our belief that further knowledge of this substance whose synthesis is controlled by the reversible photoreaction will help elucidate the details of photomorphogenesis. This paper will therefore present previously unpublished information on its distribution in the green pea plant, its rise and fall in response to physical and chemical stimuli, and some details concerning its chemical nature.

DISTRIBUTION OF INDOLEACETIC ACID OXIDASE AND ITS INHIBITOR IN LIGHT-GROWN PEAS

Materials and Methods

The experimental organisms in these studies were seedlings of light-grown Alaska and Laurel (dwarf) peas (*Pisum sativum* L.) purchased from Associated Seed Growers, New Haven, Connecticut. The seeds were soaked in tap water for 2 hr, and were then sown in coarse Zonolite vermiculite in perforated rectangular polyethylene containers. The containers were placed on stainless steel growth tables, equipped with automatic subirrigation units. These tables, constructed to our specifications by the A. B. Stanley Company, Chestnut Hill, Massachusetts, have afforded automatic and virtually trouble-free growth of plants for over a year.

The nutrient solution for each table consisted of 120 g of Hyponex (Hydroponic Chemical Company, Copley, Ohio) per 100 liters of tap water, changed every 2 weeks. The nutrient solution is circulated to the upper level by a marine type motor, equipped with a stainless steel rotor and Teflon bearings. The motor is set into operation by a time clock, fixed to operate daily for two 15-min periods, at intervals of 12 hr. During this 15-min cycle there are approximately three return flushes of the nutrient solution to the tank. Under these conditions, growth of the plants was uniform and rapid.

The growth tables were placed in air-conditioned rooms maintained at various temperatures and photoperiods. For the bulk of these experiments plants were grown under continuous illumination at 17°C. The light was provided by banks of closely packed slimline fluorescent tubes, consisting of alternate cool-white and warm-white tubes. No incandescent illumination was supplied. The light intensity at the surface of the plant was about 2000 ft-c.

Plants were usually harvested at the age of 14 days and separated into the various portions assayed. For IAA oxidase assays the tissues were converted to a brei by grinding in $0.1M$ phosphate buffer (pH 6.1) in a mortar previously stored in a deep freeze. The tissue was frozen to a slurry by contact with the mortar and was kept cold throughout the operation. Subsequent to grinding, the brei was centrifuged briefly (10 min, $2000 \times g$) to remove cell-wall debris, and the supernatant liquid was made up to volume.

For assay of inhibitor, it was essential to obtain an inhibitor-free enzyme preparation of high activity. This was done by grinding third internode tissue of etiolated 7-day-old Alaska peas in the same manner as described above, 100 mg fr. wt. tissue being present per milliliter of final enzyme solution.

The inhibitor was prepared from green tissue in three ways, all of which yielded approximately the same results. (*a*) Brei was dialyzed overnight at 2°C *vs* an equal volume of 0.01M pH 6.1 phosphate buffer, the dialyzate being used as the inhibitor. (*b*) Brei was immersed in a boiling water bath for 5 min, and the resulting precipitate was removed by centrifugation or filtration, and the supernatant liquid was used as inhibitor. (*c*) Intact tissue was boiled in distilled water or in dilute buffer (0.1M, pH 6.1), and the resulting liquid was used directly as the inhibitor.

All assays for IAA oxidase activity were made by the use of the Salkowski colorimetric technique (Tang and Bonner, 1947) readings being made 20 min after mixture of solution and reagent. Ten milliliters reaction mixture containing $10^{-4}M$ $MnCl_2$ and 2,4-dichlorophenol (DCP) (Goldacre *et al.*, 1953), $2 \times 10^{-4}M$ IAA, buffer and enzyme were placed in 50-ml Erlenmeyer flasks shaken 96 cycles/min at 30°C in an Aminco Dubnoff metabolic shaking incubator. One-milliliter aliquots were removed at intervals and pipetted vigorously into 4 ml of Salkowski reagent, then stirred vigorously. The resulting colors were read 20 min later on a Klett colorimeter equipped with a No. 54 green filter.

Protein nitrogen determinations were made as previously described (Galston and Dalberg, 1954).

The IAA was the Eastman product, and the gibberellic acid used in certain experiments was kindly supplied by Dr. P. W. Brian of Imperial Chemical Industries, England.

Results

Distribution of Enzymatic Activity in Alaska Pea Plants. Two-week-old Alaska pea plants, grown at 17°C and 24 hr photoperiod, were divided into terminal bud, successive internodes, and leaves. Five hundred milligrams of each kind of tissue was then ground, made up to 50 ml brei, and assayed for IAA oxidase activity at various levels of tissue equivalent per 10 ml reaction mixture. The results are shown in Fig. 1.

The following conclusions may be drawn from these data: (1) IAA oxidase activity is high in terminal bud and young stem tissues, but falls rapidly as the concentrations of tissue per standard volume of reaction mixture is raised. This is best interpreted in terms of a high level of inhibitor present in the brei. (2) With the older stem tissues,

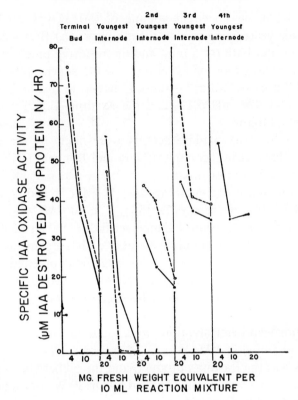

FIG. 1. The IAA oxidase activity of various portions of 14-day-old light-grown Alaska pea seedlings, measured at various concentrations.

enzyme activity is lower, but does not fall off so rapidly with increasing concentration. This is probably indicative of a lower level of inhibitor. (3) The leaves showed no activity at all, owing either to low enzymatic activity, high inhibitor level, or both.

These data were interpreted as meaning in general that IAA oxidase activity is widespread in the stem and young bud tissue of light-grown pea plants, and that there exists, in addition, a gradient in an inhibitor of this enzyme, the inhibitor being most concentrated in the youngest regions of the stem.

Direct Demonstration of the Inhibitor and Its Gradient in the Plant. The inhibitor of IAA oxidase activity has already been demonstrated to be a water-soluble, heat-stable, low-molecular-weight substance

(Tang and Bonner, 1948). It was therefore simple to demonstrate directly the presence and gradient of this substance inferred from the concentration experiments of the section above.

As before, 500-mg fr. wt. samples of the various tissues were harvested, ground to a brei, briefly centrifuged to remove debris, and made up to a final volume of 50 ml in $0.1M$ pH 6.1 phosphate buffer. The entire volume was then enclosed in a cellophane dialysis tube, and permitted to stand overnight at 2°C in contact with 500 ml of $0.01M$ pH 6.1 phosphate buffer, in a glass cylinder. The resulting dialyzed enzyme was then assayed for activity and was compared with a sample of the fresh brei, and with a sample of brei stored in a dialysis tube overnight at 2°C, but not in contact with dialysis fluid. The data for terminal bud brei are shown in Table I. The other tissues yielded similar results.

TABLE I.   Effect of Dialysis on Activity of IAA Oxidase Preparations from the Terminal Buds of 2-Week-Old Light-Grown Peas. (Concentration of *brei* was 20 mg fr. wt. equivalent per 10 ml reaction mixture. $10^{-4}M$ MnCl$_2$, $10^{-4}M$ DCP, and $2 \times 10^{-4}M$ IAA added. Salkowski technique employed)

| | Salkowski Colors after Minutes of Reaction | | | | |
Brei Used	0	30	60	90	Δ Salkowski, 60 min
Fresh	273	271	267	—	7
Aged overnight at 2°C	274	275	272	261	2
Dialyzed overnight at 2°C	269	218	89	33	185

It is clear that the activity of the enzyme is increased by dialysis, as previously reported for this enzyme (Galston and Baker, 1951). The inference is that a dialyzable inhibitor has passed out of the bag into the surrounding dialyzing fluid.

To demonstrate the latter point more directly and to obtain quantitative data on inhibitor content, the dialysis experiment was repeated with 50-ml breis of various tissues ($= 500$ mg fr. wt.) being dialyzed against 50 ml $0.1M$ buffer. This time, the dialyzate was harvested, and 0.5 ml of the fluid added to 10 ml of reaction mixture containing, as enzyme, 1 ml of inhibitor-free brei ($= 100$ mg fr. wt.) from the third internode of 7-day-old etiolated Alaska pea seedlings. The results are shown in Table II.

TABLE II. Relative Inhibitor Content of Dialyzates of Breis Prepared from Various Portions of 2-Week-Old Light-Grown Alaska Pea Plants (50 ml brei (= 500 mg fr. wt. tissue) dialyzed overnight at 2°C *vs* 50 ml 0.1M pH 6.1 phosphate buffer; 1 ml dialyzate then added per the usual 10 ml of reaction mixture; initial Salkowski color (time 0) = 270)

Tissue Used	Salkowski Color after 60 min	Δ Salkowski Color, Colorimeter Units	Per Cent Inhibition by Tissue Dialyzate
None (control)	79	191	—
Stem, youngest internode	234	36	81
Stem, all other internodes	72–85	185–198	ca. 0
Leaflets and stipules, youngest leaf	211	59	69
Leaflets and stipules, leaf 2	142	128	33
Leaflets and stipules, leaf 3	109	161	16
Petioles and tendrils, youngest leaf	137	133	30
Petioles and tendrils, leaf 2	85	185	3
Petioles and tendrils, leaf 3	75	195	0

The following facts are clearly demonstrated by the data of Table II. (1) The inhibitor is most abundant in young tissues of all kinds, decreasing in concentration in progressively older tissues. (2) It is most concentrated in the youngest internode of the stem, next most abundant in the laminar tissues of the youngest expanded leaf, least abundant in the petioles and tendrils.

Since the inhibitor is heat stable (Tang and Bonner, 1947) and since preparation of the inhibitor by dialysis requires at least 16 hr, it was reasoned that the inhibitor could be collected quantitatively more conveniently by simple boiling of either brei or intact tissue. It was found that complete recovery of inhibitor results from exposure of brei to 100°C in a boiling water bath for 5–10 min, followed by filtration to remove coagulated proteins. Approximately the same recovery can be obtained by boiling the intact tissue in distilled water. Under these conditions, the content of inhibitor in the water rises for about 20 min, then falls off slowly with time. This probably means that more and more inhibitor is extracted with increased boiling time, but that some thermal destruction occurs on prolonged boiling.

Further inhibitor assays were made, by using the technique of boiling intact tissues for inhibitor extraction (10 mg fr. wt./ml H_2O). Results of such assays confirmed the distribution of inhibitor shown in

Table II and revealed in addition the fact that the smaller the terminal bud, the higher its inhibitor concentration. Thus, terminal buds less than 7 mm in length had higher IAA oxidase activities per unit protein (at low brei concentrations) than 8-, 10-, 12-, or 14-mm buds, in that order. With increasing brei concentration, the order of activity changed. Direct inhibitor assays revealed that the youngest buds actually had the highest inhibitor content. Thus, the generalization holds that youngest tissues are richest in inhibitor.

Effect of Light-Dark Alterations on Inhibitor Content and Oxidase Activity.   Tang and Bonner (1947) showed that exposure of etiolated pea seedlings to light resulted in a fall in IAA oxidase activity and an increase in the content of inhibitor. Both of these effects were linearly proportional to the daily duration of illumination. We were able to show the same kind of response to light duration in green peas.

Seedlings were grown under daily photoperiods of 8, 16, or 24 hr for 2 weeks. The youngest internodes were then harvested, and 500 mg made up into 50 ml of brei, as usual. One-half milliliter of brei was then added per 10 ml of reaction mixture, and the IAA oxidase activity was measured. Concurrently, the inhibitor content of the youngest leaflet from the same plants was measured, inhibitor being extracted by direct boiling of intact tissue and being added to the enzyme obtained from completely etiolated plants, as before. The results, shown in Table III, demonstrate a simultaneous rise in inhibitor and decline in

TABLE III.   Effect of Daily Duration of Illumination on Inhibitor Content and IAA Oxidase Activity of Green Alaska Pea Seedlings (All seedlings 14 days old, grown under ca. 1500 ft-c of fluorescent light; initial Salkowski color = 270)

Daily Photoperiod, hr	IAA Oxidase Activity of Stem, Δ Salkowski Color/60 min	IAA Oxidase Activity of Inhibitor-Free Enzyme, Appropriate Inhibitor Extract Added, Δ Salkowski Color/60 min
— (control, no inhibitor)	—	194
8	174	185
16	135	151
24	0	17

enzymatic activity with increasing photoperiod. Although the close coincidence of the numbers in the two data columns is probably at least partly fortuitous, the simultaneous and approximately equal movement of these quantities suggests that the decreased oxidase activity is a consequence of the increased inhibitor content.

Experiments were next conducted to see whether inhibitor levels of the youngest expanded leaflets would vary with the light regime to which the plant is exposed. Groups of 2-week-old seedlings of Alaska peas which had been raised under continuous light at 17°C were placed, for varying periods of time, in a dark room maintained at 23°C. At the completion of the dark period, 500 mg of leaflets was harvested from each group, ground into a brei in the dark room, the brei was then boiled for 10 min in a water bath, and the inhibitor content was assayed as before. The data, summarized in Fig. 2, reveal a

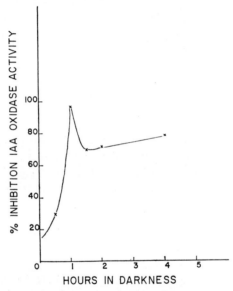

FIG. 2. The effect of transfer to complete darkness of pea plants previously grown in continuous light on the IAA oxidase inhibitor content of the youngest expanded leaflets.

sharp increase in inhibitor level in the first hour after transfer of the plant to darkness, followed by a sharp fall and gentle rise. The exact nature of the pattern depicted varied somewhat from experiment to experiment, i.e., the peak of inhibitor level varied from 0.5–2.0 hr, and the height of the peak showed considerable variation. Nonetheless, the basic pattern was the same in all six experiments done.

Several experiments performed with excised leaflets revealed that they are capable of manifesting these same variations in inhibitor content as a result of light-dark alterations. In Fig. 3 are presented data from a typical experiment, showing a rise in inhibitor level in the first

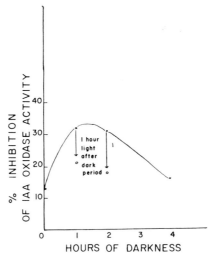

FIG. 3.   The effect of incubation in darkness of leaflets excised from pea plants previously grown in continuous light on their content of IAA oxidase inhibitor.

hour or two of darkness followed by a fall after 4 hr. It is also noteworthy that the temporary rise is largely reversed by transferring the dark-exposed leaf discs to light.

Comparative Inhibitor Content of Tall and Dwarf Peas.   The occurrence of a gradient of IAA oxidase inhibitor down the stem, together with variation in inhibitor content with light-dark alterations (see also Hillman and Galston, 1957) suggested a possible role for this substance in normal growth regulation. To test this possibility, further comparisons were made of the inhibitor content of tall (Alaska) and dwarf (Laurel) pea seedlings grown in the light. In both instances, 14-day-old plants were used, all having been grown under 24-hr photoperiods and at 17°C.

Individual leaflets of the youngest expanded leaf (fifth node) were harvested, wrapped in filter paper, and placed in the bottom of an 18 by 150 mm test tube. They were then covered with boiling distilled water and boiled in a water bath on a hot plate for 20 min. The fluid was decanted, and adjusted to such a volume that each milliliter represented 10 mg fr. wt. of the original plant material. Two-tenths milliliter (equivalent to 2 mg fr. wt.) of this inhibitor extract was then added per the usual 10 ml of reaction mixture. Results of such inhibitor assays are shown in Table IV.

TABLE IV. Comparative IAA Oxidase Inhibitor Content of Youngest Expanded Leaflets of 14-Day-Old Dwarf (Laurel) and Tall (Alaska) Pea Seedlings. (Inhibitor extracted by direct boiling in distilled water, of the intact leaflet. The equivalent of 2 mg fr. wt. of leaflet was then added as hot aqueous extract per 10 ml of usual reaction mixture. Original Salkowski color = 270.)

Variety	Leaf	Leaflet	Fr. Wt. Leaflet, mg	Salkowski Color, 60 min	Inhibition of IAA Oxidase Activity, %	Average Inhibition, %
— (control)	—		—	213	—	—
Laurel	1	A	65	103	51.7	
		B	58	151	29.1	
	2	A	58	157	26.3	
		B	50	152	28.6	27.5
	3	A	61	184	13.6	
		B	63	180	15.5	
Alaska	1	A	69	80	62.5	
		B	54	50	76.5	
	2	A	69	124	41.7	
		B	54	67	68.5	76.4
	3	A	43	2	99.2	
		B	41	0	100	

It is clear that Alaska (tall) leaflets have about three times as much inhibitor as Laurel (dwarf) leaflets per unit fresh weight. This is consistent with the view that inhibitor controls growth by sparing auxin from destruction. Similar assays of terminal buds, young stem and old stem showed smaller differences, but always in the same direction. In view of the fact that the youngest expanded leaflets are richest in the inhibitor, data obtained from these organs are considered the more significant.

Effect of Gibberellic Acid Pretreatment on IAA Oxidase Inhibitor in Leaflets of Alaska and Laurel Peas. It has been shown for peas

(Brian and Hemming, 1955) and for maize (Phinney, 1956) that gibberellic acid (GA) so enhances the growth of certain dwarf races as practically to eliminate the growth differences between tall and dwarf forms. If, therefore, the differences in inhibitor content between tall and dwarf peas shown above are physiologically meaningful, one should expect pretreatment with gibberellic acid to raise the inhibitor level of the leaflets. This result was actually obtained in many experiments, although occasionally, and without apparent reason, GA applications to the plants had no effect on leaflet inhibitor content.

GA was applied to the tissues in one of several ways. (*a*) Solutions of GA in dilute buffer were placed in large plastic tubs, and the perforated polyethylene containers holding several plants were immersed in the solution to a depth of ca. 3 cm. Uptake of GA was thus exclusively through the root system. (*b*) Stems were severed at the ground level and placed with their cut ends in GA solutions. (*c*) Individual leaflets of the youngest expanded leaves were excised and floated on GA solutions. (*d*) Discs of leaflets or cylinders of stem were removed with

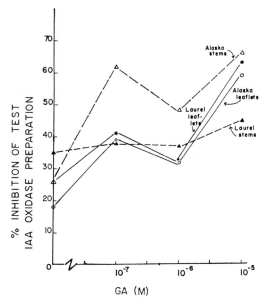

FIG. 4.   The effect of various concentrations of gibberellic acid administered via the roots to intact plants on the IAA oxidase inhibitor content of youngest expanded leaflets. GA applied 40 hr prior to harvest.

a cork borer or section cutter and floated on a GA solution. Generally four discs per leaflet could be obtained, one disc being placed in each of four petri dishes containing a different GA solution. In general, application of GA to the entire plant produced the greater effects on inhibitor level, though similar results were obtained with all techniques. Sample data are presented in Fig. 4. The results appear to permit the conclusion that GA somehow raises the inhibitor level, perhaps by itself being converted to inhibitor.

CHEMICAL NATURE OF THE INHIBITOR

Although we cannot yet present detailed information concerning the chemical nature of the inhibitor, considerable progress has been made in the preparation and fractionation of active extracts. This work has used as its starting point the leaflets of 14-day-old Alaska pea seedlings grown under continuous light, at a temperature of 17°C. Such leaflets, as mentioned previously, are relatively rich sources of the inhibitor.

The leaves are added to boiling water (1 g/10 ml), boiled vigorously for 20 min, and the supernatant is then decanted and cooled. The inhibitor activity is extremely stable, and such crude extracts have been stored in the frozen state for several months. For assay purposes, the inhibitor is added to a reaction mixture including inhibitor-free enzyme prepared from the third internodes of 7-day-old etiolated pea epicotyls, fortified with optimal concentrations (ca. $10^{-4}M$) $MnCl_2$ and 2,4-dichlorophenol. IAA at $2 \times 10^{-4}M$ is added at zero time, and aliquots removed for colorimetric assay at 15-min intervals.

The first step in the purification involves adsorption onto Darco-G-60 charcoal previously acid-washed and heated to 500°C. Small amounts of the active charcoal are added stepwise to the inhibitor solution until assay of the supernatant revealed essentially complete adsorption of the inhibitor. The charcoal can then be washed with 30% ethanol and water without loss of inhibitor, and the inhibitor finally eluted with a mixture of 50% ethanol-0.01M NH_3. The elution solvent is removed *in vacuo,* and the residue is taken up in water. Such a purified aqueous solution can be satisfactorily stored in the frozen state for long periods. Some quantitative data on recovery after adsorption and elution are presented in Table V.

TABLE V.   Recovery of Inhibitor Activity after Adsorption on Charcoal and Elution with Various Substances

Fraction	Volume, ml	Vol. Required for Standard Inhibition, ml	Total Units
Original	800	0.001	800,000
Charcoal supernatant	800	0.1	8,000
50% alcohol eluent	40	0.01	4,000
50% alcohol + 0.01M NH$_3$ eluent	27.5	0.001	27,500
	25	0.0001	250,000
50% alcohol + 0.05M NH$_3$	25	0.001	25,000
eluent	30	0.01	3,000
Total units recovered			317,500
Recovery			39.6%

Chromatographic purification of the eluted inhibitor was next attempted on a variety of materials. The best results were obtained with columns of cellulose powder and on paper strips. Some representative procedures and results are presented in the paragraphs below.

A. Chromatography on a cellulose column (Whatman cellulose powder)

Column size: 27 cm high × 1 cm wide.

Sample: Charcoal-treated preparation.

Flow rate: 1 ml/10 min.

Fraction size: 1.7 ml.

Elution results

1. Solvent: *n*-butanol; 100 ml collected. Fractions 9–13 (breakthrough) contained UV absorbing material; fractions 14–60 contained none.

2. Solvent: *n*-butanol (86): water (14); 240 ml collected. Ultraviolet absorption spectrum records indicated definite fractionation of components of the mixture.

3. Column extruded, cellulose washed with water. Ultraviolet absorption of this fraction was appreciable.

Fractions were combined as seemed best according to the spectra. The solvents were removed *in vacuo,* 40°, and the residues dissolved in small amounts of water.

Enzymatic assay results

Fractions collected under all three elution conditions which had appreciable UV absorption also showed inhibitor activity. Recovery was approximately 90% of the original.

Paper strip chromatography of eluates from above procedure

Paper: Whatman #1.

Solvent system: *n*-butanol (4): acetic acid (1): water (5) (organic phase).

1. Several UV-absorbing components were observed from each spot. Those from different fractions gave different R_f values.
2. Inhibitor activity was diffuse and not found in the spots showing greatest UV absorption. It could be recovered only when large areas of the chromatogram were recombined. In some cases activity at a well-defined R_f could be shown.

Conclusions

1. This method offers an opportunity for fractionating the solution containing the inhibitor.
2. The results suggest that not one but several compounds with inhibitor activity are present in the original extract.

B. Paper strip chromatograms

The best solvent systems used were:

1. *n*-butanol: H_2O.
2. *n*-butanol (4): acetic acid (1): water (5) (organic layer).
3. *i*-amyl alcohol (4): acetic acid (1): water (5) (organic layer).
4. *t*-butanol (7): NH_3 (1): H_2O (2).
5. 6% acetic acid.

Other systems tested include the following in which there was no movement:

1. *n*-butanol (9): NH_3 (1).
2. benzene (6): acetic acid (7): H_2O (3).
3. benzyl alcohol (4): acetic acid (1): H_2O (10).

Paper chromatography run under rigidly standardized conditions thus appears to represent a good potential tool for the separation of the inhibitory substances. Work to date has indicated that conditions must be controlled very carefully in order to obtain consistent results. It has been observed that the R_f's obtained on Whatman #1 paper and those on #3 paper are not comparable. Future runs will be made along with certain arbitrary standard substances to facilitate comparisons.

Location of the inhibitor on chromatograms is frequently difficult unless very large amounts of material are applied to the paper. Seldom is a well-defined area containing inhibitory activity obtained, but the activity can be recovered if large areas of the paper are eluted and tested together. This, in addition to the evidence from the column fractionation has suggested the presence of a multiplicity of compounds with inhibitory activity, each present in quite small amount.

STUDIES ON A COFACTOR FOR IAA OXIDASE

Various workers (Kenten, 1955; Waygood et al., 1956) have found that extracts of various plant parts contain substances, presumably phenolic in nature, which enhance the activity of IAA oxidase preparations. Such a material is also present in the terminal buds of completely etiolated peas, but it is absent from green material. The conditions of its occurrence are thus exactly the opposite of the inhibitor, and, in fact, certain experiments have suggested that the cofactor is transformed, by photomorphogenically active light, into the inhibitor. We have therefore been conducting a parallel investigation into the chemical nature of the extractable cofactor.

The cofactor is best prepared by dialysis of a brei of etiolated pea buds. It is either completely absent from or present in small quantities in stem tissue. In combination with $MnCl_2$ ($10^{-4}M$), but in the absence of 2,4-dichlorophenol, the cofactor enhances the oxidation of IAA by the etiolated pea IAA oxidase system (Fig. 5). Once again, although we depend on this system for assay, we do not necessarily imply that the biological action of the cofactor is involved with IAA destruction.

The cofactor is insoluble in ether, unstable to base, especially at elevated temperatures, and can also be destroyed by 12-min boiling in $0.1N$ acid or by ashing. It is readily adsorbed onto Dowex-1 resin, but not easily eluted. Chromatographic resolution on cellulose powder

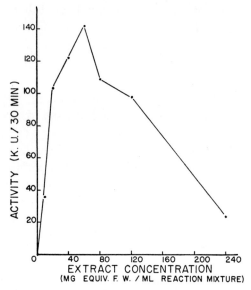

F𝕚ɢ. 5.   The effect of cofactor concentration on the IAA oxidase activity
of etiolated pea epicotyl brei supplemented with $10^{-4}M$ MnCl$_2$. The
ordinate represents the change in optical density of an aliquot mixed with
Salkowski reagent for determination of residual indoleacetic acid. (K.U.
= Klett colorimeter units.)

columns and on paper strips has been partially achieved by the use of
low concentrations of the lower alcohols, such as methyl, ethyl, iso-
propyl, and tertiary butyl. The R_f of the cofactor in 30% t-butanol is
0.7–0.8. With solvents such as benzene, methyl ethyl ketone, and
n-butanol, the active component remains at the origin. The active area
has thus far been invariably associated with a substance fluorescing
bright blue under ultraviolet.

The yield and stability of the cofactor are both improved by prior
extraction of the buds with ethyl ether, the ether extract being discarded. The residual material is then extracted with 80% ethanol
which yields a reasonably stable solution of cofactor. Addition of the
original ether extract lowers activity and decreases stability.

Removal of the alcohol *in vacuo* from the final extract yields a
cloudy aqueous solution which, upon standing, produces a copious
precipitate. Both the precipitate and supernatant liquid are completely
inactive by themselves, but when they are recombined, complete ac-

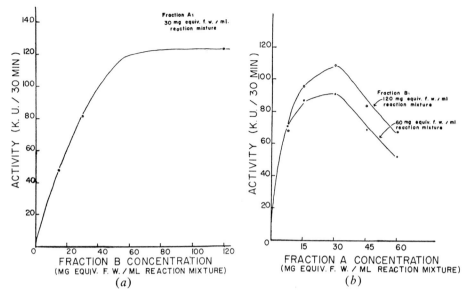

FIG. 6.   Reconstitution of cofactor activity by combination of precipitate (fraction B) and supernatant (fraction A): (*a*) supernatant constant, precipitate varied; (*b*) precipitate constant (2 levels), supernatant varied.

tivity is restored (Fig. 6). This situation parallels that described recently by Romberger (1957) for the DPNH oxidase cofactor.

The pea cofactor obviously differs from Waygood's wheat leaf cofactor in being insoluble in ethyl ether and in yielding no active precipitate with basic lead acetate.

SUMMARY

1. A substance which inhibits IAA oxidation by the IAA oxidase of etiolated peas occurs in pea buds, its synthesis being apparently controlled by the red-far red reversible photoreaction which also controls morphogenesis. This inhibitor is easily extracted from tissue by dialysis of a brei or by boiling of intact tissue.

2. In green pea seedlings, the inhibitor is most concentrated in young buds, young stem and young leaf tissue.

3. The greater the daily duration of illumination, the greater is the inhibitor content of young leaves. Transfer of the plant or of excised

leaves from light to dark results in a temporary rise in inhibitor, followed by a fall.

4. The quantity of inhibitor in young leaves of Alaska (tall) pea plants greatly exceeds that in analogous portions of Laurel (dwarf) pea plants.

5. Treatment of intact Laurel or Alaska pea plants with gibberellic acid (ca. $10^{-5}M$) results in an elevation of inhibitor content in the young leaflets. Similar results, though not so marked, can be obtained by application of GA to excised stem or leaflet tissue.

6. Both the IAA oxidase inhibitor and cofactor (from which the inhibitor may be made by a photoreaction) have been partially purified by solvent techniques and chromatography. The cofactor has been resolved into two fractions, neither of which is active alone.

7. The studies are being pursued in the hope that an understanding of the nature of the inhibitor and of the mechanism of the light control of its synthesis may shed some light on the intermediary biochemistry of photomorphogenesis.

REFERENCES

Brian, P. W., and H. G. Hemming. 1955. The effect of gibberellic acid on shoot growth of pea seedlings. *Physiol. Plantarum, 8,* 669–81.

Galston, A. W., and R. S. Baker. 1951. Studies on the physiology of light action. III. Light activation of a flavoprotein enzyme by reversal of a naturally occurring inhibition. *Am. J. Botany, 38,* 190–95.

Galston, A. W., and L. Y. Dalberg. 1954. The adaptive formation and physiological significance of indoleacetic acid oxidase. *Am. J. Botany, 41,* 373–80.

Goldacre, P. L., A. W. Galston, and R. L. Weintraub. 1953. The effect of substituted phenols on the activity of the indoleacetic acid oxidase of etiolated peas. *Arch. Biochem. Biophys., 43,* 358–73.

Hillman, W. S., and A. W. Galston. 1957. Inductive control of indoleacetic acid oxidase activity by red and near infrared light. *Plant Physiol., 32,* 129-35.

Kenten, R. H. 1955. The oxidation of indolyl-3-acetic acid by waxpod bean root sap and peroxidase systems. *Biochem. J., 59,* 110–21.

Mohr, H. 1957. Der Einfluss monochromatischer Strahlung auf das Längenwachstum des Hypocotyls und auf die Anthocyanbildung bei Keimlingen von *Sinapis alba* L. *Planta, 49,* 389–405.

Phinney, B. O. 1956. Growth response of single-gene dwarf mutants in maize to gibberellic acid. *Proc. Natl. Acad. Sci. U. S., 42,* 185–89.

Piringer, A. A., and P. H. Heinze. 1954. Effect of light on the formation of a pigment in the tomato fruit cuticle. *Plant Physiol., 29,* 467–72.

Romberger, J. A. 1957. Some characteristics of the soluble DPNH oxidase system of barley roots. *Plant Physiol., 32* (Suppl.), xxix.

Siegelman, H. W., and S. B. Hendricks. 1956. Two photochemically distinct controls of anthocyanin formation in *Brassica* seedlings. *Plant Physiol, 31* (Suppl.), xiii.

————. 1957. Photocontrol of anthocyanin synthesis in apple hypodermis. *Plant Physiol., 32* (Suppl.), ix.

Tang, Y. W., and J. Bonner. 1947. The enzymatic inactivation of indoleacetic acid. I. Some characteristics of the enzyme contained in pea seedlings. *Arch. Biochem, 13,* 11–25.

————. 1948. The enzymatic inactivation of indoleacetic acid. II. The physiology of the enzyme. *Am. J. Botany, 35,* 570–78.

Waygood, E. R., A. Oaks, and G. A. Maclachlan. 1956. The enzymatically catalyzed oxidation of indoleacetic acid. *Can. J. Botany, 34,* 905–26.

Withrow, R. B., J. B. Wolff, and L. Price. 1956. Elimination of the lag phase of chlorophyll synthesis in dark-grown bean leaves by a pretreatment with low irradiances of monochromatic energy. *Plant Physiol., 31* (Suppl.), xiii-xiv.

Wolff, J. B., L. Price, and R. B. Withrow. 1957. Stimulation of protochlorophyll synthesis in dark-grown bean leaves by irradiation in low energy. *Plant Physiol., 32* (Suppl.), ix.

*Role of Chemical Agents
in Photocontrol of Vegetative Growth*

CONTROL OF LEAF GROWTH BY AN INTERACTION OF CHEMICALS AND LIGHT [1,2]

JAMES L. LIVERMAN

Division of Biology and Medicine, U. S. Atomic Energy Commission, Washington, D. C.[3]

That photoperiodically active light controls a great many different processes in plants and animals has been known for about 35 years. In this connection, the phenomenon of flowering in particular has received wide attention (Liverman, 1955), as has also the inhibition of growth of seedlings of various kinds.

Since 1952 (Borthwick *et al.*, 1952) it has become increasingly apparent that the red and far-red portions of the spectrum are concerned in these responses and that these two qualities of light act antagonistically to each other, i.e., when one promotes a process, in most cases the other reverses this promotion. For instance, it has been shown that red light promotes expansion of etiolated leaves (Liverman *et al.*, 1955), the unbending of the hypocotyl hook (Klein *et al.*, 1956), coleoptile elongation (Schneider, 1941; Liverman and Bonner, 1953), and seed germination in a great many plants (Toole *et al.*, 1956). In most cases these promotive effects are reversed by a subsequent exposure to far-red light. Other processes involved in seedling growth that are inhibited by red light include hypocotyl, internode, and mesocotyl elongation (Downs, 1955; Goodwin, 1941; Weintraub and Price, 1947). It is reasonably certain, of course, that the same receptive pigment is involved in all these responses since their action spectra appear to be almost identical. The evidence presently available does not indicate, however, that the reactions subsequent to the actual per-

[1] Research reported herein was supported in part by grants-in-aid from the U. S. Atomic Energy Commission and the National Science Foundation.

[2] Most of the experimental work reported herein constituted part of a dissertation submitted by Dr. Ralph A. Scott to the Graduate School, Texas Agricultural and Mechanical College, 1957.

[3] On leave from Department of Biochemistry and Nutrition, Texas Agricultural Experiment Station, College Station, Texas.

ception of the light by the plant are identical. In fact, it would be difficult to explain all these different responses on the basis of a series of identical reactions. Only when we have a thorough understanding of the underlying biochemistry will we be able to show definitely the differences and similarities in reactions.

Although the biochemistry of each of these responses is important, in this paper I will concentrate on one of them, that of leaf expansion, and more specifically on the biochemistry of the light-induced reactions. This area has been selected because of our research on this problem for the past three years. To what extent these results can be extrapolated to the other light-controlled growth processes in seedlings is unknown at this time, so that one can only hazard a guess concerning the possible implications of the findings.

LIGHT CONTROL OF LEAF GROWTH

A brief review of the effect of light in controlling leaf growth will be helpful in introducing the problem. It has been known for many years that leaves on plants grown in the dark expand only slightly unless given a short exposure to light, after which they grow at approximately the maximum rate. This appears to be true whether the leaves are on intact seedlings (Downs, 1955) or are removed and grown as leaf discs on a substrate to serve as an energy source (Miller, 1952; Scott, 1957). The action spectrum for the light requirement for expansion of leaves on intact plants was indicated in the pioneering experiments of Parker *et al.,* 1949) for the Alaska pea. Downs (1955) extended these experiments to the red kidney bean and showed that the far-red portion of the spectrum was very active in reversing the red-light promotion. Although such a detailed spectrum has not been worked out for expansion of the leaf disc, it was shown in 1953 (Liverman *et al.,* 1955) that the red-far red system controlled the expansion of discs from leaves of the dwarf stringless greenpod bean. It appears, therefore, that the light requirement for expansion of the disc and for the intact leaf are identical.

With these early experiments as a basis, we turned in my laboratory to a detailed study of the biochemical nature of the light-induced expansion of leaf discs. This system permits an assay for the effect of chemicals and light and their interaction in 48 hr, whereas tests such as those on flowering require several days or weeks. In addition, this system appears to have advantages over the pea internode and the *Avena* cylinder test, because of the almost essential requirement for light in the case of leaf discs.

Our system is a modification of that of Bonner *et al.* (1939) as modified by Miller (1952) and again modified by us (Scott and Liverman, 1956) better to fit our own conditions. The growth medium used in the experiments described below consisted of the following essentials: 3% D-glucose, 0.08M potassium nitrate, 0.09M potassium dihydrogen phosphate, and a 0.018M potassium-sodium tartrate buffer, pH 5.6. Five milliliters of this basal solution was added to a petri dish so as to just moisten two sheets of Whatman No. 1 filter paper. Growth promotion due to an additive would be growth over and above that occurring in the basal medium, and the reverse would occur for inhibition. As a source of red light we used fluorescent lamps filtered through two layers of Dupont 300 MSC red cellophane. The far red was obtained by passing light from frosted incandescent bulbs through two layers of the above red cellophane and two layers of Dupont 300 MSC dark blue cellophane. The red filter transmits only those wavelengths of light longer than 6000 A except for a slight transmission (about 3%) in the region of 5500 A. Since the transmission limit for the fluorescent lights is about 7000 A, this filter system gives essentially only photoperiodically active red light. The blue plus red cellophane transmits about 3 to 5% in the region of 5500 A, transmission is almost nil between 6000 A and 7000 A, and rapidly reaches 60% beyond 7000 A. These filter systems are in general use now in a number of laboratories with apparently satisfactory results.

Several experiments have shown that the initial size and physiological age of the leaf are particularly important, so that leaf material must always be uniform. The plants were grown in washed sand for 6 to 7 days in a darkroom maintained at a temperature of 25° ± 1°C until the leaves reached an area of about 2 to 3 cm². Discs were removed under a dim green or dim orange safelight and placed on the filter paper with the upper epidermis against the paper. The discs were then exposed to light with and without supplements of chemicals to the basal medium. When the discs were exposed to red light, they attained about a 50% increase in area, whereas those grown in darkness attained a 20 to 25% increase. Under ideal conditions the discs exposed to far red and red-far red grew approximately the same as those in darkness, although they often grew slightly more, indicating a partial activation of the red-sensitive pigment system. Controls in basal medium were run for each experiment in order to estimate the variability in growth between experiments.

Before extensive experimentation was begun, it was felt that we should examine our system for its similarities to the lettuce seed system. We examined the system for infinite reversibility by red and far red and also studied the effect on growth of a time lag between the exposure to red and to far red. A series of petri dishes containing 20 discs each was placed in the darkroom. One dish was kept in continuous dark as a control. Another dish was exposed to far-red light and returned to darkness. All remaining dishes were exposed to red light simultaneously, a single dish then being removed to darkness; the remainder were then exposed to far-red light. A sequence of such red and far-red exposures was given, a single dish being removed after each light exposure. The results given in Table I show that the

TABLE I. Photoreversibility of Etiolated
Bean Leaf Disc Expansion

Treatment	Increase in Diameter, mm	
Dark	0.66	
Far-red light (I)		0.69
Red light (R)	1.36	
RI		0.97
RI–R	1.43	
RI–RI		0.93
RI–RI–R	1.36	
RI–RI–RI		0.96
RI–RI–RI–R	1.32	
RI–RI–RI–RI		0.95
RI–RI–RI–RI–R	1.43	

response is dependent upon the quality of the light given during the last exposure. In additional experiments wherein we exposed the discs to red light and waited varying periods of time before exposure to far red, we observed that the discs escape slowly from control by far red and that after 20 hr very little of the potential growth can be reversed. These results are in agreement with those of Downs (1955) on intact bean plants. Thus, for experimental purposes this system responds in the same way as the lettuce seed system, and we may assume that the same general type of light action is involved.

CHEMICAL CONTROL OF LEAF GROWTH

A number of workers have studied chemical control of leaf growth entirely apart from its control by light. Among the early workers in this field were Professor Went and his colleagues at the California Institute of Technology (Bonner *et al.*, 1939; Bonner and Haagen-Smit, 1939), who observed that a diffusate from peas stimulated the growth of radish and other leaves. In 1939 Bonner and Haagen-Smit reported that certain crystalline substances appeared to affect the growth of green leaves of radish and cosmos. Since these were green leaves, it is possible that the growth-limiting factors are different from those for etiolated leaves. In etiolated leaves certain growth-limiting requirements can be satisfied by red light. Among the active crystalline substances tried were amino acids, which promoted a 10 to 25% increase in growth as measured by wet weight when supplied at a concentration of 500 mg/1. It is not immediately obvious that this measurement reflects the same net result as a measurement of the increase in diameter. Their results indicate that the stimulation may differ for leaves from different plants; for example, arginine most actively satisfied the requirement in *Nicotiana sylvestris,* whereas proline and asparagine were most active for radish. None of these amino acids was as active as the diffusate from peas. Substances found to be inactive include vitamins and their derivatives, as well as a number of pyrimidines. Bonner and Haagen-Smit did observe that adenine, xanthine, and other purines gave about an 18% increase in wet weight. Only adenine was active at 10 mg/l, whereas higher concentrations of the other purines were necessary. In comparative tests the pea diffusate in every case showed more activity than adenine. Miller confirmed reports of Bonner (1940) that KNO_3 was also very active in promoting growth of leaves.

Miller (1951a) found that coumarin, normally considered to be a growth inhibitor, caused a very marked promotion of growth of discs from green leaves of *Chenopodium album,* although this has not yet been confirmed. Others have tried unsuccessfully to promote leaf growth with many different compounds (de Ropp, 1945, 1947; Juhren and Went, 1949).

INTERACTION OF LIGHT AND CHEMICALS

In 1951 Miller (1951b) published experiments aimed at elucidating the biochemical nature of the light-induced expansion of etiolated leaves, by using a system almost identical with the one we now use. Miller tried a number of chemical compounds, including some that Bonner *et al.* (Bonner *et al.*, 1939; Bonner and Haagen-Smit, 1939; Bonner, 1940) had tried, and observed that they were, in general, without effect. He made the interesting discovery, not yet completely understood, that the cobaltous ion produced a rather pronounced expansion even in darkness and that this promotion was in addition to that caused by exposure to light. This effect was not specific, since the nickelous and the manganous ions were also active (Miller, 1951b). It has since been observed that cobalt is active in other light-controlled responses. It produces the same effect as red light in *Xanthium* flowering (Salisbury, 1957) and in the growth of oat coleoptiles (Thimann, 1956; Liverman and Bonner, 1953), in the unhooking of the hypocotyl of bean (Miller, 1951b), and in other responses.

We have repeated Miller's experiments on cobalt in detail and have found, in addition, that the growth due to cobalt is linear with time under all our conditions of light—red, red-far red, and far red—and in darkness. We made the additional observation that the amount of growth obtained in response to cobalt is almost linearly related to the length of time the cobalt is left in contact with the leaves. The effect of light is superimposed upon the effect of cobalt, and it appears to make no difference whether the light is given before or after the cobalt is supplied. Another of our observations, the meaning of which is not yet clear, is shown in Table II. The importance of these data is in showing that a concentration of cobalt which gives maximum growth in far-red light alone gives the minimum growth in red followed by far

TABLE II. Cobalt and Light Versus Expansion

Concentration	Red	FR	R-FR	Dark
0	1.2	1.0	1.0	0.61
$0.24 \times 10^{-4}M$	1.6	1.2	1.2	0.62
$0.98 \times 10^{-4}M$	2.5	1.7	1.6	1.73
$1.48 \times 10^{-4}M$	2.9	1.8	1.1	1.99
$1.96 \times 10^{-4}M$	2.5	1.98	0.8	1.76

red. We have no ready explanation for this phenomenon but are investigating it further. There is no really definitive explanation for the action of cobalt in a great many biological responses which it affects, although it has been suggested that it may act as an anti-peroxidative agent (Galston and Siegel, 1954). Certainly the action of cobalt appears to be rather closely linked with the light action mechanism.

In connection with our studies we desired to determine the nature of chemical substances which could overcome, replace, or in some way alter the effect of light in its control of leaf expansion. Among the compounds which we wished to examine was kinetin, which had been demonstrated to be active in cell division (Miller et al., 1955). When it became generally available in the latter part of 1955, some of this compound, along with a number of similar compounds, was obtained for our studies through the courtesy of Dr. William Shive and Dr. C. G. Skinner of the Biochemical Institute, University of Texas, Austin, Texas (Skinner and Shive, 1955; Ham et al., 1956; Skinner, Shive, et al., 1956; Skinner, Ham, et al., 1956). All compounds of the first group examined, among which was kinetin, showed a pro-motive effect in darkness, and this promotion was simply additive to that obtained by red light. Although the red-light effect could be reversed by far red light, the promotive effect by kinetin could not. A second group of these compounds, on the contrary, gave an inhibition in red light as compared to its effect in darkness, i.e., the growth in red light was always less than that in darkness. Thus it appeared that red light exerted an inhibitory effect, not a promotive one, if given while these compounds were present.

Up to this time we looked upon these substances as simply foreign chemicals not really related to the action of light, until we tried the compound 6-thiopurine-2-succinic acid (Skinner, Shive, et al., 1956).

This compound gave an enormous increase which was the same in light and darkness, i.e., the effects of red and far red light were absent. About this time Carter and Cohen (1956) suggested that adenylo-succinic acid, which is simply adenylic acid with succinic acid replacing a hydrogen of the 6-amino group, could be converted to adenylic acid. There is a further report that this compound occurs naturally in mammalian liver (Joklik, 1956). The results of these workers led us to try adenylic acid and other related compounds in our system, among them, adenine. We found that adenine reacted in a manner analogous to that of thiopurinesuccinic acid. The adenylic acid itself was not very active, but this might be due to a lack of penetration into the

TABLE III. Control of Leaf Growth by Light and Kinins—Increase in Diameter

R_1[b]	R_2	R_3	Red Light 0.96	Dark 0.42
\multicolumn{5}{c}{Chemical Treatment None, Basal Solution[a]}				
		Group I		
N	H	2-Furfuryl	2.12	1.64
N	H	Benzyl	1.81	1.42
N	H	4-Pyridylmethyl	1.56	1.10
N	Pentyl	Pentyl	1.39	0.83
S	—	Pentyl	1.41	1.19
S	—	Benzyl	1.36	1.21
		Group II		
N	H	2-Thenyl	1.30	1.38
N	H	H (Adenine)	2.80	2.81
N	H	C_2H_5	0.99	0.94
N	H	3-Diethylamino-*n*-propyl	1.23	1.26
S	—	H	Completely inhibits	Completely inhibits
S	—	2-Succinic acid	2.37	2.36
		Group III		
N	H	2-Pyridylmethyl	0.92	1.10
N	H	3-Pyridylmethyl	1.13	1.55
N	H	2-Phenylethyl	0.97	1.73
N	H	3-Phenylpropyl	1.28	1.48
N	H	4-Phenylbutyl	1.04	1.20
S	—	Butyl	0.62	0.80

[a] Concentration was 0.5 mg/l.

[b] R_1 refers to the substituent on the ring at the 6 position of purine. R_2 and/or R_3 refers to the group attached to R_1.

tissue. We then began a systematic study of the relation between structure and activity of various adenine derivatives and of the many kinetin-like compounds which were available. Table III summarizes in a general way for a single concentration the relation between structure and activity of examples taken from over 60 compounds tested in this system.

One may logically inquire whether this effect, particularly of adenine and thiopurinesuccinic acid, is specific for this single concentration of these two compounds or whether it applies throughout a concentration series. The basic question is, are these compounds specific for the light reaction, or do they simply replace part of the light reaction, and if we had used lower concentrations, would we have obtained a different result? Table IV indicates that they are not simply replacing

TABLE IV.   Control of Leaf Expansion by Adenine and Thiopurinesuccinic Acid[a]

Treatment	Red	Far Red	Red-Far Red	Dark
Control	1.22	1.00	0.99	0.68
Adenine				
0.05	2.20	2.19	2.21	2.23
0.5	2.79	2.81	2.84	2.81
5.0	2.31	2.29	2.31	2.30
10.0	1.96	2.05	1.99	1.99
TPSA				
0.05	2.39	2.38	2.44	2.37
0.5	3.34	3.30	3.32	3.31
5.0	2.99	3.01	3.01	3.03
10.0	1.84	1.84	1.86	1.91

[a] Concentration, mg/l increase in diameter, mm.

a part of the light reaction, but actually obviate the need for it. The light action—either promotive or inhibitory—appears to be completely erased by adenine. These results suggested to us the following relations between structure and activity:

1. *Response Group I.* Replacement of one of the hydrogens of the amino group of 6-aminopurine by a ring compound results in a promotion which is at least partially additive to the red-light effect.

2. *Response Group II.* Either nonreplacement or replacement of one of the hydrogens by a short-chain aliphatic results in a disappearance of any light effect.

3. *Response Group III.* The exact configuration and spatial ar-

rangement of the aromatic or heterocyclic nucleus around the 6-amino group is quite important.

This last requirement is stressed particularly in the phenyl and the pyridylmethyl series of compounds. The distance of the benzene ring from the nitrogen of 6-aminopurine markedly affects the response, i.e., the benzyl substitution (in which the ring is one carbon removed from the nitrogen) gives a group I type of response. The phenylethyl, phenylpropyl, and phenylbutyl substitutions all give a group III type response wherein growth in red light is less than in darkness. It thus appears that the distance the ring is removed from the purine nucleus is critical. With the pyridylmethyl series it appears that the orientation of the ring nitrogen of pyridine with regard to the purine ring is important; compare the 2-, 3-, and 4-pyridylmethyl substitutions. From other data it appears that the pyridine orientation is concentration dependent; thus we must conduct more experiments before a final conclusion may be drawn.

Needless to say, we do not know the exact nature of this inhibitory reaction nor how the chemicals of groups II and III alter the response to light. We feel that adenine or some naturally occurring related purine or purine derivative is intimately connected with the expansion of etiolated leaves and that possibly it is the need for adenine or some similar compound which is satisfied by light. Thus light might set in motion a process that leads to the eventual formation of adenine or a like compound, which may then be used in nucleic acid or nucleo-protein synthesis. This connection needs to be studied in more detail in order to gain a thorough understanding of its nature and to extend the observations to systems other than our own.

A discordant note in our observations should be mentioned at this point. After the appearance in *Science* of our paper (Scott and Liver-man, 1957) describing these experiments in a preliminary manner, I received a letter from Dr. Carlos Miller (personal communication, 1957) saying he could not get an effect with adenine. We have since exchanged seed and chemicals, with the same net result on his part. We have not been able to get our system standardized since moving into new quarters and, therefore, are not able to clear up the point. I certainly feel that our results are correct, and I do not doubt those of Dr. Miller. This difficulty probably can be resolved by showing that there are particular conditions under which we both will be correct.

Early in 1956 gibberellic acid began to be a topic of intense research interest among plant physiologists. When it became available to us in August 1956, it was immediately tested with regard to its effect in causing leaf expansion. We observed that its promotive effect in darkness was just about additive to the effect of red light, acting like cobalt and like kinetin. Upon closer examination and after an extension to far-red reversal of the red effect, we noted a phenomenon, Table V, which we had not observed previously with any kind of

TABLE V. Control of Leaf Expansion by Gibberellic Acid[a]

Treatment	Red	Far-Red	Red-Far Red	Dark
Control	1.23	0.95	0.96	0.69
Gibberellic acid				
0.05	2.76	1.70	1.38	1.80
0.5	2.53	1.40	1.50	2.05
5.0	2.50	2.02	2.10	2.18
10.0	2.10	1.40	1.40	2.02

[a] Concentration, mg/l; increase in diameter, mm.

compound, namely, that far-red light not only reverses the red light effect but also appears to overcome a portion of the gibberellic acid effect (Scott and Liverman, 1957). There are several other possible interpretations of these results, but this is our own interpretation at the present time. Although these results are not as clear-cut as they might be, they do indicate a rather interesting aspect of light physiology as controlled by chemicals.

As a sidelight not directly related to seedling growth but which may contribute to understanding the overall physiology of light action, I would like to mention, in passing, some additional experiments which we ran. We appear to have a summer dormancy problem in Texas with many crops, but particularly with tomatoes, which appears to be brought about by an excess of far-red light (Johnson et al., 1956). We reasoned that if our results with leaf discs were correct, we should be able to reverse the dormancy of tomato fruits by spraying them with gibberellic acid. The experiment worked, and a preliminary report has been made (Liverman and Johnson, 1957). There is no positive proof that this is the same response as observed with leaf discs, but there is a strong suggestion of a similar phenomenon. It now appears that this chemical may be used for control of the tomato dormancy problem on a field scale, particularly if combined with other chemicals.

Let us now turn to another interesting area of the chemical control of the light-induced response in leaves. On the basis of experiments with the *Avena* coleoptile, James Bonner and I postulated a number of years ago that a cyclic mechanism was involved in the red-far red reaction concerned with growth of the coleoptile as affected by auxin (Liverman and Bonner, 1953). There has been some question of the validity of the conclusions that we drew from a few data, and I do not wish here to discuss the correctness of our conclusions and hypotheses —all I want to do now is to present some additional information which bears upon this topic and which may lead us eventually to the right answer concerning the nature of light actions. Let me summarize very briefly the experiments on *Avena*.

It is known that auxin is required for the growth of an oat coleoptile and that red light promotes its growth. Our experiments showed that far-red light had its effect only if both red light and auxin were supplied before the far-red exposure. It was concluded that red light generated something which led to additional growth and that, whatever the nature of this substance, its effect was erased by exposure to far red. These results were interpreted in terms of a cyclic mechanism as shown in Fig. 1. Attempts to demonstrate the existence of such a system in leaf discs by using auxin were never successful at that time. This result is not too surprising, however, since it is known that young

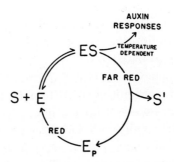

Fig. 1. The morphogenetic photocycle proposed by Liverman and Bonner (1953) as a working hypothesis for studying the light-controlled reactions in photoperiodism.

leaves serve as a source of auxin. Thus, under the above experimental conditions, auxin was never limiting, and auxin effects could not be determined in this manner. The thought occurred to me at that time, although we were unable to run the experiments, that a possible approach to this problem lay in reducing the level of native auxin in the leaf. Attempts to do this with anti-auxins were not effective (unpublished results).

Gordon showed sometime ago that x-ray would knock out the enzyme responsible for the conversion of indoleacetaldehyde to indoleacetic acid (Gordon, 1955, 1956). There is no proof that such a system operates in etiolated leaves, but this approach seemed worth while, so we set about irradiating plants with x-ray and determining the response. The method of treatment consisted of growing the plants for about 6 days, exposing them to x-ray irradiation for the required time, and returning them to the darkroom for an additional 60 hr growth before discs were removed. From this point on, the treatment was as outlined earlier. It is obvious from Table VI that x-irradiation results in a marked inhibition of expansion.

TABLE VI.   X-Ray and Light Versus Leaf Disc Expansion[a]

X-Ray Treatment	Red	Far Red	Red-Far Red	Dark
None	1.20	1.01	1.03	0.64
25 r	0.82	0.43	0.42	0.40
100 r	1.00	0.59	0.64	0.42
175 r	0.89	0.48	0.61	0.39

[a] Increase in diameter, mm.

It was next desirable to find if a portion of this loss could be overcome by the addition of auxin. In the particular case illustrated here, indoleacetic acid was used, but naphthalene acetic acid works equally well. The 175 r exposure data have been used in Table VII, but the same effect prevails at 25 and 100 r. All concentrations of auxin caused inhibition of growth in the non-x-rayed discs, whereas all concentrations of auxin promoted well above the x-ray controls, and the higher concentrations of auxin promoted well above the non-x-ray controls. Thus, whatever the nature of the action of x-irradiation, auxin effectively replaces the removed factor. This evidence, although

TABLE VII.   X-Ray, Light and IAA Versus Leaf Expansion

Treatment	Red	Red-Far Red	Dark
No X-ray control	1.20	1.03	0.64
IAA 0.05 mg/l	1.10	0.74	0.50
0.5	1.14	0.81	0.54
1.5	0.91	0.76	0.53
3.0	0.89	0.79	0.50
175 r X-ray control	0.89	0.61	0.39
IAA 0.05 mg/l	1.16	0.87	0.76
0.5	1.43	0.97	0.83
1.5	1.50	1.21	0.96
3.0	1.39	1.05	0.74

not compelling, suggests that auxin is involved in leaf expansion and that some of the mechanisms involved in oat coleoptile growth are also operative in leaf expansion. Possibly such a system is also operative in seed germination, although suitable experiments have not yet been devised to test this hypothesis.

Since it is known that nucleic acids are affected by x-irradiation (Scholes *et al.*, 1956) and since the experiments cited earlier indicate that purines may be involved in leaf expansion, it became of interest to study the ability of some of the purines to reverse the x-ray-induced inhibition of leaf expansion. Table VIII shows data from a typical

TABLE VIII.   X-Ray, Light, Purines, and Auxins Versus Leaf Expansion

Treatment	Red	Red-Far Red	Dark
No X-ray			
Control	1.24	0.97	0.81
Adenine 0.5	2.79	2.81	2.81
TPSA 0.5	3.34	3.30	3.31
100 r X-ray			
Control	0.98	0.67	0.52
Adenine 0.5[a]	1.95	1.53	1.53
TPSA[b] 0.5[a]	1.59	1.55	1.52
Adenine 0.25 + IAA 0.25	2.92	2.64	2.65
TPSA 0.25 + IAA 0.25	2.91	2.93	2.90

[a] All concentrations behave alike.
[b] TPSA thiopurinesuccinic acid.

experiment with purines in x-irradiated discs. Again x-ray reduced the control growth by an appreciable amount. The purines overcome a portion of this inhibition, but will not entirely replace the indoleacetic acid destroyed by the x-irradiation. This evidence again suggests that auxin may be involved in leaf expansion. These experiments also indicate that there is a basic difference in the reactions affected by adenine and thiopurinesuccinic acid, since a red-light effect is evident in the presence of adenine following x-irradiation, but not in the presence of thiopurinesuccinic acid.

DISCUSSION

What do these results contribute to the understanding of the many faceted phenomenon of growth as controlled by light? First of all, as suggested earlier in this presentation, because of the varied nature of the final response, it appears highly unlikely that a single series of reactions controls all the growth processes shown in Fig. 2. It seems probable that the initial phases of all these processes are quite similar because of their control by red and far-red light. We can logically ask, then, at what point between the initial light reaction and the final response—flowering, leaf expansion, etc.—do the chemicals discussed above have their action? In the endeavor to answer this question, we may begin to get an insight into the biochemical nature of each of these processes and to determine how many reactions they may have in common; or to put it another way, we may learn at what point these reactions begin to diverge.

It may be profitable to take each of the chemicals discussed above and relate its action to the hypothetical sequence shown in Fig. 2.

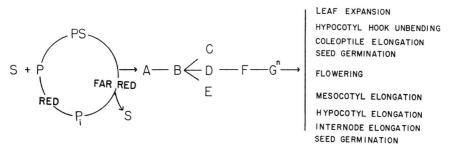

Fig. 2. Proposal concerning possible reaction sequences involved in photoperiodically controlled responses. The cycle represents the reactions closely allied with the primary light reaction. G^n represents from one to hundreds of reactions, possibly not on the same pathway, which lead to the final response—flowering, etc.

On the basis of our own earlier experiments (Liverman and Bonner, 1953) it still appears that there may be a cyclic mechanism involved in the "light reversible" reaction controlling photoperiodic responses. Certainly no evidence thus far presented would compel one to discard this possibility. Whether auxin or some physiologically related compound is involved in the primary light reaction is still not definitely known. Our own experiments with leaf discs and *Avena* suggest that auxin-like compounds are involved early in the reaction sequence indicated in Fig. 2. Additional evidence favoring this view is that auxins affect nearly all the final responses in some manner or other.

Experiments from many laboratories suggest that cobalt or a similar substance is rather intimately connected with the primary light action in some manner, possibly by preserving an "activated complex" resulting from the light exposure. The only really suggestive experiments as to the role of cobalt are those of Galston and Siegel (1954) showing its participation in antiperoxigenic type reactions. Our experiments (Table II) showing a reinforced far-red response in the presence of cobalt suggest that it or a physiologically similar factor may be complexed with the far-red receptive form of the "pigment" system. A further, more detailed analysis of the mechanism of action of cobalt may lead to a better understanding of the reactions which it affects and thus to a better understanding of light action in the photoperiodic response.

Gibberellic acid, too, appears to be effective in the early part of the reaction sequence, since a portion of its effect in causing leaf expansion is overcome by exposure to far-red light. It has not been determined whether this portion of the response is in turn reversed by subsequent red exposure. Thus it would appear particularly important to study the action of this substance in detail with a view to learning more of the biochemistry of the red-far red reaction mechanism. It is not possible to say at this time whether the action of gibberellic acid in overcoming far-red-induced summer dormancy in tomato (Johnson *et al.*, 1956; Liverman and Johnson, 1957) is directly comparable to the reaction cited above, but the implication is that the two reactions may be identical. The control of dormancy in other responses may be related to this same phenomenon. All these indications lead one to suspect that gibberellic acid or a physiologically similar substance may be closely linked to the primary light reaction, although much more research is needed to clarify this point.

The data on the participation of purines in leaf expansion presented above (Table III) give us some additional information concerning the diversity of the biochemical pathways traversed between the initial light reaction and the final response. Basically, it appears that compounds of group II, i.e., those which give the same amount of growth in light or darkness, obviate the need for light. These compounds then must have their effect many reaction steps removed from the initial act of light perception. This suggests, in leaf expansion at least, that the initial light reaction is probably concerned with the activation of a system leading to the production of adenine or a related purine, which then may be further transformed to nucleic acids, coenzymes, etc. It appears that compounds like those of group I, i.e., those which simply cause growth over and above that caused by light, are not on the principal pathway but that they in some way spare those compounds which are so situated. A study of the interaction of compounds of these two classes should contribute markedly to a better understanding of the biochemical pathways involved in leaf expansion and the site of action of both types of compounds. The compounds of group III, which show an inhibition in the presence of red light, are unique, and there is neither a really satisfactory explanation for their action nor an indication of the relative position in the sequence of reactions at which they are effective. One possible explanation could be that the compounds are light-sensitive and are simply destroyed by light, since the growth in light in the presence of the chemical in most cases is equal to or greater than growth in light without the chemical (Table III). In view of the difference in responses elicited by the 4- as compared to the 2- and 3-pyridylmethyl analogs, however, this proposal seems rather unlikely.

Whether compounds of the purine group are able to substitute for light in any of the responses shown in Fig. 2 is not definitely known. It does appear, however, that cobalt (Salisbury, 1957; Thimann, 1956), auxin (Liverman, 1955), and gibberellic acid (Long, 1956; Lockhart, 1956; Kahn et al., 1957) may be involved in a number of the responses, and in some instances at least they appear to replace light. The available data on how these various substances affect responses other than leaf expansion and flowering are insufficient to pinpoint their site of action with regard to the scheme presented in Fig. 2.

In conclusion, I would emphasize that some of the data presented above are of a preliminary nature, and the interpretations are therefore rather tenuous. The concept of a series of reactions between the initial light reaction and the final response is not new, but we have never made extensive use of it in trying to relate the similarities and differences among the various responses. It is reasonably certain that the same reactions are not involved in every step between the perceiving of the light and the final response. By recognizing this fact and by making more extensive use of the concept discusssed above, we can begin to understand better the biochemistry of the whole field of photoperiodic regulation of growth phenomena.

REFERENCES

Bonner, D. M. 1940. Leaf growth factors. Dissertation, California Institute of Technology, Pasadena.

Bonner, D. M., and A. J. Haagen-Smit. 1939. Leaf growth factors. II. The activity of pure substances in leaf growth. *Proc. Natl. Acad. Sci. U. S., 25,* 184–88.

Bonner, D. M., A. J. Haagen-Smit, and F. W. Went. 1939. Leaf growth hormones. I. A bio-assay and source for leaf growth factors. *Botan. Gaz., 101,* 128–44.

Borthwick, H. A., S. B. Hendricks, M. W. Parker, E. H. Toole, and V. K. Toole. 1952. A reversible photoreaction controlling seed germination. *Proc. Natl. Acad. Sci. U. S., 38,* 662–66.

Carter, C. E., and L. H. Cohen. 1956. The preparation and properties of adenylosuccinase and adenylosuccinic acid. *J. Biol. Chem., 222,* 17–30.

de Ropp, R. S. 1945. Studies in the physiology of leaf growth. I. The effect of various accessory growth factors on the growth of the first leaf of isolated stem tips or rye. *Ann. Botany, 9,* 369–81.

———. 1947. Studies in the physiology of leaf growth. IV. The growth and behavior *in vitro* of dicotyledonous leaves and leaf fragments. *Ann. Botany, 11,* 439–47.

Downs, R. J. 1955. Photoreversibility of leaf and hypocotyl elongation of darkgrown red kidney bean seedlings. *Plant Physiol., 30,* 468–72.

Galston, A. W., and S. M. Siegel. 1954. Antiperoxidative action of the cobaltous ion and its consequences for plant growth. *Science, 120,* 1070–71.

Goodwin, R. H. 1941. On the inhibition of the first internode of *Avena* by light. *Am. J. Botany, 28,* 325–32.

Gordon, S. A. 1955. Studies on the mechanism of phytohormone damage by ionizing radiation. *Proc. Intern. Conf. Atomic Energy*, A/8/P/97 Geneva, Switzerland.

———. 1956. The biogenesis of natural auxins. *The Chemistry and Mode of Action of Plant Growth Substances*, R. L. Wain and F. Wightman, Editors. Academic, New York, 65–75.

Ham, R. G., R. E. Eakin, C. G. Skinner, and W. Shive. 1956. Inhibition of regeneration in hydra by certain new 6-(phenylalkyl)-aminopurines. *J. Am. Chem. Soc., 78,* 2648.

Johnson, S. P., W. C. Hall, and J. L. Liverman. 1956. Growth and fruiting responses of intact tomato plants to far-red radiation. *Physiol. Plantarum, 9,* 389–95.

Joklik, W. K. 1956. The occurrence of adenine and adenyl succinic acid in mammalian liver. *Biochim. et Biophys. Acta, 22,* 211–12.

Juhren, M. C., and F. W. Went. 1949. Growth in darkness of squash plants fed with sucrose. *Am. J. Botany, 36,* 552–559.

Kahn, A., J. A. Goss, and D. E. Smith. 1957. Effect of gibberellin on germination of lettuce seed. *Science, 125,* 645–46.

Klein, W. H., R. B. Withrow, and V. B. Elstad. 1956. Response of the hypocotyl hook of bean seedlings to radiant energy and other factors. *Plant Physiol., 31,* 289–94.

Lang, A. 1956. Gibberellin and flower formation. *Naturwissenschaften, 43,* 544.

Liverman, J. L. 1955. The physiology of flowering. *Ann. Rev. Plant Physiol., 6,* 177–210.

Liverman, J. L., and J. Bonner. 1953. The interaction of auxin and light in the growth responses of plants. *Proc. Natl. Acad. Sci. U. S., 39,* 905–16.

Liverman, J. L., and S. P. Johnson. 1957. Control of arrested fruit growth in tomato by gibberellins. *Science, 125,* 1086–87.

Liverman, J. L., M. P. Johnson, and L. Starr. 1955. Reversible photoreaction controlling expansion of etiolated bean-leaf disks. *Science, 121,* 440–41.

Lockhart, J. A. 1956. Reversal of the light inhibition of pea stem growth by the gibberellins. *Proc. Natl. Acad. Sci. U. S., 42,* 841–48.

Miller, C. O. 1951a. Expansion of *Chenopodium album* leaf disks as affected by coumarin. *Plant Physiol., 26,* 631–34.

———. 1951b. Promoting effect of cobaltous and nickelous ions on expansion of etiolated bean leaf disks. *Arch. Biochem. Biophys., 32,* 216–18.

———. 1952. Relationship of the cobalt and light effects on expansion of etiolated bean leaf disks. *Plant Physiol., 27,* 408–12.

———. 1957. Personal communications.

Miller, C. O., F. Skoog, M. H. Von Saltza, and F. M. Strong. 1955. Kinetin a cell division factor from deoxyribonucleic acid. *J. Am. Chem. Soc., 77,* 1392.

Parker, M. W., S. B. Hendricks, H. A. Borthwick, and F. W. Went. 1949. Spectral sensitivities for leaf and stem growth of etiolated pea seedlings and their similarity to action spectra for photoperiodism. *Am. J. Botany, 36,* 194–204.

Salisbury, F. B. 1957. The mechanism of action of cobaltous ion, 2,4-dinitrophenol and auxins in flowering. *Plant Physiol., 32,* (Suppl.), x.

Schneider, C. L. 1941. The effect of red light on growth of the *Avena* seedling with special reference to the first internode. *Am. J. Botany, 28,* 878–86.

Scholes, G., J. Weiss, and C. M. Wheeler. 1956. Formation of hydroperoxides from nucleic acids by irradiation with x-rays in aqueous systems. *Nature, 178,* 157.

Scott, R. A., Jr. 1957. Biochemical and photochemical control of leaf disk expansion. Dissertation, Texas Agricultural and Mechanical College, College Station.

Scott, R. A., Jr., and J. L. Liverman. 1956. Promotion of leaf expansion by kinetin and benzylaminopurine. *Plant Physiol., 31,* 321–22.

———. 1957. Control of etiolated bean leaf disk expansion by gibberellins and adenine. *Science, 126,* 122–24.

Skinner, C. G., R. G. Ham, D. C. Fitzgerald, Jr., R. E. Eakin, and W. Shive. 1956. Synthesis and biological activity of some 6-(substituted)-thiopurines. *J. Org. Chem., 21,* 1330–31.

Skinner, C. G., and W. Shive. 1955. Synthesis of some 6-(substituted)-aminopurines. *J. Am. Chem. Soc., 77,* 6692–93.

Skinner, C. G., W. Shive, R. G. Ham, D. C. Fitzgerald, Jr., and R. E. Eakin. 1956. Effect of some 6-(substituted)-purines on regeneration of hydra. *J. Am. Chem. Soc., 78,* 5097–5100.

Thimann, K. V. 1956. Studies on the growth and inhibition of isolated plant parts. V. The effects of cobalt and other metals. *Am. J. Botany, 43,* 241–50.

Toole, E. H., S. B. Hendricks, H. A. Borthwick, and V. K. Toole. 1956. Physiology of seed germination. *Ann. Rev. Plant Physiol., 7,* 299–319.

Weintraub, R. L., and L. Price. 1947. Inhibition of mesocotyl elongation in various grasses by red and by violet light. *Smithsonian Inst. Publs., Misc. Collections, 106* (21), 1–15.

INTERACTION OF GROWTH SUBSTANCES AND PHOTOPERIODICALLY ACTIVE RADIATIONS ON THE GROWTH OF PEA INTERNODE SECTIONS [1]

WILLIAM S. HILLMAN
Department of Botany, Josiah Willard Gibbs Research Laboratory, Yale University, New Haven, Connecticut

A prominent role of the red-far red photomorphogenic system in plants is the control of stem elongation, a process which has long been investigated with particular emphasis on the action of growth substances. The use of excised tissues provides many advantages in studying possible radiation-growth substance interaction, but, unfortunately, most recent work on this question (see discussion) has employed materials (leaf discs, hypocotyl hooks, coleoptile sections) in which the response measured is promoted by red light. The results are thus not directly relevant to stem elongation, which is inhibited by red light.

The work of Schneider (1941) suggested that there is no direct interaction between auxin and red light action. Using *Avena* seedlings grown either in total darkness or exposed to dim red light, Schneider found that the growth of excised mesocotyl (first internode) sections was greater in sections from dark-grown plants than in those from plants previously exposed to red light. The absolute amount of the inhibition was not affected by auxin except at supraoptimal levels, which eliminated it entirely. For some reason, these results have not been considered by more recent investigators of red light-auxin interactions (e.g., Liverman and Bonner, 1953; Galston and Baker, 1953). The results to be presented below confirm and extend them, and lead to the conclusion that the effects of red and far-red radiation on pea internode sections, at least, are at most very indirectly mediated by growth substances such as indoleacetic acid or gibberellic acid.

[1] Research supported by the National Science Foundation under grant NSF G-2009 to A. W. Galston. The writer is greatly indebted to Professor Galston for his advice, particularly in the preparation of this paper.

MATERIALS AND METHODS

Seeds of *Pisum sativum,* var. Alaska, were obtained from Asgrow, Inc., of New Haven, Connecticut, sown in vermiculite (Mica-Gro Type B, supplied by Platt Seed Company, Branford, Connecticut, thoroughly washed in running water) and allowed to develop for 7 days at $26 \pm 1°C$. Experimental plants were either "dark-grown" or "red-grown." The former were kept in darkness except for exposure to dim green light at time of handling; these were selected for recurved apical crooks. Red-grown plants were obtained by exposure to red light (two 15-watt red fluorescent lamps at a distance of 30 cm, giving approximately 19.5 kiloergs $\cdot$ cm^{-2} $\cdot$ min^{-1}) for 20-min periods at 3-hr intervals during the 18 hr before harvest, and were selected for approximately 90° apical crooks.

All sections were taken from plants with third internodes 15–40 mm long. Most experiments were conducted with sections initially 8 mm long and cut 4 mm below the apex, but some were conducted with 5-mm sections cut either 1 or 6 mm from the apex in order to obtain extremes of endogenous growth or of response to auxin or gibberellic acid (see Purves and Hillman, 1958). Sections were randomized in buffer after cutting, then distributed in lots of 10 on circles of Whatman No. 1 filter paper in 10-cm petri dishes containing 8 ml of medium. The basal medium consisted of $0.02M$ KH$_2$–Na$_2$HPO$_4$ buffer, pH 6.1, with 2% sucrose. Each dish was divided into halves by a microscope slide under the filter paper; thus each experimental treatment was given to two replicate lots of 10 sections each.

Measurements were made after a 20-hr growth period in darkness (except for initial radiation treatments) at 26°C. In certain experiments, lots of sections were weighed before and after growth; most of the data on fresh weight increase so obtained were similar to those on elongation, with the exceptions to be noted. All radiation treatments were given to the sections within the first 2 hr of the growth period. Red-light treatment was for 100 min (approximately 1950 kiloergs/cm²); the effect so obtained was maximal, since even continuous exposure to red light failed to give a greater effect.[2] Far-red radiation was obtained from five 200-watt incandescent bulbs·at a distance of about 60 cm, and separated from the tissue by four layers each of red and blue cellophane and 7 cm of water. Twenty minutes was used as a standard exposure, since it gave a maximal effect, with 10 min significantly less effective.

Indoleacetic acid was obtained from Eastman Chemical Company, gibberellic acid from Merck and Company, and kinetin from Nutritional Biochemical Company.

RESULTS

All data presented and discussed have been confirmed in at least three repetitions. While absolute values varied considerably between experiments, the relationships observed were consistent throughout.

Effects of Red and Far-Red Treatments on Endogenous Growth

When excised sections are placed in basal medium, some elongation takes place without added growth substances. This will be referred to as "endogenous growth." Figure 1 shows the effects of red and far-red

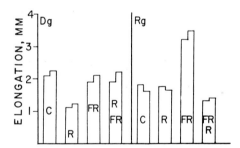

FIG. 1.   Elongation of sections from dark-grown (Dg) or red-grown (Rg) plants. Sections initially 8 mm long, cut 4 mm from apex. Treatments at start of 20-hr growth period in darkness: C, dark controls; R, red light (100 min, 1950 kiloergs/cm²); FR, far red (20 min); R FR, red followed by far red; etc. Divisions of bars represent replicate means of 10 sections. (Dg exp. 4–4–57; Rg exp. 2–22–57.)

[2] Since the presentation of these results, A. W. Galston has found that 30 sec exposure (about 10 kiloergs/cm²) has a maximal effect when the most apical section is used.

(FR) treatments given to the sections themselves on the endogenous growth of sections from dark-grown and red-grown plants. Red inhibited the elongation of sections from dark-grown plants; FR had little or no effect by itself (occasionally causing a slight inhibition), but it reversed the red inhibition when given directly after the red treatment. The elongation of sections from red-grown plants was not affected by red treatment, but was promoted by FR; the FR promotion was reversed by subsequent red light.

A relationship between the red inhibition and endogenous growth is indicated in Fig. 2, representing an experiment conducted with 5-mm

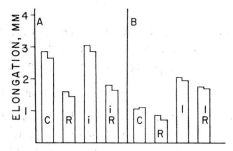

FIG. 2. Elongation of 5-mm sections from dark-grown plants, cut 1 mm (A) or 6 mm (B) from apex, as affected by red light treatment (R) in the presence or absence of optimal IAA. i, $10^{-7}M$ IAA; I, $10^{-6}M$ IAA. (Exp. 9–12–57.)

sections taken either 1 or 6 mm from the apex of dark-grown plants. Endogenous growth in the apical sections (Fig. 2A: C) was much greater than in the basal sections (Fig. 2B: C); the red-light inhibition was also greater, not only in absolute terms but also proportionally. The effects of indoleacetic acid (IAA) also shown in Fig. 2 will be discussed later.

Interaction of Gibberellic Acid with Red and Far-Red Treatments

Elongation in sections from both dark-grown and red-grown plants is promoted by gibberellic acid (GA) at concentrations from 10^{-8} to $10^{-4}M$, with what appears to be a weakly marked optimum at $10^{-6}M$ (0.346 mg/l). Figure 3 shows some interactions of red treatment and $10^{-6}M$ GA on sections from both types of plants. GA promoted elongation in both types of sections. Red light inhibited the elongation

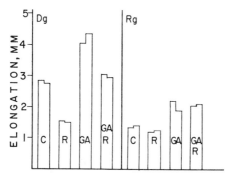

FIG. 3.   Elongation of sections from dark-grown (Dg) or red-grown (Rg) plants as affected by red light (R) treatment in the presence or absence of $10^{-6}M$ gibberellic acid (GA). Dg sections 5 mm long, 1 mm from apex. (Exp. 9–24–57.) Rg sections 8 mm long, 4 mm from apex. (Exp. 7–11–57.)

of sections from dark-grown plants in both the presence and absence of GA, and the absolute value of the inhibition was approximately the same in both cases. In some experiments, the inhibition was slightly but significantly less in the presence of GA than in its absence, but in no case was it possible to prevent the red inhibition with any GA concentration. No red-light inhibition was observed in the sections from red-grown plants either with or without GA.

Figure 4 shows the effects of $10^{-6}M$ GA and of FR on sections

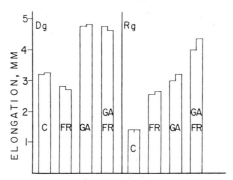

FIG. 4.   Elongation of 8-mm sections cut 4 mm from apex of dark-grown (Dg) or red-grown (Rg) plants, as affected by far-red (FR) treatment in presence or absence of $10^{-6}M$ gibberellic acid (GA). (Dg exp. 3–25–57; Rg exp. 4–5–57.)

from dark-grown and red-grown plants. GA alone promoted elongation, as usual. FR alone, as shown previously, promoted elongation only in sections from red-grown plants. GA and FR together had the same effect as GA alone on sections from dark-grown plants, but on sections from red-grown plants their effects were almost perfectly additive.

Interactions of Indoleacetic Acid with Red and Far-Red Treatments

Galston and Baker (1953) found that the optimum IAA concentration for the elongation of sections from red-grown plants was about 100 times that for sections from dark-grown plants. This was easily confirmed. With 8-mm sections cut 4 mm below the apex, an elongation optimum ca. $10^{-6}M$ (0.175 mg/l) IAA was found for sections from dark-grown plants as compared with ca. $10^{-4}M$ for the red-grown. Almost identical results were also obtained with naphthaleneacetic acid (NAA). Fresh weight increase, however, was maximal for sections from dark-grown plants at ca. $10^{-5}M$ IAA or NAA, (cf. Galston and Hand, 1949) whereas for sections from red-grown plants it was only slightly higher at $10^{-4}M$ than at $10^{-5}M$. Thus the difference in auxin sensitivity between the two types of sections is much less marked when considered in terms of fresh weight increase.

It was already shown that red treatment inhibits elongation in sections from dark-grown plants in the absence of IAA. It also inhibits at all levels of IAA up through $10^{-6}M$; the absolute value of the inhibition is approximately constant regardless of the IAA level, so that there is a decrease in percentage inhibition with increasing IAA. Figure 2 provides two examples of this. In Fig. 2A, the difference between the control (C) and red treatment (R) is the same as that between the $10^{-7}M$ IAA treatment (i) and its red-treated counterpart (iR). This level of IAA is optimal for the elongation of the 5-mm apical sections used (Purves and Hillman, 1958). In Fig. 2B, again, the difference between the control and red treatment is the same as that between the $10^{-6}M$ IAA treatment (I) and its red counterpart (IR). It is also worth noting that, while the higher red sensitivity of the apical sections (Fig. 2A) appears to be correlated with a higher endogenous growth, the increased elongation of the basal sections caused by IAA did not confer a proportional increase in red sensitivity.

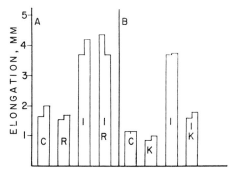

Fig. 5. Elongation of 8-mm sections cut 4 mm from apex of red-grown plants as affected by red light (R) treatment or $3 \times 10^{-5}M$ kinetin (K) in the presence or absence of $10^{-6}M$ IAA (I). (A, exp. 5–17–57; B, exp. 6–26–57.)

No red light inhibition was observed in sections from red-grown plants at any concentration of IAA (cf. Fig. 5A).

While relatively low IAA levels do not affect the red light inhibition, the data in Fig. 6 show that sufficiently high concentrations prevent both red and FR effects. The lower pair of lines represents the elongation of sections from dark-grown plants, with or without red treatment. While a significant red inhibition was present at $10^{-6}M$ IAA, none was observed at the higher levels. Similarly, the upper pair of lines indicates that FR promotion of elongation is still in evidence at $10^{-5}M$ IAA, but not at $10^{-4}M$.

Comparison of Effects of Kinetin and of Red Treatment

Several reports have appeared (Miller, 1956; Scott and Liverman, 1956; Hillman, 1957) showing that the effects of kinetin (6-furfuryl-aminopurine) frequently resemble those of red light. It was thus of interest to compare kinetin and red light effects on internode sections. Kinetin inhibited elongation at concentrations as low as $10^{-5}M$. When tested against endogenous growth, no difference was apparent between its effects on sections from dark-grown plants and sections from red-grown plants. Figure 5B shows that kinetin, unlike red light, strongly inhibited IAA-induced elongation in sections from red-grown plants, although the concentration used ($3 \times 10^{-5}M$), like the red light (cf. Fig. 5A) hardly affected endogenous growth.

DISCUSSION

Before attempting to interpret the results, one must consider previous views on red light-growth substance relationships. The work of Schneider (1941) was mentioned in the introduction, and will be referred to again below. Galston and Hand (1949) were able to obtain direct and inductive effects of low (white) light doses on excised pea internode sections. Although their results led to the conclusion that "a non-auxin system is responsible for the light growth inhibition," several subsequent papers by Galston and co-workers (cf. Galston and Baker, 1949, 1951) concentrated on the photoinactivation of IAA by blue light and riboflavin, and did not pursue the question of red light action.

Kent and Gortner (1951) and Galston and Baker (1953) showed that pretreatment of intact etiolated pea plants with red light affected the subsequent auxin sensitivity of the tissues. The results of Galston and Baker have been confirmed here, but Thomson (1954) has pointed out the complexities involved in studying light action by treatment of intact, growing plants. The light-auxin interactions so demonstrated are perhaps more likely to be consequences of photomorphogenesis than they are to be the primary mechanism; hence the desirability of studying excised sections rather than intact plants.

Liverman and Bonner (1953) showed that red light promotes growth in *Avena* coleoptile sections whether given before or during auxin treatment, while FR reverses the action of red only when given in the presence of auxin but has no effect in its absence. Kinetic treatment of the data led the authors to propose that red light increases the production of an auxin-receptive entity, and FR decomposes the active auxin-receptor complex, giving a nonreceptive entity. While the concept is attractive as an explanation for the *Avena* results, it seems a priori to be inapplicable to stem elongation, which was not considered in the paper in question, and which is promoted by both auxin and FR. The FR promotion of elongation reported for intact plants by Downs *et al.* (1957) and reported here for sections from red-grown plants can hardly be interpreted in terms of a decomposition of a growth-active complex unless the *ad hoc* assumption is made that this complex inhibits internode elongation.

Klein *et al.* (1956) found that red irradiation decreased the sensitivity of excised bean hypocotyl hooks to IAA; the reverse was also true. Since red light and auxin cause opposite responses in the tissue, no specific antagonism is necessarily implied by these results.

Hillman and Galston (1957) reported that red and FR control the apparent level of an *in vitro* IAA oxidase inhibitor found in the buds of etiolated peas, but pointed out the difficulty of ascribing any direct physiological significance to this control. While the changed auxin sensitivity of internode sections from red-grown plants might be ascribed to a change in IAA oxidase activity, this seems unlikely for several reasons. No such change could be detected in internode tissue in the work cited. In addition, Galston and Hand (1949), Kent and Gortner (1951), and the results reported here all indicate that the effects of light on apparent auxin sensitivity are as marked when NAA is used as the auxin as with IAA, although NAA is not attacked by IAA oxidase, at least *in vitro* (Stutz, 1957; also unpublished experiments in this laboratory).

A relation between gibberellin action and photomorphogenesis has been suggested by several investigations. Lona (1956) and others have observed that GA promotes dark germination of certain red-light-requiring seeds. The specificity of this effect is doubtful, since kinetin also acts in a similar fashion (Miller, 1956) as do other agents. Lockhart (1956) found that while intact dark-grown pea seedlings are only slightly affected by gibberellin, plants exposed to red light respond to gibberellin with an increased internode elongation which amounts to a complete reversal of the red light inhibition. However, gibberellin does not reverse the red light effects on leaf and node development. Vlitos and Meudt (1957) have suggested that GA may act by protecting against the light inactivation of endogenous growth hormones, although Biebel (1942) found that the hypocotyls of bean plants de-etiolated with red light contained no less *Avena*-active auxin than dark controls. Scott and Liverman (1957) reported that GA promotes the expansion of etiolated bean leaf discs, as does red light. The promotion was at least partially additive to that of red light, and was reversed by FR except at one concentration.

Although these results indicate that GA affects some of the responses also affected by red and FR, all the responses in question are promoted by GA, so that in some cases (seeds, leaf discs) it acts in the same direction as red light, while in others (internode elongation), in the same direction as FR. Any hypothesis of a close relationship between GA and the photomorphogenic system needs to explain this circumstance.

Turning to the results at hand, three summary statements can be made. (1) Qualitatively, the response of pea internode sections to red and FR depends on the previous light regime of the plants used. (2) Quantitatively, the red response depends on the endogenous growth of the tissue exposed. (3) The presence of exogenous GA or auxin has no effect on either red or FR response, with the exception of high auxin levels, which prevent both. The first statement was illustrated in Fig. 1; similar observations have been made on various materials by others. The second point, however, deserves further consideration. The data in Fig. 2 suggest that red light inhibits endogenous growth, and *endogenous growth only:* the inhibition was much greater in the rapidly growing apical (A) sections than in the basal (B) sections, but when the growth of the latter was increased by IAA, no change in the amount of red inhibition occurred. This leads to a more extended consideration of the third statement.

The amount of inhibition caused by red light is approximately the same whether GA is present or not (Fig. 3, Dg); in tissues which are not sensitive to red light, the increased growth due to GA remains insensitive to red light (Fig. 3, Rg). Similarly, the amount of elongation caused by FR is approximately the same in the presence or absence of GA (Fig. 4, Rg); and tissues insensitive to FR remain so in the presence of GA (Fig. 4, Dg). For similar results with GA and FR on intact plants see Downs *et al.* (1957). Statements similar to those on GA above can also be made for IAA in concentrations thru $10^{-6}M$, and are illustrated by the data in Figs. 2, 5A, and 6. All these results agree with the concept that what is inhibited by red light is a portion of endogenous growth, that this component is already completely repressed in sections from red-grown plants, and that neither IAA-induced growth nor GA-induced growth is red sensitive. The converse would be true for FR action.

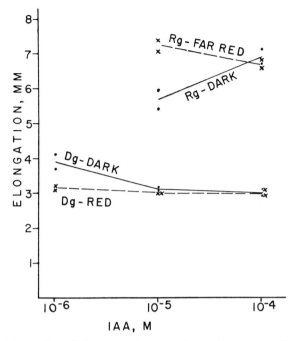

FIG. 6.   Elongation of 8-mm sections cut 4 mm from apex of red-grown (Rg) or dark-grown (Dg) plants, as affected by red or far-red treatment at indicated IAA levels. (Rg exp. 5–9–57; Dg exp. 5–15–57.)

A concept that calls for a qualitative distinction between endogenous growth and that induced by growth substances, particularly IAA, is admittedly disturbing. The assumption that IAA-induced growth is identical and coextensive with endogenous growth is implicit in most of the literature on section growth. While this general question cannot be discussed here, the writer is unaware of any systematic attempts to compare endogenous growth to IAA-induced growth with respect to inhibitor sensitivity, for example, or any other characteristic, and the assumption has remained an assumption. It is difficult to maintain against the present evidence.

Endogenous growth is clearly red sensitive in sections from dark-grown plants (Figs. 1, 2). If it is identical with IAA-induced growth, then as growth is increased with IAA the red inhibition should increase in proportion, which it does not do. If all endogenous growth is identical with IAA-induced growth, it is difficult to explain why the

FR-induced endogenous growth in sections from red-grown plants is completely suppressed by red, while IAA-induced growth in the same material is unaffected. Exactly parallel arguments will also suggest that GA-induced growth and endogenous growth are not identical. Thus the postulation of a light-sensitive endogenous growth component of unknown nature appears to offer fewer difficulties than the traditional assumption. This is not to say that no portion of endogenous growth is IAA-mediated; there is a great deal of evidence against such a position. It is only necessary to assume that a portion of it is not IAA-mediated, and that this is the portion controlled by red light. This interpretation is in complete agreement with the results of Schneider (1941), who pointed out that "the effect is much as though [red] light caused a given absolute amount of inhibition, the amount being nearly the same under all conditions of auxin supply."

A diagram summarizing this concept is presented in Fig. 7, in which

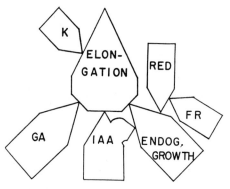

Fig. 7.　Summary of effects of various agents on elongation of pea stem sections. See Discussion.

the pointed ends of the figures indicate promotion or inhibition of elongation depending on their direction relative to that of the central figure. Figure 7 represents elongation in excised sections as contributed to by (at least) three more or less independent components: endogenous growth, IAA-induced growth, and GA-induced growth. The separation of IAA- and GA-induced growth is based primarily on the results of Purves and Hillman (1958) for the same material, but also on the belief that it is better to assume a lack of any direct relation until there is unequivocal evidence of interaction. Red and FR are represented as acting only on endogenous growth. Note that IAA is also represented as inhibiting endogenous growth, an effect easily demonstrated with sections taken very close to the apex (Purves and Hillman, 1958). This interaction provides an explanation for the fact that high IAA levels suppress both the red and FR response (Fig. 6).

If a sufficiently high IAA level, while causing elongation on its own, completely represses that portion of the endogenous growth also inhibitable by red light, no red inhibition will be detected in its presence. This interpretation is strengthened by the fact that, for sections from dark-grown plants, the concentration of IAA required to prevent red inhibition is supraoptimal, so that it is evident that an inhibition of some sort is occurring. On the assumption that all endogenous growth is identical with IAA-induced growth, this inhibition would simply be due to excess IAA in a single system, but only on this assumption. It is equally likely that the IAA response curve of sections from dark-grown plants is the resultant of a promoting action on one system (IAA-induced growth) and an inhibiting action on another (endogenous growth). Significantly, the prevention of red inhibition by high IAA is not a true reversal, since elongation is not restored to the peak given by $10^{-6}M$ IAA in the absence of red. A similar observation was made for the *Avena* first internode by Schneider (1941, Fig. 12).

The suppression of FR promotion by high IAA can be similarly interpreted. An alternative explanation is that elongation at high IAA is limited here by other factors, such as energy-rich substrate or structural materials, but several experiments have shown that GA can still increase elongation at high IAA levels, so that this seems unlikely.

In terms of this scheme, then, sections from dark-grown plants are inhibited by red light because an endogenous growth component is inhibited; sections from red-grown plants are not inhibited by red because this component no longer contributes to elongation unless it is de-inhibited by FR; this same component is also inhibited by sufficiently high levels of IAA. The results of Galston and Baker (1953) may perhaps be explained on this basis. If the apparently lower IAA optimum of sections from dark-grown plants is due simply to an inhibition of endogenous growth by IAA, and if this inhibition is already "saturated" in sections of red-grown plants, then elongation will be promoted in the latter by considerably higher IAA levels.

The position of kinetin in Fig. 7 is easily explained. It inhibits endogenous growth in both types of sections. It also appears to be an effective inhibitor of IAA-induced elongation (Fig. 5B) and, in similar experiments, GA-induced elongation. Hence its effect on elongation cannot be referred to any of the individual "components" described.

Thomson (1954) studied the effects of occasional (white) light treatment on etiolated pea and *Avena* seedlings. She concluded that "Exposure very early in the course of either cell division or cell elongation accelerates the early part of the phase of growth. Exposure after either phase is well under way hastens the transition to the next phase and reduces the final number or length of cells." In short, light hastens maturation. The relevance of this work to the present results is that the "components" discussed above may simply represent phases in internode development, arbitrarily isolated from the developing organism at a given time.

On this basis, red inhibition of elongation in an intact plant might also result in increased sensitivity to a growth factor such as GA (Lockhart, 1956), if the light accelerates the development to a phase requiring that growth factor. In this regard it is significant that apical sections, which show a high endogenous growth and red sensitivity, are also more responsive to GA than more basal sections (Purves and Hillman, 1958), although no direct relation between endogenous growth and GA response could be established. As sheer speculation, it is possible to suppose that the development of very young internode tissue passes through at least three stages: (1) endogenous growth, highly red sensitive; (2) a stage limited by GA; (3) a stage limited by auxin. Thus the light-induced increase in GA response found in intact plants would be due to the fact that cell maturation proceeds unhindered, which would not be true for sections.

It should be clear that the intent of the scheme presented in Fig. 7 and of this discussion is not to propose a mechanism for the interaction of radiations and growth substances; on the contrary, it is to show how "interactions" might be observed even if red-FR control is exerted on completely unknown processes. Admittedly, the results of Liverman and Bonner (1953) remain unexplained by this concept, perhaps because coleoptile tissue is somewhat anomalous in being promoted by both auxin and red light. However, the results of Schneider (1941), Thomson (1954), and those reported here, as well as the general consiforation that red and FR control diverse processes in both plants and animals, make it seem unlikely that this control is exerted in any but the most indirect manner through interactions with plant growth substances such as IAA or GA.

The conclusion that photomorphogenesis is not mediated by known growth substances suggests that a much closer examination of endogenous growth in both excised tissues and intact plants should be undertaken, preferably coupled with anatomical and cytological studies. If a guess were to be made as to the kind of system which might be involved in photomorphogenesis, one affecting purine metabolism might be suggested. Purines and related compounds have been implicated in photomorphogenesis by several groups (cf. Scott and Liverman, 1957), and their basic role in nucleic acids and energy transfer at least makes it possible to conceive that a system affecting them might in turn control overall cell maturation and differentiation in many diverse ways.

SUMMARY

The growth response of pea seedling internode sections to red or far-red (FR) radiations depends upon the previous light regime of the plants used. Red light inhibits elongation in sections from completely dark-grown plants, but it has little or no effect on sections from plants exposed to red light during the preceding 18 hr (red-grown plants). Elongation of sections from red-grown plants is promoted by FR, but sections from dark-grown plants are not affected. For sections from dark-grown plants, the greater the endogenous growth (no added growth substances) the greater is the inhibition by red light.

Neither the direction nor the absolute magnitudes of the red or FR responses are affected by gibberellic acid (GA) or auxin (IAA), except in the case of high IAA, which prevents both responses. Kinetin, unlike red light, inhibits the elongation of both types of sections equally, and is an effective inhibitor of IAA- and GA-induced growth.

These results suggest that the radiations act primarily on a component of endogenous growth which is distinct from IAA- or GA-induced growth. Some implications of this view are discussed.

REFERENCES

Biebel, J. P. 1942. Some effects of radiant energy in relation to etiolation. *Plant Physiol. 17,* 377–96.

Downs, R. J., S. B. Hendricks, and H. A. Borthwick. 1957. Photoreversible control of elongation of pinto beans and other plants under normal conditions of growth. *Botan. Gaz., 118,* 199–208.

Galston, A. W., and R. S. Baker. 1949. Studies on the physiology of light action. II. The photodynamic action of riboflavin. *Am. J. Botany, 36,* 773–80.

——. 1951. Studies on the physiology of light action. IV. Light enhancement of auxin-induced growth in green peas. *Plant Physiol., 26,* 311–17.

——. 1953. Studies on the physiology of light action. V. Photoinductive alteration of auxin metabolism in etiolated peas. *Am. J. Botany, 40,* 512–16.

Galston, A. W., and M. E. Hand. 1949. Studies on the physiology of light action. I. Auxin and the light inhibition of growth. *Am. J. Botany, 36,* 85–94.

Hillman, W. S. 1957. Nonphotosynthetic light requirement in Lemna minor and its partial satisfaction by kinetin. *Science, 126,* 165–166.

Hillman, W. S., and A. W. Galston. 1957. Inductive control of indoleacetic acid oxidase by red and near-infrared light. *Plant Physiol., 32,* 129–35.

Kent, M., and W. A. Gortner. 1951. Effect of pre-illumination on the response of split pea stems to growth substances. *Botan. Gaz., 112,* 307–11.

Klein, W. H., R. B. Withrow, and V. B. Elstad. 1956. Response of the hypocotyl hook of bean seedlings to radiant energy and other factors. *Plant Physiol., 31,* 289–94.

Liverman, J. L., and J. Bonner. 1953. The interaction of auxin and light in the growth of plants. *Proc. Natl. Acad. Sci. U. S., 39,* 905–16.

Lockhart, J. A. 1956. Reversal of the light inhibition of pea stem growth by the gibberellins. *Proc. Natl. Acad. Sci. U. S., 42,* 841–48.

Lona, F. 1956. L'acido gibberellico determina la germinazione dei semi di *Lactuca scariola* in fase di scoto-inibizione. *Ateneo parmense, 27,* 641–44.

Miller, C. O. 1956. Similarity of some kinetin and red light effects. *Plant Physiol., 31,* 318–19.

Purves, W. K., and W. S. Hillman. 1958. Response of pea stem sections to indoleacetic acid, gibberellic acid, and sucrose as affected by length and distance from apex. *Physiol. Plantarum, 11,* 29–35.

Schneider, C. L. 1941. The effect of red light on growth of the *Avena* seedling with special reference to the first internode. *Am. J. Botany, 28,* 878–86.

Scott, R. A., Jr., and J. L. Liverman. 1956. Promotion of leaf expansion by kinetin and benzylaminopurine. *Plant Physiol., 31,* 321–22.

——. 1957. Control of etiolated bean leaf-disk expansion by gibberellins and adenine. *Science, 126,* 122–24.

Stutz, R. E. 1957. The indole-3-acetic acid oxidase of *Lupinus albus* L. *Plant Physiol., 32,* 31–39.

Thomson, B. F. 1954. The effect of light on cell division and cell elongation in seedlings of oats and peas. *Am. J. Botany, 41,* 326–32.

Vlitos, A. J., and W. Meudt. 1957. Relationship between shoot apex and effect of gibberellic acid on elongation of pea stems. *Nature, 180,* 284.

EFFECTS OF GIBBERELLIC ACID, KINETIN, AND LIGHT ON THE GERMINATION OF LETTUCE SEED

ALAN H. HABER and N. E. TOLBERT [1]
Biology Division, Oak Ridge National Laboratory,[2] Oak Ridge,
Tennessee

A reversible red, far-red photoreaction can profoundly affect many aspects of plant morphogenesis (Wassink and Stolwijk, 1956). Heretofore, attempts to mimic the effects of red light by chemical treatment achieved only slight success. Within the last few years, two groups of chemicals, the gibberellins (Stowe and Yamaki, 1957) and the kinins (Skoog and Miller, 1957) have been shown to affect plant development greatly and in some instances to produce changes similar to effects of red light (Hillman, 1957; Kahn *et al.*, 1957; Miller, 1956; Scott and Liverman, 1957; Stowe and Yamaki, 1957). It has been suggested that natural gibberellin-like (Phinney *et al.*, 1957; Radley, 1956; Stowe and Yamaki, 1957) and kinin-like (Danckwardt-LilliestrÖm, 1957; Skinner *et al.*, 1957; Skoog and Miller, 1957) substances occur in higher plants. It is thus conceivable that the red light effects on some systems could be related to the production or activity of endogenous gibberellin- or kinin-like substances.

The effect of red light on the germination rate of Grand Rapids lettuce seed can be mimicked by treatment with either gibberellin (Kahn *et al.*, 1957) or kinin (Miller, 1956; Skinner *et al.*, 1957). Moreover, promotion of germination by gibberellin or kinetin was apparently not reversed by far-red light treatment (Kahn *et al.*, 1957; Miller, 1956). These results are consistent with hypotheses that the photoreaction regulates levels of endogenous gibberellin- or kinin-like substances.

In this paper it is demonstrated that gibberellic acid and kinetin

---

[1] Present address: Department of Agricultural Chemistry, Michigan State University, East Lansing, Michigan.

[2] Operated by Union Carbide Nuclear Company for the U. S. Atomic Energy Commission.

have distinct effects on the germination of Grand Rapids lettuce seed, and that treatment with either of these chemicals cannot substitute for red light treatment under selected conditions. Thus the effect of any one of these three agents can be separated from the effects of the other two. The results contradict the hypothesis that the photoreaction controls germination of Grand Rapids lettuce seed solely by regulating the levels of endogenous gibberellin- or kinin-like substances.

MATERIALS AND METHODS

Seeds of *Lactuca sativa,* var. Grand Rapids, were obtained from Mayo Seed Co., Knoxville, Tennessee. They were germinated in covered 9-cm petri dishes containing pads of filter paper moistened with appropriate solutions at pH 5.8 and exposed to light only at the times indicated. Dishes were transferred to and from rooms at different temperatures in a light-tight box. Red and far-red treatment affected only the *rate of* germination in darkness at 22°C, since germination of far-red treated seeds was complete if subsequently given sufficient time in darkness. This behavior corresponds to that exhibited by the Grand Rapids seed used by Evenari *et al.* (1953). The criterion for germination at any time was the visible appearance of the radicle.

Unless otherwise indicated, each treatment was represented by two dishes, each containing approximately 120 seeds. Germination among replicates was shown, by the chi-square test, to be attributable to chance variations among seeds drawn at random from a single population. On the basis of this test, the replicate data were pooled for further analysis. Chi-square tests were then applied to the 2×2 contingency tables formed by considering all possible treatment pairs within one experiment. Differences concluded significant were those for which $P < 0.001$. It should be noted that within any one experiment, the chi-square tests so applied are not independent. This formal objection was overcome by the application of Tukey's method for comparison of means after percentage germination in each dish had been transformed by the inverse sine transformation. This procedure yielded differences significant at the 5% level. A description of these statistical procedures is given by Snedecor (1956).

RESULTS AND DISCUSSION

1. *Separation of the Gibberellic Acid from the Kinetin Effect by Temperature and Evidence for the Distinct Effects of These Compounds on Germination.* Effects of gibberellic acid and kinetin on germination at 35°C are illustrated in Fig. 1a. Kinetin promoted germination over water controls at this temperature; gibberellic acid had no effect. The concentration of $5 \times 10^{-5}M$ kinetin used in this experiment was optimal at this temperature. No concentration of gibberellic acid increased germination over water controls. Germination was greater with the combination of gibberellic acid and kinetin than with kinetin alone. This synergism suggests that gibberellic acid somehow retained the capacity to affect cellular processes in conjunction with kinetin at 35°C, even though gibberellic acid alone had no apparent effect on germination. A direct test demonstrating that gibberellic acid was not irreversibly inactivated by high temperature was made. Dishes containing seeds with $3 \times 10^{-4}M$ gibberellic acid or none at all were left in darkness at 37°C for 48 hr. The dishes were then transferred, in darkness, to a room at 22° and examined 24 hr later. At that time, 86% of the seeds treated with the gibberellic acid had germinated, compared with 12% of the similarly treated water controls. These last results agree with those of Kahn *et al.* (1957), which show that germination of certain seeds at 21° was decreased by similar pretreatment at 36° and that gibberellin reversed this inhibition.

It has been reported that gibberellin or kinin can stimulate germination of Grand Rapids seeds at room temperature either in darkness or with far-red treatment (Kahn *et al.*, 1957; Miller, 1956). Since germination was very rapid at 22°C, it was desirable to give the seeds at this temperature a saturating exposure to far-red light (Borthwick *et al.*, 1954) to slow the germination so that differences in germination rates caused by gibberellic acid or kinetin could be more accurately observed. The optimal concentrations for stimulating germination of seeds so treated were $3 \times 10^{-4}M$ for gibberellic acid and $5 \times 10^{-5}M$ (as at 35°C) for kinetin. In the presence of these optimal

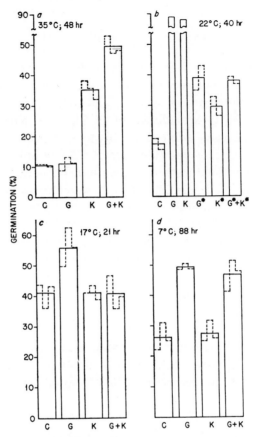

FIG. 1. Effects of gibberellic acid and kinetin on germination at different temperatures. Seeds in *a, c,* and *d* were germinated in darkness; seeds in *b* were exposed to far-red light during the first 16 hr (see text). Each dotted bar represents one dish of seeds. Solid bars represent average of replicates. Approximately 180 seeds were used per dish in *a* and *b*; 120 per dish in *c* and *d*. It is not intended that comparisons be drawn between experiments at different temperatures. Letters below columns: C, control. G, $3 \times 10^{-4}M$ gibberellic acid; G*, $3 \times 10^{-6}M$. K, $5 \times 10^{-5}M$ kinetin; K*, $5 \times 10^{-7}M$.

concentrations, germination rates were very rapid. Therefore, $3 \times 10^{-6}M$ gibberellic acid and $5 \times 10^{-7}M$ kinetin (each 1% of optimal) were used for more accurate evaluation of the effect of gibberellic acid and kinetin in combination (Fig. 1*b*). Whereas either gibberellic acid or kinetin at the lower concentrations promoted germination over water controls, the increase effected by the combination was much less than the sum of the increases effected by each alone under these conditions. This is in contrast to the synergism observed at 35°C.

Effects of gibberellic acid and kinetin on germination at 17°C are illustrated in Fig. 1c. Kinetin alone did not promote germination over water controls at this temperature, but gibberellic acid did. The combination of gibberellic acid plus kinetin, however, did not promote germination over water controls at this temperature. Thus, although kinetin alone did not seem to affect germination rate, it did appear to cancel the effect of gibberellic acid at this temperature.

Effects of gibberellic acid and kinetin on germination at 7°C are shown in Fig. 1d. As at 17°, gibberellic acid promoted germination over similarly treated water controls and kinetin did not. In the presence of the combination of gibberellic acid plus kinetin, however, germination was about the same as with gibberellic acid alone. At 7°, kinetin did not affect the germination rate and did not modify the overall response of the seeds to gibberellic acid.

Gibberellic acid alone did not stimulate germination over similarly treated water controls at 35°C, but did so at 22°, 17°, and 7°C. Kinetin alone stimulated germination over similarly treated water controls at 35° and 22°, but did not at 17° and 7°C. These results indicate that temperature can be used as a means of separating gibberellic acid and kinetin effects in the overall germination process. This suggests that gibberellic acid and kinetin affect germination by distinct mechanisms, but it does not in itself rule out the hypothesis that gibberellic acid and kinetin ultimately affect the same basic process(es) controlling germination.

At 35°C, gibberellic acid did not promote germination in the absence of kinetin, but did in its presence. This effect was observed even in the presence of kinetin at optimal concentration for promoting germination at this temperature. At 17°, gibberellic acid promoted germination in the absence of kinetin but not in its presence. The quite different apparent interactions of gibberellic acid plus kinetin at 35°, 22°, and 17° provide presumptive evidence against the hypothesis that gibberellic acid and kinetin affect the same process(es) controlling germination. A more likely possibility is that gibberellic acid and kinetin affect different (groups of) processes that share in the regulation of germination.

2. *Separation of Red Light Effect from Either Gibberellic Acid or Kinetin Effect.* Seeds germinated for 36 hr at 7°C gave 0% germination, owing to the slow rate of germination at this temperature (Table I). Seeds germinated at 37° gave 0% germination regardless of the

TABLE I.   Germination at 37° or 7° after Holding at 22°C[a]

	Percentage Germination	
Time at 22°, hr	37°, 48 hr	7°, 36 hr
0	0	0
4	0	0
8	2	4
12	22	37

[a] Seeds were always in darkness during these experiments.

length of the experiment or the concentration of gibberellic acid. However, seeds will germinate in water under these unfavorable conditions if they are first held in darkness at 22°C for some time (Table I). Presumably, changes occur in the seeds during the 8 or 12 hr at 22° and lead to subsequent germination at 37° and an increased rate of germination at 7°. Effects of gibberellic acid, kinetin, or light treatments on seeds during the first 12 hr at 22° could conceivably be separated by transferring the seeds after the 12 hr to the temperature unfavorable for further action of either chemical on germination—37° to inhibit further action of gibberellic acid or 7° to inhibit the action of kinetin.

For experiments run entirely at room temperature, Kahn *et al.* (1957) pointed out that "since gibberellin that has entered the seeds cannot be removed, the lack of reversal of the gibberellin effect by far red light cannot be considered definitive." In an attempt to perform a definitive experiment, we held seeds for the first 12 hr at 22°C in the presence of $3 \times 10^{-4}M$ gibberellic acid and exposed them to 20 min of far-red light at various times during this period. They were then transferred in darkness to a 37° incubator; this treatment might be considered tantamount to removing the gibberellic acid that had en-

TABLE II. Germination at 37°C of Gibberellic Acid-Treated Seeds Held for 12 hr at 22° in Darkness Interrupted by 20 min Exposure to Far-Red Light

Far-Red Treatment	Molarity of Gibberellic Acid	Germination after 48 hr at 37°, %
None	0	14.5
	3×10^{-4}	27.4
After 2 hr	0	0
	3×10^{-4}	1.7
After 4 hr	0	0.4
	3×10^{-4}	4.6
After 6 hr	0	3.0
	3×10^{-4}	8.0

tered the seeds. The results of this experiment (Tables II and III) demonstrated that gibberellic acid did not greatly protect against the inhibiting effect of exposure to far-red light during the 12 hr at 22°. Data in Table III demonstrate that exposure to red light immediately after the far-red exposure reversed the far-red effect under conditions where treatment with gibberellic acid did not. The same results were obtained with concentrations of gibberellic acid as high as $2.9 \times 10^{-3}M$ (1000 ppm).

After each of the four far-red light treatments of Table II, the increased germination of the gibberellic acid-treated seeds over the water controls was significant. If we assume that germination at 37°C was not affected by gibberellic acid, these differences must have resulted from changes induced by gibberellic acid during the 12 hr at 22°. Also significant was the trend of decreasing effectiveness of the far-red treatment with increasing time from the beginning of the imbibition, both within the gibberellic acid-treated and the control series.

TABLE III. Red Light Reversal of Far-Red Inhibition for Gibberellic Acid-Treated Seeds Held at 22°C for 12 hr

Light Treatment[a]	Germination after 48 hr at 37°, %	
	$0 M$	$3 \times 10^{-4} M$
None	23	39
Red	24	32
Far red	1	6
Far red + red	26	30

[a] 20 minutes exposure to red or far red after second hr at 22°.

In analogous experiments with kinetin, seeds were held at 22° for 12 hr in darkness interrupted after 2 hr with far-red and red light treatments (Table IV). After the 12-hr period the seeds were trans-

TABLE IV. Red Light Reversal of Far-Red Inhibition for
Kinetin-Treated Seeds Held at 22°C for 12 hr

	Germination after 36 hr at 7°, %	
Light Treatment[a]	0 M	$5 \times 10^{-5}\ M$
None	49	66
Red	42	53
Far red	5	3
Far red + red	28	42

[a] Twenty minutes exposure to red or far red after second hour at 22°.

ferred in darkness to 7°, a temperature detrimental to further action of kinetin. After 36 hr at 7°, it could be seen that kinetin had been ineffective in reversing the far-red effect under conditions where red light gave nearly complete reversal.

The experiments summarized in Tables III and IV show that, under given conditions, gibberellic acid or kinetin did not protect against the inhibition of germination by far-red light, whereas subsequent exposure to red light did. Thus the effect of the red, far-red photoreaction on the germination of these seeds at 22° cannot be explained in terms of its regulating the production of *either* endogenous gibberellin-like *or* endogenous kinin-like substances. Moreover, the fact that the effects of gibberellic acid plus kinetin on far-red treated seeds was less than additive at 22° (Fig. 1*b*) further suggests that the photoreaction cannot be explained solely in terms of regulating the production of *both* gibberellin *and* kinin.

Whereas gibberellic acid or kinetin apparently reversed the far-red effect during 40 hr at 22° (Fig. 1*b*), they failed to do so when the seeds were transferred after 12 hr at 22° to 37° or 7°C, respectively (Tables II–IV). One possible explanation is that the seeds begin to respond to one or both of these chemicals at around 12 or more hr after the beginning of imbibition. Alternatively, it is possible that one or both of these agents was fully active within the first 12 hr, but that its effect was reversed by the temperature change.

SUMMARY

Gibberellic acid and kinetin have different temperature ranges of activity for promoting germination of Grand Rapids lettuce seed over similarly treated water controls. Kinetin was effective at high temperatures where gibberellic acid was ineffective; gibberellic acid was effective at low temperatures where kinetin was ineffective. The apparent interactions of combinations of gibberellic acid plus kinetin at different temperatures rule out the possibility that these chemicals produce their effects by influencing the same process(es) regulating germination.

The different temperature ranges of activity of gibberellic acid and kinetin were used to nullify their effects on germination after a 12-hr period at room temperature, during which time red and far-red light treatments were applied. During the 12-hr period neither gibberellic acid nor kinetin could reverse the far-red light inhibition of germination though red light could. Thus the actions of gibberellic acid, kinetin, and red light on promoting lettuce seed germination were experimentally separated from one another. The effect of the red, far-red photoreaction can not be explained in terms of its regulating endogenous levels of gibberellin-like or kinin-like substances.

Acknowledgment

We gratefully acknowledge the advice on statistical procedures given by Dr. M. A. Kastenbaum of the Mathematics Panel of the Oak Ridge National Laboratory.

REFERENCES

Borthwick, H. A., S. B. Hendricks, E. H. Toole, and V. K. Toole. 1954. Action of light on lettuce-seed germination. *Botan. Gaz., 115*, 205–25.

Danckwardt-Lillieström, C. 1957. Kinetin induced shoot formation from isolated roots of *Isatis tinctoria. Physiol. Plantarum, 10*, 794–97.

Evenari, M., G. Neumann, and G. Stein. 1953. Factors modifying the influence of light on germination. *Nature, 172*, 452.

Hillman, W. S. 1957. Nonphotosynthetic light requirement in *Lemna minor* and its partial satisfaction by kinetin. *Science, 126*, 165–66.

Kahn, A., J. A. Goss, and D. E. Smith. 1957. Effect of gibberellin on germination of lettuce seed. *Science, 125*, 645–46.

Miller, C. O. 1956. Similarity of some kinetin and red light effects. *Plant Physiol., 31,* 318–19.

Phinney, B. O., C. A. West, M. Ritzel, and P. M. Neely. 1957. Evidence for "gibberellin-like" substances from flowering plants. *Proc. Natl. Acad. Sci. U. S., 43,* 398–404.

Radley, M. 1956. Occurrence of substances similar to gibberellic acid in higher plants. *Nature, 178,* 1070–71.

Scott, R. A., and J. L. Liverman. 1957. Control of etiolated bean leaf-disk expansion by gibberellins and adenine. *Science, 126,* 122–24.

Skinner, C. G., J. R. Claybrook, F. Talbert, and W. Shive. 1957. Effect of 6-(substituted)thio- and amino-purines on germination of lettuce seed. *Plant Physiol., 32,* 117–20.

Skoog, F., and C. O. Miller. 1957. Chemical regulation of growth and organ formation in plant tissues cultured *in vitro. Symposia Soc. Exptl. Biol., 11,* 118–31.

Snedecor, G. W. 1956. *Statistical Methods,* 5th ed. Iowa State College Press, Ames, Iowa.

Stowe, B. B., and T. Yamaki. 1957. The history and physiological action of the gibberellins. *Ann. Rev. Plant Physiol., 8,* 181–216.

Wassink, E. C., and J. A. J. Stolwijk. 1956. Effects of light quality on plant growth. *Ann. Rev. Plant Physiol., 7,* 373–400.

INTERACTION OF GROWTH FACTORS WITH PHOTOPROCESS IN SEEDLING GROWTH [1]

WILLIAM H. KLEIN
Smithsonian Institution, Washington, D. C.

Test Object

During the germination of a bean seedling a hook develops in the hypocotyl. As growth proceeds in the dark, the hook moves up into the epicotyl. In total darkness this hook does not completely disappear by the time the food reserves are depleted. However, when exposed to low values of irradiance in the red between 600 and 700 mμ, the hook opens and completely disappears in several days. This hypocotyl hook can be excised and used to determine quantitatively the photomorphogenic response (Klein *et al.,* 1956).

Histology of Dark and Red-Exposed Hooks

Red-treated and control hooks (dark) were fixed with formalin-aceto-alcohol and embedded in paraffin. Sections were cut longitudinally 10 μ in thickness and stained. Since no stage of cells undergoing mitosis has been detected in any of the numerous prepared slides, it can be assumed that the growth response is due to cell elongation. The degree of hook opening depends upon the relative growth rates of the inner and outer sides of the hook. The cells on the inner (concave) side are stimulated to elongate by the red treatment, while the cells on the outer side (convex) are relatively unaffected. The elongation is proportional to the incident energy. This work was done in cooperation with Dr. C. C. Moh. Figure 1 is a photomicrographic drawing of the inner and outer sides of the dark-treated and red-treated hooks.

[1] Published with the approval of the Secretary of the Smithsonian Institution.

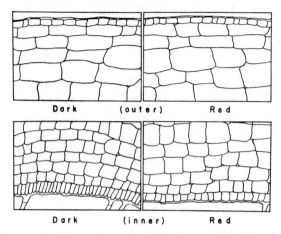

FIG. 1. Camera lucida tracings of photomicrographs of sections through the center of excised bean hook ($\times$700). The hooks were marked and then exposed to 20 hr of development in the dark and to 1 μw/cm^2 of red energy (625–700 mμ). The two upper sections are from the outer part of the hook; lower sections are from the inner portion. Note the marked elongation of the cells on the inner portion when the hook was exposed to red radiant energy.

IAA and Red Irradiance

The relationship between 3-indoleacetic acid and red energy is presented graphically in Fig. 2 for concentrations of IAA from 10^{-8} to $10^{-5}M$ and red irradiance (625–700 mμ) from 10^{-3} to 10 μw/cm^2. In complete darkness, IAA caused closure of the hook, which increased in magnitude with concentration. All concentrations of IAA decreased the effect of the photoreaction. Low concentrations of IAA between 10^{-8} and $10^{-6}M$ did not alter either the linearity of the opening response to the log of the irradiance or the slopes of the curves above a 10° opening value.

Effect of Gibberellin on Hook Response

Hooks developed in the dark with gibberellin responded negatively at all concentrations greater than $10^{-9}M$. Hooks exposed to both red radiant energy and gibberellin opened to a lesser degree than the water controls, if the concentration of gibberellin was greater than $10^{-10}M$. These results indicate that gibberellin opposes the opening of

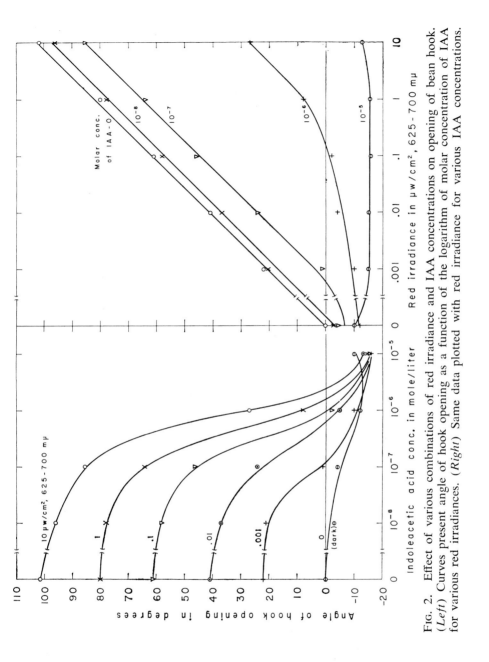

FIG. 2. Effect of various combinations of red irradiance and IAA concentrations on opening of bean hook. (*Left*) Curves present angle of hook opening as a function of the logarithm of molar concentration of IAA for various red irradiances. (*Right*) Same data plotted with red irradiance for various IAA concentrations.

209

TABLE I. Effect of Gibberellin on Photoreversibility in Bean Hook

Gibberellin Concentration, M	Angular Response, Degrees		
	Dark	Red[a]	Red-Far Red[b]
0	0	45	10
10^{-7}	−4	19	−4
10^{-6}	−7	25	−4
10^{-5}	−3	21	0

[a] Red, 625–700 mμ for 15 min (250 mj/cm²).
[b] Far red, 720–800 mμ for 25 min (12 mj/cm²).

the hypocotyl hook in both light and dark conditions in a manner similar to that of auxin.

Gibberellin brings about the same result whether the red activation is given continuously over a 20-hr period or for only a brief interval. The presence of gibberellin does not affect the reversal mechanism of the hook, but is additive to the normal reversal action as indicated in Table I. Table II presents evidence showing that gibberellin initiates

TABLE II. Interaction of Gibberellin ($10^{-6}\,M$) and Red Radiant Energy (250 mj/cm²) on Elongation of Straight Section of Hypocotyl Hooks[a]

Radiant Energy	Elongation, cm
Dark	3.02
Dark + gibberellin	3.30
Red	2.92
Red + gibberellin	3.19

[a] L.S.D. 1% = 0.05.

elongation responses in both light and dark conditions; also, that red radiant energy initiates a separate response independent of gibberellin and distinguishable from the gibberellin action.

Kinetin

Figure 3 presents the effect of kinetin on the hook response in darkness and in red radiant energy. Kinetin induces a response very similar to that of IAA, although the red is more effective in reducing the negative response at higher concentrations. In general, the response is similar to the effect of other growth regulators.

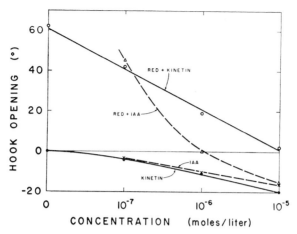

FIG. 3.   Effect of various molar concentrations of kinetin on the opening of the bean hook in the dark and on those exposed to 1 μw/cm^2 red irradiance (625–700 mμ). IAA curves are also plotted for comparison.

Cobalt

Except for red light, cobalt is the only additive we used that had any appreciable positive effect on the opening of the hypocotyl hook. Figure 4 presents typical cobalt responses. The optimum concentration of cobalt is $10^{-3}M$, both in light and dark. The cobalt effect is essentially additive to the red light effect in the same manner as reported for leaf expansion (Miller, 1952). Our results also indicate that cobalt can counteract the negative responses induced by kinetin, either with or without red light.

Flavinmononucleotide (FMN), IAA and Blue Irradiance

Blue radiant energy alone is relatively ineffective in inducing a photomorphogenic response (Withrow *et al.*, 1957). However, when hooks are presoaked in $10^{-3}M$ FMN for 1 hour and then exposed to blue irradiance, an increased response results; when red radiant energy is used as a treatment, no change is observed. IAA ($10^{-5}M$) produces the normal inhibition of the hook response in the presence of FMN. If FMN-infiltrated hooks are developed in conjunction with IAA and blue radiant energy, an increased response is obtained at the higher energy values. When the control H$_2$O curve values are subtracted from

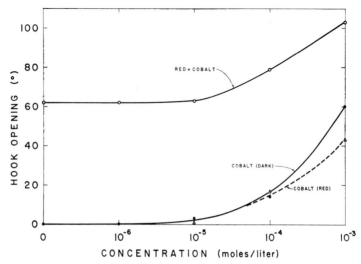

FIG. 4.   Response curves of the hypocotyl hook showing the effect of cobalt in the dark and with exposure to 0.1 μw/cm^2 red irradiance (625–700mμ). Dashed line is the difference curve between cobalt in the dark and cobalt in the red, indicating the additive nature of cobalt to the red reaction.

the FMN curve values, a difference curve is obtained. This curve is almost identical with the difference curve between IAA and IAA + FMN (Figs. 5 and 6), indicating that FMN produces the same response on the hook opening, regardless of the presence or the absence

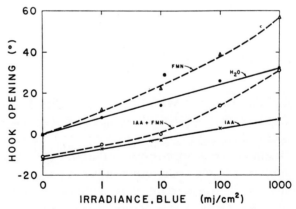

FIG. 5.   Response curves of the hypocotyl hook to blue irradiances with water, FMN (10^{-3}M), IAA (10^{-5}M), and FMN + IAA.

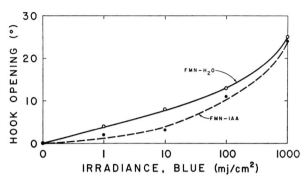

FIG. 6. Graph showing the marked similarity of the difference curves between FMN and water and between FMN + IAA and IAA.

of added IAA. The IAA merely shifts the level of the curve and does not alter its shape, indicating that there is no interaction between FMN and the added IAA. The interaction between FMN, blue irradiance, and the hook opening occurs at relatively high concentrations of FMN ($10^{-3}M$) and at high levels of irradiance.

Discussion

Numerous reports have indicated that gibberellin and kinetin can produce a photomorphogenic response in the absence of light (Miller, 1956; Scott and Liverman, 1956; and Kahn et al., 1957). The biological assay used in most cases consisted of etiolated bean leaf discs or lettuce seeds. In either of these assays, KNO_3 causes an increase in diameter of the leaf discs and increased germination in lettuce seeds (Toole et al., 1956), as compared to a H_2O control. This would indicate that any additive which produces a more nearly optimal condition for growth would act in a positive manner. While the above positive influence does not invalidate the use of seeds and leaves as test objects, it makes more difficult the evaluation of a light effect. On the other hand, the bean hook test has a more specific requirement for light. Indoleacetic acid, gibberellin, and kinetin all produce a negative curvature in darkness and oppose the light response. The outer (convex) cells of the bean hook respond in a manner similar to leaf discs upon addition of growth regulators, but the inner (concave) cells do not respond until application of a light treatment. In general, most of the additives produce a growth response that is kinetically separable from that induced by light. None of them has been capable of substituting for a light treatment in the bean hook test, with the exception of the cobalt ion. Cobalt has the ability to cause the hook to open about 60° at $10^{-3}M$; this effect is additive to a light stimulus and would indicate that two different sites are affected. Cobalt is the only stimulus we have tested which can stimulate, even partially, the response produced by light in the hypocotyl hook of bean.

There is a definite interaction between infiltrated FMN and blue irradiance on the opening of the hypocotyl hook. However, it does not appear to have any relationship to added IAA. Since FMN can absorb the blue radiation and fluorescence in the yellow-green portion of the spectrum, one possible explanation for the added response induced by the presence of FMN is that the yellow fluorescent energy emitted by FMN is reabsorbed by the photomorphogenic pigment. Measurements of the fluorescent energy indicate that the emitted energy is sufficiently high to produce a hook response, and experiments using the fluorescent emission from FMN solutions do cause a considerable hook opening.

SUMMARY

1. The opening of the excised hypocotyl hook of bean is brought about by the stimulation of cell elongation on the inside (concave) of the hook and not by cell division, since no mitotic stages have been detected in any prepared slides. The elongation is proportional to the incident energy.

2. IAA, gibberellin, and kinetin can affect the growth response of the hypocotyl hook in a negative manner, either in the dark or in the presence of red radiant energy. There is no evidence to indicate any interaction between red radiant energy and the added substances.

3. Cobalt at $10^{-3}M$ is the only additive found that can induce a hook opening in the dark to an appreciable degree. This effect of cobalt is additive to the red light response and the magnitudes of the responses are not comparable. It appears to cause hook opening via some other pathway than the photoreaction. The maximum response induced by the optimum concentration ($10^{-3}M$) of cobalt is only about 60°, whereas red radiant energy can produce about three times this response.

4. Hooks infiltrated with $10^{-3}M$ FMN interact with blue radiant

energy to produce a greater hook opening than noninfiltrated hooks. There is no interaction between added IAA and FMN stimulation with blue irradiance.

REFERENCES

Kahn, A., J. A. Goss, and D. E. Smith. 1957. Effect of gibberellin on germination of lettuce seed. *Science, 125,* 645–46.

Klein, W. H., R. B. Withrow, and V. B. Elstad. 1956. Response of the hypocotyl hook of bean seedlings to radiant energy and other factors. *Plant Physiol., 31,* 289–94.

Miller, C. O. 1952. Relationship of the cobalt and light effects on expansion of etiolated bean leaf disks. *Plant Physiol., 27,* 408–12.

———. 1956. Similarity of some kinetin and red light effects. *Plant Physiol., 31,* 318–19.

Scott, R. A., Jr., and J. L. Liverman. 1956. Promotion of leaf expansion by kinetin and benzylamino-purine. *Plant Physiol., 31,* 321–22.

Toole, E. H., S. B. Hendricks, H. A. Borthwick, and V. K. Toole. 1956. Physiology of seed germination. *Ann. Rev. Plant Physiol., 7,* 299–324.

Withrow, R. B., W. H. Klein, and V. B. Elstad. 1957. Action spectra of photomorphogenic induction and its photoinactivation. *Plant Physiol., 32,* 453–62.

CONTROL OF STEM GROWTH BY LIGHT AND GIBBERELLIC ACID

JAMES A. LOCKHART
Kerckhoff Laboratories of Biology, California Institute of Technology,
Pasadena, California

It has already been reported that application of gibberellic acid reverses the low-intensity light inhibition of pea stem growth (Lockhart, 1956). Similar results have been obtained by Vlitos and Mendt (1957) with light of higher intensities for the green and blue as well as the red region of the spectrum. Lona and Bocchi (1956) have also shown that application of gibberellic acid reverses the red light inhibition of light-grown *Cosmos*.

The effect of gibberellic acid on the light inhibition of stem growth has now been examined in several additional species. In all cases (with one important exception), a marked interaction between light and gibberellic acid has been found (Fig. 1). *Pisum sativum* and *Helianthus annuus* show an essentially complete reversal of light inhibition at both low (60 ergs $\cdot$ cm^{-2} $\cdot$ sec^{-1}) and relatively high (2000 ergs $\cdot$ cm^{-2} $\cdot$ sec^{-1}) light intensities. This is true for both blue and red radiation.

Cucurbita pepo (Dark Green Zucchini) and *Cucumis sativus* (National Pickling) are very sensitive to light. Thus, in the case of *Cucurbita*, maximum inhibition (ca. 50%) is induced by even the low-intensity red light. *Cucumis* is also markedly inhibited by the low-intensity light and even further inhibited by the high-intensity radiation. Application of gibberellic acid usually causes only partial reversal of the light inhibition of stem growth in these species. It is interesting to note that in those species in which the gibberellic acid is fully effective, the optimum dose is approximately 0.04–0.4 μg/plant, whereas in *Cucurbita* and *Cucumis* a dose of 4.0–10.0 μg/plant is required for maximum response. In the latter species gibberellic acid

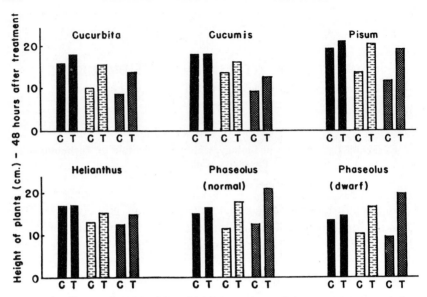

FIG. 1.　Interaction of gibberellic acid and red light on stem growth in several species. The effect on species grown in darkness (black bars); low intensity red light (light shading); high-intensity red light (darker shading). T, gibberellic acid treatments; C, untreated controls.

may differ sufficiently from the natural gibberellin to make it physiologically less effective (cf. Phinney *et al.,* 1957).

In the case of *Phaseolus vulgaris,* application of gibberellic acid reverses the light inhibition of stem growth and, in light, elicits a growth which is much greater than that characteristic of dark-grown plants (either of control or of gibberellic acid-treated plants). It has been established that this promotion of growth by light (in the presence of added gibberellic acid) is a red light response, which may be fully reversed by subsequent irradiation in the far red (Fig. 2). If the far-red radiation is not given immediately after the red, but is delayed several hours, then the growth promotion is proportional to the time the pigment remains in the far-red-absorbing (red light-induced) form (Table I).

Dwarf and pole beans respond to gibberellic acid application in an apparently identical manner. Neither responds in darkness. Both respond to the application if also supplied with light, either as brief exposures to red radiation or to greenhouse conditions with bright sun-

FIG. 2.   The response of dark-grown *Phaseolus vulgaris* seedlings to red and far-red radiation and to gibberellic acid. From left to right: Darkness, untreated; darkness, gibberellic acid treated; red light, no gibberellic; red light, gibberellic acid; red followed by far red, no gibberellic acid; red followed by far red, gibberellic acid. Two days after treatment.

light. The absence of a response to gibberellic acid in dwarf beans grown in darkness is unique among the dwarfs so far examined. This result might be interpreted as suggesting that the beans are dwarfed only in light. The growth of these plants in darkness, then, would be identical with that of the "normals" and limited only by the red light factor. The natural gibberellin in the dwarfs, however, would be more sensitive to "destruction" by light.

TABLE I.   Effect of Proportion of Time Red-Far Red Pigment Is Present in Far-Red-Absorbing Form on Growth Response of *Phaseolus vulgaris*, Variety Black Valentine to Gibberellic Acid Treatment (4.0 µg/Plant) (Light treatments repeated daily)

| | Height of Plants, cm | | Treated Minus Control Values, cm |
	Control	Gibberellic Acid-Treated	
Dark	19.4 ± 0.62	24.4 ± 0.64	5.0
Red	23.8 ± 0.37	33.3 ± 0.44	9.5
Red + far red (immediately)	23.9 ± 0.48	27.8 ± 0.62	3.9
Red + far red (after 6 hr)	24.0 ± 0.31	29.9 ± 0.46	5.9
Red + far red (after 24 hr)	24.1 ± 0.29	32.5 ± 0.79	8.4

Mohr (1957) has recently distinguished between a low-energy (red and far-red) inhibition and a high-energy (blue and red) inhibition of stem elongation. He found that stem growth of *Sinapis alba* is not inhibited by brief exposures to red light, but after long exposures to relatively high-intensity light, inhibition of stem elongation is clear, but both with red and with blue radiation. In the present experiments it was found that the application of gibberellic acid (4.0 μg/plant) to this species does not reverse the inhibition of stem elongation by light. It should be noted that in all other plants studied, the high-energy inhibition of stem growth is partially or completely reversed by gibberellic acid treatment.

The gibberellic acid-induced reversal of light inhibition may be most readily demonstrated by comparison of the responses of plants grown in continuous light and of those grown in complete darkness. Growth inhibition is much less pronounced in the case of plants given intermittent light exposures owing, in part, to compensatory growth. When a plant (e.g., *Pisum*) is given a single exposure to light, an inhibition of growth results. After return of the plant to darkness, however, its growth rate exceeds that of the normal until the height of the light-treated plants is approximately equal to that of the plants which remained in complete darkness (Went, 1941). The compensatory growth phenomenon was originally demonstrated on a variety of dwarf pea (Little Marvel) whose growth has since been found to be promoted by gibberellic acid (in both light and dark). Apparently, then, the growth of this variety is limited in both light and darkness by the endogenous gibberellin. The phenomenon of compensatory growth means that the endogenous gibberellin has not been destroyed by light, but rather it is "saved" for use at a later time. Since the plant can respond to added gibberellic acid even in light (and at almost equally low doses), it appears that the capacity of the plant to respond to and utilize the gibberellin is not impaired in light. Apparently the gibberellin is simply not present in a usable form during irradiation. Some precursor (or alternate product) presumably builds up during irradiation. During the following dark period this material is then converted to the active gibberellin in unusually large amounts. The amount of the precursor should be just sufficient to restore the height of the treated plants to that of the controls.

Application of gibberellic acid reverses the light inhibition of stem elongation in several species of higher plants. One species has been found that shows no response to applied gibberellic acid. It appears that the light inhibition of stem growth in many plants involves a mechanism by which the synthesis of the endogenous gibberellin is temporarily blocked, or diverted to a side product which accumulates. When plants are returned to darkness, this product appears to be converted to active gibberellin. Promotion of stem growth by the red light reaction has been found in *Phaseolus vulgaris*.

REFERENCES

Lockhart, J. A. 1956. Reversal of the light inhibition of pea stem growth by the gibberellins. *Proc. Natl. Acad. Sci. U. S., 42*, 841–48.

Lona, F., and A. Bocchi. 1956. Interferenza dell'acido gibberellico nell'effecto della luce rossa e rosso-estrema sull'allungamento del fusto di *Perilla ocymoides* L. *Ateneo parmense, 27*, 645–49.

Mohr, H. 1957. Der Einfluss monochromatischer Strahlung auf das Langenwachstum des Hypocotyls und auf die Anthocyanbildung bei Keimlingen von *Sinapis alba* L. (= *Brassica alba* Boiss.). *Planta, 49*, 389–405.

Phinney, B. O., C. A. West, M. Ritzel, and P. M. Neeley. 1957. Evidence for "gibberellin-like" substances from flowering plants. *Proc. Natl. Acad. Sci. U. S., 43*, 398–404.

Vlitos, A. J., and W. Mendt. 1957. Interactions between gibberellic acid and the shoot apex of Alaska pea seedlings. *Plant Physiol.* (Suppl.), *32*, xlvii.

Went, F. W. 1941. Effects of light on stem and leaf growth. *Am. J. Botany, 28*, 83–95.

PHYSIOLOGICAL AND MORPHOLOGICAL EFFECTS OF GIBBERELLIC ACID ON EPICOTYL DORMANCY OF TREE PEONY [1]

LELA V. BARTON and **CLYDE CHANDLER**
Boyce Thompson Institute for Plant Research, Inc., Yonkers, New York

Gibberellic acid has been found to promote the growth of dormant epicotyls of tree peony replacing the need for low-temperature pretreatment for the production of green shoots in the greenhouse. Application of 1, 10, or 100 μg to the hypocotyl of the germinated seed before planting in soil caused the emergence of green shoots above ground in 3 weeks or less. Most rapid development of the epicotyl followed treatment with 100 μg gibberellic acid, but more normal growth resulted from the lower dosages. This is the only chemical which has been found to break epicotyl dormancy of tree peony.

Morphological studies have shown that differentiation of epicotyledonary tissues and elongation of the epicotyl axis proceeds slowly in untreated seedlings in soil in the greenhouse. After application of gibberellic acid, however, both differentiation and elongation were rapid, as shown by microscopic examination of sectioned material. Elongation of the epicotyl induced by gibberellic acid or by a period of 8 weeks at 5°C was characteristic of seedlings which were capable of green-shoot production in soil in the greenhouse. Such elongation did not occur in untreated seedlings that failed to produce green shoots. Elongation of the epicotyl axis is due to an increase in cell size and cell number.

[1] Complete paper published in *Contribs. Boyce Thompson Inst.*, *19*, 201–14 (1957).

PHOTOPERIODIC EFFECTS IN WOODY PLANTS: EVIDENCE FOR THE INTERPLAY OF GROWTH-REGULATING SUBSTANCES [1]

J. P. NITSCH and COLETTE NITSCH
Laboratoire du Phytotron, Gif-sur-Yvette (Seine-et-Oise), France

Although the effect on vegetative growth of the relative duration of day and night was recognized early in the history of photoperiodism (Garner and Allard, 1923), the majority of plant physiologists have neglected this aspect somewhat and until recently focused their attention on the flowering phenomenon. Woody plants, that is trees and shrubs which take years to reach the flowering stage, are excellent materials for investigating photoperiodic effects on vegetative growth.

PHOTOPERIODIC CONTROL OF GROWTH AND DORMANCY

If, for example, one divides a lot of actively growing dogwoods (*Cornus florida* L.) into two groups and places one of them under long days of 15 hr or more and the other one under short days of 12 hr or less, one will observe that vegetative growth will continue almost indefinitely under long days, but it will cease rapidly under short days. In the latter case, both the elongation of the stem and the development of new leaves will be arrested; instead of leaves, cataphylls (scales) will be produced, and will enclose the terminal meristems: in short, the plant will become dormant. In the dogwood (Waxman, 1957), in *Platanus occidentalis* L., or in *Rhus typhina* L. (Nitsch, 1957b), stem elongation completely stops after 2 weeks of short days. The onset of dormancy is a complex phenomenon. Part of it is a growth process and, therefore, can be investigated with the techniques which have been developed in the field of plant growth. Such an attempt is pre-

[1] Research supported in part by the National Institutes of Health, Bethesda, Maryland (grant No. RG 4840) and in part by the National Science Foundation (grant No. G 4046).

225

sented in the discussion which follows. It will attempt (1) to define the organ which is responsible for setting the dormancy mechanism into motion, (2) to find a lead pointing toward the kind of substance one should look for, and (3) to present preliminary studies of the fluctuations caused by photoperiodic treatments, in the levels of endogenous auxins and inhibitors.

RECEPTOR ORGAN

In many cases, the receptor organ for the photoperiodic stimulus has been found to be the leaf. Such is the case in the induction of flowering in *Xanthium* (Hamner and Bonner, 1938) and in the control of vegetative growth in *Weigela* (Downs and Borthwick, 1956). The following experiments, taken from the work done in this laboratory by Waxman (1957), show conclusively that the photoperiod regulates the amount of growth produced by terminal or axillary buds through the intermediary of certain well-defined leaves.

Induction of Growth Inhibition through Leaves

Let us consider plants of *Cornus florida* var. *rubra* growing under long days. If we decapitate a vigorously growing branch, the buds existing in the axil of the two top (opposite) leaves will start to develop and produce new shoots (Fig. 1A). If we subject to short days one of the two top leaves, by placing a lightproof envelope over that leaf every day from 5 P.M. until 8 A.M. (starting on the day the decapi-

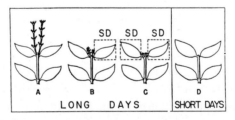

FIG. 1. Decapitated branches of *Cornus florida rubra* kept under long, 18-hr days (A, B, C) or under short, 12-hr days (D). The development of the top axillary shoots is completely prevented when the whole plant is placed under short days and partially prevented when only one or two of the uppermost leaves are subjected to short days (adapted from Waxman, 1957).

tation has been performed), the development of the axillary buds is reduced, the most inhibited bud being the one situated in the axil of·the
shaded leaf (Fig. 1B). If both the two top leaves are given short days,
then the growth of the two axillary buds is more strongly inhibited, although all the rest of the plant continues to receive long days (Fig.
1C). When the whole plant is kept under short days before and after
the operation, decapitation causes no growth whatsoever in the axillary
buds (Fig. 1D). Thus, this first set of experiments shows that the top
young leaves, having reached approximately their full size, are able
to inhibit strongly the development of buds in their axils when they,
alone, are subjected to short days.

Prevention of Growth Inhibition through Leaf Removal

Let us now consider another photoperiodically sensitive plant,
Weigela florida, clone Eva Rathke. This time, we will use plants which
have two equal branches and which have been growing vigorously
under long days. We will divide them into five equal groups. At time
0, we place groups A–E under short, 9-hr days, after having treated
them in the various ways depicted in Fig. 2. For about 2 weeks, there
is some residual growth which we will not consider here, but, after
that time, the effect of the short-day treatment becomes fully visible.
We will measure, therefore, the new growth some 23, 37, and 50 days
after the beginning of the short-day treatment. The plants of group A,
which have all their leaves on, stop growing completely; no stem
elongation and no development of new leaves occur, at least from 23
days on after the beginning of the short-day treatment. On the contrary, the plants of group B from which all the leaves have been
stripped (the newly unfolded leaves being removed as they reach about
three-fourths of their full size), continue to grow, and produce new
stem and new leaves. Plants of group C, in which only the three first
pairs of leaves are kept removed, also continue to grow under short
days, although at a slower rate than the plants of group B. However,
the plants of group D, which had all their leaves removed except the
first pair (not counting leaves less than 1 cm long) stop growing completely under short days, as did those of group A which had all their
leaves on. The above-mentioned results, which confirm those of Downs
and Borthwick (1956), allow the two following conclusions to be

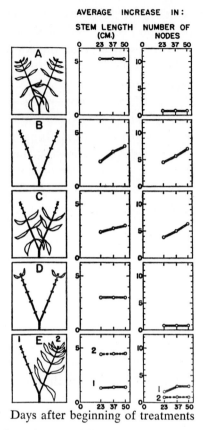

FIG. 2. Effect of various defoliation treatments on the growth of *Weigela florida* plants which have been shifted from long to short days at time 0 (adapted from Waxman, 1957).

drawn: (1) short days stop growth in *Weigela* via a mechanism present in the leaves; when all the leaves are removed, growth continues until the food reserves present in the stem and roots are exhausted; (2) the young leaves, i.e., the ones which have reached from one-half to three-fourths of their final size, are the ones which are most effective in the photoperiodic control of growth and dormancy; the older leaves have a much less pronounced effect.

The experiment done with group E was an attempt to find out if the regulatory principle made in the leaves under short days could be transported from one branch to another. On each plant of group E, one branch was completely defoliated while the other was kept intact. The branch with all the leaves on stopped growing under short days. The defoliated branch produced one more node, then stopped growing also, suggesting that some of the inhibitory principle made in the intact branch was reaching the defoliated one.

NATURE OF GROWTH-REGULATORY PRINCIPLE

The experiments which have just been presented suggest that some growth-regulating principle is formed in the leaves and that its production is controlled photoperiodically. The question is now to find out what type of a principle this may be. Fundamentally, long days favor continuous growth, short days bring growth to a stop. At first sight, one could try to explain this pattern in two different ways: (1) under short days, an inhibitor is produced, which causes growth to stop; or (2) a growth-promoting substance is formed under long days, but not under short days. In order to avoid making too quick a judgment on this alternative, let us examine various bits of evidence pertaining to the general problem of growth and dormancy.

Evidence from Leaf Removal Experiments

The experiments presented under "Receptor Organ" point toward the inhibitor hypothesis. In the case of *Weigela,* it is clear that the *removal* of leaves, under short days, *promotes* growth. The simplest explanation would be to postulate that, under short days, leaves manufacture an inhibitory substance which causes vegetative growth to stop.

Evidence from Rooting Experiments

Horticulturists know from practical experience that cuttings root more readily at certain times of the year than at others. If we make poplar cuttings, for example, on July 10, when the day length is 15 hr at Ithaca, New York, we get 80% rooting after 3 weeks and an average of 5.8 roots per cutting. If we take the same type of cuttings, from the same tree, when the day length is 14, 13, and 12 hr, then we observe that the number of roots per cutting decreases progressively to less than one root per cutting (Fig. 3). In other words, as days become short in the fall, the rooting capacity of the poplar branches decreases.

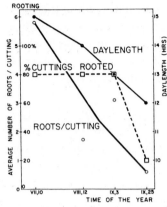

FIG. 3. Rooting behavior of cuttings taken from the same tree (*Populus canadensis* Moench) at various dates between July and September. White circles, average number of roots per cuttings (10 replicates). Squares, percentage of cuttings rooted after 3 weeks. Black circles, daylength at Ithaca, New York.

This phenomenon, which was described by Moshkov and Kocher-zhenko (1939), has been studied in some detail by Waxman (1957), who showed that when cuttings are taken from *Weigela* or *Cornus florida* plants growing under long days and rooted under various photoperiodic treatments, the number of roots produced per cutting is lower under short-day than under long-day treatments (Fig. 4). As a

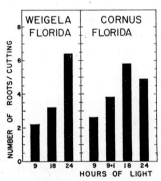

FIG. 4. Number of roots produced after 30 days on similar cuttings of *Weigela florida* and *Cornus florida* subjected to various photoperiodic treatments while rooting. Each figure is the average of 10 measurements. 9 + 1 means: 9-hr day plus one hr of light (25 ft c) in the middle of the dark period (from Waxman's data, 1957).

matter of fact, in the case of *Cornus florida,* a light break of 1 hr of low-intensity, incandescent light, given in the middle of the dark period, increased the number of roots per cutting when compared with a similar short-day treatment with uninterrupted night. In other words, photoperiodic treatments influence the number of roots produced on leafy cuttings.

It is well known (see, for example, Went and Thimann, 1937) that the number of root primordia produced on cuttings is linked to the level of auxins. It has also been demonstrated that factors other than auxin and sometimes grouped under the name "rhizocaline" (Went, 1938) modify the extent of rooting obtained. The fact that photoperiodic treatments influence the formation of adventitious roots suggests that these treatments may change the level of growth substances in the cuttings, whether auxins or rhizocaline. Spiegel (1954) demonstrated the existence of natural rooting inhibitors, however, which opens a different explanation for the results presented in Figs. 3 and 4. Perhaps in these cases also, the results of the photoperiodic treatments may be explained in terms of inhibitors formed under short days.

Effect of Gibberellic Acid

Gibberellic acid has been reported to break dormancy of the buds of *Fagus sylvatica* (Lona and Borghi, 1957) and of various other species in early spring (Marth *et al.,* 1956). Also, it has been shown to replace the cold treatment necessary to break the dormancy of embryos of *Malus arnoldiana* (Barton, 1956). Similar results have been obtained by Nitsch (1957a) in the case of peaches. If peach embryos of the variety Lowell are dissected out of the seed and germinated at room temperature, they give rise to seedlings which remain dwarf, the terminal buds being dormant (Fig. 5, right). If the terminal buds of these seedlings are treated with about 5 μg of gibberellic acid in lanolin, they start to elongate, and the seedlings become undistinguishable from those derived from cold-treated seeds (Fig. 5, left).

Gibberellic acid was also applied to sumac seedlings in the following manner. Plants growing vigorously under long days were divided into four equal groups. At time zero, two of these groups, one treated with 10 μg of gibberellic acid in lanolin, the other untreated, were placed under short days of 10 hr of light; the two other groups, one of them

Fig. 5. Lowell peach seedlings produced by unchilled embryos dissected out of the seeds. Left, plants having received each about 5 μg of gibberellic acid in lanolin. Right, untreated controls. Photographs taken 1 month after the treatment (Nitsch, 1957a).

similarly treated with gibberellic acid, remained under long, 18-hr days. The plants under 18-hr days grew regularly, the ones treated with gibberellic acid growing significantly faster than the untreated ones. Under short days, the untreated group stopped growing completely after 2 weeks, the terminal growing points abscising, which caused a slight diminution in the overall length; the gibberellic acid-

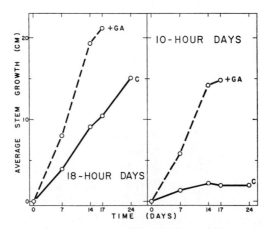

Fig. 6. Average stem growth of *Rhus typhina* seedlings moved at time 0 from long days to long, 18-hr days or to short, 10-hr days. The dotted lines represent the average growth of plants treated with about 10 μg of gibberellic acid at time 0 (Nitsch, 1957b).

treated group, on the contrary, continued to grow as if the dormancy-inducing effect of the short days had been completely overcome. However, the growth rate of the latter group started to decline 2 weeks after the treatment (Fig. 6).

The experiments reported here show that the addition of a growth-promoting substance, gibberellic acid, overcomes, at least temporarily, the growth-inhibiting effect of short days.

Photoperiodic After Effects

It has been shown above that photoperiodic treatments given to cuttings while they are being rooted can influence the number of roots produced. A comparable effect can also be obtained in a slightly different way. Let us divide into 4 groups a lot of poplars growing in pots under 24 hr of light. At various dates, we will move one of these lots to a short-day treatment (10 hr of light), so that, on a given day, lot A will have been exposed to short days for 13 weeks, lot B for 6 weeks, and lot C for 4 weeks, lot D being still under continuous light. On that

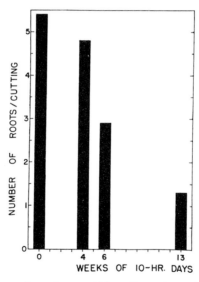

FIG. 7.   Average number of roots (10 replicates) produced after 3 weeks by *Populus canadensis* cuttings rooted under the same photoperiod but which had been taken from stock plants previously subjected to 0, 4, 8, and 13 weeks of short, 10-hr days.

day, 10 similar cuttings will be taken from all the lots and rooted under identical conditions. Figure 7 gives the root counts obtained 3 weeks after the cuttings were made. It shows that, although the cuttings were all rooted under the same conditions, the number of roots produced varied according to the treatments which had been given to the stock plants. In other words, the cuttings "remembered" under which photoperiodic regime they had been before being cut away from the plant. This "after effect" had already been clearly shown by Waxman (1957). One of his data was used in Fig. 8A, which gives the average number of roots produced on cuttings of *Cornus florida rubra* taken from plants which had been subjected previously to the indicated

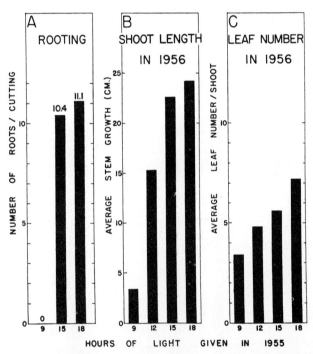

FIG. 8. *Cornus florida rubra.* A: average number of roots produced after 80 days by cuttings rooted under the same 18-hr photoperiod but taken from comparable side shoots of plants maintained previously for 125 days under 9-, 15-, and 18-hr days. Averages of 10 replicates per treatment. B and C, average shoot length (B) and leaf number of (C) produced under a uniform photoperiod in 1956 by large dogwood plants having received the indicated treatments in 1955. Averages of 10 measurements (from Waxman's data, 1957).

photoperiods. These results show that, whatever substances photo-periodic treatments cause to be produced in woody plants, they can be stored in twigs and branches. Are these growth-promoting or growth-inhibiting substances? If we recall Spiegel's work which gives evidence for the existence of rooting inhibitors, then it might be difficult, at this point, to decide whether the substance which regulates rooting in the cited experiments is a growth-promoting or a growth-inhibiting one.

Another experiment by Waxman (1957), however, gave evidence that growth-promoting substances must be formed under long days and stored in stems. A series of large plants of *Cornus florida rubra* were subjected to 9-, 12-, 15- and 18-hr days during the year 1955. In November 1955, the plants from all treatments were placed in the same greenhouse under natural short days and at 5°C. After a while, all the plants dropped their leaves. The low temperature broke the dormancy of the buds in all cases and, in May 1956, when the tem-perature reached a suitable level in the greenhouse, buds started to open. No trace of dormancy remained in the plants which had been grown previously under short days; as a matter of fact, these very plants were the first ones to open their buds. Nevertheless, the average shoot growth produced by short-day plants was far below the growth produced by plants previously subjected to long days. As shown in Fig. 8B,C, the average shoot length of plants subjected to 18-hr days in 1955 was nearly 6 times greater than that of plants previously grown under 9-hr days. Thus, when differences due to varying degrees of dormancy had been erased by the cold treatment, there remained a difference in the amount of growth-promoting material stored in the plants.

In summary, the various examples given in this section point toward the photoperiodically controlled production of factors which some-times inhibit growth, sometimes promote it. To clarify this dilemma, it is necessary to find out what substances are actually produced in the plant as a result of photoperiodic treatments.

PRELIMINARY STUDY OF AUXINS AND INHIBITORS IN PHOTOPERIODICALLY TREATED PLANTS

Ethylacetate extracts of fresh shoot tips of *Cornus florida rubra* grown under long and short days were made by Waxman (1957),

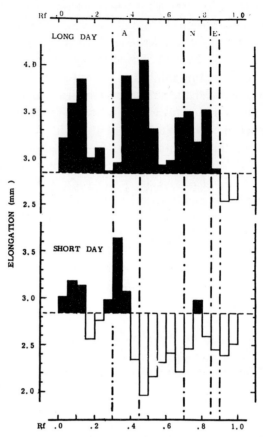

FIG. 9. Histograms giving the biological activity (on coleoptile segments) of 1-cm sections of paper strips. On these strips had been chromatographed the extracts of *Cornus florida rubra* grown under long days (top) and short days (bottom). The black bars represent the average growth (10 replicates each) over the controls (dotted lines), the white bars the average growth below the controls. Extracts: 0.61 and 0.66 g fresh weight, respectively, of tips of branches extracted 5 times at 0°C with ethylacetate. Extracts evaporated to dryness, taken back into ether and chromatographed on Whatman 3MM paper in isopropanol (80) + ammonia (10) + water (10) (V/V). The positions of indoleacetic acid (A), indoleacetonitrile (N), and ethylindoleacetate (E) have been indicated (from Waxman, 1957).

chromatographed in isopropanol (80) + ammonia (10) + water (10) (V/V), and assayed with oat coleoptiles according to Nitsch's method (1955). The results (Fig. 9) showed drastic differences: the extract of long-day plants contained several growth-promoting substances and practically no inhibitory ones, whereas the extract of short-day plants had less auxins and more inhibitors. Thus, it became apparent at once that the story of dormancy might be a complex one, involving *both* an increase in inhibitors and a decrease in growth-promoting substances. However, in the case of Waxman's experiment, the short-day tissues had been taken from plants which had been dormant for 12 weeks and which, therefore, were considerably older than the long-day tissues. A more detailed study was necessary.

A detailed study was made with sumac tissues, in this laboratory also. The sumac seedlings of which the growth behavior has been shown in Fig. 6, were harvested at various times and lyophilized. The upper leaves and the tips were extracted separately. The extracts were chromatographed on paper strips and assayed biologically for growth-regulating substances. Figure 10 gives the results obtained with the first internode bioassay (Nitsch and Nitsch, 1956). This bioassay is very sensitive (one-thousandth of a microgram of indole-3-acetic acid (IAA) produces a significant increase in growth), but responds little to inhibitors. Consequently, the results given in Fig. 10 reflect changes in the level of growth-promoting substances of the auxin type without giving much information about the inhibitor picture. As shown on the left part of Fig. 10, the tips of plants grown under long days contain a growth-promoting substance which moves to the same Rf position as IAA. After 1 week of short days, when the growth rate is declining (Fig. 6), there is still a large amount of this substance in the tips, an amount slightly larger, on a concentration basis, but slightly smaller, on a per plant basis, than that of long-day seedlings (Table I). After 2 weeks of short days, the level of growth-promoting substances drops. At that time, the growth of the sumac seedlings has stopped completely (Fig. 6). A first result of this investigation is, therefore, the observation that as the length of the short-day treatment increases, the level of growth-promoting substances decreases. However, from the results presented here, it is not possible to determine whether the lowering of the auxin level is a cause or a consequence of the decreased growth rate produced by short days.

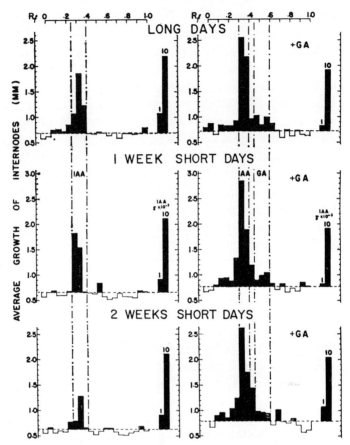

FIG. 10. Histograms corresponding to tips of the *Rhus typhina* plants used in the experiment of Fig. 6. Methanol extracts of 25 mg dry weight in each case. Chromatography on 3 MM Whatman paper strips in iso-propanol (80) + ammonia (1) + water (19). Assay: oat first internodes. Left, controls. Right, plants treated with about 10 μg of GA. The positions of IAA and GA on the chromatograms have been indicated, as well as the amount of growth obtained with 1 and 10 thousandths of a microgram of IAA.

As was shown in Fig. 6, when 10 μg of gibberellic acid was applied to sumac tips, the growth rate of the plants increased under both long and short days. The tips (including all the unfolded leaves) of these plants were lyophilized, extracted, and chromatographed as previously. The first internode test showed that the level of the auxin which

TABLE I.   Quantitative Changes in Amount of Endogenous IAA (?)[a] Caused by Photoperiodic and Gibberellic Acid Treatments

	Endogenous IAA (?)[a] in $\mu g \times 10^{-3}$	
	Per 100 mg Dry Weight	Per Plant
In tips (+ unfolded leaves) of sumac		
Controls		
Continuous long days	17.5	36.4
After 1 week of short days	22.8	18.2
After 2 weeks of short days	6.6	8.6
Treated with GA (10 μg/plant)		
Long days: 1 week after GA treatment	110.0	39.6
After 1 week of short days, 1 week after GA treatment	171.2	109.6
After 2 weeks of short days, 2 weeks after GA treatment	75.8	62.0
In tips (above the first two true leaves) of dwarf red kidney bean seedlings:		
Controls	54.0	3.9
Two days after GA treatment (5 μg/plant)	573.0	49.9

[a] Auxin moving to the IAA position when chromatographed in isopropanol (80) + ammonia (1) + water (19) (V/V).

chromatographs at the IAA position had increased markedly (Fig. 10). A large increase in the concentration of this auxin was found 7 days after the application of gibberellic acid (GA), even though the plants were growing under short days. Thus, a second result of this investigation is that gibberellic acid, which increases stem elongation and prevents, at least temporarily, short days from stopping growth, also produces a clear-cut increase in the level of endogenous auxin. As a matter of fact, we have found that only 2 days after the application of gibberellic acid to dwarf kidney bean seedlings, the level of an auxin that chromatographs at the position of indoleacetic acid increases ten fold (Table I). The results may help, possibly, to understand the mode of action of gibberellic acid.

In short, the experiments summarized in Fig. 10 show that, whenever growth is kept active, either by means of long days or with gibberellic acid, a relatively high level of endogenous auxins can be found. As far as the photoperiodic mechanism is concerned, however, this is not the entire story. If we use a test which detects inhibitors, such as the oat coleoptile test as modified by Nitsch and Nitsch (1956), then we obtain the results of Fig. 11. The pattern detected previously with the first internode test holds true here, since the level of auxins is found to decrease sharply after 2 weeks of short days and

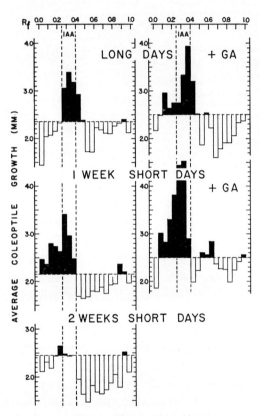

FIG. 11.   Histograms similar to those of Fig. 10 except that coleoptiles were used instead of first internodes. Left, controls. Right, plants treated with about 10 μg of GA (from Nitsch 1957b).

to increase after the treatment with gibberellic acid. In addition, however, one can see on the left side of Fig. 11 that under short days a growth-inhibitory zone increases in size and intensity between Rf's 4.0 and 9.0. Indeed, after 2 weeks of short days, the sumac tips contain more inhibiting than stimulating substances.

SUMMARY AND CONCLUSIONS

In woody plants such as *Cornus florida, Rhus typhina,* long days produce apparently unlimited vegetative growth, whereas short days cause growth to stop completely after about 2 weeks of treatment. The effect of the photoperiodic treatments is mediated through the young leaves, those which have reached one-half to three-fourths of their mature size. The manner in which the photoperiodic regulation of growth is brought about seems to be complex. Experiments in which the removal of leaves produced an increased growth suggested that some inhibitory mechanism is involved in the process. On the other hand, after effects, visible 1 year after the application of photoperiodic treatments and after the destruction of all inhibitory substances through a cold treatment, suggested that some growth-promoting principle (the actual substance or a precursor of it) may be stored in the tissues of long-day-treated plants. The study of growth-regulating substances which can be extracted from stem tips revealed the presence of both growth-promoting and growth-inhibiting substances. Treatments inducing dormancy cause the level of auxins to decrease and that of inhibitors to increase. The application of gibberellic acid, which stimulates growth under both long and short days, also caused a rise in the level of endogenous auxin. Thus, both indirect evidence and actual extraction studies concurred in pointing out that the regulation of vegetative growth of woody plants by photoperiodic treatments involves changes in the levels of both the growth-promoting and the growth-inhibiting substances.

REFERENCES

Barton, L. V. 1956. Growth response of physiological dwarfs of *Malus Arnoldiana.* Sar. to gibberellic acid. *Contribs. Boyce Thompson Inst., 18,* 311–17.

Downs, R. J., and H. A. Borthwick. 1956. Effect of photoperiod upon vegetative growth of *Weigela florida* var. *variegata. Proc. Am. Soc. Hort. Sci., 68,* 518–21.

Garner, W. W., and H. A. Allard. 1923. Further studies in photoperiodism, the response of the plant to relative length of day and night. *J. Agr. Research, 23,* 871–920.

Hamner, K. C., and J. Bonner. 1938. Photoperiodism in relation to hormones as factors in floral initiation and development. *Botan. Gaz., 100,* 388–431.

Lona, F., and R. Borghi. 1957. Germogliazione di gemme di *Fagus sylvatica* L. in periodo di quiescenza invernale, a fotoperiodo breve, per azione dell' acido gibberellico. *Ateneo parmense, 28,* 116–18.

Marth, P. C., W. V. Audia, and J. W. Mitchell. 1956. Effects of gibberellic acid on growth and development of plants of various genera and species. *Botan. Gaz., 118,* 106–11.

Moshkov, B. S., and I. E. Kocherzhenko. 1939. Rooting of woody cuttings as dependent upon photoperiodic condition. *Compt. rend. acad. sci. U.S.S.R., 24,* 392–95.

Nitsch, J. P. 1955. Methods for the investigation of natural auxins and growth inhibitors. *The Chemistry and Mode of Action of Plant Growth Substances.* R. L. Wain and F. Wightman, Editors. Butterworths, London. pp. 3–31.

Nitsch, J. P. 1957a. Photoperiodism in woody plants. *Proc. Am. Soc. Hort. Sci., 70,* 526–44.

Nitsch, J. P. 1957b. Growth responses of woody plants to photoperiodic stimuli. *Proc. Am. Soc. Hort. Sci., 70,* 512–25.

Nitsch, J. P., and C. Nitsch. 1956. Studies on the growth of coleoptile and first internode sections. A new, sensitive, straight-growth test for auxins. *Plant Physiol., 31,* 94–111.

Spiegel, P. 1954. Auxin and inhibitors in canes of *Vitis. Bull Research Council Israel, 4,* 176–83.

Waxman, S. 1957. The development of woody plants as affected by photoperiodic treatments. Ph.D. thesis, Cornell University, Ithaca, New York.

Went, F. W. 1938. Specific factors other than auxin affecting growth and root formation. *Plant Physiol., 13,* 54–80.

Went, F. W., and K. V. Thimann. 1937. *Phytohormones.* Macmillan, New York.

Photoperiodic Control of Reproduction in Plants

THE PHOTOPERIODIC PROCESS

JAMES BONNER
**Division of Biology, California Institute of Technology,
Pasadena, California**

We will in this discussion consider the series of events which characterize the photoperiodic process as it occurs in plants. I wish it to be
understood that I approach this discussion in all humility. A great
many facts about photoperiodism have accumulated since the formulation of the principle by Garner and Allard in 1920. These facts are not
only numerous but complex, and it does not appear to be possible
today to put all of them together into one coherent model. Perhaps it is
impossible for one individual even to remember simultaneously all the
relevant facts. This discussion will be limited principally to the photoperiodic lore relating to the flowering process, to reproduction. The
photoperiodic control of flowering is on the whole inductive, a term
which will be defined below. Photoperiodic control of vegetative
growth, on the contrary, is largely noninductive. A clear distinction
can therefore be made between these two important sets of photoperiodic responses.

Biologists are now aware that plants may be classified with respect
to their responses to relative length of day and night. Thus we have
short-day plants, long-day plants, and day-neutral plants. Day-neutral
plants are those which disregard relative length of day and night and
in which flowering is controlled by other factors, as by age, number of
nodes, and previous history of cold treatment. The flowering behavior
of short-day and long-day plants, on the other hand, is determined by
relative length of day and night. Thus, the short-day plant flowers only
under day lengths shorter than some critical value. The long-day plant,
on the contrary, flowers only under day lengths longer than a critical
value. Actually the two groups might better be referred to as long-night
and short-night plants respectively, since the length of the dark period
is the primary determinative factor in each case (Hamner and Bonner,

1938; Lang and Melchers, 1943). Generally speaking, short-day plants flower when exposed to light-dark cycles containing dark periods longer than the critical value. Long-day plants, on the contrary, flower only when exposed to light-dark cycles containing dark periods shorter than the critical value. Or we may define short-day and long-day plants roughly in still another way based upon their responses to interruptions of a long dark period by a light flash. Short-day plants produce flowers when grown on a regime of long nights, and this flowering is inhibited by a light flash given during the night (Hamner and Bonner, 1938). Long-day plants, on the contrary, do not flower when grown on a regime of long nights, but do flower if this long night is interrupted by a light flash (Katunskij, 1936).

There are special cases, however, for which these generalizations do not hold true. Harder and Gümmer (1947) and Lang (1954), for example, grew short-day, and therefore long-night plants, under conditions in which flowering occurred only if flashes of light were supplied at periodic intervals. This is, however, a special variant of the more general propositions stated above and can be understood in terms of further responses to be described below.

The photoperiodic effectiveness of a dark period, then, may be negated by light, even of very low intensities, and the photochemical characteristics of the process by which this takes place can be determined. A great deal of information about photoperiodism has resulted from such studies (Parker et al., 1946, 1950). This information may be summarized by saying that plants behave as though they contain in the dark a pigment which absorbs red light, thereby negating the photoperiodic effectiveness of a long dark period. By absorption of red light the pigment appears to be converted to a different pigment which absorbs at longer wavelengths, with a peak in the near infrared (Borthwick et al., 1952; Downs, 1956). Thus if a red light treatment is immediately followed by a near infrared treatment, the plant behaves as though it had been maintained in darkness. Photoperiodic behavior is thus mediated in part by what we refer to as the pigment system.

It is of course well known that the leaves of the plant are the perceptors of the radiant energy. Thus if we subject one leaf of the short-day plant *Xanthium* to long nights, the remainder of the leaves being maintained in long-day conditions, the plant flowers in response to the long-night treatment of the single leaf and flowers systemically (Hamner and Bonner, 1938). This also holds true for long-day plants (Knott, 1934). Since it is the bud that flowers in response to photoperiodic treatment of the leaf, it is obvious that there must be some transmission of stimulus between leaf and bud. This stimulus could be either something that promotes flowering and travels from leaf to bud, or something that inhibits flowering, which is normally stored in the bud and which is somehow absorbed by the leaf as the result of photoperiodic treatment. It is now generally assumed that in short-day plants something that promotes flowering is produced by the leaf as the result of appropriate photoperiodic treatment and then travels from leaf to bud. We know some of the characteristics of the transport of this stimulus (Moshkov, 1937; Kuiper and Wiersum, 1936). Thus we know that transport of the flowering stimulus takes place only in living tissue. It may travel either up or down the stem, and it moves in general in the direction of flow of photosynthate, from photosynthesizing leaves to growing, photosynthate-consuming organs (Stout, 1945). For this peripatetic stimulus the name "florigen" was proposed by Cajlachjan in 1936, and this is the term we use today. That the florigen which is produced in long-day plants as the result of exposure of their leaves to long days is physiologically identical with the florigen produced by short-day plants as the result of exposure of their leaves to long nights has been shown by reciprocal grafting experiments summarized by Lang (1952). Thus, if we graft together the long-day plant *Hyoscyamus niger* and the short-day plant Maryland Mammoth Tobacco, and if we keep both plants on long days, the Maryland Mammoth Tobacco flowers in response to something which it receives from the *Hyoscyamus* donor (Lang and Melchers, 1948). Reciprocally, if we keep both partners on short days, the *Hyoscyamus* flowers in response to something which it receives from the Maryland Mammoth Tobacco donor (Melchers and Lang, 1941). Similar grafting experiments have been carried out with the long-day *Callistephus* and the short-day *Xanthium* (Thurlow, 1948).

The photoperiodic response is in a sense a qualitative one in short-day plants. Each bud and each plant is either reproductive or vegetative. And in this sense the photoperiodic response is all or none. But in another sense the response of plants to photoperiodic treatment is a quantitative one, as first shown by experiments of Hamner with soybean (1940). In this experiment soybean plants were removed from long-day conditions and placed in short-day conditions for varying numbers of days, after which they were returned to long-day conditions. After a further time—2 weeks in this case—the plants were classified as to number of flowers formed per plant. The results of this experiment are clear-cut. Number of flowers per plant is a linear function of the number (greater than one) of short-day, long-night cycles to which the plants have been subjected. Similar experiments may be done with the short-day plant *Xanthium,* as has been shown by Lockhart and Hamner (1954) and by Salisbury and Bonner (1955). In the case of *Xanthium* we use as a measure of the extent and effectiveness of photoperiodic treatment the subsequent rate of development of reproductive buds. *Xanthium* plants are grown on long day, treated with one, two, or more short-day, long-night cycles, and returned to long day. After a further period of time the plants are dissected and the stage of development of each bud noted. Rate of development of the reproductive buds of *Xanthium* is a linear function of the number of short days to which the plant has been subjected. Similarly, rate of development of reproductive buds is a linear function of the extent by which the length of the dark period exceeds the critical value, 8.5 hr.

It would appear then that the substances that promote flowering which are produced in one favorable dark period can be accumulated and added to those produced during the next dark period. The effects of successive cycles of photoperiodic treatment are additive. Thus, although induction of flowering of itself is an all or none phenomenon, the effectiveness of photoperiodic treatment as measured by number of flowers or rate of flower bud development is a modulated response, and this modulation persists over weeks or months. Plants treated with a minimum of photoperiodic induction flower slowly over long periods of time (Naylor, 1941). Plants treated with a greater number of cycles or with dark periods of greater length flower rapidly and vigorously over long periods.

The facts described above help us to interpret many details concerning the photoperiodic behavior of plants. Thus, if we give many successive long dark periods to a short-day plant, these dark periods need be only infinitesimally longer than the critical value in order to produce rapid flowering. This is in fact the classical method for determination of the critical night length. If, on the other hand, few dark periods are given to our short-day plant, these must be much longer than the critical value in order to elicit the same flowering response. The amount of flowering stimulus necessary to elicit a rapid rate of flowering may thus be produced all at once during one or a few nights much longer than the critical value, or it may be made little by little during a long succession of dark periods which need then be but little longer than the critical value. It helps us, too, to understand the effects of temperature upon photoperiodic treatment. The critical dark length is changed but little by temperatures as low as 5°C, but the number of short-day, long-night cycles needed to achieve a given level or intensity of flowering is greater, the lower the temperature (Hamner and Bonner, 1938). Evidently the events which determine the critical dark length are not greatly temperature-dependent (Long, 1939). The events which follow the critical dark period and which result in the quantitative aspect of flowering are, on the other hand, apparently highly temperature-dependent. And this fact in turn tells us that we must differentiate sharply between at least two kinds of processes which occur during the long-night treatment of long-night plants. Clearly the temperature-independent processes which are rate-limiting for the first 8.5 hr are different from the temperature-dependent processes that follow.

Now let us consider photoperiodic induction. We select a plant and give it an appropriate photoperiodic treatment. For soybeans of the Biloxi variety, at least two short-day, long-night cycles are required in order to assure subsequent flowering. In the case of *Xanthium, Chenopodium amaranticolor,* and *Pharbitis nil,* but one short-day, long-night cycle is required. In the case of *Hyoscyamus,* a long-day plant, four long-day cycles must be given to the plant in order to assure subsequent flowering. During the photoperiodic treatment, nothing happens in the bud which can be detected even by the most skilled anatomist. But suddenly and some time after the expiration of the photoperiodic treatment, flower bud development begins. In the case of *Xanthium,* the visible changes in the bud which initiate the reproductive state are apparent to the anatomist about 2.5 days after the beginning of the long-night treatment which incited this new pathway of differentiation. By the photoperiodic treatment a chain of events has been set in motion which causes the *Xanthium* plant, say, to remember that it once had one long night. We say then that the plant has been induced.

With many plants induction does not persist for long, and the plant may ultimately revert to a vegetative condition. But with some species and with *Xanthium* in particular induction is very persistent indeed. A classical example is that carried out by Hamner (1938) with *Xanthium*. Young plants were subjected to a few long nights and returned to continuous light, under which they grew, within a year, into small trees. But during the entire year, during this great multiplication of cells and tissues, the cocklebur plants flowered continuously. They "remembered" over an extended period of time that they had once had a few short days. Or again, we may take our induced *Xanthium* plant, return it to long days, and graft it as a graft partner to a vegetative *Xanthium* plant which has been maintained continuously on a long-day regime. The receptor is induced to flower. Something has passed from the induced donor to the vegetative receptor to bring about flowering in the latter. We may now sever the graft union, throw away the donor, and use our indirectly "induced-to-flower" receptor in turn as a graft partner for a second vegetative plant. Our indirectly induced-to-flower donor acts in turn as a donor and brings about flowering in its graft partner. And it has been possible in this way to transmit the flowering impulse with apparently undiminished vigor through as many as five to seven graft transfers (Thurlow, 1948).

How are we to interpret induction—the persisting after effect of photoperiodic treatment? One possibility would be that during the photoperiodic treatment a great deal of flowering stimulus is produced in the induced plant and that this is stored, to leak slowly out over a long period of time. But this interpretation appears an unlikely one in view of the fact that the induced leaves may be cut from the donor plant a few days after induction without apparent diminution in the vigor of induction of the buds of this plant. The hypothesis is made unlikely also by consideration of the great dilution of any material originally produced in the induced leaves in the experiments of Hamner and of Thurlow alluded to above. It appears more probable that some persistent change has taken place in the photoperiodically induced plant—some change which causes the plant to continue the production of those materials which result in flowering. And this changed state, the state which results in persistent flowering after photoperiodic treatment, photoperiodic induction, is known as the induced state.

We can think of photoperiodic induction as a catenary sequence of processes. This catenary sequence has been most studied and most ambitiously (if tentatively) separated into its individual steps in the case of the short-day, long-night plants. This separation has been formulated by the work of many investigators, among whom the names of Hamner, Borthwick, Hendricks, Liverman, Salisbury, Lockhart, and other attendants at this symposium are prominent. And I think that all would agree that we can, for the time being, describe the catenary sequence by the mnemonic HPTHSTI. The letters of this mnemonic stand respectively for: initial high-intensity light reaction, pigment decay, time measuring, hormone synthesis, stabilization, translocation, and induction.

Let us summarize in a few words what is known of each of these factors. The short-day plant, in order to be responsive to a long dark period, must have been subjected to an immediately previous period of high-intensity light, as has been so elegantly shown by Hamner (1940). During this period of high-intensity light, sugars or other photosynthetic products are made which are required for effectiveness of the following dark period (Liverman and Bonner, 1953). And, as appears in the work of Bünning, reported to this symposium, the light during the high-intensity light period must also be such as to maintain the pigment system in the far-red-absorbing form. At the end of the high-intensity light period our plant is placed in darkness. During the first 2 to 3 hr of this dark period something happens which we may call "pigment decay." The pigment system is in the far-red-absorbing form at the end of the light period. In the dark it transforms thermally and spontaneously to the red-absorbing form, as is indicated by experiments of Salisbury and Bonner (1956) and of Lockhart (1956). After the completion of pigment decay the time-measuring process starts measuring time and ticks off a further 6 hr or so—measures the length of time required to attain the total critical dark length of 8.5 hr. The time-measuring process may very well be the temperature-independent critical night-length-determining process which we have mentioned earlier. Pigment decay and time measuring having been consummated, the processes which we know as hormone synthesis begin. These are the processes which we know by virtue of the proportionality between number of flowers or rate of flowering and amount by which the dark period exceeds the critical value. Hormone synthesis is inhibited by applied auxin in short-day plants (Bonner and Thurlow, 1949), by dinitrophenol, by cyanide, and by other respiratory inhibitors (Salisbury, 1957; Nakayama, 1955). We do not know the nature of the active material which is produced. We do know, however, that during the succeeding light period this material must be stabilized, must be transformed, in the presence of high-intensity light, into a new form with thermal sensitivity different from that of the material produced during the dark (Lockhart and Hamner, 1954). Hormone stabilization in the light having been achieved, the floral stimulus now begins its exit from the leaf: the process of translocation gets underway. It is possible for us to time and determine the characteristics of the translocation of the flowering substance by experiments on defoliation such as those of Lockhart and Hamner (1954), of Salisbury and Bonner (1956), and of Lincoln (1954). Suffice it to say that the translocation of the flowering hormone is a slow process and is not finished until perhaps 20 to 45 or more hr after the end of the dark period. When the flowering stimulus arrives at an actively growing bud, the processes of induction proper get underway (Carr, 1953). These are the processes which lead to differentiation, to the initiation of reproductive growth.

Such are some of the characteristics of the photoperiodic process and of photoperiodic induction. These facts constitute a part of the framework upon which a conference on photoperiodism may build.

REFERENCES

Bonner, J., and J. Thurlow. 1949. Inhibition of photoperiodic induction in *Xanthium* by applied auxin. *Botan. Gaz., 110*, 613–24.
Borthwick, H. A., S. B. Hendricks, and M. W. Parker. 1952. The reaction controlling floral initiation. *Proc. Natl. Acad. Sci. U. S., 38*, 929–34.
Cajlachjan, M. Ch. 1936. New facts in support of the hormonal theory of plant development. *Compt. rend. acad. sci. UR.S.S., 4*, 79–83.

Carr, D. J. 1953. On the nature of photoperiodic induction. II. Photoperiodic treatments of debudded plants. *Physiol. Plantarum, 6,* 680–84.

Downs, R. J. 1956. Photoreversibility of flower initiation. *Plant Physiol., 31,* 279–84.

Garner, W. W., and H. A. Allard. 1920. Effect of relative length of day and night and other factors of the environment on the growth and reproduction in plants. *J. Agr. Research, 18,* 553–606.

Hamner, K. C. 1938. Unpublished, University of Chicago, Illinois.

———. 1940. Interrelation of light and darkness in photoperiodic induction. *Botan. Gaz., 101,* 658–87.

Hamner, K. C., and J. Bonner. 1938. Photoperiodism in relation to hormones as factors in floral initiation and development. *Botan. Gaz., 100,* 388–431.

Harder, R., and G. Gümmer. 1947. Über die untere kritische Tageslänge verschiedener Lichtdunkelrythmen. *Planta, 35,* 88–99.

Katunskij, V. M. 1936. Short periodical illumination as a method of controlling the development of plant organisms. *Compt. rend. acad. sci. U.R.S.S., 3,* 303–304.

Knott, J. E. 1934. Effect of a localized photoperiod on spinach. *Proc. Am. Soc. Hort. Sci., 31,* 152–54.

Kuiper, J., and L. K. Wiersum. 1936. Occurrence and transport of a substance causing flowering in the soybean. *Proc. Kon. Acad. Sci. Amsterdam, 39,* 1114–22.

Lang, A. 1952. Physiology of flowering. *Ann. Rev. Plant Physiol., 3,* 265–306.

———. 1954. Unpublished. University of California, Los Angeles.

Lang, A., and G. Melchers. 1943. Die photoperiodische reaktion von *Hyoscyamus niger. Planta, 33,* 653–702.

Lang, A., and G. Melchers. 1948. Auslösung von Blütenbildung bei Langtagpflanzen unter Kurztztagbedingungen durch Aufpfropfung von Kurztztagpflanzen. *Z. Naturforsch., 3b,* 108.

Lincoln, R. 1954. Unpublished. University of California, Los Angeles.

Liverman, J. L., and J. Bonner. 1953. Biochemistry of the photoperiodic response: the high intensity light reaction. *Botan. Gaz., 115,* 121–28.

Lockhart, J. A. 1956. Unpublished. California Institute of Technology, Pasadena.

Lockhart, J. A., and K. C. Hamner. 1954. Partial reactions in the formation of the floral stimulus in *Xanthium. Plant Physiol., 29,* 509–13.

Long, E. M. 1939. Photoperiodic induction as influenced by environmental factors. *Botan. Gaz., 101,* 168–88.

Melchers, G., and A. Lang. 1941. Weitere untersuchungen zur Frage der Blühhormone. *Biol. Zentr., 61,* 16.

Moshkov, B. S. 1937. Flowering of short day plants under continuous day as a result of grafting. *Bull. Appl. Botany Genet. Plant Breeding, 21A,* (Suppl.) 145–56.

Nakayama, S. 1955. The effects of certain metabolic inhibitors on the dark reaction during photoperiodic treatment. *Botan. Mag. Tokyo, 68,* 61–62.

Naylor, F. L. 1941. Effect of length of induction period on floral development of *Xanthium pensylvanicum. Botan. Gaz., 103,* 146–54.

Parker, M. W., S. B. Hendricks, H. A. Borthwick, and N. J. Scully. 1946. Action spectrum for the photoperiodic control of floral initiation of short day plants. *Botan. Gaz., 108,* 1–26.

Parker, M. W., S. B. Hendricks, and H. A. Borthwick. 1950. Action spectrum for the photoperiodic control of floral initiation of the long day plant Hyoscyamus niger. *Botan. Gaz., 111,* 242–52.

Salisbury, F. B. 1957. Growth regulators and flowering. I. *Plant Physiol., 32:* 600–608.

Salisbury, F. B., and J. Bonner. 1955. Interaction of light and auxin in flowering. *Beitr. Biol. Pflanzen, 31,* 419–30.

———. 1956. The reactions of the photoinductive dark period. *Plant Physiol., 31,* 141–47.

Stout, M. 1945. Translocation of the reproductive stimulus in sugar beets. *Botan. Gaz., 107,* 86–95.

Thurlow, J. 1948. Certain aspects of photoperiodism. Thesis, California Institute of Technology, Pasadena.

DEVELOPMENT OF VEGETATIVE
AND FLORAL BUDS

**RALPH H. WETMORE,[1] ERNEST M. GIFFORD, JR.,[2]
and MARGARET CORNETT GREEN** [3]
**Biological Laboratories, Harvard University, Cambridge,
Massachusetts**

In the higher plants, a bud is defined as an undeveloped state of a
main stem or a branch; it usually has embryonic leaves, some possibly
modified as protective scales. Whether a bud is terminal, axillary, or
adventitious, whether it is in vegetative or flowering phase, its distal
end is characteristically terminated by an apical meristem. This apical
meristem is of unique importance to the plant. It is known, for example, that (1) its component cells are capable of cell division under
favorable conditions, thereby increasing the number of cells comprising it and so adding to the length of the axis concerned; (2) leaf
primordia are produced in regular, orderly sequence from aggregates
of these newly produced cells; aggregates of cells of the apical meristem in or above the axils of these newly formed leaf primordia
become the new bud primordia. The development of buds from these
primordia may be deferred until correlative relations between them
and the apex no longer interfere with their growth; (3) the apical
meristem and the young, derived leaves collectively are effective in
the induction of vascular tissues in the axis proximal to them.

An examination of buds of various plants and in various states of
development shows that differences of pattern occur in their apices.
Stated briefly, a major conclusion is that they are constructed on no
single histological pattern (Wetmore and Wardlaw, 1951). While

[1] This work was supported in part by a grant from the National Science
Foundation to the senior author and Prof. K. V. Thimann.
[2] This work was done while a Merck Senior Postdoctoral Fellow at the Biological Laboratories, Harvard University.
[3] Work on this research was completed while holding a Junior Fellowship
from the Canadian Federation of University Women at Radcliffe College.

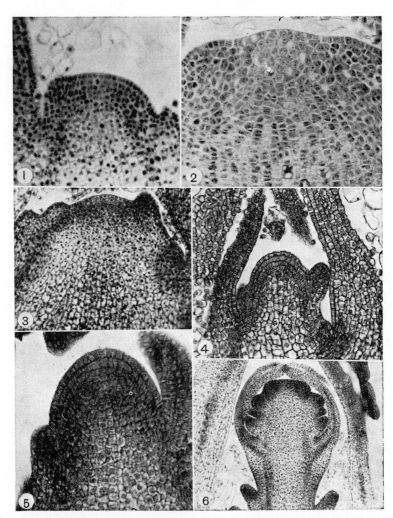

Figs. 1–6.

one may still utilize the term *tunica* to designate the outer layer or layers, with the characteristic anticlinal divisions, and apply the term *corpus* to the remainder, the main body of the apical meristem, with no regular orientation of mitotic figures, these terms are probably only of topographical value. Recent workers tend rather to recognize cytohistological zonation patterns in the apical meristems of angiosperms (Buvat, 1952, 1955; Gifford, 1956; Philipson, 1947, 1949; Popham, 1951), gymnosperms (Camefort, 1956; Foster, 1938, 1941), and even of certain ferns (Steeves, 1951) and lycopods (Freeberg and Wetmore, in preparation). These zones are usually three in number; they have been designated the central zone, the peripheral zone, and the pith rib meristem zone (Foster, 1938), irrespective of the variation in their extent and position in different species (Figs. 1–5). Even if we assume a common set of morphogenetic interrelations of zones in which all shoot meristems participate, we fail to find histological uniformity to correlate with this morphogenetic unity.

Recent trends toward recognizing patterns of zonation as possibly significant in the material and energy turn-over in the apex command serious attention. That the cells of the central zone, however distributed, and in whatever patterns, have in common certain characteristics is probably more than coincidence (Figs. 1–5). They habitually are of larger size, are more highly vacuolated, divide less frequently, and often, perhaps characteristically, possess larger nucleoli

---

FIGS. 1–6.   Vegetative and flowering apices.

1. Vegetative apex of *Nicotiana tabacum*. Note central zone with a mitotic metaphase near the top. ×150.

2. Vegetative apex of *Ginkgo biloba*. Note conspicuous cup-shaped central zone of very large, vacuolated cells; mitosis showing near bottom of zone. ×100.

3. Vegetative apex of *Xanthium pensylvanicum*. Note central zone of a layer of cells in the middle of the second row capped by a few conspicuous cells in the top row. ×100.

4. Vegetative apex of *Chenopodium album*. Note less conspicuous V-shaped central zone of about 7 cells each of first two rows, 4 to 5 cells in the third row, and 2 cells in fourth row. ×150.

5. Vegetative apex of seedling *Papaver somniferum*. Note faintly outlined V-shaped central zone of large cells, the outer three layers conspicuously in rows, the peak of the V less conspicuously so. ×200.

6. Flowering apex of *P. somniferum*. Note absence of central zone at top of apex. ×50.

than the component cells of the peripheral zone and the pith rib mother cell zone. If one follows the fundamental belief that, given the same heritage of size initially, larger cells are larger because they have grown more, and that such increased growth implies a greater net availability of growth hormones at the time of growth, then one has to admit that the cellular environment of these central cells must be different from that of the enveloping cells of the peripheral zone. It may well be true that the conditions which foster frequent cell divisions in the peripheral zones are different from those which produce only occasional cell divisions in the central zone (Figs. 1, 2), and even these occasional divisions are more frequent on the margins of the central zone than in the middle. In fact, it is not improbable that these two situations are related causally. As far as the authors know, no one yet has been able to devise methods which have given answers to the problems suggested here at the level at which the plant resolves them. We believe such methods may yet be devised.

Some facts have proved suggestive. Histochemical tests for oxidases and dehydrogenases give indication of greater amounts of both in the mitochondria of the cells of the central zone over those in the peripheral or pith rib meristem zones. Janus Green B, as found effective by Sorokin (1938, 1941, 1955a,b, 1956a,b), was used on longitudinal sections of the apex. The bluish stain was especially prominent in the central zones of sections immersed in well-oxygenated isotonic sugar solutions. Also sections placed in a similar sugar solution with 0.002% neotetrazolium chloride (Nutritional Biochemicals Corp.) (Sorokin, 1956b) and contained in a chamber through which purified nitrogen was passed by bubbling it through the solution overnight gave indication of more reddish granules of diformazan in the mitochondria of the central region than in those in the cells of the peripheral region or the pith rib meristem region. Even when the results can be duplicated, these tests are certainly no more than somewhat qualitative and therefore unsatisfying. At present one can record only a working idea and not a conviction. Other techniques must be brought into effective use before anything more than a suspicion of contrastive metabolic activity can be recognized between the central cells and their peripheral and subjacent counterparts.

Perhaps the most suggestive results so far recorded in this connection are those of Robert Brown and his co-workers. In the past two years, they have made comparative growth studies on the apex of *Lupinus albus* (Sunderland and Brown, 1956). As defined for their studies, the apex included the apical meristem or dome and the first seven nodes and internodes below. Determination of cell numbers, average cell volumes and total volume in the apical dome, the successive leaf primordia and the apical units (e.g., the first apical unit would include the apical meristem or dome and the axis with the first leaf primordium; the second apical unit, the apical dome with that part of the stem bearing the first two leaves; and so on) has enabled them to compare on a cellular level, or at least approach a comparison of, the growth of individual successive primordia with their respective subjacent internodes, that is, growth units. A second study (Sunderland *et al.*, 1956, 1957) has enabled these investigators to get a picture of the concentration of protein and of the related respiration rates in the apical dome, in apical units, in growth units, and in their component parts, the leaf primordia and internodes, the oxygen uptake being determined through the use of minute Cartesian divers. The importance that they attach to their findings can be indicated in their statement (1957, p. 69), "Clearly many of the properties of the system are a consequence of the state established in the first growth unit, and the origin of the differentiation in this unit is a matter of critical importance." The first growth unit consists of the small-celled first leaf primordium and a central portion, which is the initiating stage of the first internode. As the authors indicate (1957, p. 69), "Thus the position in the first primordium is likely to represent the situation in the surface of the system, and the position in the internode is likely to be determined by the cells of the central core." While it is true that the authors take no note of the central zone of the apex as different and distinct from the pith of the first four internodes and of the small-celled pith rib meristem that separates the central zone from the internodal pith below, yet one cannot but be arrested by the findings of the high oxygen uptake reported for the predominantly large-celled region in the first four internodes. In fact, a recent personal communication from Dr. Brown indicates that in *Lupinus* the oxygen uptake in this large-celled middle region is some 20 times as great as that in the small-celled peripheral leaf primordia.

Brown and his co-workers suggest that the higher protein turnover in the large-celled region may conceivably be related to the production of certain mobile substances which are utilized extensively in the synthesis of macromolecules made available to the enveloping, dividing peripheral cells. Although no evidence exists of the similarity in metabolic turnover of the large-celled central zone and the incipient pith of the first four internodes, the results are sufficiently provocative to justify attempts to determine the oxygen uptake of the cells in the central zone of the apical meristem. It is of more than passing note that cells of internodes 5 to 7 show a greatly decreased oxygen uptake from those of internodes 1 to 4.

The suggestive results of our own cytochemical studies find support in the studies of Sunderland, Heyes, and Brown. A more critical statement of their units in terms of the apical organization of *Lupinus,* together with an extension of their studies to other plants, may lead to a better understanding of the organization and metabolic behavior of the apices of vascular plants.

This extended consideration of the vegetative apex has seemed necessary if we are to examine it as that same apex which becomes modified in the production of reproductive devices, whether spore-bearing leaves in the ferns, or cones in the conifers, or flowers in the angiosperms (Figs. 6, 13, 14, 17, 20). Differences of opinion exist (Buvat, 1952, 1955; Gifford, 1956; Grégoire, 1938; Plantefol, 1947, 1951) concerning the interpretation of the dramatic changes in the transformation of angiospermous apices from vegetative to flowering conditions. Is the apex gradually and progressively‹ altered, either anatomically or physiologically or both, with the advent of the reproductive period? Or is it replaced by a derived apex which can produce only inflorescence or floral parts? Grégoire (1938) has hypothesized a complete replacement of the vegetative apex with a reorganized terminal portion having a "massif parenchymateux," or a massive central core, covered by a few-celled "manchon méristématique," or mantle, of small, actively dividing cells from which the floral organs arise as well as those of the underlying core. To Grégoire, the vegetative and floral apices were "irreducible types" of morphological organization. More recently Plantefol (1947), Buvat (1952, 1955), and their co-workers have fostered the Grégoire concept and have given it substance by suggesting that it is the central zone, essentially inactive during the vegetative life of the plant, which gives rise to the reproductive axis, receptacle, and flowers. In their thesis, the peripheral zone plays no persisting part in this rebuilding.

In the studies reported here, a comparative histological examination was made of the apical regions of three short-day and two long-day plants. Collections were made of apices in the vegetative period and at regular intervals throughout the period of transition to flowering during and after photoinduction. We are convinced that it is not necessary to disregard the vegetative apex and invoke a new flowering apex to envision the changes which take place.

METHODS

In our studies, we have utilized the short-day plants *Xanthium pensylvanicum* Wallr., *Chenopodium album* L., and *Glycine max* (L.) Mer., and the long-day plants *Hyoscyamus niger* L., annual form, and *Papaver somniferum* L. For the supply of seeds of all these we are grateful to Dr. Harry Borthwick and the United States Department of Agriculture.

The procedure employed will be described in some détail for *Xanthium;* for the other species, variations in procedure were planned to fit the individual needs in keeping with their long- or short-day habits.

Plants of *Xanthium* were grown in the greenhouse under long-day conditions. Before induction was initiated, vegetative apices were killed and fixed for the histological preparation of microscopic slides. A large number of plants were then placed in a light room on an 8-hr day, 16-hr night schedule. After one photocycle, apices were killed and fixed from two plants, and a number of plants were returned to the greenhouse with long-day illumination. Collections for histological study were made from apices of these plants every other day. After two photocycles in the light room, more plants were moved to the same greenhouse conditions, two terminal regions collected at once for histological study, and two every other day thereafter until the plants were recognizably flowering. On each succeeding day, the same procedure was followed until the seventh day, when even casual inspection indicated that all apices of plants in the light room were of flowering nature. The experiment in the light room was then terminated.

Histological preparations representative of photoinduction with the subsequent changes in the apices with the onset of flowering have been followed in the species listed. Only the changes in *Xanthium pensylvanicum* will be considered in detail. Others will be dealt with in a broad way, as differences reflect essentially only individual differences in the organization of the vegetative apex and not in fundamental changes during flowering.

RESULTS

In Fig. 3, a vegetative apex shows a section of a caplike zone of central cells in the second row, the outer row of the corpus, usually 6 to 9 cells in diameter.[4] Overlying it, the tunica shows a section of a cap, often fewer (5 to 7) cells in diameter. Because of cytological similarities, these can, for the present, be considered as part of the central zone. Flanking the central zone, and therefore completely surrounding it circumferentially, is the small-celled peripheral zone. Beneath it, and merging laterally with the peripheral zone, is the subjacent rib meristem zone, below which lie the radiating rows of pith cells. Between the central zone and the rib meristem zone is a flat zone, only a few cells in thickness, in which, as will be pointed out, demonstrable activity preceding flowering, after induction, is initiated. Sections of leaf primordia are evident on the flanks of the apex.

Apices of plants with one short day before being brought back to long days in the greenhouse showed no recognizable histological change until the fourth day. In Figs. 7 and 8, sections of a 4-day and a 6-day apex, one can recognize considerable increase in the number of cells below the central zone and above the rib meristem, a result

---

[4] The description that we give to the vegetative apex of *Xanthium pensylvanicum* results from our own studies; it is, however, in accord with the excellent, detailed and well-illustrated study of the vegetative apex of this species given recently by Millington and Fisk (1956). The subsequent account of the transition from the vegetative to the flowering apex which the authors present in this paper is also in agreement with the corresponding study by Millington (1951). We are grateful for access to this information, some of it unpublished.

of mitotic activity, as the first sign in an effect of the single photoperiod, so that the initiation of ribs or files of cells of the pith can now be seen to be separated from the latter by several rows of cells where only three or four rows were previously present. Though they are not easily visible here, numerous mitotic figures can be seen in practically every section. At least 3 were present in Fig. 8. It should be pointed out that this first sign of induction by photoperiodic treatment was found in every species of plant studied, whether long-day or short-day type.

In Fig. 9, with 1 short day of photoperiodic treatment and 8 subsequent days in the greenhouse, more extensive multiplication of cells in the subcentral cell zone is evident. Generally, too, the apex is beginning to show this increase in cells by appearing more extensively mounded. It must be pointed out that the cells in this region of mitotic activity soon begin a period of cell enlargement as do those of the rib meristem region below, thereby giving definite extension to the pith of the newly forming flower and inflorescence axis.

In Fig. 10, after 10 days in the greenhouse, the inception of a flowering apex is well advanced. Much has happened in the last 2 days. As mentioned, the multiplication of cells below the central region has continued, but so has the collateral process of cell enlargement with the progressive vacuolation of many of these cells, the result being that the top of the pith seems to be close to the region of the central zone. The progressive steps of this change become apparent. The central cells have divided anticlinally, as is indicated by the smaller components; this row has also been extended well down the flanks of the mound by like-appearing cells from recent divisions in the cells of the remaining peripheral part of the flanking meristem, so that the tunica-like second row of cells and even parts of a regular third layer can be followed easily, though the cells are somewhat smaller and less vacuolated than earlier. Anticlinal divisions were present in the section but they are hard to detect at the magnification of Fig. 10.

The next series of four figures, Figs. 11 to 14 inclusive, is of plants which were exposed to two photoperiods before being removed to the greenhouse. Figure 11 is the section of an apex of a lateral bud at the time of removal from the light room. Even at the end of two photo-

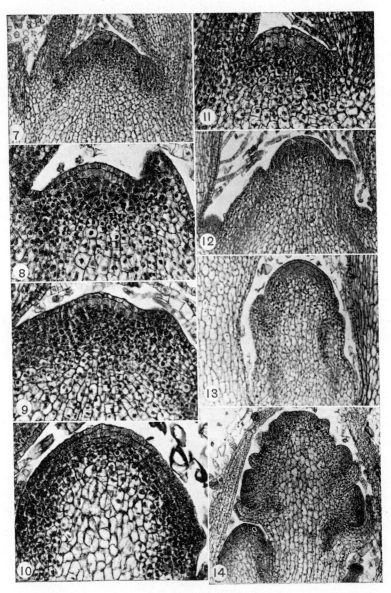

Figs. 7–14.

periods, mitotic activity, as well as the enlargement of some of the recently divided cells, can be seen below the mother cell zone. Also certain cells of the mother cell zone itself show signs of divisions, one cell on the left dividing and others having divided so that the zone appears to be two cells thick. It has not yet shown signs of extension down the flanks of the already somewhat mounded apex. Figure 12, with 2 days in the greenhouse, and Fig. 13 with 6 days, are somewhat comparable to Figs. 9 and 10, though somewhat more mounded. The apex of Fig. 12 was slightly more advanced toward flowering after 2 days in the greenhouse with two photoperiods than the apex of Fig. 9 was after 8 days on one photoperiod. Figure 13 already gives evidence of growth of many of the proliferated subjacent cells with vacuolation causing much mounding of the whole apex. The cap of central zone cells has extended down the flanks, and the larger cells of the zone itself have been cut up to smaller units.

Figure 14 represents a stage of a two-photoperiod plant 8 days after removal from the light room. Here clearly is a young head or inflorescence elaborated, with bracts and axillary flower primordia indicated. Presumably the top florets would have been male; that present on the low left would probably have produced a female flower. As indicated above, histological evidence of floral induction follows after one photoperiod, but it takes 6 to 8 days for its appear-

---

Figs. 7–14.   Apices of *Xanthium pensylvanicum* during induction.

7. Terminal apex 4 days after one photoperiod. ×175.

8. Apex of lateral bud 6 days after one photoperiod. Note increased number of cells below prominent central zone cap in first and second layers. ×175.

9. Terminal apex 8 days after one photoperiod. Even more prominent multiplication of cells between central zone and pith rib meristem. ×155.

10. Terminal apex 10 days after one photoperiod. Note enlargement of cells of region of recent cell multiplication, referred to in 8 and 9, and cutting up by anticlinal divisions of cells of central zone. ×160.

11. Apex of lateral bud at end of two photoperiods. Some mitotic activity below and in central zone. ×160.

12. Terminal apex 2 days after two photoperiods. ×100.

13. Apex of lateral bud 6 days after two photoperiods. Note apex in about same state as 10, 10 days after one photoperiod. ×100.

14. Terminal apex 8 days after two photoperiods. Note flower buds in axils of bracts. ×125.

ance; the same stage was reached at the end of two photoperiods, with no subsequent wait in the greenhouse.

Subsequent photoperiods gave evidence of incipient changes already present in the apex when removed from the light room. Figure 15 shows a transitional stage not pictured in Figs. 7-14, for it is often missed in collections made every second day. This apex had had three photoperiods and 2 days in the greenhouse. Subapical multiplication of cells had taken place as usual, as had the acropetal growth of incipient pith. The flanks of the central zone had extended and precocious enlargement of the peripheral cells had occurred just adaxial to each leaf primordium, in the region of the leaf gaps. Lateral extension of the pithlike parenchyma is at once obvious above and near each leaf primordium as soon as the extension of the pith has occurred acropetally after induction. Moreover, not infrequently did these enlarged cells show mitoses, indicating that both cell division and cell enlargement may take part in this parenchymatization of the peripheral region. In all species studied, this seems to be present as a step in sequential events following the initiation of reproduction. The same picture can be readily recognized in Fig. 18, a section of the apex of a bud 2 days after removal from the light room in which it had been exposed to five photoperiods; this stage was already present in buds of plants at the end of 6 days in the light room (Fig. 19). Buds from similar plants which had had 2 days in the greenhouse in addition show a later stage in the apex (Fig. 20) than found following two photoperiods and 6 days in the greenhouse (Fig. 13) or than after 10 days in the greenhouse subsequent to a single photoperiod (Fig. 10).

When one examines such an apex as is shown in Fig. 14, it seems clear that floral bracts and axillary florets are borne all around the axis. If one considers that bracts are leaves borne at nodes, in the ordinary concept of an inflorescence, then the stem bearing these can be followed, as such, very close to the tip. In other words, almost no apex is left. Across this small portion can be seen no large central cells of the central zone, rather the characteristic small cells of the subdivided central cells which follow induction. It would seem difficult to consider this inflorescence axis or head as other than a short stem, or short shoot, bearing bracts, with axillary florets. As is

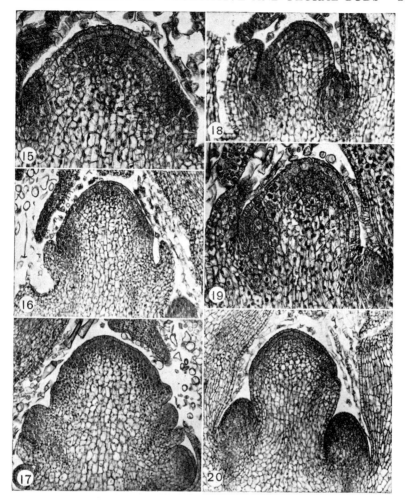

FIGS. 15–20.   Apices of *Xanthium pensylvanicum* during induction.

15. Terminal apex of 2 days after three photoperiods. Compare with Figs. 18, 19; note extension of cell growth into peripheral zones in region of gaps of flower bud primordia. ×150.

16. Terminal apex 4 days after three photoperiods. Compare with 13. ×75.

17. Terminal apex 6 days after three photoperiods. Note flower buds forming in axils of bracts. ×100.

18. Terminal bud 2 days after five photoperiods. ×65.

19. Terminal apex following six photoperiods. ×150.

20. Terminal apex 2 days after six photoperiods. ×75.

well known, the terminal bud gives a head of male florets with the basal ones sometimes female. Lower heads tend to be female.

In another short-day plant, *Chenopodium album,* chosen as possessing a branched inflorescence rather than a head or capitulum, transition to flowering has been followed through the same routine treatment in the same detail as was done in *Xanthium.* A vegetative terminal apex is pictured in Fig. 4. Though not too clear, it can be noted that the central zone embodies not only the first and second layers but also a few cells in the third and fourth layers until the whole resembles almost a letter V in section, or actually something of an inverted cone, the apex of the cone being essentially against the top of the pith rib meristem. The first signs of initiation of flowering, seen histologically, again appear just above the pith rib meristem, involving the bottom of the central zone; these signs take the form of cell multiplication which show up on the second day in the greenhouse under long days after two short-day (8 hr in light and 16 hr in darkness) photoperiods. By the sixth day in the greenhouse, similar plants with two photoperiods possessed essentially the same basic organization as Figs. 14 and 17 indicate for *Xanthium.* Instead of forming a capitulum or head of flowers as does *Xanthium,* in *Chenopodium* the inflorescence axis is more elongate as is characteristic of a developing spiked panicle. The successive changes involve the enlargement of the newly divided cells above the rib meristem extending the pith well up into more mounded apex. The cells of the central zone undergo division, mostly anticlinal, and the regular, even, outer rows can be seen extended well down the flanks of the developing axis of the inflorescence. Bracts and axillary buds, which produce the axes of the branched inflorescence, develop rapidly so that plants subjected to two photoperiods have an entire inflorescence recognizable in bud form by the eighteenth day in the greenhouse, involving even the last of the apical meristem in a terminal flower. When such inflorescences were removed on the sixth day from like plants, and planted *in vitro* on a medium which permits the growth of angiosperm apices, the inflorescences produced flowers that appeared normal in all respects for *Chenopodium album,* shedding pollen and showing a receptive stigma. No attempt was made to pollinate these flowers and no seeds were set.

As with *Xanthium,* so with *Chenopodium,* it would be difficult to state with Buvat (1952, 1955) that the central zone, which has become active mitotically, is responsible for the formation of the bracts, branches of the inflorescence, and the resulting flowers. Rather, mitotic activity appears to begin in that group of cells just beneath the central zone or just distal to the pith rib meristem, and ultimately involves the whole apex which becomes transformed into a condensed stem tip or short shoot. Certainly the peripheral meristem continues to be the active peripheral region which gives rise to appendages, both bracts and axillary buds; these early appear spaced on the axis of the inflorescence.

Papaver somniferum is a long-day plant. Whereas *Xanthium,* when flowering, produces a head and *Chenopodium* illustrates a branching inflorescence, *Papaver* has the whole axis closed by a single flower (Fig. 6). The transition to flowering is little different from that in *Xanthium* or *Chenopodium.* The central zone, like that in *Chenopodium,* is a kind of cone, somewhat V-shaped in section; it can be recognized in Fig. 5 as about 8 cells in diameter in the tunica region. This central zone has entirely disappeared before or concomitant with the development of the single flower.

Although this investigation has included the changes in the apical region accompanying flowering in the soy bean, *Glycine max,* a short-day plant, and in the annual form of *Hyoscyamus niger,* a much studied long-day plant, we need only state in this brief account that little more information was added by including these two species. The story of either of these apices as modified in flowering is essentially the story for the other, and neither is fundamentally different from that of *Chenopodium,* except as related to individual differences in development of inflorescences.

DISCUSSION

To the authors, it seems impossible to follow Grégoire (1938) in the belief that irreducible differences exist between the vegetative and the flowering apex. Philipson in a series of papers, ending in two summaries (1947, 1949), points out (1949) that "the constitutional tendency of the vegetative apex is to produce growth in length of an axis; that of the reproductive axis is to produce a meristematic surface from which the floral organs may develop, the meristem being carried on a parenchymatous support." In his discussion, he notes "that the zonation of the meristem in the inflorescence rudiment of *Bellis* and *Succisa* is derived from that of the vegetative apex by suppression of the central initial zone, its place being taken by an extension of the peripheral zone." That this gradual and progressive change of the vegetative apex to a flowering apex is a common phenomenon following floral induction in various angiosperms (Popham and Chang in *Chrysanthemum,* 1952; Boke in *Vinca,* 1947; Rauh and Reznik in nine different species, 1951) proves to be true in the present study for at least those short-day (*Xanthium pensylvanicum, Chenopodium album,* and *Glycine max*) and long-day plants (*Papaver somniferum* and *Hyoscyamus niger*) studied. In these species, although individual variations occur in the timing of response, the orderly sequence of demonstrable histogenic changes are essentially the same. The initial observable effect found in the five species studied proved to be mitotic activity just below the central zone and above the rib meristem zone. Gradually, this activity spread into the central cells, irrespective of the pattern of the central zone, so that the peripheral zone of small, more or less isodiametric cells now had added to it progressively the whole region distal to the pith rib meristem zone. This set of descriptive changes is followed by a cessation of mitotic activity and an increase in size of all cells of the pith rib meristem, the newly formed parenchymatous region below the former central zone region, and laterally into the regions above all newly forming primordia. Thereby seemingly the apex becomes a parenchymatous core of pith covered with a thin mantle of meristematic cells from which arise the bracts, the axillary branches of the inflorescence, and the flowers as required genetically for each of the several species. The apex has ceased extension in species developing floral heads or single flowers and has slowed down any increase in length of axis even in forms with limited inflorescences such as *Chenopodium* and *Hyoscyamus.* What happens in rapidly growing inflorescences such as *Agave* or the Talipot palm (*Corypha umbraculifera*) is unknown.

It is clear that the changes just dealt with are descriptive and histological only; even so, they must represent fundamental morphogenetic modifications involving physiological and biochemical processes. As Popham and Chang (1952) point out, dominance of the apex disappears, for lateral flower buds and even inflorescence branches are no longer correlatively inhibited, as were lateral buds, by the vegetative apex. Moreover, if it is found that the central zone plays a significant part in the biochemical division of labor of the vegetative apex, then certainly the change in nature of the cellular components of this zone must imply a change in their function. Unless this loss is compensated elsewhere, it may well prove true that the loss of capacity for growth in length, the shift to the production of reproductive axes instead of vegetative buds, and the loss of apical dominance are concomitants of the change in visible structural pattern. Presumably the effects of the leaf-produced "flowering hormone" must include the initiation and promotion of these histogenic changes.

SUMMARY

In this investigation, the significant aspects of the inception of flowering by photoperiodic induction must include the following assertions:

1. The chain of events is repeated alike in short-day and long-day plants. Whatever the inducing agent (or agents), it seems to be capable of bringing about the same results in the different plants investigated. The sample is small, but noteworthy.

2. The zonation of the apex is affected similarly in all plants studied. The central zone, envisioned by Buvat as the source of the meristems from which arise inflorescences and flowers, cannot be so interpreted in its changes by the present investigators. Rather, the entire apical meristem becomes involved ultimately as floral induction proceeds, more and more of the peripheral region of the apex producing floral leaves in single flowers or developing into an axis and bearing bracts and floral buds in inflorescences.

3. The elimination of a central zone and whatever biochemical functions may be associated with it in the metabolic economy of the apex undoubtedly is correlated with the fundamental set of changes set into action by floral induction. The act of flowering therefore must have as associated physiological changes at least the limitation of growth of the apex, a changing phyllotaxy and loss of apical domi-

nance. It would seem that a very different distribution of energy expenditure is called for. Each flower, single or collective, is on an axis in which no elongation takes place, resulting in a short shoot. Moreover, the leaves of the flower—the floral parts—have an entirely different order of development from vegetative leaves. Auxin and other growth-controlling substances must be greatly changed quantitatively, if not qualitatively, under floral induction, for the characteristics of growth expression are startlingly different both in pattern and in extent.

REFERENCES

Boke, Norman H. 1947. Development of the adult shoot apex and floral initiation in *Vinca rosea* L. *Am. J. Botany, 34,* 433–39.

Buvat, R. 1952. Structure, évolution et fonctionnement du méristème apical de quelques Dicotylédones. *Ann. sci. nat., botan., 11ᵉ sér. 13,* 199–300.

———. 1955. Le méristème apical de la tige. *Ann. Biol., 31,* 595–656.

Camefort, H. 1956. Étude de la structure du point végétatif et des variations phyllotaxiques chez quelques Gymnospermes. *Ann. sci. nat., botan., 11ᵉ sér. 17,* 1–185.

Foster, A. S. 1938. Structure and growth of the shoot apex in *Ginkgo biloba*. *Bull. Torrey Botan. Club, 65,* 531–56.

———. 1941. Comparative studies on the structure of the shoot apex in seed plants. *Bull. Torrey Botan. Club, 68,* 339–50.

Freeberg, J. A., and R. H. Wetmore. 1958. Developmental patterns in the Lycopsida. *Am. J. Botany,* in preparation.

Gifford, E. M., Jr., 1956. The shoot apex in Angiosperms. *Botan. Rev., 20,* 477–529.

Grégoire, V. 1938. La morphogénèse et l'autonomie morphologique de l'appareil floral. I. Le carpelle. *Cellule, 47,* 287–452.

Millington, W. F. 1951. Shoot development and inflorescence initiation in *Xanthium pensylvanicum* Wallr. Thesis, University of Wisconsin, Madison.

Millington, W. F., and Emma L. Fisk. 1956. Shoot development in *Xanthium pensylvanicum.* I. The vegetative plant. *Am. J. Botany, 43,* 655–65.

Philipson, W. R. 1947. Apical meristems of leafy and flowering shoots. *J. Linnaean Soc. London, Botany, 53,* 187–93.

———. 1949. The ontogeny of the shoot apex in Dicotyledons. *Biol. Revs. Cambridge Phil. Soc., 24,* 21–50.

Plantefol, L. 1947. Hélices foliaires, point végétatif et stèle chez les Dicotylédones. La notion d'anneau initial. *Rev. gén. botan., 54,* 49–80.

———. 1951. Phyllotaxie et point végétatif. *Scientia,* sér. 6, 45th ann., 91–98.

Popham, R. A. 1951. Principal types of vegetative shoot apex organization in vascular plants. *Ohio J. Sci., 51,* 249–70.

Popham, R. A., and A. P. Chang. 1952. Origin and development of the receptacle of *Chrysanthemum morifolium*. *Am. J. Botany, 39,* 329–39.

Rauh, W., and H. Reznik. 1951. Histogenetische Untersuchungen an Blüten- und Infloreszenachsen. I Teil. Die Histogenese becherförmigen Blüten- und Infloreszenachsen, sowie der Blütenachsen einiger Rosoideen. *Sitzber. heidelberg. Akad. Wiss., Math.—naturw. Kl., 1951,* 139–207.

Sorokin, H. P. 1938. Mitochondria and plastids in living cells of *Allium cepa. Am. J. Botany, 25,* 28–33.

———. 1941. The distinction between mitochondria and plastids in living epidermal cells. *Am. J. Botany, 28,* 476–85.

———. 1955a. Mitochondria and spherosomes in the living epidermal cell. *Am. J. Botany, 42,* 225–31.

———. 1955b. Mitochondria and precipitates of A-type vacuoles in plant cells. *J. Arnold Arboretum, 36,* 293–304.

———. 1956a. Staining of mitochondria with neotetrazolium chloride. *Am. J. Botany, 43,* 183–90.

———. 1956b. Studies on living cells of pea seedlings. I. Survey of vacuolar precipitates, mitochondria, plastids, and spherosomes. *Am. J. Botany, 43,* 787–94.

Steeves, T. A. 1951. Morphogenesis in *Osmunda cinnamomea* L. Thesis, Harvard University, Cambridge, Mass.

Sunderland, N., and R. Brown. 1956. Distribution of growth in the apical region of the shoot *Lupinus albus. J. Exptl. Botany, 7,* 127–45.

Sunderland, N., J. K. Heyes, and R. Brown. 1956. Growth and metabolism in the shoot apex of *Lupinus albus. The Growth of Leaves,* T. L. Milthorpe, Editor. Butterworths, London. Chapter 6, pp. 77–90.

———. 1957. Protein and respiration in the apical region of the shoot of *Lupinus albus. J. Exptl. Botany, 8,* 55–70.

Wetmore, R. H., and C. W. Wardlaw. 1951. Experimental morphogenesis in vascular plants. *Ann. Rev. Plant Physiol., 2,* 269–92.

PHOTOPERIODIC CONTROL OF FLOWERING

H. A. BORTHWICK

Agricultural Research Service, United States Department of Agriculture, Beltsville, Maryland

Plants are responsive to very small differences in photoperiod such as occur in nature from day to day or from one latitude to another. This responsiveness reveals one important feature of the photoperiodic mechanism that regulates flowering: it operates as a graduated control. The extent to which plants are able to detect and respond to small photoperiodic differences is illustrated by a recent experiment with several varieties of soybean (*Glycine max* (L.) Merr.).

In this experiment, performed at Beltsville, Maryland, we attempted to simulate the natural photoperiods of three different localities in Maryland, Virginia, and North Carolina, in which field plantings of soybean were grown. The latitudes of these places are 39°N, 36°40′N, and 34°20′N, respectively. The daily photoperiod, the period from sunrise to sunset plus the parts of the morning and evening twilight during which the light intensity was 2 ft-c or greater, was calculated for each latitude and date. The amounts of twilight included in the photoperiods proved to be 20.9% of the twilight periods listed for the appropriate latitudes and dates in the American Nautical Almanac.

The soybeans were planted in soil boxes on trucks that could be kept outside in the daytime and in dark rooms at night. Incandescent lamps on time switches were used to complete the photoperiods after the trucks were moved inside. The switches were reset at 2-day intervals to maintain the calculated natural changes in day length of the three latitudes. Four plantings of six varieties were made at 2-week intervals beginning May 23.

The mean times of flowering and maturity for all varieties became progressively earlier with decreasing day length (Table I) even though the difference between photoperiods 2 and 1 or 3 for any date was about 17 min near the end of June, and became less as the season

CONTROL OF REPRODUCTION

TABLE I. Mean Developmental Responses of Six Soybean Varieties Planted on Four Different Dates and Subjected to Three Different Photoperiodic Schedules

Planting Date	Period from Planting to Flowering on Indicated Photoperiod, Days[a]			Period from Planting to Pod Maturity on Indicated Photoperiod, Days		
	1	2	3	1	2	3
May 23	62	58	54	146	141	138
June 6	54	50	48	135	132	124
June 20	51	46	44	127	124	118
July 4	45	41	40	119	116	113

[a] Photoperiods were changed at 2-day intervals to simulate the seasonal change in day length at latitudes of 39°N for photoperiod 1, 36°40′N for photoperiod 2, and 34°20′N for photoperiod 3. The calculated photoperiod for each latitude and date included the period from sunrise to sunset as tabulated in the American Nautical Almanac plus 20.9% of the morning and evening twilight periods.

progressed. The photoperiodic control mechanism is thus very sensitive and delicately balanced.

Action Spectra

A discussion of a plant's mechanism for the control of flowering can best start with a summary of information obtained from action spectra (Fig. 1). Action spectra for control of flowering were measured for two short-day plants, cocklebur (*Xanthium pensylvanicum* Wallr.) and soybean (*Glycine max* var. Biloxi) (Parker *et al.*, 1946), and for two long-day ones, barley (*Hordeum vulgare* L.) (Borthwick *et al.*, 1948) and henbane (*Hyoscyamus niger* L.) (Parker *et al.*, 1950). Important features of these action spectra are as follows: (1) They are closely similar from about 5800 A to about 7000 A (Borthwick *et al.*, 1948, 1950); (2) the action of radiant energy of this spectral region is reversed by that of the so-called far-red region, which extends roughly from 7000 to 7600 A (Hendricks and Borthwick, 1955); and (3) they are very similar to the action spectra of a number of other plant responses such as germination of light-sensitive seeds (Borthwick *et al.*, 1952, 1954), elongation of internodes (Downs *et al.*, 1957), and pigmentation of parts of fruits (Piringer and Heinze, 1954).

The region of maximum effectiveness for the so-called red reaction is centered near 6500 A and is broad. Maximum effectiveness for the reverse reaction is centered near 7300 A. The nearness of the peaks of

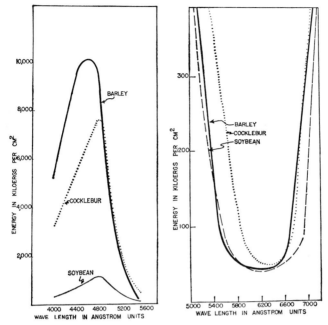

FIG. 1.   Composite action spectra for Wintex barley, cocklebur, and soybean. Left, in "blue-violet" region of spectrum; right, in "red" region of spectrum. Action spectra for short-day plants, cocklebur and soybean, give energy required to suppress floral initiation when applied as a dark-period interruption. Action spectrum for Wintex barley gives energy required to initiate spike development and stem elongation when applied at middle of a 12.5-hr dark period (Borthwick, Hendricks, and Parker, 1948).

activity of these two opposed reactions results in a very rapid change of response with wavelength in a narrow spectral region near 7000 A. This wavelength region of rapid change is identical for the various kinds of plant tested, the apparent differences in the curves not exceeding the errors inherent in measurement of the response.

The principal differences in the action spectra of the four plants listed occur at the blue end of the spectrum. Response to radiant energy in this region was found in soybean and cocklebur, but in barley it was very low, and in henbane it was not clearly detected. Responses of soybean, cocklebur, and barley were at a minimum between 4400 and 4800 A, and they increased again at shorter wavelengths. At 4000 A the effectiveness of radiant energy for soybean was about 15% of that at 6500 A and for cocklebur 1 or 2%.

Repromotion of Flowering by Far Red

Although the action of red on flowering has been reversed in all four plants mentioned as well as in others (Borthwick *et al.*, 1952; Cathey and Borthwick, 1957; Downs, 1956), no detailed action spectrum for the repromotion of flowering by far red is available. The best information is from experiments with cocklebur (Borthwick *et al.*, 1952). The cocklebur plants grew in long dark periods and short photoperiods during the period of treatment. The dark periods except for those of the unirradiated control plants were interrupted near the middle with a brief red irradiance to inhibit flowering. These inhibited plants were then given various brief irradiances with the spectrograph at different wavelengths longer than about 6000 A. Results of such an

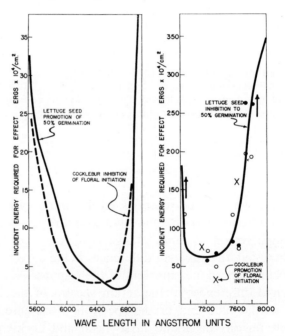

WAVE LENGTH IN ANGSTROM UNITS

Fig. 2. Action spectra for promotion (left) and inhibition (right) of lettuce seed (*Lactuca sativa* var. Grand Rapids) germination and for inhibition (left) and promotion (right) of floral initiation of cocklebur (*Xanthium pensylvanicum*). (From Hendricks and Borthwick, 1955.)

experiment are shown on an action-spectrum curve for the inhibition
of the germination of seed of lettuce (*Lactuca sativa* L. var. Grand
Rapids) (Hendricks and Borthwick, 1955). The various points obtained for repromotion of flowering in cocklebur agree very well with
the curve for inhibition of seed germination (Fig. 2).

Red, Far-Red Reaction in Chrysanthemum

The discovery of reversibility in the controlling reaction of flowering
immediately opened the way to experiments that deal with other
features of this photoreaction and of the responses it controls. Such
studies have been made with a number of different kinds of plants, but
illustrations here are drawn largely from recent work with chrysanthemum (*Chrysanthemum morifolium* Ramat) (Cathey and Borthwick, 1957).

Young chrysanthemum plants grown from cuttings recently rooted
and under photoperiodic conditions inhibitory to flowering were given
an inductive treatment consisting of 8 cycles of 9 hr of high-intensity
light alternating with 15 hr of darkness. Irradiation treatments were
given in the form of brief dark-period interruptions during these 8
cycles. A post-inductive period of 6 more daily cycles of 9 hr of light
gave time for development of flower primordia initiated by the induction treatment. During this 6-day period 4 hr of incandescent-filament
light was given in the middle of each dark period to make sure that
further induction did not occur. The plants were dissected on the
fourteenth day after the start of induction. The results were recorded
as coded numbers identifying the stage of floral development of each
plant; zero represented complete vegetativeness and 10 indicated that
perianth primordia were present on all florets.

Experiments were performed to test the effectiveness of different
energy levels of red light on the inhibition of flowering of chrysanthemums, the light source being a group of 8-foot slimline fluorescent
lamps equipped with a red filter consisting of two layers of red cellophane. In a typical experiment (Table II) the terminals of each of the
unirradiated control plants, which received 8 daily photoperiods of
9 hr, enlarged to form a globular structure, the receptacle of the
inflorescence, that had either no evidence of floret primordia (stage
4) or 1 to 3 rows of them around its lower part (stage 5). In both of

TABLE II. Inhibition of Floral Initiation in Indianapolis Yellow Chrysanthemum by Red Light

Period of Irradiation with Red, Min	Stage[a] of Flowering of 6 Individual Plants						Total for 6 Plants[b]
	1	2	3	4	5	6	
0	5	5	5	4	5	5	29
1/2	3	3	3	2	2	2	15
1	2	2	2	2	2	1	11
2	2	1	1	2	1	2	9
4	0	1	0	0	1	1	3
8	0	0	0	0	0	0	0

[a] See text for description of stages of development.
[b] Called relative stage of floral development in Tables IV to VII.

these stages the involucral bracts of the inflorescence were present, and at the time of dissection they enveloped the receptacle.

Irradiation of plants for half a minute in the middle of each 15-hr dark period with light from the red source reduced flower formation to stage 2 (terminal just starting to become capitate and very few bract primordia present) or stage 3 (terminal clearly capitate and 12 or more bracts present). Complete vegetativeness of all plants (stage 0) resulted from 8-min treatments and almost complete vegetativeness (stage 1, terminal meristem elevated higher than in vegetative plants but not yet starting to become capitate) from 4-min treatments. The effectiveness of light from the red source varied slightly in successive experiments, but usually 4 min was adequate to prevent initiation of flower primordia.

Repromotion of Flowering in Chrysanthemum by Far Red

In a typical experiment flowering of chrysanthemums, which was completely inhibited by 9 min of red light, was repromoted by 1 min of far red (Table III). The far-red source consisted of three 300-watt internal-reflector tungsten-filament lamps mounted about 50 cm apart and about a meter from the plants. Radiant energy from this source was filtered through two layers each of blue and red cellophane. In this particular experiment 3 min of far red had as strong a repromotive effect on flowering as 9 min and only slightly more than 1 min. The flowering stage attained by repromotion with far red was appreciably less advanced than that of the controls in this experiment and in many others done with the same (Table IV) or similar varieties.

TABLE III. Repromotion of Flowering in Indianapolis Yellow Chrysanthemum by Far-Red-Radiant Energy Applied after Inhibition by Red

Period of Irradiation, Min		Stage[a] of Flowering of 6 Individual Plants						Total for 6 Plants[b]
Red	Far Red	1	2	3	4	5	6	
9	0	0	0	0	0	0	0	0
0	0	5	5	3	3	5	3	24
9	1	1	1	1	3	2	3	11
9	3	1	3	3	3	3	3	16
9	9	2	1	2	3	3	3	14

[a] See text for description of stages of development.
[b] Called relative stage of floral development in Tables IV to VII.

In some other chrysanthemum varieties that are normally early flowering it was possible by repromotion with far red to obtain flower primordia that were just as far advanced as those of the unirradiated controls (Table V). Plants of these varieties produced much more advanced floral stages under the same inductive treatments than those of the Indianapolis Yellow (Tables II and III). In the unirradiated lots and in the lots exposed to far red the receptacle was completely covered with florets on many of which the primordia of the individual flower parts were recognizable. The 4-min red treatments, which were highly inhibitory to flowering of Indianapolis Yellow (Table II), were only moderately inhibitory to flowering of most of these varieties; they prevented the production of floret primordia on the receptacle but not the formation of the receptacle itself.

TABLE IV. Repromotion of Floral Initiation in Indianapolis Yellow Chrysanthemum by Far-Red-Radiant Energies Given Immediately after Red

Date of Experiment	Period of Irradiation, Min		Relative Stage of Floral Development[a]		
	Red	Far Red	Dark Control	Red	Red + Far Red
September 7	9	9	24	0	14
September 22	9	9	25	0	20
October 25	9	9	27	0	16
November 14	3	3	29	0	15
December 12	4	4	28	6	18
January 2	4	4	42	14	26

[a] Values are totals for 6 plants. See text for description of stages of development.

TABLE V. Repromotion of Floral Initiation in Several Early-Flowering Varieties of Chrysanthemum by Far Red Given Immediately after Red

Relative Stage of Floral Development[a]

Variety	Unirradiated Control	4 Min of Red	4 Min of Red + 4 Min of Far Red
Amber Bright	42	4	32
Benora	46	42	46
Blizzard	42	20	42
Butterball	40	16	42
Harvest Golden	38	18	42
Pristine	48	14	42

[a] Values represent totals for 3 plants adjusted to basis of 6 plants for comparison with other tables. See text for description of stages of development.

Far-red repromotion of flowering of cocklebur resembles that of these early chrysanthemum varieties in that the flower primordia of the reinduced plants usually develop almost as well as those of the unirradiated controls (Downs, 1956). Far red almost always repromotes flowering of all plants of Indianapolis Yellow, Shasta, and certain other varieties, but the primordia are almost invariably less advanced than those of the controls. Repromotion of flowering by far red often fails in lamb's-quarters (*Chenopodium album* L.) and when it succeeds, the flower primordia are not well developed.

Repromotion of Flowering by Far Red Dependent on Time between Red and Far-Red Treatments

The maximum degree of repromotion of flowering attainable in various kinds of chrysanthemums with far-red treatments usually occurs when treatments of about 1 to 10 min are given as quickly as possible after the red treatment. If the time between red and far-red treatments exceeds about 45 min, the effectiveness of the far red in repromoting flowering decreases, and if it is as much as 90 min, repromotion of flowering often fails completely (Table VI).

This effect was observed first in cocklebur (Downs, 1956), in which repromotion of flowering failed in about 30 min. The red light apparently forms a product, the far-red-absorbing form of the pigment, which in short-day plants such as cocklebur and chrysanthemum starts reactions that lead to prevention of flowering. If these reactions are permitted to run a sufficient part of their course, flowering will ob-

TABLE VI.   Dependence of Repromotion of Floral Initiation in Plants of Indianapolis Yellow Chrysanthemum on Duration of Darkness between 3-Min Irradiations with Red and Far-Red-Radiant Energy

Relative Stage[a] of Floral Development

Date of Experiment	Dark Control	Red Control	0 Min of Dark	15 Min of Dark	30 Min of Dark	45 Min of Dark	90 Min of Dark
Nov. 14, 1956	29	0	15	16	—	8	—
April 30, 1957	16	5	14	14	—	15	4
May 15, 1957	27	0	13	19	—	10	0
June 3, 1957	25	0	12	13	11	4	—
July 2, 1957	26	2	18	—	11	3	0

[a] Values are totals for 6 plants. See text for description of stages of development.

viously be prevented even though the initial photoreaction is reversed. In chrysanthemum this period is about an hour.

Repeated Reversibility of Flowering Response

The flowering response like other phenomena controlled by the red, far-red reaction is repeatedly reversible. In an experiment involving two varieties of chrysanthemum the lots of plants were given various numbers of alternating 3-min irradiations with red and far red as shown in Table VII. One variety, Honeysweet, was similar to

TABLE VII.   Repeated Reversal of Flowering Response of Chrysanthemums by Alternating Treatments of Red and Far Red

Relative Stage[a] of Floral Development

Treatment	Honeysweet	Harvest Golden
R	0	10
R, FR	8	17
R, FR, R	0	8
R, FR, R, FR	7	14
R, FR, R, FR, R, FR, R	0	8
R, FR, R, FR, R, FR, R, FR	4	12
Dark control	18	20

[a] Values are totals for 6 plants. See text for description of stages of development.

Indianapolis Yellow in that its flowering was completely inhibited by 3 min of red and incompletely promoted by 3 min of far red. Flowering of the other, Harvest Golden, was only partly inhibited by 3 min of red, but it was reasonably well repromoted by 3 min of far red

Repromotion of flowering occurred in response to the fourth application of far red in such a series of alternating red and far-red treatments, but it was not so strong in the final cycle as in earlier ones. This is attributed to the fact that performance of the experiment required more than 45 min each day, and thus the plants were probably in the red-irradiated condition long enough so that they began to escape from control by the photoreaction.

Effect of Prolonged Treatments with Far Red

Another feature of the reaction shown by chrysanthemum is that about 90 min of far red causes the same response as 2 or 3 min of red, namely, failure of flowering. The far red does this, moreover, when used alone or when immediately preceded by a brief inhibitory irradiation with red. In the latter case one knows from results such as those of Table III that during the first few minutes of the 90-min period of irradiation with far red the flowering stimulus is reestablished only to be redestroyed during the remainder of the period.

The brief treatment with far red apparently changes most of the far-red-absorbing form of the pigment to the red-absorbing form. If the plant is then placed in darkness, the conversion of the remainder of the far-red-absorbing form presumably occurs thermally. If the plant is maintained in far red for as long as 90 min, however, the fractional distribution of the pigment in the two forms probably remains the same as at the end of 3 min and inhibition of flowering results from the slow action throughout that time of the small amount of the far-red form of the pigment.

Of course, the actions of far red first to repromote and then to reinhibit flowering might depend on the simultaneous functioning of two photoreactions, one the reversible, red, far-red one and the other a reaction such as that controlling anthocyanin production in red cabbage (*Brassica oleracea*) (Siegelman and Hendricks, 1957) and white mustard (*Sinapis alba*) (Mohr, 1957). Experimental results thus far do not indicate which of these two possible explanations is correct.

Time Measurement in Photoperiodism

Experimental results of the type described give much information about the photoperiodic mechanism but leave many questions unanswered. We know reasonably well, for example, that the plant measures the duration of darkness, but we still do not know how it does this even though time-requiring events that occur during the dark period are known. For example, the plant is unresponsive to red light at the beginning of darkness, but it becomes responsive after a measurable period of a few hours. Reappearance of responsiveness to red probably must occur before actual flower-promoting reactions start, and these presumably must run for a time to reach the threshold of flowering. The time required for change of the pigment system from the far-red- to the red-absorbing form is probably an important feature of the time-measuring mechanism, but it still is not clear why these two events have a combined time requirement equal to a critical dark period.

The reappearance of reversibility itself also is not completely understood. In germination of light-sensitive seeds, which is controlled by the same reversible reaction as flowering, there is good evidence that the pigment undergoes thermal change in darkness. One surmises that the reappearance of reversibility of flowering results from a similar type of pigment change, but the time periods involved in flowering are only a few hours whereas in seed germination they are about a day, the length of the period depending on temperature. Lack of agreement of these time periods in seed germination and flowering, however, is not a serious argument against dependence of both types of response on dark conversion of the pigment from the far-red- to the red-absorbing form.

Effect of Far Red at Beginning of Dark Period

The promotion of flowering in millet (*Setaria italica* (L.) Beauv.) (Downs, 1958) by a short far-red treatment at the beginning of each 8-hr dark period is in agreement with what one might expect of a short-day plant. It was mentioned earlier that during a critical dark period two things happen: first is the dark conversion of the pigment from the far-red- to the red-absorbing form, which is followed by the onset of flower-forming reactions. In the Downs experiment with millet the dark period was less than the critical one for millet, but he converted the pigment in 5 min in far-red-radiant energy instead of in a longer time in darkness and thereby left almost the entire 8 hr for the second event of the dark period, the flower-promoting reactions.

The experiment was remarkably successful, but its success raises other questions for which I do not have answers. First, why does not chrysanthemum, another short-day plant, flower under similar conditions? Such a response would be of real use to the growers, but thus far brief irradiations with far red at the beginning of subcritical dark periods have been completely ineffective. Secondly, how does it happen that flowering was also promoted in two long-day plants, henbane and dill (*Anethum graveolens* L.), tested in the same experiment with the millet? According to their action spectra the flowering of long-day plants on short days is promoted by interrupting the dark periods with red light. Reversal experiments show further that far red given immediately after a red interruption incompletely reverses the red action on flowering and stem elongation. But far red given immediately after a long photoperiod promotes these two responses. The reason for these apparently opposite actions of far red is not apparent. One notes, however, that far red had an inhibitory action when it followed a brief period of light and a promotive action when it followed a long one. In the latter case, in which the red light was present continuously for several hours, certain of the flower-promoting reactions presumably escaped from reversible control whereas others, such as stem elongation, were perhaps still subject to control and favored by far-red treatment.

Differences between Long- and Short-Day Plants

The basis of the differences between long- and short-day plants is still not clear. Action spectra show that the controlling photoreaction in the two is the same even though the responses are opposite. Reversibility also occurs in long-day plants just as it does in short-day ones. In long-day plants red promotes flowering and in short-day ones it inhibits, but in both types far red counteracts the red. Further study of the occurrence of reversibility in long-day plants is needed. The change in the apparent direction of action of far red in millet and henbane suggests that flowering depends in some way on two or more light-influenced processes that must proceed concurrently or in close succession. If these are not equally influenced by the same light treatment, possibly their relative sensitivity to light is in some way responsible for the display of the various types of photoperiodic response or lack of it now recognized.

REFERENCES

Borthwick, H. A., S. B. Hendricks, and M. W. Parker. 1948. Action spectrum for photoperiodic control of floral initiation of a long-day plant, Wintex barley (*Hordeum vulgare*). *Botan. Gaz., 110,* 103–18.
———. 1952. The reaction controlling floral initiation. *Proc. Natl. Acad. Sci. U. S., 38,* 929–34.
Borthwick, H. A., S. B. Hendricks, M. W. Parker, E. H. Toole, and V. K. Toole. 1952. A reversible photoreaction controlling seed germination. *Proc. Natl. Acad. Sci. U. S., 38,* 662–66.
Borthwick, H. A., S. B. Hendricks, E. H. Toole, and V. K. Toole. 1954. Action of light on lettuce seed germination. *Botan. Gaz., 115,* 205–25.
Borthwick, H. A., M. W. Parker, and S. B. Hendricks. 1950. Recent developments in the control of flowering by photoperiod. *Am. Naturalist, 84,* 117–34.
Cathey, H. M., and H. A. Borthwick. 1957. Photoreversibility of floral initiation in chrysanthemum. *Botan. Gaz., 119,* 71–76.
Downs, R. J. 1956. Photoreversibility of flower initiation. *Plant Physiol., 31,* 279–84.
———. 1958. Photocontrol of vegetative growth.
Downs, R. J., S. B. Hendricks, and H. A. Borthwick. 1957. Photoreversible control of elongation of Pinto beans and other plants under normal conditions of growth. *Botan. Gaz., 118,* 199–208.
Hendricks, S. B., and H. A. Borthwick. 1955. Photoresponsive growth. *Aspects of Synthesis and Order in Growth,* Dorothea Rudnick, Editor. Princeton University Press, Princeton, N. J. Pages 149–69.
Mohr, Hans. 1957. Der Einfluss Monochromatischer Strahlung auf das Langerwachstum des Hypokotyls und auf die Anthocyanbildung bei Keimlingen von *Sinapis alba* L. (= *Brassica alba* Boiss.). *Planta, 49,* 389–405.
Parker, M. W., S. B. Hendricks, and H. A. Borthwick. 1950. Action spectrum for the photoperiodic control of floral initiation of the long-day plant *Hyoscyamus niger. Botan. Gaz., 111,* 242–52.
Parker, M. W., S. B. Hendricks, H. A. Borthwick, and N. J. Scully. 1946. Action spectra for photoperiodic control of floral initiation in short-day plants. *Botan. Gaz., 108,* 1–26.
Piringer, A. A., and P. H. Heinze. 1954. Effect of light on the formation of a pigment in the tomato fruit cuticle. *Plant Physiol., 29,* 467–72.
Siegelman, H. W., and S. B. Hendricks. 1957. Photocontrol of anthocyanin formation in turnip and red cabbage seedlings. *Plant Physiol., 32,* 393–98.

METABOLIC ASPECTS OF PHOTOPERIODISM
IN PLANTS

IRWIN SPEAR
University of Texas, Austin

It is well known that the photoperiod controls a great many physiological, morphological, and anatomical processes of plants and animals. However, the metabolic changes that bring about these responses are largely unknown. Two lines of evidence suggested that a study of the CO_2 metabolism of short-day plants would be fruitful. The first of these was the need for a supply of CO_2 during the light phase for the flowering response of short-day plants (Harder and von Witsch, 1941; Parker and Borthwick, 1940). The second came from other experiments (Bode, 1942; Schmitz, 1951) with isolated leaves and shoots of *Kalanchoë* plants exposed to different day lengths, which demonstrated that both the photosynthetic rate in the light and the pattern of CO_2 production in the dark are affected by day length.

In our experiments (Gregory *et al.*, 1954; Spear, 1953; Spear and Thimann, 1954), the diurnal CO_2 metabolism of the short-day plant *Kalanchoë blossfeldiana* was studied as a function of day length. The plants for these experiments were grown on long days (16 hr light and 8 hr dark) in air-conditioned light rooms maintained at 19°C and 75% relative humidity with a light intensity of 1500 ft-c from incandescent and fluorescent light sources. The plants were then enclosed in gastight chambers as shown in Fig. 1, the seal being effected by affixing a slit piece of gum rubber tubing around the lower portion of the stem and filling the space with latex. The base of the chamber is assembled and bolted together around the rubber tubing, thus forming a gastight seal. Air was passed over the plants at a rate of 27.5 ± 0.5 liters per hour, and the CO_2 content of the air entering and leaving the chamber was measured with an infrared gas analyzer.

The CO_2 exchange of plants which had always been grown on non-flower-inducing long days was studied for several long-day cycles, after

FIG. 1.   Gastight plant chamber used to study CO_2-metabolism of *Kalanchoë blossfeldiana*. Description in text.

which they were transferred to 8-hr photoperiods (short days). The gas exchange was then measured under short-day conditions after the plants had received an increasing number of short days.

EFFECT OF SHORT DAYS ON CO_2 METABOLISM IN THE DARK

In Fig. 2, the data for the CO_2 metabolism during the dark phase are presented. The broken lines show the CO_2 uptake during two successive nights under long-day conditions. When the lights go off at midnight (24 hr) photosynthesis ceases, but there remains a small, though significant, net dark uptake of CO_2. When the lights come on at 8:00 A.M., photosynthesis resumes and there is a marked increase in the rate of uptake of CO_2. This behavior is what would be expected from a succulent plant.

The solid lines show the corresponding behavior during the 16-hr

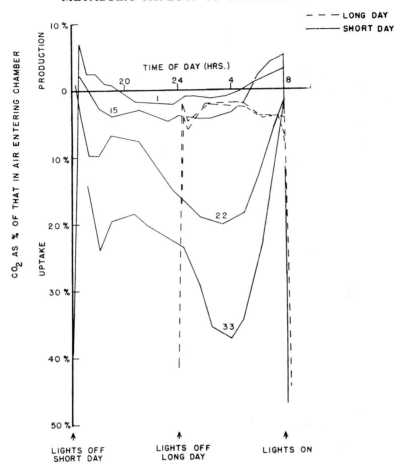

FIG. 2.   Carbon dioxide metabolism of *Kalanchoë* in dark phase under long-day conditions (broken lines) and during the 1st, 15th, 22nd, and 33rd long nights (solid lines).

dark period after exposure to an increasing number of short days. As the number of short-day cycles is increased, there is a marked increase in the ability of the plant to fix CO_2 in the dark. The maximum fixation usually occurs 11 to 12 hr after the onset of darkness, after which the rate of CO_2 uptake decreases to about zero before the lights come on at 8:00 A.M.

EFFECT OF SHORT DAYS ON CO_2 METABOLISM IN THE LIGHT

The CO_2 metabolism during the light phase is shown in Fig. 3. Under long-day conditions (broken lines) there is a marked photosynthetic uptake of CO_2. After exposure to short days (solid lines) the rate of uptake of CO_2 decreased during the early part of the light phase giving way to a net CO_2 production after pretreatment with 15 to 20 long nights. Thus, plants that have received 33 short days show a net production of CO_2 in the light and a net uptake of CO_2 in the dark.

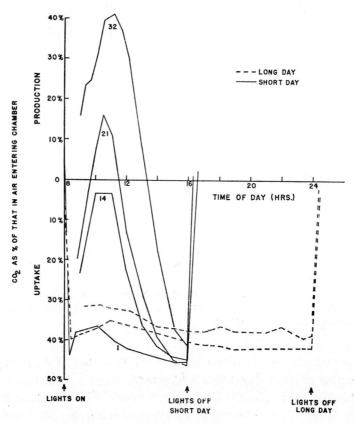

FIG. 3. Carbon dioxide metabolism of *Kalanchoë* in light phase under long-day conditions (broken lines) and after 1, 14, 21, and 32 long nights (solid lines). Same plants as in Fig. 2.

Similar results have been obtained with several dozen plants similarly treated.

The production of CO_2 in the light is due to both heat-labile and light-labile components because evolution of CO_2 can be obtained in the dark by raising the temperature from 20°C to 30°C. After the CO_2 evolution has ceased at 30°C, an additional burst of CO_2 can be obtained by turning on the lights (Spear and Thimann, 1954).

EFFECT OF INTERRUPTING LONG DARK PERIOD

It is well known that interrupting the long dark period by a short period of illumination completely annuls its effectiveness (Hamner and Bonner, 1938), especially when the interruption is given near the midpoint of the dark period (Harder and Bode, 1943). Short-day plants fail to flower under these conditions. It was therefore of considerable interest to ascertain whether the CO_2 metabolism responded in the same way.

Plants grown in long days were exposed for prolonged periods to cycles of 8 hr light and 16 hr darkness, with and without interruption (with 10 min of light) halfway through the long dark period. One such experiment is shown in Fig. 4. The solid line represents a plant given uninterrupted long nights, and the broken line a plant given a 10-min interruption by 1500 ft-c at midnight. It is evident that the uninterrupted plant developed the characteristic CO_2 metabolism of short-day plants, just described, while the companion plant that received 35 interrupted long nights failed to develop the ability to fix large amounts of CO_2 in the dark. The corresponding burst of CO_2 in the light is largely absent. This experiment has been repeated five times with similar results.

EFFECT OF PROLONGED DARK AND PROLONGED LIGHT PERIODS

It is clear from Figs. 2 and 4 that the CO_2 fixation in darkness decreases rapidly after the first 12 hr and has usually ceased before the end of the 16 hr dark period. A study was therefore made of the CO_2

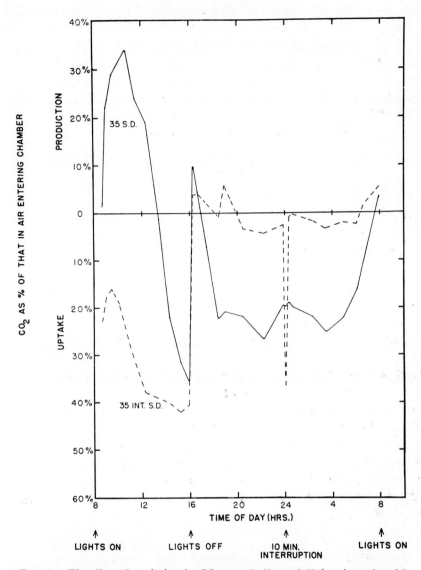

FIG. 4.   The diurnal variation in CO_2 metabolism of *Kalanchoë* after 35
long nights with (broken lines) and without (solid lines) 10-min interruptions of the long dark period by 1500 ft-c. The interrupting light was
given at midnight (24 hr).

relations in prolonged darkness, and Fig. 5 shows the results with a plant pretreated with 34 short-day cycles. During the first 12 hr of this dark period, the characteristic increase in dark CO_2 fixation occurs, but after 4:00 A.M. the rate of fixation decreases, giving way to CO_2 evolution after 8:00 A.M. For the remainder of this 48-hr dark period,

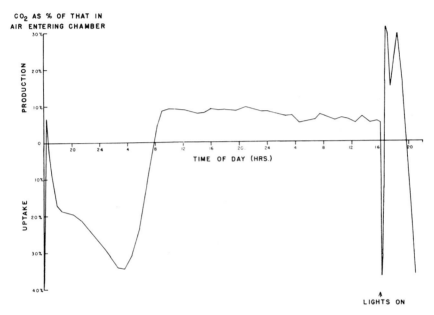

FIG. 5.   The CO_2 metabolism of *Kalanchoë* during a prolonged dark period of 48 hr and 4 additional hr in the light.

there is a continuous production of CO_2 with no endogenous rhythm apparent. When the lights are turned on after the prolonged dark period, there is a burst of CO_2 production similar to that observed with 16-hr dark periods.

The effect of a prolonged light period on a plant pretreated with 34 short-day cycles is shown in Fig. 6. After the usual burst of CO_2 production is over (4 to 6 hr after the light comes on), the uptake of CO_2 rapidly increases and then remains relatively constant. Again there is no sign of an endogenous rhythm.

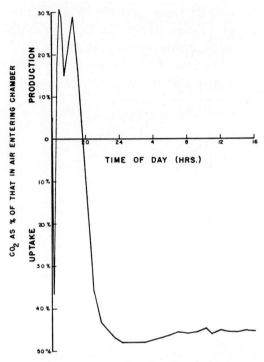

FIG. 6. The CO_2 metabolism of *Kalanchoë* during a prolonged light period of 24 hr.

INDUCTION OF CO_2 FIXATION

The flowering response to photoperiodism may be induced; that is, after a certain number of cycles of a favorable day length have been given, flower formation will proceed even though the plant is maintained under unfavorable day lengths. In *Xanthium* only one photoinductive cycle is required, but with *Kalanchoë,* under the conditions employed in these experiments, 13 to 14 short-day cycles are required for a minimum flowering response and 20 to 25 short-day cycles for a maximum response. The result of an experiment to determine whether the CO_2 metabolism associated with short days could also be induced is shown in Fig. 7. The broken line represents the metabolism of this plant under long-day conditions; the solid line the CO_2 metabolism during the twentieth short-day cycle; and the dotted line the CO_2 metabolism after the plant had received 21 short days followed by 15 long days. By comparing the dotted and broken curves, it is evident

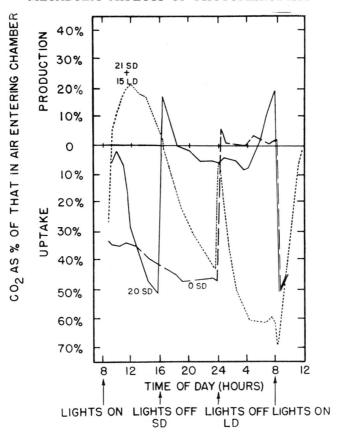

FIG. 7. Carbon dioxide metabolism of *Kalanchoë* under long-day conditions (broken lines), after 20 short-day cycles (solid lines), and after 21 short-day plus 15 long-day cycles (dotted lines). Lights on at 8:00 A.M. under long- and short-day conditions. Lights off at 4:00 P.M. (16 hr) for the short-day conditions, and at midnight (24 hr) for the long-day conditions (broken and dotted lines).

that the CO_2 metabolism can be induced to develop after treatment with 21 short days, although the plant is returned to long days.

POSSIBLE RELATIONSHIP BETWEEN CO_2 METABOLISM AND FLOWERING

It is interesting to speculate on the possible relationship between the CO_2 metabolism and the initiation of flowering. The similarities are striking.

1. Both are promoted by short days.

2. The peak of CO_2 fixation occurs 11 to 12 hr after the onset of darkness, and this is the critical dark period for the onset of flowering in *Kalanchoë*.

3. CO_2 fixation ceases after 16 hr of darkness, and this is the optimal dark period for flowering as determined by Harder (1948).

4. CO_2 fixation does not occur unless preceded by a light phase (Fig. 5) and this is also true of the initiation of flowering by long dark periods (Hamner, 1940; Harder and Gümmer, 1947).

5. Both are inhibited by interrupting the long dark period.

6. Both are induced after sufficient short-day cycles have been received.

7. In other experiments (Spear, unpublished) we have found that in using 96-hr cycles with a long (84-hr) dark period interrupted at different intervals, treatments that inhibit flowering also inhibit the characteristic CO_2 metabolism.

On the other hand, it should be noted that we have been unable to inhibit flowering by withholding CO_2 during the dark period in *Kalanchoë* (Spear, 1953). However, a succulent such as *Kalanchoë* undoubtedly has a tremendous store of metabolic CO_2 available in the form of carboxyl groups of organic acids. Inhibition of floral initiation in soybeans and *Xanthium* by CO_2-free dark atmospheres has been reported by Langston and Leopold (1954). These authors have also noted the promotion of $C^{14}O_2$ fixation in the dark by these plants after photoinduction.

In studying the organic acid content of *Kalanchoë* leaves on different photoperiods, Neyland and Thimann (1956) found that the total acidity rose slowly in the first part of the dark phase, then at an increasing rate, and reached the highest measured level at the end of the dark period. In the subsequent light period, the acidity dropped rapidly at first, 2 hr of light being sufficient to reduce the acid gained in the dark by one half. In all other respects the organic acid pattern followed what would be predicted from the CO_2-fixation studies above. The principal organic acids formed were malic, citric (isocitric), and glycolic, with lesser amounts of succinic.

Kunitake *et al.* (1957), using $C^{14}O_2$, have confirmed the effect of short days in inducing an increase in dark CO_2 fixation by *Kalanchoë blossfeldiana*. However, they found that in the products of fixation, the difference was only quantitative rather than qualitative. Neither the pattern of labeled compounds (malate, aspartate, glutamate, alanine, glutamine, citrate, isocitrate, succinate, and fumarate) nor the relative distribution of radioactivity in these compounds showed any significant differences between leaves of induced and noninduced plants.

In recent work, with total titratable acids, Neyland and Thimann (personal communication) have found that while much of the fixation goes into organic acids, which decompose again in light or warmth, there is sufficient difference between CO_2 fixation and organic acid measurements to suggest that important fixation products remain unidentified.

Although at present it is impossible to say whether or not there is a causal relationship between the CO_2 metabolism and flowering, it should be noted that this metabolic response is more amenable to investigation than the morphological responses most often studied. A morphological response such as flowering involves cell division, cell enlargement, and cell differentiation, and each of these processes must include many distinct biochemical steps. The CO_2 fixation response would appear to be a much simpler system. In addition, these metabolic responses may indicate less obvious metabolic changes which could be causally related to flowering.

EFFECT OF ANAEROBIC CONDITIONS ON FLOWERING

In addition to treating *Kalanchoë* with CO_2-free air during the long dark periods, we have also treated *Kalanchoë* and *Xanthium* with anaerobic conditions and carbon monoxide. We will present only some of the anaerobic experiments at this time. In 14 out of 15 cases where *Xanthium* was given anaerobic conditions during 2 to 5 long (16-hr) dark periods, flowering was inhibited. The one plant that flowered had received five short-day cycles and showed a delayed marginal response. Anaerobic conditions during the dark period had no effect on *Kalanchoë* plants treated for 15 short-day cycles. Perhaps more interesting are the experiments of Melchers and Claes (1945; Claes, 1947) with the long-day plant *Hyoscyamus niger*. This plant was able to flower under short-day conditions if nitrogen was given throughout the long dark period.

These experiments lend support to the idea that some of the dark processes involve the aerobic metabolism of constituents formed in the light.

REFERENCES

Bode, O. 1942. Über Zusammenhänge zwischen CO_2-Assimilation und Photoperiodismus bei *Kalanchoë blossfeldiana. Planta, 33,* 278–89.

Claes, H. 1947. Die Beteiligung des dissimilatorischen Stoffwechsels an der photoperiodischen Reaktion von *Hyoscyamus niger. Z. Naturforsch., 2b,* 45–55.

Gregory, F. G., I. Spear, and K. V. Thimann. 1954. The interrelation between CO_2 metabolism and photoperiodism in *Kalanchoë. Plant Physiol., 29,* 220–29.

Hamner, K. C. 1940. Interrelation of light and darkness in photoperiodic induction. *Botan. Gaz., 101,* 658–87.

Hamner, K. C., and J. Bonner. 1938. Photoperiodism in relation to hormones as factors in floral initiation and development. *Botan. Gaz., 100,* 388–431.

Harder, R. 1948. Vegetative and reproductive development of *Kalanchoë blossfeldiana* as influenced by photoperiodism. *Symposia Soc. Exptl. Biol., 2,* 117–38.

Harder, R., and O. Bode. 1943. Über die Wirkung von Zwischenbelichtungen während der Dunkelperiode auf das Blühen, die Verlaubung und die Blattsukkulenz bei der Kurztagpflanze *Kalanchoë blossfeldiana. Planta, 33,* 469–504.

Harder, R., and G. Gümmer. 1947. Über die untere kritische Tageslänge bei der Kurztagspflanzl *Kalanchoë blossfeldiana. Planta, 35,* 88–99.

Harder, R., and H. von Witsch. 1941. Über die Bedeutung der Kohlensäure und der photoperiodische Belichtung für die Blütenbildung bei *Kalanchoë blossfeldiana. Naturwissenschaften, 29,* 770–71.

Kunitake, George M., P. Saltman, and A. Lang. 1957. The products of CO_2 fixation in leaves of long- and short-day treated *Kalanchoë blossfeldiaha. Plant Physiol., 32,* 201–203.

Langston, R., and A. C. Leopold. 1954. The dark fixation of carbon dioxide as a factor in photoperiodism. *Plant Physiol., 29,* 436–40.

Melchers, G., and H. Claes. 1945. Auslosing von Blütenbildung bei der Langtagpflanze *Hyoscyamus niger* in Kurztagbedingungen durch Hemmung der Atmung in den Dunkelphasen. *Naturwissenschaften, 31,* 249.

Neyland, M., and K. V. Thimann. 1956. Organic acid content of *Kalanchoë* leaves on different photoperiods. (Abstract) *Plant Physiol., 31* (Suppl.), xxxv–xxxvi.

Parker, M. W., and H. A. Borthwick. 1940. Floral initiation in Biloxi soybeans as influenced by photosynthetic activity during the induction period. *Botan. Gaz., 102,* 256–68.

Schmitz, J. 1951. Über Beziehnungen zwischen Blütenbildung in verschiedenen Licht-Dunkelkombinationen und Atmungsrhythmik bei wechselnden photoperiodischen Bedingungen (Untersuchungen an *Kalanchoë blossfeldiana). Planta, 39,* 271–308.

Spear, I. 1953. The interrelation between carbon dioxide metabolism and photoperiodism. Thesis, Harvard University, Cambridge, Mass.

Spear, I., and K. V. Thimann. 1954. The interrelationship between CO_2 metabolism and photoperiodism in *Kalanchoë.* II. Effect of prolonged darkness and high temperatures. *Plant Physiol., 29,* 414–17.

A CORRELATION OF PHOTOPERIODIC RESPONSE OF *Xanthium* AND GERMINATION OF IMPLANTED LETTUCE SEED [1]

LAWRENCE BOGORAD and WAYNE J. McILRATH
Department of Botany, The University of Chicago, Chicago, Illinois

Several of the papers presented at this symposium have reviewed and documented the marked similarity in action spectra for a number of responses; these include the control of photoperiodic induction of floral initiation, germination of seeds of certain varieties of lettuce, leaf expansion, and internodal elongation. The diversity in types of responses is evident. The present experiments were designed to investigate the following problems: Does the similarity in these systems extend beyond the identity in photoreceptor, and does the photoreaction (and some ensuing steps) in each of these systems lead to the production of the same substance which, in each case, elicits a different and specific response (Bogorad and McIlrath, 1955; McIlrath and Bogorad, 1954; McIlrath and Bogorad, 1958)?

Lettuce seed germination and the photoperiodic control of floral initiation, two well-characterized red, far-red reversible systems, were chosen for investigation. The experimental approach was simple. When *Xanthium* plants, grown in the greenhouse under a 20-hr photoperiod, had reached a suitable size, slight incisions were made on the abaxial surface of the petioles of the second, third, and fourth leaves from the terminal bud. Up to about seventy dry lettuce seeds (achenes) were implanted in each petiole. The petioles were then covered with either a light-tight wrapper of aluminum foil (Fig. 1) or a transparent cover of Saran Wrap (Dow Chemical Co.) (Fig. 2), sealed on with masking tape (Minnesota Mining & Manufacturing Co.). The plants with implanted petioles were then subjected to various regimes of light and

[1] This investigation was supported in part by the National Science Foundation (G-4018) and in part by the Dr. Wallace C. and Clara A. Abbott Memorial Fund of the University of Chicago.

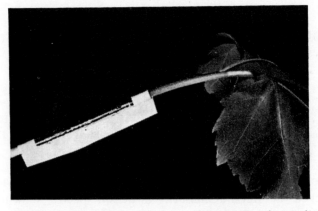

FIG. 1.   Lettuce seeds implanted in the petioles of *Xanthium* plants and covered with aluminum foil.

darkness at 20–21°C. After 4 to 6 days the leaves with implanted petioles were removed and the number of germinated seeds was determined; all the *Xanthium* plants were then returned to the greenhouse where they were maintained on a 20-hr photoperiod and observed for appearance of flowers. Seeds of Grand Rapids Tipburn Resistant No. 1 lettuce were used in all but a few experiments in which seeds of White Paris Self-Folding Cos lettuce, a variety which is not photosensitive, were used. Several different lots of seed of each variety were used in the course of the experiments, and the same trends were observed with the various lots, although absolute values varied. Generally, at least three plants (nine implanted petioles) implanted with a total of 150 to 400 seeds were used in each treatment.

Figure 3 (upper) shows a dissected petiole from a cocklebur plant

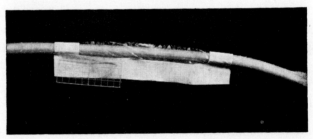

FIG. 2.   Lettuce seeds implanted in *Xanthium* petioles and covered with Saran Wrap.

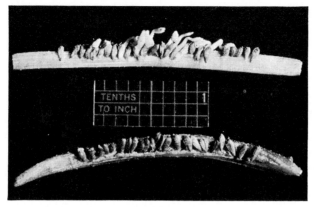

FIG. 3.   Germination of Grand Rapids lettuce seeds implanted under light-tight aluminum foil wrappers in the petioles of *Xanthium* plants maintained on 8-hr (above) and 20-hr (below) photoperiods.

which had been exposed to five 8-hr photoperiods after Grand Rapids lettuce seeds had been implanted and covered with a light-tight wrapper. Approximately 40% of the implanted seeds germinated. Figure 3 (lower) illustrates a petiole from a *Xanthium* plant which had been exposed to five 20-hr photoperiods. This petiole contains no germinated seed; in related experiments, however, in which larger samples of seeds from the same lot were similarly treated, up to 5% germination was observed.

The implanted petioles shown in Fig. 4 were covered with transparent Saran Wrap rather than with light-tight aluminum foil. A direct

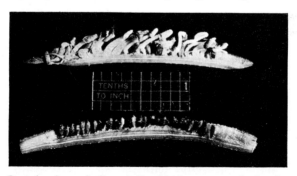

FIG. 4.   Germination of Grand Rapids lettuce seeds implanted under transparent Saran Wrap covers in petioles of *Xanthium* plants maintained on 8-hr (above) and 20-hr (below) photoperiods.

promotive effect of illumination on the germination of the seeds implanted in petioles of plants maintained on 8 hr of light daily (Fig. 4, upper) is apparent, but there was no comparable influence on seeds implanted in petioles of plants subjected to 20-hr photoperiods daily (Fig. 4, lower).

The first questions raised by these observations were: Is the response of implanted Grand Rapids lettuce seed a result of *stimulation* of germination when the *Xanthium* host plants are subjected to several 8-hr photoperiods; are these results a consequence of *inhibition* of germination of seed implanted in *Xanthium* plants maintained on 20 hr of light daily; or, does a combination of these influences lead to these results? These questions are not easily answered by germinating the lettuce seeds in darkness on moist filter paper in petri dishes (designated hereafter as "germination *in vitro*") because germination *in vitro* is not entirely comparable to germination in *Xanthium* petioles. There is no readily available independent control situation, so one must compare the results when the *Xanthium* hosts are subjected to different experimental conditions. The question of *inhibition* vs. *stimulation* of germination was approached experimentally in two ways.

First, two groups of seeds of Grand Rapids lettuce were treated in the following manner. "High dark germination seeds" were prepared by exposing imbibed seed to red light (660 mμ-G.A.B. Interference filter) and then drying them. "Low dark germination seeds" were prepared by germinating lettuce seeds in petri dishes on moist filter paper for 48 hr in darkness at 20°C and then drying all the seeds in darkness. The seeds of the latter group which had germinated were then removed and discarded.

Table I shows the results obtained in implantation experiments when either high dark germination seed (80% germination *in vitro* at 20°C in darkness in 48 hr) or low dark germination seed (less than 2% germination *in vitro*). The results with low dark germination seed implanted in *Xanthium* petioles and covered with aluminum foil support the conclusion that there is little or no stimulation of lettuce seed germination when the hosts are maintained under 8-hr photoperiods. On the other hand, the results with the high dark germination seeds indicate a marked inhibition of germination when the host plants are exposed to 20 hr of light daily. These results suggest, too, the possibil-

TABLE I. Germination of Grand Rapids Lettuce Seeds
Implanted in Petioles of *Xanthium* Plants

Photoperiod, hr (*Xanthium*)	Germination of Lettuce Seed, %	
	In Light[a]	In Darkness[b]
High Dark Germination Seed[c]		
8	62.4	35.3
20	3.7	3.6
Low Dark Germination Seed[d]		
8	46.0	1.3
20	3.3	1.1

[a] Implanted petioles covered with Saran Wrap.
[b] Implanted petioles covered with aluminum foil.
[c] Eighty percent germination *in vitro* in darkness at 20°C in 48 hr.
[d] Two percent germination *in vitro* in darkness at 20°C in 48 hr.

ity of some inhibition of germination even when the *Xanthium* hosts are exposed to 8 hr of light daily.

Direct illumination of seeds implanted in petioles of *Xanthium* plants on 8-hr photoperiods results in an increase in the percentage of seeds which germinate. On the other hand, as seen in Figs. 3 and 4 and Table I, illumination of the seeds appears to have little or no effect on germination when the cocklebur plants are under 20-hr photoperiods; inhibition is not reversed by illumination of implanted seeds.

The source of the inhibitory influence appears to be in the leaf blades. If the leaf blades are removed after the petioles have been implanted and wrapped with aluminum foil, the germination of the implanted seed is unaffected by the subsequent photoperiodic treatment of the *Xanthium* host.

In the second approach to the *stimulation* vs. *inhibition* problem, seeds of White Paris Self Folding Cos, a nonphotosensitive variety of lettuce, were used in implantation experiments. Table II shows ger-

TABLE II. Germination of Seeds of White Paris Self Folding
Lettuce (Dark) Implanted in *Xanthium* Petioles

Photoperiod, hr (*Xanthium*)	Germination of Seed,[a] %	
	Expt. 1	Expt. 2
8	86.5	61.7
20	37.8	8.0

[a] Implanted petioles covered with aluminum foil.

mination data obtained in two series of experiments performed at different times and using different lots of seed. These results again suggest that the effects observed are probably largely or entirely a consequence of an inhibition of germination of seed implanted in petioles of cocklebur plants exposed to long days. These experiments also show that photosensitive seeds are not required in order to obtain the germination response. Thus, the initial objective, to determine whether a common active material is produced as a consequence of the photoreactions in the lettuce seed germination and photoperiodic induction systems, was not achieved. Instead, lettuce seed germination appears to serve as a bioassay for some metabolic change or changes associated with photoperiodic induction of flowering in *Xanthium*.

What evidence is there that the responses are reflections of photoperiodic induction of *Xanthium* and not, for example, responses to duration or intensity of photosynthesis? In one set of experiments *Xanthium* plants, the petioles of which were implanted with Grand Rapids lettuce seed, were sprayed with a 5% sucrose solution daily during the photoperiodic treatment. This application of sugar failed to result in any appreciable alteration in the response of the implanted seed (Table III). Another series of experiments was performed to

TABLE III.   Effect of Sucrose Applications to *Xanthium* on the Germination of (Dark) Implanted Grand Rapids Lettuce Seed

Photoperiod, hr (*Xanthium*)	Germination, %	
	With Sugar	Without Sugar
8	29.4	28.8
20	17.9	15.3

determine the relation between the percentage of germination of the implanted lettuce seed and photoperiodic treatment of the host. Table IV contains the results of experiments using Grand Rapids lettuce which showed about 80% germination *in vitro* in darkness at 20°C in 48 hr. It is interesting, though perhaps coincidental, that the break in the germination response curve falls somewhere between 16 and 20 hr of light daily and that the critical day length for these *Xanthium* plants is very close to 16 hr. Furthermore, the lettuce seed germination response was about the same whether the cocklebur plants were exposed for 8 hr each day to light intensities of 2000 or of 5000 ft-c (at the tops of the plants). Seeds implanted in *Xanthium* plants exposed for 8 hr per day to 5000 ft-c light (total of 40,000 ft-c hr/day) responded like seeds in cockleburs exposed to 8 hr of 2000 ft-c light (total, 16,000 ft-c hr/day) and not like similar seed implanted in

TABLE IV. Effect of Day Length on Germination of
(Dark) Implanted Grand Rapids Lettuce Seed

Photoperiod, hr (*Xanthium*)	Germination, %	No. of Experiments
8	35.3	7
12	23.3	3
16	12.9	2
20	3.6	6
24	3.8	1

plants which were exposed to 20 hr of light daily of 2000 ft-c intensity (total, 40,000 ft-c hr/day). Thus, within the experimental limits described, the lettuce seed germination response is related to the length of the photoperiod to which the host plants are exposed, and not to the total light energy which these plants received.

Investigations were also made to determine whether treatments, other than variation in day length, which interfere with photoperiodic induction affect the lettuce seed germination response. Petioles of a number of *Xanthium* plants were implanted with Grand Rapids lettuce seed and enclosed in light-tight wrappers. The leaf blades of one lot of plants was sprayed with an aqueous solution of 500 mg per liter of indoleacetic acid (IAA) before each of the six 16-hr dark periods to which the plants were subjected. This treatment is known to interfere with the flowering of *Xanthium* exposed to photoperiods which are normally inductive (Bonner and Thurlow, 1949). Only about 2% of the seeds which were implanted in the sprayed plants germinated; the plants which were sprayed with the IAA solution failed to flower when they were subsequently maintained on a regime of 20 hr of light daily. These data again support the conclusion that the lettuce seed germination response is related to metabolic changes associated with photoperiodic induction of the host cocklebur plants. One disquieting note has been the failure to get consistent support for this conclusion from a few experiments in which interruption of the critical dark period by light has been used to interfere with floral induction. This point requires considerable further study.

Finally, the effects of a few possible inhibitors of lettuce seed germination were examined. The effects of xanthinin, coumarin, and IAA were investigated. Crystalline xanthinin was prepared according to the method of Geissman *et al.* (1954). This compound had no effect on the germination of lettuce seed *in vitro* at any concentration tried, including 1000 mg per liter. Earlier reports on the inhibitory effect of coumarin on the germination of lettuce seed and the reversal of this inhibition by light (Evenari, 1957) were confirmed. The reversal by light appears to be inconsistent with the nature of the inhibition of germination of seed implanted in plants exposed to long photoperiods (e.g., Table I). Thus, inhibitors of the coumarin type seem to act differently from the inhibitor or inhibitors which are active in the implantation experiments.

The germination *in vitro* of the Grand Rapids lettuce seed used in these experiments was little affected by IAA in concentrations up to 1 mg per liter. Fifty percent of the seed germinated in the presence of 10 mg per liter IAA. At concentrations of IAA which did not affect seed germination, a swelling of the seedling radicle was observed. At concentrations at which the percentage of germination was decreased, the cotyledons emerged but the radicles did not. By contrast, seedlings produced from those seeds which had germinated in the petioles of *Xanthium* plants exposed to long-day conditions appeared normal. Thus, it appears that the pattern of inhibition of germination by IAA *in vitro* does not correspond to that observed in the implantation experiments. The active material in cocklebur plants is being sought.

Summary

The germination of lettuce seed implanted in petioles of cockelbur plants shows an inverse correlation with the duration of the daily light period to which the hosts are exposed. The evidence thus far obtained strongly suggests that the germination response is a function of metabolic changes associated with floral induction of the *Xanthium* plant. Additional evidence along this line is being sought. The germination response can be interpreted as an inhibition of germination of seeds implanted in petioles of *Xanthium* plants exposed to long-day conditions, although a stimulation of germination of implanted seed, when the hosts are under short-day conditions, is not excluded. The nature of the naturally accurring inhibitor is being investigated further.

REFERENCES

Bogorad, L., and W. J. McIlrath. 1955. Indirect photoperiodic effects on lettuce seed germination. *Plant Physiol., 30.*

Bonner, J., and J. F. Thurlow. 1949. Inhibition of photoperiodic induction in *Xanthium* by applied auxin. *Botan. Gaz., 110,* 613–24.

Evenari, M. 1957. The physiological action and biological importance of germination inhibitors. *Symposia Soc. Exptl. Biol., 11,* 21–43.

Geissman, T. A., P. Deuel, E. K. Bonde, and F. A. Addicott. 1954. *Xanthinin:* a plant growth-regulating compound from *Xanthium pensylvanicum.* I. *J. Am. Chem. Soc., 76,* 685–87.

McIlrath, W. J., and L. Bogorad. 1954. Germination of lettuce seed implanted in *Xanthium* petioles. Abstracts 29th Annual Meetings, Am. Soc. Plant Physiol.

McIlrath, W. J., and L. Bogorad. 1958. Photoperiodic floral induction of *Xanthium* and germination of lettuce seeds implanted in the petioles. *Botan. Gaz., 119,* 186–91.

THE INDUCTION OF FLOWERING IN *Xanthium pensylvanicum* UNDER LONG DAYS

J. P. NITSCH [1] and **F. W. WENT** [2]

Laboratoire du Phytotron, Gif-sur-Yvette (Seine-et-Oise), France and
Earhart Plant Research Laboratory, California Institute of Technology,
Pasadena

Since ancient times, it has been well known that flowering can be brought about by many diverse influences. In numerous cases, apparently, it is a question of physiological age. When the plant has reached a certain development, it initiates flower buds. Environmental and nutritional factors, of course, may accelerate or delay this basic trend. Recently, studies in the field of photoperiodism have focused attention upon one mechanism: the regulation of flowering by the relative duration of day and night. According to this view, plants can be classified into groups such as "short-day plants," "long-day plants," and "day-neutral plants." The day-neutral plants constitute a very large group. Among the species which do respond to photoperiodic induction, most numerous are those which are not strictly photoperiodic. Other factors, such as temperature, profoundly alter their behavior. Physiologists, however, have tended to select one or two species known to be strictly photoperiodic, forgetting that the plants they work with have been picked out of hundreds of species and constitute, therefore, exceptions rather than examples of a general behavior. The prototype of such exceptions is the plant most commonly used in photoperiodic experiments, namely the cocklebur, *Xanthium pensylvanicum*.

Even in *Xanthium,* however, the photoperiodic mechanism is not the only one that is conducive to flowering. This fact has been recently reported by De Zeeuw (1957) who obtained flowering cockleburs under long days by submitting the plants to cold treatments. In view of the importance of such a claim, new experiments were started along the same line. The results in brief follow.

[1] The work reported here was done in the Earhart Plant Research Laboratory under Grant G4046 from the National Science Foundation, which made it possible for one of us to go to Pasadena as a part of a more general investigation on the regulation of growth in plants.
[2] Present address: Missouri Botanical Garden, St. Louis, Missouri.

311

Vigorous *Xanthium* plants (J. Bonner's strain) were raised under smog-free air in the Earhart Laboratory under long days (full day of July plus additional incandescent light to produce days of 18 hr). The temperature was 23°C (day) and 17°C (night). At time zero, the plants were distributed among the various treatments, 8 replicates being used per treatment. During the following 13 days, the plants received, during the light periods, artificial light of about 1,000 ft-c (mixture of fluorescent and incandescent light). At the end of the experiment, the plants were returned to the original, long-day condition under natural light. At that time, the flower buds were macroscopically visible on the plants in which flowering had been induced. Photographs were taken 2 days later.

The results are presented in Table I. At 23°C (day and night), no

TABLE I. Effect of Various Light and Temperature Treatments on the Flowering of
Xanthium pensylvanicum

Light Period		Dark Period		
Duration, hr	Temperature, °C	Duration, hr	Temperature, °C	Plants Flowering,[a] %
24	23°	0	—	0
20	23°	4	23°	0
16	23°	8	23°	0
16	{ 8 hr at 4° / 8 hr at 23°	8	23°	100
8	23°	16	23°	100
24	{ 20 hr at 23° / 4 hr at 4°	0	—	0
24	{ 16 hr at 23° / 8 hr at 4°	0	—	0
24	{ 8 hr at 23° / 16 hr at 4°	0	—	0
24	4°	0	—	0

[a] Eight replicates in each case.

flowering was obtained when the dark period was 0, 4, or 8 hr, but complete flowering was obtained when the length of the dark period was 16 hr. Complete flowering could be achieved with a 16-hr day, however, when low temperature (4°C) was given during the first 8 hr of this long day. Various temperature treatments given during continuous illumination were unable to cause flowering.

Figures 1 and 2 give the aspect of typical growing points produced under some of the treatments. The flowers which had been initiated under 8-hr days were the most advanced in their development (Fig. 1A). Under 16-hr days, there were no flowers at 23°C (Fig. 1B) but definite inflorescences when a 4°C temperature was given during the first 8 hr of the light period (Fig. 1C). A similar 8-hr treatment with a

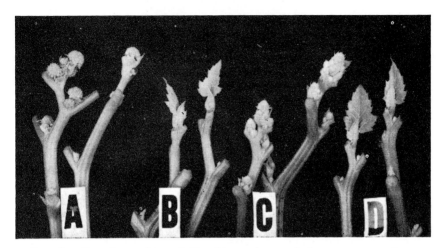

FIG. 1. Growing points of *Xanthium* plants of the same age photographed 15 days after the beginning of the following treatments. A. 8-hr days at 23°C. B. 16-hr days at 23°C. C. 16-hr days at 4°C during the first 8 hr, 23°C during the subsequent 8 hr of light. D. 24-hr days at 4°C during 8 hr, 23°C during the remaining 16 hr. (In all cases, the leaves have been removed in order to photograph the growing points.)

4°C temperature produced no flowers under continuous light (Fig. 1D).

In summary, cockleburs which do not flower under long days of 16 hr at 23°C can be induced to flower under the same long days when the temperature is dropped to 4°C during the first 8 hr of the long days (Fig. 2).

This experiment may be interpreted by saying that a labile compound promoting flowering is formed during the first part of the dark period. When the dark period is too short, this labile compound does not have time to be transformed into a stable one and is destroyed during the subsequent light phase. This destruction may be prevented by dropping the temperature.

The results presented here have also a more general meaning. They

FIG. 2. The induction of flowering in *Xanthium* with a cold treatment. Both plants were grown under long days of 16 hr of light. The plant at the left was maintained at 23°C. The plant at the right received 8 hr of 4°C temperature during the first 8 hr of the light period; temperature during the rest of the time was 23°C. Photograph taken 15 days after the beginning of the treatments.

show that factors other than photoperiod alone are able to regulate flowering even in a species which has been regarded up to now as most strictly photoperiodic. This is not an isolated case. The photoperiodic behavior of many plants is greatly changed by temperature. This is true not only of the flowering response, but also of dormancy (Downs and Borthwick, 1956; Waxman, 1957), winter hardiness (Moshkov, 1935), and seed germination (Vaartaja, 1956). Thus, as has been demonstrated in the case of *Hydrocharis morsus ranae* by Vegis (1955), the photoperiodic mechanism may be operative inside certain temperature limits only.

REFERENCES

De Zeeuw, D. 1957. Flowering of *Xanthium* under long-day conditions. *Nature, 180,* 588.

Downs, R. J., and H. A. Borthwick. 1956. Effect of photoperiod on growth of trees. *Botan. Gaz., 117,* 310–26.

Moshkov, B. S. 1935. Photoperiodismus and Frosthärte ausdauernder Gewächse. *Planta, 23,* 774–803.

Vaartaja, O. 1956. Photoperiodic response of germination of seed of certain trees. *Can. J. Botany, 34,* 377–88.

Vegis, A. 1955. Über den Einfluss der Temperatur und der täglichen Licht-Dunkel-Periode auf die Bildung der Ruheknospen zugleich ein Beitrag zur Entstehung des Ruhezustandes. *Symbolae Botan. Upsalienses, 14,* 1–175.

Waxman, S. 1957. The development of woody plants as affected by photoperiodic treatments. Ph.D, thesis, Cornell University, Ithaca, N. Y.

DUAL DAY LENGTH REQUIREMENTS
FOR FLORAL INITIATION

ROY M. SACHS
Department of Floriculture, University of California, Los Angeles

In the years 1930 to 1935 there was considerable interest in the interaction between vernalization and photoperiodism in the winter varieties of wheat, rye, and barley; in four separate investigations attention was called to the fact that some period of short-day (SD) preceding long-day (LD) induction had a stimulatory effect upon reproductive development (McKinney and Sando, 1930; Maximov, 1930; Forster *et al.*, 1932; Purvis, 1934; McKinney and Sando, 1935). Prior to this, winter cereals were considered to be simple long-day plants (LDP) with a preceding low-temperature requirement. As a result of their studies McKinney and Sando (1935) obtained sufficient evidence for the Harvest Queen variety of winter wheat to suggest that it be called a short-long day plant (SLDP). Their suggestion was based on the fact that, following emergence of the vernalized or unvernalized seedling, a 6-week period of SD induction decreased the number of days to heading by as much as 33%. This was the first description of a dual day length requirement for floral initiation. Little attention has been paid to McKinney and Sando's paper even though their data present serious difficulties for recent theories on the photoperiodic control of floral initiation (Borthwick *et al.*, 1948a; Bakhuyzen, 1951; Liverman and Bonner, 1953). Gott *et al.* (1955), continuing some earlier work of Purvis (1934), have shown recently that floral initiation in unvernalized winter rye is promoted by a sequence of SD followed by LD induction, and Wellensiek (1953) has presented evidence indicating that *Campanula medium* should also be placed in the SLDP category. Winter wheat and rye are winter annuals and *C. medium* is a biennial, so in all three cases floral initiation is promoted by a cold treatment at some stage in the development of the plant. Since SD induction in these plants can replace, partially or wholly, the

315

vernalization requirement, it has sometimes been referred to as "SD-vernalization" (Lang, 1952). The data of Gott *et al.* indicate that SD induction is possible only when vernalization is incomplete, that is, the two treatments are interchangeable, and perhaps the term "SD-vernalization" is acceptable here (although Gott *et al.* believe that vernalization and SD induction act upon different steps in the synthesis of the floral stimulus); however, McKinney and Sando (1935) have clearly demonstrated that vernalization and SD induction were not additive in winter wheat, even after 54 days of vernalization, and in this case "SD-vernalization" does not properly describe the action of SD induction or of the cold treatment.

Resende (1952) recently reported that floral initiation in several species of the Liliaceae and Crassulaceae required a sequence of LD followed by SD induction, and he suggested that these plants be classified as long-short day plants (LSDP). Since then, *Cestrum nocturnum,* a member of the Solanaceae, has also been described as a LSDP (Sachs, 1956a). *Cestrum* will remain vegetative if grown continuously in LD or SD conditions, the sequence of LD followed by SD cannot be reversed, and there is no morphological change at the terminal or axillary buds until sometime after SD induction is completed.

To the author's knowledge these are the only descriptions of plants with a dual day length requirement for floral initiation, although it has been suggested that the intermediate-day plants described by Allard (1938) may be specal cases of either SLDP or LSDP (Sachs, 1956a).

One of the most important criteria used in recent years to classify plants as either LDP or SDP has been the light interruption of the dark period associated with short photoperiods (on a 24-hr cycle); the light break inhibits floral initiation in SDP and promotes it in LDP (Lang, 1952). In the few cases in which this criterion has been applied to SLDP and LSDP, it has been shown that both the SD and LD induction requirements are comparable with those in SDP and LDP, respectively (Resende, 1953; Gott *et al.*, 1955; Sachs, 1956a). Unfortunately action spectra for the light-interruption phenomena in the dual day length-requiring plants are not available to compare with those for barley, *Hyoscyamus* and *Xanthium* (Borthwick *et al.*, 1948b; Parker *et al.*, 1950; Parker *et al.*, 1946), and it cannot be said with certainty that the photoreceptor is the same in all cases. In two respects

LD induction in *Cestrum nocturnum*, a LSDP, differs from that in LDP: continuous light is not as effective as a 16-hr photoperiod in *Cestrum* (Sachs, 1956b), whereas in LDP no combination of light and dark has been found to be more favorable than continuous light (Lang, 1952); the temperature of the photoperiod has a greater effect than the associated dark period in *Cestrum* (Sachs, 1956c), whereas in the two LDP for which the effect of temperature has been investigated the reverse was found to be true (Lang and Melchers, 1943; Liverman and Lang, 1952). These differences have been discussed elsewhere (Sachs, 1956b,c), and attempts were made to compare the various experiments; owing to great differences in experimental technique the discussion was highly speculative. For this reason it will not be repeated here, and the interested reader is referred to the original papers.

Of what help are the dual day length-requiring plants in understanding the photoperiodic control of floral initiation? Before considering this problem two assumptions will be made in order to facilitate the discussion. There have been an increasing number of reports of interspecific and intergeneric flower-inducing grafts between plants of the same and different photoperiodic type (Lang, 1952; Okuda, 1953; Khudairi and Lang, 1954), and the first assumption is that the floral stimulus is the same in all plants. The second is that the synthesis of the stimulus proceeds along the same pathway in all plants; although there is no evidence supporting this assumption, it is one that has proved valid for the biosynthesis of a number of compounds found in plants. It is recognized that both assumptions may be oversimplifications of the actual situation.

In LSDP and SLDP both LD and SD induction occur in the same plant, and, therefore, there must be at least two photosensitized reactions involved in the synthesis of the floral stimulus. In *Cestrum* it has been shown that the product of LD induction is not translocated from the treated leaves, whereas shortly after SD induction the floral stimulus moves to the axillary and terminal buds; hence, in a physiological sense, the products of LD and SD induction are easily separable. On this basis alone it is reasonable to ask whether LD induction in the LDP affects the same or a different step in the synthesis of the floral stimulus from that affected by SD induction in SDP. Furthermore, a theory of the photoperiodic control of floral initiation based on a single photosensitized reaction controlling the synthesis or destruction of the floral stimulus, or precursor (as proposed in Borthwick *et al.,* 1948a; Bakhuyzen, 1951) is not applicable to the LSDP and SLDP.

The sequence of photoperiodic requirements in the dual day length-requiring plants is obligatory, that is, the order of LD and SD induction cannot be reversed, and the following argument can be made.

In the LSDP:

$$LD_1 \quad \rightarrow \quad SD_1 \quad \rightarrow \text{floral stimulus}$$
$$\text{induction} \qquad \text{induction}$$

In the SLDP:

$$SD_2 \quad \rightarrow \quad LD_2 \quad \rightarrow \text{floral stimulus}$$
$$\text{induction} \qquad \text{induction}$$

Let the assumption be made that SD induction in the LSDP is identical with that in the SLDP, i.e., $SD_1 = SD_2$. Then, since LD_1 precedes and LD_2 follows SD induction, LD_1 cannot be identical with LD_2. Therefore, LD induction in the LSDP does not control the same step in the synthesis of the floral stimulus as it does in the SLDP. If it is assumed that $LD_1 = LD_2$, SD_1 cannot be identical with SD_2, and one can show that SD induction in the LSDP does not affect the same reaction as that in the SLDP. On the basis of our present criteria for classifying photoperiodic reactions, LD induction in the LSDP is indistinguishable from that in the SLDP, and the same is true for SD induction in these two groups. It can be concluded then that our criteria must be augmented, and we should be wary of the assumption that LD induction affects the same stage of synthesis of the floral stimulus in every LDP (the same doubt exists with regard to SD induction in all SDP).

When the chemical identity of the floral stimulus is known, an investigation of the intermediary metabolism involved in its synthesis will be feasible, and the two assumptions made at the beginning of the discussion, namely, that the floral stimulus and the pathway to its synthesis are common to all plants, can be tested. Until that time comes there is a need for more information about the characteristics of photoperiodic induction among plants of the same category. Although the dual day length-requiring plants have not contributed to a better understanding of photoperiodism and floral initiation, they present a challenge to our present concepts. With regard to the synthesis of the floral stimulus they demonstrate that there may be more than one photosensitized reaction involved in the same plant (though the photoreceptor may be concerned in the different reactions). Perhaps even more important, they show that our criteria for classifying plants as LDP or SDP do not permit us to conclude that LD or SD induction controls the same step in the synthesis of the floral stimulus in all cases.

REFERENCES

Allard, H. A. 1938. Complete or partial inhibition of flowering in certain plants when days are too short or too long. *J. Agr. Research, 57,* 775–89.

Bakhuyzen, H. L. van de Sande. 1951. Flowering and flowering hormones (one single scheme for both long and short day plants). IIA. Photoperiodism in long day plants. *Proc. Koninkl. Ned. Akad. Wetenschap,* C56, 603–23.

Borthwick, H. A., M. W. Parker, and S. B. Hendricks. 1948a. The reaction controlling floral initiation. *Vernalization and Photoperiodism,* A. E. Murneek and R. O. Whyte, Editors. Chronica Botanica, Waltham, Massachusetts. Pp. 71–78.

Borthwick, H. A., S. B. Hendricks, and M. W. Parker. 1948b. Action spectrum for photoperiodic control of floral initiation of a long day plant, Wintex barley (*Hordeum vulgare*). *Botan. Gaz., 100,* 103–18.

Forster, H. C., M. A. H. Tincker, A. J. Vasey, and S. M. Wadham. 1932. Experiments in England, Wales, and Australia on the effect of length of day on various cultivated varieties of wheat. *Ann. Appl. Biol., 19,* 378–412.

Gott, M. B., F. G. Gregory, and O. N. Purvis. 1955. Studies in vernalization of cereals. XIII. Photoperiodic control of stages in flowering between initiation and ear formation in vernalized and unvernalized Petkus winter rye. *Ann. Botany, 21,* 87–126.

Khudairi, A., and A. Lang. 1954. Flowering hormone of short day and long day plants. *Congr. intern. bot. Rapports et Communications aux Sections 11 et 12,* 331.

Lang, A. 1952. The physiology of flowering. *Ann. Rev. Plant Physiol., 3,* 265–306.

Lang, A., and G. Melchers. 1943. Die photoperiodische Reaktion von *Hyoscyamus niger. Planta, 33,* 653–702.

Liverman, J. L., and J. Bonner. 1953. The interaction of auxin and light in the growth responses of plants. *Proc. Natl. Acad. Sci. U. S., 39,* 905–16.

Liverman, J. L., and A. Lang. 1952. *The Physiology and Biochemistry of Flowering,* J. L. Liverman. Ph.D. thesis, California Institute of Technology, Pasadena.

Maximov, N. A. 1930. Physiological control of length of the vegetative period. *5th Intern. Congr. Botany Cambridge,* Abstract Commun., 275–76.

McKinney, H. H., and W. J. Sando. 1930. The behavior of winter wheat in artificial environments. *Science, 71,* 668–670.

————. 1935. Earliness of sexual reproduction in wheat as influenced by temperature and light in relation to growth phases. *J. Agr. Research, 51,* 621–41.

Okuda, M. 1953. Flower formation of *Xanthium canadense* under long day conditions induced by grafting with long day plants. *Botan. Mag. (Tokyo), 66,* 247–55.

Parker, M. W., S. B. Hendricks, H. A. Borthwick, and N. J. Scully. 1946. Action spectrum for the photoperiodic control of floral initiation of short day plants. *Botan. Gaz., 108,* 1–26.

Parker, M. W., S. B. Hendricks, and H. A. Borthwick. 1950. Action spectrum for the photoperiodic control of floral initiation of the long day plant, *Hyoscyamus niger. Botan. Gaz., 111,* 242–52.

Purvis, O. N. 1934. An analysis of the influence of temperature during germination on the subsequent development of certain winter cereals and its relation to the effect of length of day. *Ann. Botany, 1,* 919–55.

Resende, F. 1952. "Long-short" day plants. *Portugaliae Acta Biol. A3,* 318–21.

————. 1953. Acerca do impulso floral em plantas de "dia curto-lungo" e plantas de "dia lungo-curto." *Rev. fac. cienc. Lisboa, 2C3,* 447–534.

Sachs, R. M. 1956a. Floral initiation in *Cestrum nocturnum.* I. A long-short day plant. *Plant Physiol., 31,* 185–92.

————. 1956b. Floral initiation in *Cestrum nocturnum,* a long-short day plant. II. A 24-hour versus a 16-hour photoperiod for long day induction. *Plant Physiol., 31,* 429–30.

————. 1956c. Floral initiation in *Cestrum nocturnum,* a long-short day plant. III. The effect of temperature upon long day and short day induction. *Plant Physiol., 31,* 430–33.

Wellensiek, S. J. 1953. De physiolgie der bloemvormung in *Campanula medium. Proc. Koninkl. Ned. Akad. Wetenschap., 62,* 115–18.

CHEMICAL NATURE OF THE PHOTORECEPTOR PIGMENT INDUCING FRUITING OF PLASMODIA OF *Physarum polycephalum*

FREDERICK T. WOLF

Vanderbilt University, Nashville, Tennessee

The Myxomycetes are organisms characterized by a vegetative stage which is a plasmodium. Under proper conditions the plasmodium fruits, and is transformed into a number of sporangia containing spores. The conditions required for fruiting include nutritional factors and a favorable temperature. The present work is concerned with fruiting of plasmodia of *Physarum polycephalum* Schw., a species which is rather easily grown in the laboratory on 1.0% water agar, upon the surface of which are scattered sterile oat grains.

Fruiting of *P. polycephalum*, which has yellow plasmodia, has previously been studied by Gray (1938, 1939, 1953). Except in a very few cases, plasmodia grown from stock cultures maintained in the dark will not form fruiting bodies in the complete absence of light. After exposure to light, however, fruiting can then occur in darkness. The length of the vegetative phase is conditioned by the total amount of light received; the more intense the light, the shorter is the time required for fruiting.

Gray observed that the shorter wavelengths of the visible spectrum (blue) were more effective in stimulating the fruiting response than was yellow or red light. The blue line of the mercury arc (436 mμ) was more effective than either the green line at 546 mμ or the yellow at 578 mμ. The yellow pigment was extracted from the plasmodium with acetone, and its spectrum showed an absorption maximum in the blue. It was therefore concluded that the yellow pigment of the plasmodia is a photoreceptor which interacts with light to bring about the morphogenetic response of fruiting.

In studying the influence of pH upon fruiting, by using McIlvaine's citric acid-NaH_2PO_4 buffers of pH 3.0–8.0, Gray found that a higher percentage of the cultures fruited, and that less time was required for fruiting, at pH 3.0 or 4.0.

The chemistry of the pigment is not known, although Seifriz and Zetzmann (1935) have shown that it possesses the properties of an indicator, and Allman (1955) has studied it intensively in connection with the problem of estimation of the quantity of plasmodium by the amount of pigment produced. We are presently concerned with certain of the chemical and physical properties of the pigment, which appears to be important in the photoinduction of fruiting.

METHODS

Complete removal of the yellow pigment present in the plasmodia may be achieved by extraction with methanol, as recommended by Allman (1955). As mentioned by Gray (1938), the yellow plasmodia begin to lose their color shortly before fruiting begins. They eventually become white or colorless. When the black sporangia of cultures which had fruited one day previously were extracted with methanol, with thorough grinding in a mortar, no trace of yellow pigment was apparent. It seems clear that the yellow pigment characteristic of plasmodia disappears completely upon fruiting.

When examined with an ultraviolet light, the plasmodia of P. polycephalum are strongly fluorescent. Methanol extracts containing the pigment are likewise fluorescent. A fluorescence spectrum was taken, which showed two peaks at 473 mμ and 505 mμ. It was therefore suspected that two pigments are present in the plasmodium.

Accordingly, the methanol extract was chromatographed on strips of Whatman No. 1 filter paper, by the ascending technique, with $3N$ NH$_4$OH as the developing solvent. Two yellow spots were found on visual inspection. These spots were characterized by Rf values of 0.44–0.62 and 0.67–0.77. The two substances will be subsequently referred to as component 1 and component 2, respectively.

In order to separate quantities of the two pigments greater than would be possible by paper chromatographic techniques, column chromatography was employed. With a column of alumina measuring approximately 1 × 10 cm, the methanol solution of the two pigments could be separated. Component 1 is strongly adsorbed, and remains

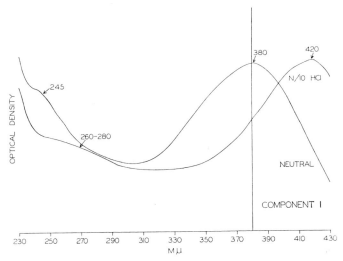

FIG. 1.   The absorption spectrum of component 1 from *Physarum poly-cephalum* in neutral and acid solution.

within 2 to 3 cm of the top of the column. It could not be eluted with organic solvents, but was readily eluted by 0.1*N* HCl. Component 2 is weakly adsorbed, and its methanol solution was collected at the foot of the column.

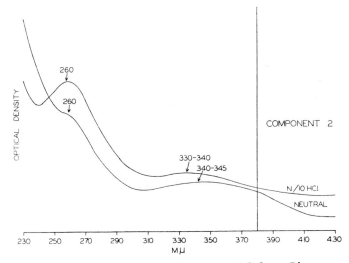

FIG. 2.   The absorption spectrum of component 2 from *Physarum poly-cephalum* in neutral and acid solution.

RESULTS AND DISCUSSION

The fluorescence spectrum of component 1 in 0.1N HCl showed a maximum at 505 mμ. The fluorescence spectrum of component 2 in methanol has a maximum at 473 mμ.

Absorption spectra of the two substances were taken in both the ultraviolet and visible regions with a model DU Beckman spectrophotometer. Previous spectral studies by Gray (1953) and Allman (1955) had been restricted to the visible. It was the ultraviolet spectra which first provided us with a clue as to the chemical nature of the two pigments. Component 1 in acid solution has a very prominent peak in the visible at 420 mμ, and a smaller inconspicuous maximum in the region of 260–280 mμ. In neutral solution, the position of these peaks is changed to 380 mμ and 245 mμ. In alkaline solution, the 380-mμ peak is unchanged, but the other peak shifts to 265 mμ.

Component 2 in acid solution likewise has a spectrum with two maxima, located at 330–340 mμ and at 260 mμ. In neutral solution, the 260-mμ peak is unchanged, but the longer wavelength maximum is shifted slightly to 340–345 mμ. In alkaline solution, the short-wavelength peak is shifted to 265 mμ, and the long-wavelength maximum is broadened in the region of 330–350 mμ.

The possession of two absorption maxima in the ultraviolet or near ultraviolet, the shifts in position of maxima with change in pH, and the fluorescence of the compounds in question indicate that component 1 and component 2 are pteridines (Gates, 1947; Wolstenholme and Cameron, 1954; Albert, 1954). It has not been possible to identify either component 1 or component 2 with any known compound of this group.[1]

Through the kindness of Dr. Ernest A. Jones, the two pigments

[1] Biological verification of the identity of component 1 as a pteridine was obtained by microbiological assay with the flagellate *Crithidia fasciculata*, which requires for growth both a conjugated and an unconjugated pteridine (Nathan *et al.*, 1956). The growth factor activity of component 1 in the presence of low levels of folic acid, but not in the presence of *Crithidia* factor, indicates that component 1 is an unconjugated trisubstituted pteridine. The author gratefully acknowledges the kindness of Miss Helene A. Nathan, Haskins Laboratories, New York 17, N. Y., in performing this bioassay.

were examined in the infrared region, with a Perkin-Elmer model 21 spectrophotometer. Component 1 showed a large peak at 3400 cm^{-1} attributed to an —OH group, a small peak at 1600 attributed to an —NH$_2$ group, a large peak at 1440 attributed to an —OH group, a small peak at 1120 attributed to an —NH$_2$ group, and a small peak at 880 cm^{-1} possibly due to meta-disubstituted or trisubstituted ring structure. The infrared spectrum of component 2 was somewhat more complex. There was a large peak at 3300 cm^{-1} attributed to an —OH group, a large peak at 2900, small peaks at 2300 and 1750, a large peak at 1560 attributed to an —NH$_2$ group, a large peak at 1420 attributed to an —OH group, a small peak at 1240, a large peak at 1050 attributed to an —NH$_2$ group, and small peaks at 920 and 830 cm^{-1}. Thus the infrared spectra, demonstrating the presence of —OH and —NH$_2$ groups, support the conclusion that both pigments are pteridines.

Component 2 cannot possibly be the photoreceptor of blue light which activates fruiting in *P. polycephalum,* since its longest wavelength absorption maxima lie fairly deep in the ultraviolet. Component 1, however, appears to have the characteristics expected for the photoreceptor. In acid solution, it has a prominent peak at 420 mμ, and a large amount of absorption in the lower limits of the visible spectrum. In neutral (or alkaline) solution, the peak shifts to 380 mμ, so that the amount of absorption in the visible is greatly reduced. These absorption characteristics, and their shift with pH would seem to offer a reasonable explanation of both the influence of blue light in the photoinduction of the fruiting response and the superiority of acid conditions for fruiting.

The preceding results were obtained with pigments extracted from plasmodia grown under the normal conditions of alternate light and darkness in the laboratory. It became of interest to determine whether both pigments would be produced in plasmodia grown in constant darkness. In such plasmodia, both components are present, and no indication was obtained that their quantities are grossly different from those which characterize light-grown cultures. This result is consistent with the hypothesis that it is not component 1 per se which triggers the fruiting response, but rather the interaction of this compound with light. The role of component 2 remains problematical. It may have no influence whatever upon fruiting. It may conceivably be either a precursor or a degradation product of component 1.

SUMMARY

Plasmodia of *Physarum polycephalum,* grown either under alternate light and darkness, or in constant darkness, contain two yellow fluorescent pigments, which disappear upon fruiting. The two pigments are separable by paper chromatography or column chromatography. Absorption spectra of these compounds in the ultraviolet, visible, and infrared regions, and the fluorescence spectra of these compounds have been studied. Both pigments have been identified as pteridines.

The spectral properties of one pigment and the shifts in its spectrum with pH are such as to offer an explanation of the effectiveness of low pH and blue light in bringing about the morphogenetic response of fruiting.

REFERENCES

Albert, Adrien. 1954. The pteridines. *Fortschr. Chem. org. Naturstoffe, 11,* 350–403.

Allman, Wm. T., Jr. 1955. Methods for the quantification of Myxomycete plasmodia. Ph.D. thesis, Vanderbilt University, Nashville, Tenn.

Gates, Marshall. 1947. The chemistry of the pteridines. *Chem. Revs., 41,* 63–95.

Gray, W. D. 1938. The effect of light on the fruiting of Myxomycetes. *Am. J. Botany, 25,* 511–22.

————. 1939. The relation of pH and temperature to the fruiting of *Physarum polycephalum. Am. J. Botany, 26,* 709–14.

————. 1953. Further studies on the fruiting of *Physarum polycephalum. Mycologia, 45,* 817–24.

Nathan, H. A., S. H. Hutner, and H. L. Levin. 1956. Independent requirements for *Crithidia* factor and folic acid in a trypanosomid flagellate. *Nature, 178,* 741–42.

Seifriz, W., and M. Zetzmann. 1935. A slime mould pigment as indicator of acidity. *Protoplasma, 23,* 175–79.

Wolstenholme, G. E. W., and M. P. Cameron. 1954. *Chemistry and Biology of Pteridines.* Ciba Foundation Symposium. Little, Brown & Co., Boston, Mass.

Growth Factors and Flowering

THE INFLUENCE OF GIBBERELLIN AND AUXIN ON PHOTOPERIODIC INDUCTION [1]

ANTON LANG

Department of Botany, University of California, Los Angeles

The influence of auxin and gibberellin on flower formation, specifically on photoinduction, to which this discussion will be limited, has been studied in an attempt to get a toehold on the biochemistry of flowering. It has been somewhat of an act of desperation, for even though auxin and gibberellin control a great number of growth processes in the plant, there is no advance reason to believe that they should control flower formation, too. However, all more direct and more logical attempts to penetrate into the biochemistry of flowering which were made in the past have remained inconclusive. Thus, there is considerable physiological evidence for the existence of floral stimuli or flowering hormones, but all attempts at isolating and identifying these materials have been conspicuous by their lack of success, and some investigators—though not myself—are presently inclined to relegate them into the realm of scientific myth.

Extensive efforts have also been made to discover biochemical differences between induced and noninduced plants and to relate them to the process of flower induction. With respect to the first of these two goals, this work has been quite successful. More plant constituents, sugars, nitrogenous substances, vitamins, etc., are changed, at least quantitatively, after photoinduction than are not. The same is true for enzyme activities and various other processes in the plant. Some of them go up, and others go down; however, the second goal has not been reached; a clear-cut causal relation between these changes and flower induction has not been established. The most promising

[1] The author's personal research, referred to in this paper, has been generously supported by research grants from the National Institutes of Health, U. S. Public Health Service (RG-3939), the National Science Foundation (G-3388), The Lilly Research Laboratories, and the Committee for Research, University of California.

case was the discovery by Gregory *et al.* (1954) that photoinduction causes a spectacular increase in the dark fixation of CO_2 in the short-day plant *Kalanchoë blossfeldiana.* The parallelism between this change and the progress of photoinduction is such as to suggest a close relation. However, an analysis of the products of induced and non-induced CO_2 dark fixation did not reveal any significant differences (Kunitake *et al.,* 1957). The level of CO_2 dark fixation and metabolism in an induced *Kalanchoë* plant is raised, but this rise is one across the board; no part of the existing system seems to be favored above the other, and there is no evidence that a new pathway of CO_2 metabolism is established. This does not exclude a causal relation with flowering, but it is not clear, if such a relation does exist, at which point CO_2 dark metabolism and the processes of flower induction are linked.

After thus having down-rated the more direct efforts at penetrating into the biochemistry of flower formation, I might be expected to up-rate the auxin and gibberellin approaches by showing that they have done the trick and, logical or not, have crashed the gate into that fascinating field. But I am afraid it would be too sanguine to make such a claim. A skeptic might even summarize the status of these approaches by saying, there is much to talk about and little to say concerning the influence of auxin on flower formation, and there is little to talk about concerning the influence of gibberellins—and likewise little to say. However, at least gibberellin does produce dramatic effects on flower formation in certain types of plants, and it is reasonable to assume, as a working hypothesis, that gibberellin-like materials play a part in the biochemical events that underlie flower formation. But what part this is remains for future work to determine.

AUXIN

Influence of Auxin on Photoinduction in Short-Day Plants

The influence of auxin on photoinduction was first noted about 20 years ago. In 1937, Dostál and Hosek reported that flower formation in long-day-grown cuttings of *Circaea lutetiana,* a long-day plant, is delayed by auxin treatment; in 1938, Hamner and Bonner showed that the flower-inducing effect of a long dark period in *Xanthium,* a short-day plant, is greatly reduced by simultaneous auxin application. However, this early work failed to attract much notice, and further studies along these lines did not start until about 10 years later. In 1949, Bonner and Thurlow, and Harder and van Senden published extensive data on *Xanthium* and on *Kalanchoë blossfeldiana,* which confirmed and extended the earlier observations. Today, the inhibitory effect of applied auxin on photoinduction in short-day plants is well established for several species; some typical data are shown in Table I.

TABLE I.   Inhibition of Photoinduction in *Kalanchoë blossfeldiana* by Applied Auxin
(Harder and van Senden, 1949)

3-Indoleacetic Acid, mg/liter	Plants Treated	Plants Flowering	Days to Visible Flower Buds	Flower Buds per Plant, No.
0	6	6	24	79
1	8	7	25	35
10	8	6	33	9
100	8	0	—	—

Once the inhibitory effect of auxin on photoinduction in short-day plants can be accepted as a fact, a number of questions immediately arise: (1) Is this auxin effect a physiological one? (2) Is it a genuine auxin action? (3) Where, precisely, in the complex process of photoinduction is the point of auxin attack? (4) Does the native auxin of a short-day plant play a part in its photoinduction? And if this is so, the most important of all: (5) what is the role of the native auxin of the short-day plant in photoinduction?

Question 1 may be answered with "Yes." A significant decrease in photoinduction may be caused by auxin concentrations which have only a slight and passing effect on the growth of the treated plants.

The answer to question 2 seems also to be in the affirmative. All typical auxins that have been tried (indoleacetic acid, naphthaleneacetic acid, 2,4-dichlorophenoxyacetic acid, and perhaps one or two more) exhibited an inhibitory effect on photoinduction in short-day plants. Moreover, Bonner and Thurlow (1949) have reported that this effect of auxin can be offset by simultaneous application of an antiauxin. The experimental evidence on this latter point is very limited (see Table II) and ought to be expanded. However, the evidence that is available, taken in its entirety, supports the conclusion

TABLE II. Reversal of Auxin Inhibition of Photoinduction in
Xanthium pensylvanicum by Simultaneous Application of an
Antiauxin (Bonner and Thurlow, 1949)

		Number of Plants	
α-Naphthaleneacetic Acid, mg/liter	2,4-Dichloroanisol, mg/liter	Vegetative	With Inflorescence or Flower Primordia
—	—	2	10
10	—	11	1
30	—	12	0
—	10	0	10
10	100	1	8
30	10	6	4

that the inhibition of photoinduction in short-day plants by applied auxin is a typical auxin response.

A definitive answer to question 3, is, to my mind, not yet possible, but there exists some pertinent information on this point which should ultimately help us to obtain such an answer. Photoinduction in short-day plants can be subdivided into a series of consecutive partial reactions or "steps." If any of these steps is blocked, flower formation will not take place. The first step is a "high-intensity-light reaction" (Hamner, 1940). It is followed by a series of reactions which can take place only in the dark. Hamner (1940) showed that the events in the early part of an inductive dark period, the period before the "critical length" of the dark period has been reached, are different from those in its later part, which probably consist in the actual synthesis of the floral stimulus. The earlier events are completely negated by a light interruption; they thus constitute the "timing mechanism" of photoinduction. Floral stimulus synthesis is stopped by light, quite likely because some condition which has been created by the "timing mechanism" is now abolished, but the stimulus which had time to accumulate is preserved. Salisbury and Bonner (1956) presented evidence suggesting that the "timing mechanism" involves two distinct steps, the first being the conversion of the "photoperiodic pigment" from the far-red- into the red-absorbing form, the second a "preparatory reaction" of unknown nature, but quite distinct from pigment conversion. Lockhart and Hamner (1954), on the other hand, by terminating an inductive dark period by a brief period of light and then subjecting the plant to another dark period, showed that the floral stimulus does not appear in its final form, but first in the form of some labile precursor; this precursor is then converted to the floral stimulus proper, this "stabilization" requiring high-intensity light, or at least being greatly promoted by such a light. Thus, five partial reactions have been proposed: (1) the "first" high-intensity-light reaction; (2) pigment conversion; (3) "preparatory reaction"; (4) synthesis of the floral stimulus precursor; (5) stabilization of the stimulus (second high-intensity-light reaction). All these reactions occur in the leaf; export of the floral stimulus to the buds does not, as a rule, begin until several hours after the end of the dark period.

It ought to be stated that, the evidence for the above reactions being strictly physiological in nature, it is entirely possible that any of these reactions, perhaps with the exception of pigment conversion, is of a compound character. On the other hand, it is equally possible that some of the reactions are actually identical. Thus, it seems conceivable to me that the two high-intensity-light reactions are the same, and I am also not entirely convinced that the separation of the "preparatory reaction" and the floral stimulus (precursor) synthesis is sufficiently justified.

These questions are important for the final interpretation of the "locus" of auxin action in photoinduction of short-day plants. At present, we can say three things. First, auxin affects some of the reactions which occur in the leaf; secondly, auxin does not seem to interfere with the "timing mechanism" of induction, but rather with floral stimulus synthesis; thirdly, its action seems to depend on the (first) high-intensity-light reaction.

Salisbury (1955) and Salisbury and Bonner (1956) showed in *Xanthium* that auxin applied after the floral stimulus has left the leaf does not reduce the flowering response any more and may even promote it (see later). They also showed that auxin application does not affect the critical length of the dark period, and that auxin must therefore interfere with the later events of the dark period, that is, with some of the events in flower hormone synthesis. Lockhart and Hamner (1954) found that auxin application greatly enhances the flower-reducing action of the "second dark period" (see above). Hamner and Nanda (1956), on the other hand, showed that the inhibitory effect of auxin on photoinduction in *Xanthium* is very much greater if the light period preceding the dark period is short. They also observed (in Biloxi soybean) a simple, linear relation between the logarithm of auxin concentration and the effect (reduction of the flowering response) and assume that auxin reacts directly with some high-intensity-light product and renders it unavailable for the subsequent reactions of photoinduction. If it can be assumed that the first and the second high-intensity-light reactions are identical, and if it is furthermore assumed that the product of these reactions is necessary for the stabilization of the floral stimulus, it becomes possible to interpret auxin inhibition of photoinduction in short-day plants in a unified and specific manner.

Question 4. Does their native or endogenous auxin—or, as we can now say more specifically, the native auxin in their leaves—play a part in photoinduction of short-day plants? Several studies suggest that the efficiency of photoinduction can be increased by measures which result in a decrease of the endogenous auxin level in the plant. Bonner (1949) showed that application of antiauxin caused a weak flowering response in *Xanthium* plants which were kept just below the threshold of flower formation (by irradiation with weak red light during the night periods of inductive cycles). Khudairi and Hamner (1954a) obtained a similar effect by applying ethylene chlorohydrin, a substance that seems to lower the auxin content of plant tissues. Lona and Bocchi (1955) found that *Perilla* plants which had been treated with eosin required fewer photoinductive cycles for flower formation than untreated plants, and it may be assumed that eosin lowers the auxin content of the plants because of photosensitized auxin destruction. All these results, even though they can hardly be considered as definite, still make it likely that a relatively high auxin level in a short-day plant reduces the effectiveness of photoinduction.

Question 5. What, exactly, is the role of the native auxin in photoinduction? Two possibilities can be envisaged: either that auxin is directly involved in photoinduction, that it is, in other words, an integral part of the inductive mechanism itself; or that it modifies the operation of this mechanism, without being an actual part of the latter. If the first alternative were true, one might expect that the auxin level in the leaf would change in the course of an inductive cycle, particularly in the course of its dark period. If the second alternative were right, no such change need be expected, but there should be a relation between the auxin content of the leaf and its effectiveness in photoinduction.

A number of authors have analyzed the auxin content of induced and noninduced short-day plants. The results were rather heterogeneous. Von Witsch (1941) reported that plants in short day had less auxin than plants in long day. Cooke (1954) found that, after transfer to short days, auxin content first increases and later decreases. Vlitos and Meudt (1954) reported that induced soybean plants contain about 100 times more auxin than noninduced ones; other short-day plants did not exhibit similar differences, but induced individuals seemed to contain more indolepyruvic acid than vegetative ones. Except for that of Vlitos and Meudt, who used paper chromatographic separation, most of this work is open to question, since the possibility of the presence of inhibitory materials does not seem to have received due attention. But the main shortcoming of all this work is that the analyses were done either at certain intervals during the course of the inductive treatment, or—more frequently—long after photoinduction had been consummated. However, as stated before, if auxin is a part of the inductive mechanism, the crucial fluctuations should occur in the course of the inductive dark period. Therefore, the available results of the analytical approach must be termed inconclusive.

The fluctuations in the auxin content of leaves of different age, on the other hand, argue against a direct role of auxin in photoinduction. No measurements of the age changes of auxin content seem to have been made in the leaves of any of our photoperiodic war horses, such as *Xanthium* or Biloxi soybean. But if one may judge from such determinations in other plants, it appears that leaves with a high auxin content may be highly sensitive to photoinduction. The auxin content of a leaf is at a peak when the leaf undergoes most rapid expansion; it drops off sharply as the leaf reaches full size, and then may stay at a fairly uniform level until the onset of senescence (Goodwin, 1937; Jacobs, 1952; Shoji *et al.*, 1951). In *Xanthium*, however, highest photoinduction sensitivity is reached in a leaf which has attained about half its final size and is at its most rapid phase of expansion (Khudairi and Hamner, 1954b; Salisbury, 1955), that is, a leaf which is presumably at its top auxin level. In Biloxi soybean, expanding leaves seem somewhat less sensitive to photoinduction than leaves which have just reached full size (Borthwick and Parker, 1940), but this sensitivity change is much less than the change in auxin content of bean leaves during a comparable age interval (see Shoji et al., 1951).

One may of course argue that this evidence is not conclusive; photoperiodic sensitivity of a leaf may be limited by some other factor that changes with age. One can also raise other arguments, for example, that only one of the several auxins which seem to occur in plant tissues is important in induction, or that it is not the total auxin of a leaf but only a small, "physiologically effective" fraction thereof. I cannot deny that the evidence I can present leaves many loopholes through which a staunch defender of a more direct part of auxin in photoinduction can wiggle out; in fact, he does not have to wiggle at all, he can walk out, his head high in the air with disdain. But what evidence there is is not in favor of auxin being more than a modifying influence in photoinduction of short-day plants.

One last argument that I would like to make also supports this conclusion. Photoinduction in obligate short- (and long-) day plants contains a qualitative or all-or-none element; above (or below) a certain photoperiod, no flower formation whatever will occur, regardless of the duration of the treatment. The auxin effect on photoinduction in short-day plants, however, seems to be a purely quantitative matter. If a plant is given minimum induction, for example, a cocklebur one dark period of, say, 10 or 12 hr, it is fairly easy to suppress its effect completely by applying a moderate concentration of auxin. But if the inductive treatment is repeated, some flowering response will as a rule be obtained even in plants treated with high auxin concentrations. In one experiment in which I used a concentration of 1000 mg/liter of indoleacetic acid, I was not able to suppress induction completely when the plants (Xanthium) received continuous short-day treatment. This pronouncedly quantitative character of the auxin effect, in contrast to the partly qualitative of photoinduction, likewise suggests that auxin has only a modifying influence on photoinduction in short-day plants.

Influence of Auxin on Photoperiodic Induction in Long-Day Plants

In long-day plants, the only information on auxin effects on photo-induction that was available for quite some time was similar to the original observation of Dostál and Hosek (1937), that is, auxin may reduce the effectiveness of photoinduction. Von Denffer and Gründler (1950) found that auxin treatment delayed flower formation in long-day-grown *Calendula officinalis;* von Denffer and Schlitt (1951) showed that UV irradiation, which, somewhat similar to ethylene chlorohydrin treatment, seems to decrease the auxin content of plants, promoted flower formation in long-day-grown flax and *Statice bonduelli.* In many other long-day species, neither of these treatments had any specific effect on the flowering response, but this may well be due to quantitative differences in the sensitivity of the plants to auxin.

A few years ago, however, Liverman and Lang (1956) were able to demonstrate a promotive effect of auxin on photoinduction in two long-day plants, *Hyoscyamus niger* and *Silene armeria*. When these plants were grown in short days (8 hr of light daily), but were given subsaturating intensities of supplementary light during the night period, simultaneous auxin treatment resulted in flower formation, or increased

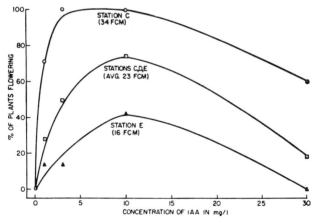

FIG. 1.   Promotion of photoinduction in annual *Hyoscyamus niger* by simultaneous treatment with auxin. The plants received various levels of supplementary light during the 16-hr night period and were sprayed with auxin daily before the start of the dark period.

the flowering response. An experiment with *Hyoscyamus* is shown in Fig. 1. The auxin used in these original experiments was indole-acetic acid. Since then, I have been able to obtain similar results with indolebutyric acid and naphthaleneacetic acid (unpublished data).

From these results, it might appear that auxin has opposite influence on photoinduction in short- and long-day plants: inhibitory in the former, and promotive in the latter. Such a situation might be very interesting. Short- and long-day plants respond to photoperiod in the opposite manner. Their photoreceptors, however, appear to be the same, and so do their floral stimuli. In view of this situation, one might expect that in the course of the processes of photoinduction which follow the initial photoreaction there appears a compound which has opposite effects on flower stimulus formation in the two response types. This compound would occupy a pivot position in the photo-periodic "mechanism," and auxin, on the basis of the above results, seemed to fit this position.

A German saying goes, "One should stop eating when it tastes best," and I suppose we should have stopped our work at this point. However, we were ambitious and wanted to make the story perfect, and in trying to do so we lost what story we did have. It turned out

TABLE III.   Effect of Applied Auxin and Antiauxin on Photoinduction in Annual *Hyoscyamus niger*

Substance	Concentration, molar $\times 10^{-6}$	Flowering Response, % [a]	
		Supplementary Light during Night	No Supplementary Light during Night
Control	—	0	0
3-Indoleacetic acid	20	33	—
	60	100	—
	200	100	0 [b]
2,3,5-Triiodobenzoic acid	0.6	0	0
	2	25	0
	6	50	0
2,4-Dichlorophenoxy-isobutyric acid	6	100	—
	20	100	—
	60	100	—
	200	20	—

[a] Percent plants with flower buds.
[b] Approximately 100 molar $\times 10^{-6}$.

(Lang, unpublished data) that antiauxins influence photoinduction in *Hyoscyamus* in much the same manner as auxins, a finding which renders the above explanation rather improbable. An example of this effect is shown in Table III, and Table IV lists the auxins and antiauxins

TABLE IV. Effect of Applied Auxins and Antiauxins on Photoinduction in Annual *Hyoscyamus* (Plants were given short days with weak supplementary light during night periods)

Auxins	Antiauxins
Promotion at Relatively Low Concentrations, Inhibition at Higher Ones	
3-Indoleacetic acid	2,3,5-Triiodobenzoic acid
3-Indolebutyric acid	2,6-Dichlorophenoxyacetic acid
α-Naphthaleneacetic acid	2,4,6-Trichlorophenoxyacetic acid
	p-Chlorophenoxyisobutyric acid
	2,4-Dichlorophenoxyisobutyric acid
	2,4-Dichloroanisol (weak effect)
	2,4-Dichlorophenetol (weak effect)
No Promotion; Inhibition at Higher Concentrations	
3-Indolepropionic acid	Skatol
β-Naphthoxyacetic acid	
2,4-Dichlorophenoxyacetic acid	

which promoted the flowering response in *Hyoscyamus* plants receiving subsaturating intensities of supplementary light. The few negative cases are probably without significance, indolepropionic acid being a rather weak auxin, β-naphthoxyacetic acid and 2,4-D producing injurious effects which would mask any flower-promotive action that might be present, and the inactivity of skatol probably being a question of insufficient penetration. The salient point in Table IV is that at least 3 auxins and 5 to 7 antiauxins had a similar promotive effect on photoinduction in *Hyoscyamus*.

Auxin and antiauxin producing the same effect is not easy to explain, particularly since in short-day plants they seem to obey law and order, antiauxin offsetting the effect of auxin (see Table II). One explanation is that auxin inhibits photoinduction in long-day plants just as it does in short-day plants, but that the endogenous auxin in long-day plants is at a level which is already optimal for this effect. In this event, both the addition of auxin and of antiauxin would reduce the auxin effect, that is, lower the degree of inhibition and thus promote flower formation.

Unfortunately, this hypothesis will not be easy to test, for the flowering response does not lend itself to the precise quantitative treatment which would be necessary for such a test. And on second thought, perhaps this is not so unfortunate at all. For would even a complete explanation of the auxin and antiauxin effect on photoinduction in long-day plants contribute to our understanding of the induction process itself? I am dubious about this, for the same statement can be made about the effect of auxin on photoinduction in long-day plants as had to be made in short-day plants. The effect seems to be a strictly quantitative one. If the auxin or antiauxin treatment is done under strict short-day conditions, without any supplementary light, that is, if we are in the qualitative range of photoinduction, no flowering response whatever is obtained (see Table III). If, on the other hand, the intensity of the supplementary light is raised to a saturating level and all plants initiate flowers, auxin has no promotive effect either, its only influence being inhibition of flower formation by relatively high concentrations. Auxin thus does not seem to be a decisive factor in photoinduction of long-day plants either; it seems rather to be able to *modify* the effectiveness of induction within a fairly narrow range of specific light conditions.

Postinductive and Preinductive Auxin Effects in Short- and Long-Day Plants

The auxin picture in relation to photoinduction is complicated by the fact that in addition to the auxin effects about which I have spoken so far, and which seem to be on induction itself, there are some other auxin effects on flower formation which may be superimposed on the induction effects. I have mentioned before, that, according to Salisbury (1955), auxin which is applied after the floral stimulus has left the leaf may promote flower formation. This promotion is most evident when the postinductive light conditions are not too good. An apparently similar effect has been observed by Leopold and Thimann (1949) in a long-day plant, Wintex barley. These authors found that auxin application increased the number of spikelets formed upon long-day treatment. They interpreted this as an effect on induction, but Hussey and Gregory (1954) showed that it is an effect on the development on the initiated spikelets which goes hand in hand with enhanced vegetative growth. Some other cases have been reported in which auxin seems to promote the manifestation of induction, but lack of time makes it impossible to discuss them here.

I would, however, like to mention briefly that, although relatively high auxin levels are unfavorable to photoinduction—in short-day plants for certain, and perhaps in long-day plants as well—effective induction may possibly depend on the presence of a certain, minimum auxin level in the plant. De Zeeuw and Leopold (1955) found that young Brussels Sprouts plants, which were not yet capable of responding to floral induction, could be made to do so by auxin application. It is conceivable that plants too young to flower have too low an auxin level, and that at least one of the physiological meanings of the "ripeness-to-flower" state of Klebs is the attainment of a certain auxin level in the plant. Brussels Sprouts requires thermoinduction (a period of low temperature), and I do not know of similar experiments with long- and short-day plants; such experiments, however, might prove very interesting.

In addition to auxin effects on photoinduction, we thus have postinductive effects of auxin in flower formation, and we may have preinductive effects. These effects may be opposite; that is, some may promote the visible response, others may inhibit it. In different species, these various effects may be quantitatively different, and this may account for differences in the auxin responses which we may encounter in different plants. We must examine very carefully with what kind of auxin effect on flower formation we may be dealing, before we try to classify and to generalize it.

GIBBERELLIN

With gibberellin there was more direct reason to check for effects on flower formation than there was with auxin. Most cold-requiring and long-day plants, when kept in a noninductive environment, grow in the habit of rosettes, without any elongate stem. Gibberellin was discovered as a promoter of stem elongation (Yabuta and Hayashi, 1939; see also review by Stowe and Yamaki, 1957). It was obviously desirable to see whether this substance would also cause stem formation in a stemless plant, and whether this might result in flowering. It soon was found that the one and the other did occur.

The first observation was made in a cold-requiring plant, a biennial strain of *Hyoscyamus niger* (Lang, 1956a,b). It soon was followed by numerous similar observations in other cold-requiring and likewise in long-day plants, all grown under strictly noninductive conditions. I want to show just one example, *Samolus parviflorus,* a long-day plant (Fig. 2), and then give a list of those long-day plants in which positive

Fig. 2.   Gibberellin-induced flower formation in *Samolus parviflorus,* a long-day plant, grown on a 9-hr short-day. From left to right: controls; plants treated with 1, 2, 5, 10, and 20 µg of gibberellin daily.

results have been reported (Table V). Of particular interest is a study by Bünsow and Harder (1956a). These authors found that gibberellin induces flowering in some long-short-day plants (two species of *Bryophyllum*) when grown on short day, that is, substitutes for the long-day part of their induction.

As in the case of auxin, after having established the effect of a substance on the response in which we are interested, a number of questions will promptly arise. The first one is, has this effect any physiological meaning? The chemically known gibberellins are products of certain strains of a mold (*Fusarium moniliforme,* sexual stage *Gibberella fujikuroi*) and have not been found to occur in any other organism.[2] Can we put any faith o nthe effects of such as extraneous material? The most direct and conclusive way of answering this question would be to see whether our plants contain some gibberellin-

[2] *Note added in proof:* Recently, one of the *Fusarium* gibberellins, gibberellin A_1, has been reported to occur also in bean seeds (J. Macmillan and P. J. Suter, *Naturwissenschaften, 45,* 46, 1958).

TABLE V. Long-Day Plants in Which Flower Formation Has Been Induced or Promoted under Short-Day Conditions by Gibberellin Treatment

Family	Species	Response[a]	Authority
Caryophyllaceae	*Silene armeria*	I	Lang, 1956c, 1957
Chenopodiaceae	*Spinacia oleracea* (spinach), 2 var.	I	Wittwer and Bukovac, 1957a,b
Compositae	*Crepis tectorum*	I	Lang, 1956c, 1957
	Crepis leontodontoides	I	Lona, 1956a
	Lactuca sativa (lettuce), 2 var.	I	Wittwer and Bukovac, 1957a,b
	Lactuca sativa (lettuce), 2 var.	P(7–20 days)	Wittwer and Bukovac, 1957a,b
	Lactuca dentata		Wittwer and Bukovac, 1957a,b
	La(m)psana communis	I	Bünsow and Harder, 1956b
	Rudbeckia bicolor	I	Bünsow and Harder, 1957
	Rudbeckia hirta	I	Bünsow and Harder, 1957
Cruciferae	*Brassica juncea* (mustard)	P(9–29 days)	Wittwer and Bukovac, 1957a,b
	Raphanus sativus (radish), 4 var.	I	Wittwer and Bukovac, 1957a,b
Onagraceae	*Oenothera* sp.	I	Sachs, unpublished data
Primulaceae	*Samolus parviflorus*	I	Lang, 1956c, 1957
Ranunculaceae	*Adonis flammeus*	P(3 months)	Bünsow and Harder, 1957
	Delphinium ajacis (larkspur)	P	Lindstrom, Wittwer, and Bukovac, 1957
	Myosurus minimus	I	Lona and Bocchi, 1956
Solanaceae	*Hyoscyamus niger*, 2 annual var.	I	Lang, 1956c, 1957
	Petunia hybrida, 6 var.	P(1–4 weeks)	Lindstrom, Wittwer and Bukovac, 1957
Umbelliferae	*Anethum graveolens* (dill)	I	Wittwer and Bukovac, 1957a,b

[a] I, flower formation induced (controls vegetative, at least for duration of experiment); P, flowering promoted (in parentheses: difference of flowering time between treated plants and controls). In some cases, this information is preliminary in character.

like materials, and whether these are affected by photoinduction or thermoinduction. I cannot yet present results of such experiments, but Dr. Lona will fill in this gap to some extent (next paper).[3] However, I

[3] *Note added in proof:* In the meantime, I have been able to obtain evidence for the presence of gibberellin-like materials in annual *Hyoscyamus* plants and for quantitative and/or qualitative differences in the "gibberellin" content of vegetative and photoinduced individuals of the species (unpublished data).

was able to obtain at least a good indication in a somewhat devious manner. Gibberellin-like materials have been found in other seed plants (Phinney *et al.*, 1957, and others), and we applied one such gibberellin-like material, contained in the endosperm of a wild cucurbit, *Echinocystis macrocarpa*, to a vegetative long-day plant and obtained an entirely similar response as with the *Fusarium* gibberellins (Lang *et al.*, 1957; see Fig. 3). This result suggests that gibberellin-

FIG. 3. Induction of flower formation in short-day-grown *Samolus parviflorus* by endosperm of *Echinocystis macrocarpa* (left) and by gibberellin (right).

like native materials are capable of regulating flower formation in certain plants, specifically, that they can overcome the flower-preventing effect of short day in long-day plants.

Another piece of evidence suggesting that gibberellins are involved in the natural regulation of flower formation is that it seems possible to enhance the effect of suboptimal photoinduction in long-day plants with suboptimal gibberellin dosages, or vice versa. Some such information has just been published by Bünsow and Harder (1957) for two species of *Rudbeckia,* and I am presently in the process of gathering what seem to be similar data. I should like to say, however, that these data are not yet sufficient for a conclusive statement, and I am mentioning them here subject to change without notice.

The next question will logically be: What precisely is the role of gibberellin in flower formation, specifically, in the photoperiodic control of this process? Let us approach this problem step by step and first examine the effect of gibberellin on flower formation in short-day plants. Not nearly as many species have been examined as in the case of cold-requiring and long-day plants, but in those obligate short-day species that were examined (*Kalanchoë blossfeldiana:* Harder and Bünsow, 1956, 1957; *Xanthium* and Biloxi soybean: Lang, 1957; *Perilla ocymoides:* Lona, 1956a) gibberellin did not induce flower formation under long-day conditions. Dr. Wittwer found promotion of flowering in a facultative or quantitative short-day plant, *Cosmos* (later in this part), and some authors report promotive effects of gibberellin treatment on short-day induction in various short-day induction in *Xanthium* (Lincoln and Hamner, 1958; Greulach and Haesloop, 1958), but gibberellin does not seem to substitute for photo-induction in this class of plants, nor, very significantly, for the short-day part of induction in the long-short-day plants studied by Bünsow and Harder (see Harder and Bünsow, 1957). On the other hand, all physiological evidence that we have (from grafting experiments) suggests that the floral stimuli of long- and short-day plants are identical (Lang, 1952; Zeevart, 1958; Lang and Khudairi, unpublished data). We must therefore conclude that gibberellin is not the "photoperiodic" floral stimulis, nor a substitute for this stimulus.

Another conclusion can be drawn by taking a closer look at the gibberellin response in long-day plants. Two things can be said in this connection. The great majority of rosette type long-day plants to which gibberellin has been applied, has responded with flower formation. A few negative results have been reported (Lona, 1956b; Lona and Bocchi, 1957; see also Lona's report in the next paper); however, I am not sure whether by extending and intensifying the treatment positive responses could not be obtained at least in some of these plants. However, the degree of response varies very much from one long-day plant to the other. This can be seen by comparing Fig. 2, *Samolus,* with Fig. 4, *Silene armeria. Silene* needs considerably more gibberellin and more time, and makes considerably more stem growth before it responds with flower formation. But in their photoperiodic sensitivity the two plants do not differ very much. This situation indicates that gibberellin is only one of several factors in the photo-

FIG. 4. Induction of flower formation in short-day-grown *Silene armeria* by treatment with gibberellin. From left to right: controls; plants treated with 2, 5, 10, 20, and 50 μg of gibberellin daily. Flower formation occurred only with the two highest dosages. The plants on the extreme right are about 1.5 meter high.

inductive process. We know that this process is a composite of several "partial reactions" (see above), and that some of these reactions are promotive with respect to flower formation, while others are inhibitory. Gibberellin seems to be one of the promotive elements in the overall process, but its effect will depend on the efficiency of the other reactions and on their balance. In some plants gibberellin may be actually the limiting factor in flower induction; such plants will respond to applied gibberellin with prompt flower formation. However, in other plants of the same response type the balance of the partial reactions of induction may be different; another partial step may be more critical than gibberellin; gibberellin application will have little effect on flower formation, and may have none at all.

All this sounds rather general, but I do not want it to sound otherwise. If our basic idea is right, and gibberellin, in contrast to auxin, is directly involved in the light reaction process, it must in some manner be tied in with the photoreaction of this process, and we shall have to prove this and also to assign it some specific place in the overall process. But I do not feel that our present information is sufficient even to permit us to make a guess. It seems to me particularly premature to equate or connect the action of gibberellin with that of red or far-red light. In lettuce seed germination, gibberellin causes the same response as red light, that is, the seeds do germinate (Kahn *et al.*, 1957). In stem growth, gibberellin and far red have similar effects: they both promote stem elongation; but here, at least in some cases, their effects are clearly independent (Downs *et al.*, 1957). As to flower formation, it is readily induced by gibberellin both in typical "red-sensitive" and typical "far-red-sensitive" plants such as spinach and radish, respectively (Stolwijk, 1952; Wittwer and Bukovac, 1957a,b). Even if there were more grounds for believing in a connection between the effects of far red and red light and gibberellin, it could hardly be a close and direct one, for it seems inconceivable that the small amounts of red or far red which are needed for determining the response in some plants can directly cause the appearance and disappearance of a substance which is needed in the amounts gibberellin is needed for flower induction. We would have to assume at least one intervening, amplifying event.

After having thus cautioned you against rash assumptions, I want to take yet another step toward pinning down gibberellin action in flower formation; but this may well be a step backward. When a cold- or long-day-requiring rosette plant is induced in the natural way, by cold or by long day, stem elongation and flower initiation occur almost simultaneously. If these plants are treated with gibberellin, stem elongation in most cases precedes flower initiation in a conspicuous manner. There are exceptions to this rule; flower initiation seems to be as early in gibberellin-treated *Samolus* plants as in long-day-induced ones. Still, we must consider the possibility that the primary effect of gibberellin is on stem formation and that flower initiation is brought about secondarily, the bolting (elongating) plant becoming capable of forming floral stimulus. This possibility is strengthened by the fact that gibberellin seems incapable of causing flower formation in caulescent long-day plants (that is, long-day plants with an elongate stem also in short-day conditions) (Lona, 1956b; Lang, unpublished data). If this interpretation is true, we would still not have succeeded in opening the door into the biochemistry of flower formation. However, we should not be utterly disappointed even if this were true. Gibberellin is the first native material which is capable of causing stem elongation and flower formation in at least numerous representatives of two large physiological plant groups, the cold-requiring and the long-day plants, under strict noninductive conditions. It has also quite a number of other effects (on seed germination, cell division, dormancy phenomena). It is thus a very powerful tool in regulating various plant responses, and if used judiciously and critically it cannot but help us in furthering our understanding of plant growth and development, including flower formation and its photoperiodic control.

REFERENCES

Bonner, J. 1949. Further experiments on flowering in *Xanthium*. *Botan. Gaz.*, *110*, 625–27.

Bonner, J., and J. Thurlow. 1949. Inhibition of photoperiodic induction in *Xanthium* by applied auxin. *Botan. Gaz.*, *110*, 613–24.

Borthwick, H. A., and M. W. Parker. 1940. Floral initiation in Biloxi soybeans as influenced by age and position of leaf receiving photoperiodic treatment. *Botan. Gaz.*, *101*, 800–17.

Bünsow, R., and R. Harder. 1956a. Blütenbildung von Bryophyllum durch Gibberellin. *Naturwissenschaften*, *43*, 479–80.

———. 1956b. Blütenbildung von Lapsana durch Gibberellin. *Naturwissenschaften*, *43*, 527.

———. 1957c. Blütenbildung von *Adonis* und *Rudbeckia* durch Gibberellin. *Naturwissenschaften*, *44*, 453–54.

Cooke, A. R. 1954. Changes in free auxin content during the photoinduction of short-day plants. *Plant Physiol.*, *29*, 440–44.

von Denffer, D., and H. Gründler. 1950. Über wuchsstoffinduzierte Blühhemmung bei Langtagpflanzen. *Biol. Zentr.*, *69*, 272–82.

von Denffer, D., and Liesellore Schlitt. 1951. Blühförderung durch Ultraviolettbestrahlung. *Naturwissenschaften*, *38*, 564–65.

Dostál, R., and M. Hosek. Über den Einfluss von Heteroauxin auf die Morphogenese bei *Circaea* (das Sachssche Phänomen). *Flora*, *131*, 263–86.

Downs, R. J., S. B. Hendricks, and H. A. Borthwick. 1957. Photoreversible control of elongation of Pinto beans and other plants under normal conditions of growth. *Botan. Gaz.*, *118*, 199–208.

Goodwin, R. H. 1937. The role of auxin in leaf development in Solidago species. *Am. J. Botany*, *24*, 43–51.

Gregory, F. G., I. Spear, and K. V. Thimann. 1954. The interrelation between CO_2 metabolism and photoperiodism in *Kalanchoë*. *Plant Physiol.*, *29*, 220–29.

Greulach, V. A., and J. G. Haesloop. 1958. Influence of gibberellin on *Xanthium* flowering as related to number of photoinductive cycles. *Science, 127,* 646–47.

Hamner, K. C. 1940. Interrelation of light and darkness in photoperiodic induction. *Botan. Gaz., 101,* 658–87.

Hamner, K. C., and J. Bonner. 1938. Photoperiodism in relation to hormones as factors in floral initiation and development. *Botan. Gaz., 100,* 338–431.

Hamner, K. C., and K. K. Nanda. 1956. A relationship between applications of indoleacetic acid and the high-intensity-light reaction of photoperiodism. *Botan. Gaz., 118,* 13–18.

Harder, R., and R. Bünsow. 1956. Einfluss des Gibberellins auf die Blütenbildung bei *Kalanchoë blossfeldiana. Naturwissenschaften, 43,* 544.

―――. 1957. Zusammenwirken von Gibberellin mit photoperiodisch bedingten blühfördernden und blühhemmenden Vorgängen bei *Kalanchoë blossfeldiana. Naturwissenschaften, 44,* 454.

Harder, R., and Helene van Sender. 1949. Antagonistische Wirkung von Wuchsstaff und "Blühhormon." *Naturwissenschaften, 36,* 348–49.

Hussey, G., and F. G. Gregory. 1954. The effect of auxin on the flowering behavior of Wintex barley and Petkus rye. *Plant Physiol., 29,* 292–96.

Jacobs, W. P. 1952. The role of auxin in differentiation of xylem around a wound. *Am. J. Botany, 39,* 301–309.

Kahn, A., J. A. Goss, and D. E. Smith. 1957. Effect of gibberellin on germination of lettuce seed. *Science, 125,* 645–47.

Khudairi, A. K., and K. C. Hamner. 1954a. Effect of ethylene chlorohydrin on floral initiation in *Xanthium. Botan. Gaz., 115,* 289–91.

―――. 1954b. The relative sensitivity of *Xanthium* leaves of different ages to photoperiodic induction. *Plant Physiol., 29,* 251–57.

Kunitake, G. M., P. Saltman, and A. Lang. 1957. The products of CO_2 dark fixation in leaves of long- and short-day treated *Kalanchoë blossfeldiana. Plant Physiol., 32,* 201–203.

Lang, A. 1952. Physiology of flowering. *Ann. Rev. Plant Physiol., 3,* 265–306.

―――. 1956a. Stem elongation in a rosette plant, induced by gibberellic acid. *Naturwissenschaften, 43,* 257–58.

―――. 1956b. Induction of flower formation in biennial *Hyoscyamus* by treatment with gibberellin. *Naturwissenschaften, 43,* 284–85.

―――. 1956c. Gibberellin and flower formation. *Naturwissenschaften, 43,* 544.

―――. 1957. The effect of gibberellin upon flower formation. *Proc. Natl. Acad. Sci. U. S., 43,* 709–17.

Lang, A., J. A. Sandoval, and A. Bedri. 1957. Induction of bolting and flowering in *Hyoscyamus* and *Samolus* by a gibberellin-like material from a seed plant. *Proc. Natl. Acd. Sci. U. S., 43,* 960–64.

Leopold, A. C., and K. V. Thimann. 1949. The effect of auxin on flower initiation. *Am. J. Botany, 36,* 342–47.

Lincoln, R. G., and K. C. Hamner. 1958. An effect of gibberellic acid on the flowering of *Xanthium,* a short-day plant. *Plant Physiol., 33,* 101–104.

Lindstrom, R. S., S. H. Wittwer, and M. J. Bukovac. 1957. Gibberellin and higher plants. IV. Flowering responses of some flower crops. *Quart. Bull. Mich. Agr. Expt. Sta., 39,* 673–81.

Liverman, J. L., and A. Lang. 1956. Induction of flowering in long-day plants by applied indoleacetic acid. *Plant Physiol., 31,* 147–50.

Lockhart, J. A., and K. C. Hamner. 1954. Partial reactions in the formation of the floral stimulus in *Xanthium*. *Plant Physiol., 29,* 509–13.

Lona, F. 1956a. L'azione dell'acido gibberellico sull'accrescimento caulinare di talune piante erbacee in condizioni esterne controllate. *Nuovo giorn. botan. ital., 63,* 61–76.

————. 1956b. Osservazioni orientative circa l'effetto dell'acido gibberellico sullo sviluppo riproduttivo di alcune longidiurne e brevidiurne. *Ateneo parmense, 27,* 867–75.

Lona, F., and Ada Bocchi. 1955. Reduzione dell'esigenze fotoperiodiche in *Perilla ocymoides* Lour. var. *nankinensis* Voss. per ipoauxinizzazione da Eosina. *Beitr. Biol. Pflanz., 31,* 333–47.

————. 1956. Sviluppo vegetativo e riproduttivo di alcune longidiurne in rapporto all'azione dell'acido gibberellico. *Nuovo giorn. botan. ital., 63,* 469–86.

Phinney, B. O., C. A. West, M. Ritzel, and P. M. Neely. 1957. Evidence for "gibberellin-like" substances from flowering plants. *Proc. Natl. Acad. Sci. U. S., 43,* 398–404.

Salisbury, F. B. 1955. The dual role of auxin in flowering. *Plant Physiol., 30,* 327–34.

Salisbury, F. B., and J. Bonner. 1956. The reactions of the photoinductive dark period. *Plant Physiol., 31,* 141–47.

Shoji, K., F. T. Addicott, and W. A. Swets. 1951. Auxin in relation to leaf blade abscission. *Plant Physiol., 26,* 189–91.

Stolwijk, J. A. J. 1952. Photoperiodic and formative effects of various wavelength regions in *Cosmos bipinnatus, Spinacia oleracea, Sinapis alba* and *Pisum sativum*. I, II. *Proc. Konink. Ned. Akad. Wetenschap., C55,* 489–502.

Stowe, B., and T. Yamaki. 1957. The history and physiological action of the gibberellins. *Ann. Rev. Plant Physiol., 8,* 181–216.

Vlitos, A. J., and W. Meudt. 1954. The role of auxin in plant flowering. III. Free indole acids in short-day plants grown under photoinductive and non-photoinductive day-lengths. *Contribs. Boyce Thompson Inst., 14,* 413–17.

von Witsch, H. 1941. Über den Zusammenhang zwischen Membranbau, Wuchsstoffwirkung und der Sukkulenzzunahme von *Kalanchoë blossfeldiana* im Kurztag. *Planta, 31,* 638–52.

Wittwer, S. H., and M. J. Bukovac. 1957a. Gibberellin effects on temperature and photoperiodic requirements of flowering of some plants. *Science, 126,* 30–31.

————. 1957b. Gibberellin and higher plants. III. Induction of flowering in long-day annuals grown under short days. *Mich. Agr. Expt. Sta. Bull., 39,* 661–72.

Yabuta, T., and T. Hayashi. 1939. Biochemical studies on the bakanae disease of rice. III. Studies on the physiological action of gibberellin in the plant. (In Japanese). *J. Agr. Chem. Soc. Japan, 15,* 403–13.

de Zeeuw, D., and A. C. Leopold. 1955. Altering juvenility with auxin. *Science, 122,* 925–26.

Zeevart, J. A. D. 1958. Flower formation as studied by grafting. *Mededel. Landbouwhogesch. Wageningen, 58,* No. 3.

SOME ASPECTS OF PHOTOTHERMAL AND CHEMICAL CONTROL OF GROWTH AND FLOWERING

FAUSTO LONA

Institute of Botany, University of Parma, Parma, Italy

On studying the action of gibberellic acid (GA) on vegetables, we became aware that plants treated with this substance assumed features similar in some respects to those produced by special environmental conditions such as low light intensity, long photoperiod, and relatively high night temperature. With regard to light conditions which possibly should have a similarity of action with that of GA, our attention was focused, of course, on the most noted morphogenetical radiations. Concerning the photoperiodic factor, the action of GA, in this paper, will be considered especially in relation to the quality of light used as a periodic supplement to a basic natural short day. In concluding this principal argument, we shall briefly mention temperature interference.

We investigated the possibility of a relationship between GA morphogenesis and plants responses to light through the reaction of perceptive systems and related processes. Our first experiments included rapid tests for the effects of red and far-red light on germination of photoblastic seeds and on shoot lengthening (Lona, 1956a; Lona and Bocchi, 1956). Similarities in the responses of intact plants were found in many instances between the effect of far-red irradiation and that of GA. At the same time we noted that red light frequently had an effect opposite to that of GA, notably in shoot lengthening, chlorophyll pigmentation, anthocyanin production, and of other secondary products of metabolism (phenol compounds and such). On the other hand, we found that *Lactuca* seed germination responded in an opposite fashion and that GA promoted germination just as red irradiation does. The same is true of the expansion of excised leaf discs (see Liverman, Section III, pp. 161–180).

351

During some preliminary observations of flowering phenomena, we noted that here again the action of GA resembles in certain cases that of far-red irradiation. In fact, there are LDP which react to GA in short-day conditions as they do in short-day plus far-red extension (9 + 15 hr). We received the impression, moreover, that this reaction to GA was not manifested by plants that react positively, with respect to flowering, to red light extension (Lona, 1957a).

Successive experiments, however, did not yield such clear-cut results. GA action on the flowering process did not always appear similar to that of far red, and moreover it seemed, in a few rosette plants, to substitute somehow for the red, perhaps also independently from their flowering processes. After these conflicting results, the interest in comparing light and GA action still remained very strong and also more stimulating. Therefore we continued our tests on these lines.

Realizing that knowledge of the reaction of our test plants to duration and quality of supplementary light was incomplete, it was necessary to go deeper and more precisely into the question of the specific ways in which different plants (even of the classical categories) react to various types of long day.

A set of trials on the effect of light extension to a basic short day, on certain LDP, concerned red and far-red light of the standard type at low energy (1 kiloerg/cm^2·sec) and at temperatures ranging from 18° to 22°C. The few data available at present concern not only flowering but also stem growth in the photoperiodic picture. It is convenient from certain points of view to treat the two subjects in parallel, trying to distinguish the direct action of the external factors of the two phenomena and, possibly, avoiding eventual confusion due to some reciprocal influence between them. It will be particularly useful to ascertain how differently growth and flowering depend on the quality of light applied during the scotophil phase.

Experimenting with the following three different photoperiod conditions, i.e., (a) 8 hr natural light + 16 hr dark (SD), (b) 8 hr natural light + 8 hr red light + 8 hr dark (rLD), or (c) 8 hr natural light + 8 hr far-red light + 8 hr dark (f-rLD), we could distinguish a series of reaction types. One example is *Centaurea cyanus*. It flowers quickly when the long day is obtained through red light extension, whereas under a far-red extension its flowering behavior appears similar to that reached by aged plants even on SD (i.e., it flowers only after a long time and after having produced a great number of leaves). It is interesting to note that its growth behavior is quite different, as the plant responds quickly to f-rLD with a vegetative bolting. To this type, which corresponds to a standard one, belongs also a strain of *Crepis leontodontoides,* of our test material. This also behaves, however, as a quantitative LDP. It differs from *Centaurea* as it does not elongate under f-rLD.

A second type was found which, on the contrary, flowers under f-rLD and remains vegetative on rLD. An annual strain of *Brassica napus,* cultivated by us, behaves in this way. Probably many crucifers of Funke's Group IV belong to this class.

A third type with a further different reaction is exemplified by *Mimulus luteus.* This species (or at least the strain used by us) flowers both under rLD and f-rLD, although more rapidly under the red. We have observed a similar behavior in other plants, as *Aethusa cynapium.* This latter flowers better under f-rLD.

After similar results, it seemed clear that very consistent differences exist among plants of the same standard category. We cannot consider the manifold aspects of this fact here, but it is well to be aware that we can no longer depend upon the uniformity of responsiveness to chromoperiodical conditions of plants pertaining to a standard photoperiod type. For instance, many LDP that react quite similarly to an extension of white incandescent light may behave very differently toward the red and far-red extension. Their reaction may consequently be different also toward various sources of artificial white light if the red and far-red components are differently represented in them (Lona, 1957b).

What we have just referred to is perhaps a picture that, besides being limited, is simplified with respect to the actual situation.

Stolwijk and Zeevart (1955) have observed that the LDP *Hyoscyamus niger* does not flower, or flowers with difficulty, when cultivated with a red light extension, while it flowers quickly with a far red. Worthy of remark, on the other hand, is Down's observation (1956) that *Hyoscyamus niger* flowers well when long nictophases are interrupted by a flash of red light while, if this is immediately followed by a far-red irradiation, the red action is hindered. In connection with these data, one may suspect that a short stimulus of red light may be favorable to flowering as well as a long irradiation period with far red, while a long treatment with red may produce negative results, and flowering may also fail by treatment with a brief flash of far red.

In short, we may assume that the same irradiation may have a different effect, or even an antithetic one, depending upon the length of action or perhaps also on the photocyclic period in which it is applied. Apart from the legitimacy of such an assumption, and neglecting for the present the case of *Hyoscyamus,* with which we have not yet experimented, we wished to learn whether there is an equal effect from applying a short irradiation (½ hr) in the middle of the night phase and that of giving a prolonged irradiation of several hours (8 hr natural light + 8 hr extension of colored light + 8 hr dark, or also 9 hr natural light + 15 hr colored light). The results of the experiments in this regard (including SDP) have not yet reached an advanced stage; they may, however, facilitate our further comments with relation to the action of GA. They have been carried out only on a few species, namely, *Centaurea cyanus, Brassica napus,* and *Xanthium italicum.*

The results revealed that *Centaurea cyanus* and *Brassica napus* behaved in practically the same manner toward both a long and a short extension made up respectively with red and far-red light. *Centaurea* flowered, say under a long red extension, and also on a short one, and so did *Brassica* under f-rLD. As far as our LD tests are concerned, we may consequently assume that three groups are to be distinguished, namely: (*a*) typical red positive (*Centaurea*); (*b.*) typical far-red positive (*Brassica*); (*c*) red and far-red-positive (*Mimulus*). A further category probably may be individuated in those plants, such as *Hyoscyamus,* that flower under a long far-red extension and also on a brief night breakage with red light, but not under a long red extension or a brief far red. Experiments are to be pursued to demonstrate whether these characteristics are really distinct or only relatively so.

In *Xanthium italicum* it appeared that, while a flash of far red acts positively on flowering, a prolonged far-red irradiation (8 hr natural day + 8 hr fr + 8 hr dark) tends to act negatively. Indeed, the flowering of individuals cultivated under f-rLD was visibly delayed in respect to those cultivated under SD. If the treatment was limited to one photocycle, only some of the SD individuals reached the flowering stage. Such behavior on the part of a SDP toward far-red extension seems very remarkable and may correspond, in an inverse sense, to that of some LDP.

We cannot consider now the mechanism of such an effect of a far-red overdosage. The datum may help us, however, to understand better several aspects of GA action on flowering as discussed below.

In the meantime we shall comment on some results concerning shoot lengthening. From these last experiments, we could clearly observe that plants generally grow tall under both prolonged and very short periods of far-red supplementary irradiation, whereas they are kept in a dwarfed condition, as in SD (!), even by a short flash of red light given in the middle of the nictophase. This is a characteristic response, especially of the caulescent type. However, in some rosette plants the rLD seems to act somewhat positively in shoot lengthening, even before the eventual formation of flowering structures. Very frequently after flowering, a new condition favorable to shoot lengthening appears. This latter may then be rather independent from photoperiod, as lengthening may continue also in SD. This argument is developed somewhat elsewhere (Lona, 1957b).

The effect of red and far-red irradiations on growth phenomena appears therefore to be, in several cases, distinct from their effect on flowering processes. It clearly appears that growth response of plants to light conditions (quality and dosage) is more uniform than flowering response. It is interesting to note that *Xanthium* flowers in conditions of growth inhibition (SD) and under conditions very favorable to shoot lengthening (f-rLD).

In view of all the foregoing results we may now consider the action of GA observed in parallel or distinct experiments.

The trials with GA showed that our annual strain of *Brassica napus* characteristically sensitive to far-red extension (a typical f-rLD) was also sensitive to GA both for growth (shoot lengthening) and flowering manifestations. GA had a general far-red-like effect on this crucifer. In *Centaurea cyanus*, a typical rLDP, only shoot lengthening was stimulated by GA, its effect being similar to that of far-red extension; flowering was not qualitatively promoted. So, this rLDP it not GA-positive for flowering, at least at the young stage of the individuals considered in our trials. Also in this case, however, GA had a general far-red-like effect. Another rLDP, *Crepis leontodontoides,* flowered rather quickly when treated with GA, but also in this case the reaction was not specific, judging by the number of leaves produced by treated plants and those formed by old plants flowering in SD (!). Shoot elongation is promoted by GA but not by far-red extension, at least under the basic conditions of our experiments. Also *Mimulus luteus,* a plant flowering both under red and f-rLD (long extension) appeared to be in no way stimulated to flower formation by GA, even if the shoot was very much lengthened under the treatment. Thus, in this case, GA had, as in *Centaurea,* a far-red-like effect on growth but not on flowering even though flowering of *Mimulus* is also allowed by f-rLD. We must note, however, that *Mimulus* may easily escape flowering also in natural conditions when cultivated in deep shadow, in which case vegetative bolting takes place. The action of GA must be interpreted in connection with this fact. We shall add here that in the annual *Hyoscyamus* the flower-promoting action of GA is a f-rLD-like one, the flowering response of this plant being positive toward a long far-red extension.

If we now consider SDP, we find undoubtedly that they respond to GA in a far-red-like way for shoot lengthening, but we cannot say exactly the same of their flowering behavior (Lona, 1956b). In this connection, in fact, we have never observed a real specific substitution of GA for a far red flash in *Xanthium* cultivated on relatively LD, but, conversely, we did find that GA action on SD individuals appears to be very similar to that of a SD supplemented with a long far-red extension.

From these observations, although they are limited, we may draw the impression that a similarity between the effect of GA and that of f-rLD (or far-red predominant action in the photoperiodic cycle) is frequently exhibited by caulescent and also rosette plants in their growth processes as intact plants. A few exceptions may be found in rosette plants that also require some red supplementary light for shoot elongation. In general, red light has the inverse effect of GA. As far as flowering is concerned, the similarity of the two actions appears even less general, but it still seems to be discernible in some of our experimental tests. Frequently GA action does not correspond to that of a rLD, especially when red light operates for a long time.

The second very significant factor for growth and flowering phenomena is the influence of temperature. We know that night temperature has an important role in the slow pigment conversion and consequently in the whole reaction to photoperiod. Noteworthy is the fact that temperature does act on growth in a simpler way than on flowering. Liverman (1955) demonstrated that for the LDP *Silene armeria,* the critical day length for flowering is shorter at 17° and 30°C (night temperature) than at either 14° or 23°C. Liverman (1955) says: "these results serve to point out that in experiments on the effect of temperature on flowering response, it is necessary to use a number of different temperatures in combination with a number of daylengths to obtain results which are meaningful. [We can now suggest] a number of different temperatures in combination with a number of photochromoperiod conditions." In this way we may perhaps approach a better understanding of the problems with which we have dealt above.

Again, simple relationships are likely to be found only between the action of night temperature and that of GA in the sector of growth manifestations (Lona, 1957b). Probably we cannot say the same thing in regard to flowering; this problem, however, is rather unexplored and we are now beginning some trials on it.

As far as the vernalization phenomena are concerned, Lang (1956) found a similarity of action between GA and a long treatment with low temperature leading to flower formation. This homology does not appear to be constant.

In conclusion we observe that the actual experimental evidence allows us to foresee the points of contact between the action of several external factors on the primary receptive systems and related secondary processes with that of GA. Consequently GA-like substances of the plant may find their places in the near future inside the schemes of the various processes of growth and developmental phenomena. Other substances of primary importance in these schemes would be kinetin or kinetin-like substances and the auxins such as IAA and other indole compounds (Lona, 1957b). For a more precise understanding of these relationships, further investigations should encompass a broader variety of light and temperature conditions to include varying duration and intensity of supplementary light as well as different wavelengths (for extension of blue light) and, moreover, the light conditions of the photophase. The rhythmical different exigencies of light in connection with endogenous rhythm and sensitivity appear to be of fundamental importance for distinguishing the different processes leading to growth and flowering.

When the specific environmental exigencies of every single phenomenon (growth, flowering, seed germination, etc.) are clearly discernible so as to discriminate their particular mode of initial reaction to external stimuli and their successive processes, which are also evidently different, we shall be able to understand the true significance of the various physiologically active substances on the plant. The very consistent differences between the modalities of response to light by flowering processes and those of growth should be studied also according to cytological manifestations distinguishing cell elongation and cell reproduction.

REFERENCES

Downs, R. J. 1956. Photoreversibility of flower initiation. *Plant Physiol., 31,* 279–84.

Lang, A. 1956. Induction of flower formation in biennial *Hyoscyamus* by treatment with gibberellin. *Naturwissenschaften, 43,* 284–85.

Livermann, J. L. 1955. The physiology of flowering. *Ann. Rev. Plant Physiol., 6,* 177–210.

Lona, F. 1956a. L'acido gibberellico determina la germinazione dei semi di *Lactuca scariola* in fase di scoto-inibizione. *Ateneo parmense, 27,* 641–44.

––––––. 1956b. Osservazioni orientative circa l'effetto dell'acido gibberellico sullo sviluppo riproduttivo di alcune longidiurne e brevidiurne. *Ateneo parmense, 27,* 867–75.

––––––. 1957a. Vegetative and developmental manifestations of some plants in connection with gibberellin compounds activity. Abstract from the lecture given at the University of Wageningen on May 23, 1957.

Lona, F. 1957b. Brief accounts on the physiological activity of gibberellic acid and other substances in relation to photothermal conditions. Colloque Int. sur le photo- et thermoperiodism, etc. (Parma, June 1957). *Bull. No. 34 IUBS, ser. B.*

Lona, F., and Ada Bocchi. 1956. Interferenza dell'acido gibberellico nell'effetto della luce rossa e rosso-estrema sull'allungamento del fusto di *Perilla ocymoides* L. *Ateneo parmense, 27,* 645–49.

Stolwijk, J. A. J., and J. A. D. Zeevaart. 1955. Wavelength dependence of different light reactions governing flowering in *Hyoscyamus niger. Proc. Ned. Akad. Wetenschap., C58,* 386–96.

INFLUENCE OF GIBBERELLIC ACID ON THE FLOWERING OF *Xanthium* IN RELATION TO NUMBER OF INDUCTION PERIODS

VICTOR A. GREULACH and JOHN G. HAESLOOP

Department of Botany, University of North Carolina, Chapel Hill

Lang (1956) reported that biennial *Hyoscyamus niger* treated with gibberellin bolted and bloomed the first season without cold or long-day treatment, and that the annual form (a long-day plant) bloomed under short days when treated with this growth substance. Soon after his initial papers appeared Lang (1957) and other investigators, including Lona (1956), Marth *et al.* (1956), and Wittwer and Bukovac (1957), reported on the initiation or promotion of reproductive development by gibberellin in various other species of plants. Some 38 species have been investigated, 17 of them long-day annuals, 9 biennials, 9 day-neutral annuals, and 3 short-day annuals. Gibberellin proved to be a substitute for long-day and cold treatments for all species in the first two groups, except for the long-day plants rye and *Perilla*. While induction of reproductive development was not a similar problem in the day-neutral species, flowering was hastened by gibberellin in all species studied except pepper and geranium. No success has been reported, however, with the few short-day species which have been studied. Lang (1957) found that Biloxi soybeans and *Xanthium* treated with gibberellin and kept under long days remained strictly vegetative, and although Marth *et al.* (1956), observed earlier blooming in gibberellin-treated *Salvia,* these plants were apparently under inductive photoperiods.

Lang (1957) came to the following conclusion: "It thus appears that application of gibberellin allows numerous plants to overcome cold and long-day requirements in flower formation but that it does not substitute for any short-day requirement."

The present study, initiated before the publication of Lang's results with the two short-day species, was designed to obtain information on the effects of gibberellin on this photoperiodic class, *Xanthium pensylvanicum* being selected as the experimental species. The first experiment, which will be reported on elsewhere, included an analysis of the effects of gibberellin on the vegetative as well as the reproductive development of *Xanthium* under long and short days. Only the data relating to reproductive development will be considered here.

The seeds were planted in a greenhouse on April 1, 1957, and the plants were kept under long days (16.5 hr minimum) until 28 days after planting, when 12 plants were treated with a $10^{-3}M$ solution of gibberellic acid in 0.25% Dreft, each plant receiving 1 ml of solution in the form of drops applied to the leaves with a pipette. Twelve controls were similarly treated with the 0.25% Dreft solution alone. Six plants of each group were retained under long days, the other six being placed under short days of 8 hr in the greenhouse by means of an automatic short-day device. The final data were taken 71 days after treatment.

In the second experiment the plants were similarly treated with gibberellin after being retained under long days (18 hr minimum) for 28 days after planting (July 15). Five control plants and five treated with gibberellin were retained under long days, while 25 of each were placed under 8-hr days. After two long dark periods, 5 of these plants from each group were returned to long days, the process being repeated on alternate days, providing groups of plants which had received 2, 4, 6, 8, and 10 induction periods. The final data were taken 21 days after the beginning of the treatments.

In the first experiment all plants under long days remained strictly vegetative, while all plants under short days bloomed profusely at about the same time. Although the gibberellin-treated plants averaged 54.8 burs per plant as compared with 50.7 for the controls, the difference was not statistically significant. The burs of the control plants were slightly heavier than those of the treated plants, on both a fresh and dry weight basis (Table I).

In the second experiment, growth of the stems of the treated plants was much greater than that of the controls regardless of photoperiodic treatment (Table II). While the stems of the control plants given four or more long nights were somewhat inhibited in growth, gibberellin apparently overcame such photoperiodic inhibition. Contrary to the

TABLE I. Effect of Gibberellic Acid on Fresh and Dry Weights of Burs of *Xanthium*

	Mean Fresh Weight, g		Mean Dry Weight, g	
	Controls	Gibberellic Acid	Controls	Gibberellic Acid
Per plant	9.60	8.52	2.54	1.72
Per bur	0.19	0.16	0.05	0.03

usual findings, all gibberellin-treated plants had more nodes than the control plants, though this may have been due to more prompt internode elongation rather than to the formation of additional nodes. Although stem diameter was not measured, it was obvious that the stems of the treated plants were uniformly more slender than those of the

TABLE II. Influence of Gibberellin and Photoperiod on Growth and Reproductive Development of *Xanthium*

No. of Long Nights	Mean Stem Growth, cm		No. of Nodes Formed		Inflorescence Buds Formed	
	Controls	Gibberellin	Controls	Gibberellin	Controls	Gibberellin
0	27.0	54.7	5	8	—	—
2	25.6	62.3	5	8	—[a]	+[b]
4	17.0	55.1	4	8	—[a]	+
6	20.6	66.7	5	8	+	+
8	15.6	57.2	5	7	+	+
10	18.9	57.4	4	7	+	+
12	15.7	50.1	5	6	+	+

[a] Inflorescence primordia present in all five plants.
[b] Four plants with macroscopic flower buds, one with inflorescence primordia.

controls (Fig. 1). All plants under long days were still strictly vegetative at the end of the experiment, while all plants given six or more long nights had well-developed macroscopic flower buds. However, the control plants given two and four induction periods had developed only microscopic inflorescence primordia, stages 2 and 3 of Salisbury (1955)—while all but one of the gibberellin-treated plants given these photoperiodic treatments had macroscopic flower buds (Table II, Fig. 1). Acceleration of reproductive development by gibberellin was also evident in the plants given six to ten induction periods, particularly as regards pistillate influences in the 10-day group.

These results substantiate Lang's conclusion that gibberellin does not substitute for any short-day requirement as far as flower initiation

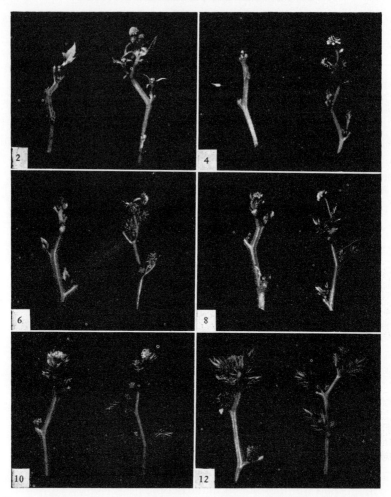

Fig. 1. Stem tips of representative *Xanthium* plants showing response to treatments with various numbers of photoinductive cycles (figures in lower left-hand corners) and gibberellin. In each pair of tips the controls are on the left, the gibberellin-treated plants on the right.

is concerned. Mann (1940), Naylor (1941), Salisbury (1955), and others have shown that while one long dark period is sufficient for photoperiodic induction of *Xanthium,* additional long dark periods increase the rate of reproductive development. Gibberellin can substitute for such additional induction periods in promoting the reproductive development of induced *Xanthium* plants.

REFERENCES

Lang, A. 1956. Induction of flower formation in biennial *Hyoscyamus* by treatment with gibberellin. *Naturwissenschaften, 43,* 284–85.

———. 1957. The effect of gibberellin upon flower formation. *Proc. Natl. Acad. Sci. U. S., 43,* 709–17.

Lona, F. 1956. L'azione dell'acido gibberellico sull'accrescimento caulinare di talune piante erbacee. *Nuovo giorn. botan. ital., 63,* 61–76.

Mann, L. K. 1940. Effect of some environmental factors on floral initiation in *Xanthium. Botan. Gaz., 102,* 339–56.

Marth, P. C., W. V. Audia, and J. W. Mitchell. 1956. Effects of gibberellic acid on growth and development of plants of various genera and species. *Botan. Gaz., 118,* 106–11.

Naylor, F. L. 1941. Effect of the length of the induction period on floral development of *Xanthium pensylvanicum. Botan. Gaz., 103,* 146–54.

Salisbury, F. 1955. The dual role of auxin in flowering. *Plant Physiol., 30,* 327–33.

Wittwer, S. H., and M. J. Bukovac. 1957. Gibberellin effects on temperature and photoperiodic requirements for flowering of some plants. *Science, 126,* 30–31.

EFFECTS OF GIBBERELLIN AND AMO-1618 ON GROWTH AND FLOWERING OF *Chrysanthemum morifolium* ON SHORT PHOTOPERIODS

HENRY M. CATHEY

Agricultural Research Service, United States Department of Agriculture, Beltsville, Maryland

Chemicals that modify the growth of plants have interested physiologists for many years. Among these growth regulators is gibberellin (Kurosawa, 1932), which is effective in accelerating elongation and flowering of many kinds of plants (Marth *et al.*, 1956). Several nicotinium and quaternary ammonium compounds have been reported (Mitchell *et al.*, 1949; Wirwillie and Mitchell, 1950) to inhibit elongation of a limited number of kinds of plants. The most active of these compounds, (4-hydroxy-5-isopropyl-2-methylphenyl) trimethylammonium chloride, 1-piperidine carboxylate, has been designated Amo-1618.[1] Application of Amo-1618 greatly inhibited elongation and delayed flowering as compared with the development of untreated plants. Among the responsive plants were chrysanthemums, short-photoperiod plants (Marth *et al.*, 1953). Later, Marth and Mitchell concluded from unpublished data that gibberellin and Amo-1618 applied in a lanolin paste were mutually antagonistic on the stem elongation of pinto beans. The photoperiod-controlled effects of gibberellin and Amo-1618 on the growth and flowering of *Chrysanthemum morifolium* were studied in the experiments reported here.

GENERAL MATERIALS AND METHODS

Rooted chrysanthemum cuttings planted in 3-inch pots containing a mixture of soil and peat were grown in a greenhouse where the minimum night temperature was 15.6°C. They were kept on long photo-

---

[1] Amo-1618 was supplied by the Growth Regulator and Antibiotic Laboratory, Crops Research Division, Agricultural Research Service, Beltsville, Maryland.

periods, obtained by interrupting the dark period with at least 10 ft-c of light from incandescent filament bulbs from 10 P.M. to 2 A.M. nightly, to keep them vegetative. They were then subjected to short (8-hr) photoperiods until anthesis. Five plants were used for each treatment.

The plants were sprayed with aqueous mixtures of gibberellin and Amo-1618. The mixtures were prepared by dissolving the required amount of the chemical in as little ethanol as would dissolve it, adding sufficient Tween 20 to produce a 0.1% solution, and then diluting the mixture to the desired volume with distilled water. The aqueous solutions were held at 10°. The immature part of the plant was sprayed with a hand atomizer until the excess solution began to run off. Approximately 0.5 ml of solution was required per plant.

The data collected at the time of anthesis included length of stem and number of lateral inflorescences.

REACTION OF PLANTS ON SHORT PHOTOPERIODS

Sensitivity to Gibberellin

Indianapolis Yellow chrysanthemum, which requires 10 weeks of short photoperiods to induce flowering, was tested for reaction to gibberellin. Short photoperiods were started on December 3, 1956. Certain plants were sprayed with aqueous solutions containing 100 ppm of gibberellin on 5 consecutive days after beginning of the short photoperiods as follows:

Week	Stem Length at Anthesis More Than That of Control, cm
1st	4.2
2nd	14.2
3rd	20.2
4th	16.3
5th	11.7
6th	11.2
7th	1.8
L.S.D. (1% level)	4.0

As shown, the stems of Indianapolis Yellow plants elongated most when treated during the third week of short photoperiods, which was after initiation of the inflorescences but before extensive floret development. The same concentration of gibberellin in the first week of short photoperiod or in the seventh week of short photoperiods had little effect on stem elongation. Untreated plants averaged 9.2 lateral inflorescences. Treatment of similar plants with 100 ppm solution of gibberellin five times in the fourth week of the short photoperiods re-duced the number of inflorescences to 4.2; the remaining flower primordia did not develop. Plants treated in the seventh week of short photoperiods developed 8.6 lateral inflorescences.

When a concentrated solution of gibberellin (1000 ppm) was applied for 5 consecutive days when the outer florets of the inflorescences were showing color (during the seventh week of short photoperiods), the florets developed faster than did those of untreated plants; anthesis occurred 10 to 14 days earlier than on untreated plants.

Sensitivity to Amo-1618

Yellow Lace chrysanthemum, which requires 9 weeks of short photoperiods to induce flowering, was tested for reaction to Amo-1618. Short photoperiods were started on June 7, 1957. Certain plants were sprayed with aqueous solutions containing 500 ppm of Amo-1618 on 3 alternate days after beginning of the short photoperiods as follows:

Week	Stem Length at Anthesis Less Than That of Control, cm
1st	42.8
2nd	42.0
3rd	30.8
4th	23.0
5th	7.3
6th	5.8
7th	0.9
L.S.D. (1% level)	6.3

Maximum inhibition of elongation occurred in the first week of short photoperiods. As shown, growth of stems of Yellow Lace was exhibited less the later the Amo-1618 treatment was given after the start of short photoperiods. Whenever inhibition of growth due to Amo-1618 occurred, the plants flowered 14 to 18 days later than untreated plants. Application of Amo-1618 in the sixth week after the start of short photoperiods did not significantly affect the elongation of stem or the time of flowering of the plants, but it did inhibit the elongation of the ray florets.

Sensitivity to Simultaneous Applications of Gibberellin and Amo-1618

Rooted cuttings of Yellow Lace chrysanthemums were planted on May 10, 1957, in 3-inch clay pots and placed on long photoperiods to test the reaction to simultaneous applications of gibberellin and Amo-1618. Short photoperiods were started June 7, 1957. Plants were sprayed four times semi-weekly during the first 2 weeks of short photoperiods first with 500-ppm solution of Amo-1618, which was allowed to dry, and then with 12.5-, 25-, 50-, and 100-ppm solution of gibberellin at each spraying; such treatments will be referred to as simultaneous applications of gibberellin and Amo-1618.

Although gibberellin applied at the beginning of photoperiodic induction was ineffective, it neutralized the inhibitory effect of Amo-1618 when the two were applied simultaneously during the first 2 weeks of induction as follows:

Solution, ppm	Stem Length at Anthesis More (+) or Less (−) Than That of Control, cm
Gibberellin	
12.5	+5.3
25	+5.8
50	+6.0
100	+9.8
Amo-1618	
500	−34.7
Amo-1618 (500 ppm) + gibberellin	
12.5	−19.6
25	−12.8
50	−3.2
100	+6.2
L.S.D. (1% level)	2.9

Amo-1618 induces maximum suppression of growth at that time. The combination of the two compounds (50-ppm solution of gibberellin and 500-ppm of Amo-1618) during the first 2 weeks of short photoperiods neutralized their growth-regulating properties; growth was similar to that of untreated plants. With mutual antagonism there was no delay in flowering of the plants (Fig. 1). Plants treated with 500-ppm solution of Amo-1618 flowered 14 days later than untreated

FIG. 1. Neutralization of growth-regulating properties on Yellow Lace chrysanthemums: Left to right: untreated plant, plants treated with 50 ppm gibberellin spray, 500 ppm Amo-1618 spray, 50 ppm gibberellin spray plus 500 ppm Amo-1618 spray semiweekly during the first 2 weeks of short photoperiods.

plants or plants treated with both 50-ppm solution of gibberellin and 500-ppm solution of Amo-1618.

Delay in flowering caused by inhibition of the growth of chrysanthemums by Amo-1618 can be counteracted without applying gibberellin simultaneously. Plants were sprayed four times semiweekly during the first 2 weeks of short photoperiods with 500-ppm solution of Amo-1618. When the outer florets were showing color (5 weeks later) the inflorescences were sprayed for 5 consecutive days with 1000-ppm solution of gibberellin. The plants treated in this way flowered at the same time as untreated plants, but they were no taller than plants treated with Amo-1618 alone.

DISCUSSION

Simultaneous applications of gibberellin and Amo-1618 in the first 2 weeks of short photoperiods neutralized their growth-regulating properties. Growth and flowering similar to those of untreated plants were obtained when four applications of 50-ppm solution of gibberellin and 500-ppm solution of Amo-1618 were given in the first 2 weeks of short photoperiods. Separately, gibberellin promoted and Amo-1618 inhibited elongation of the stems. The specific proportions of the two compounds for mutual antagonism depend upon the photoperiod and the stage of development of the plant on a specific photoperiod. Thus far, the growth-regulating properties of the two compounds have been antagonized in the first 2 weeks of short photoperiods; at different proportions, mutual antagonism should be possible at any period of growth.

Hastening of flower development is caused only by treatment with gibberellin at the time the outer florets are showing color. Application of gibberellin earlier during the short photoperiod induces elongation of the stem but does not affect time of flowering. In contrast, the period of maximum inhibition of growth and delay of flowering occurred simultaneously when the plants were treated with Amo-1618 at the start of short photoperiods. Treatment with Amo-1618 at the time the outer florets were showing color inhibited the development of the florets, but did not affect the time of anthesis as compared with that of untreated plants.

SUMMARY

Mutual antagonism of gibberellin and a quaternary ammonium compound (Amo-1618) on the growth and flowering of chrysanthemums, short-photoperiodic plants, has been demonstrated. Gibberellin by itself induces maximum elongation when applied in the third week of short photoperiods; Amo-1618 by itself induces maximum suppression of growth when applied at the start of short photoperiods. They are mutually antagonistic when applied simultaneously in the approximate concentration of 50-ppm solution of gibberellin to 500-ppm solution of Amo-1618 four times in the first 2 weeks of short photoperiods. At other times in the growth of the plant, different proportions of the two compounds may be necessary to antagonize their growth-regulating properties.

REFERENCES

Kurosawa, E. 1932. On certain experimental results concerning the over elongation of rice plants which owe to the filtrate got from the culture solution of the "Bakanae" fungi. *Rept. Taiwan Nat. Hist. Soc.*, 22, 198–201. (*From abstr.*)

Marth, P. C., W. V. Audia, and J. W. Mitchell. 1956. Effects of gibberellic acid on growth and development of plants of various genera and species. *Botan. Gaz., 118*, 106–11.

Marth, P. C., W. H. Preston, Jr., and J. W. Mitchell. 1953. Growth-controlling effects of some quaternary ammonium compounds on various species of plants. *Botan. Gaz., 115*, 200–204.

Mitchell, J. W., J. W. Wirwillie, and L. Weil. 1949. Plant growth regulating properties of some nicotinium compounds. *Science, 110*, 252–54.

Wirwillie, J. W., and J. W. Mitchell. 1950. Six new plant growth-inhibiting compounds. *Botan. Gaz., 111*, 491–94.

EFFECTS OF GIBBERELLIN ON THE PHOTOPERIODIC RESPONSES OF SOME HIGHER PLANTS [1]

S. H. WITTWER and M. J. BUKOVAC
Department of Horticulture, Michigan State University, East Lansing

One of the unique effects of gibberellin on higher plants is its alteration of photoperiodic responses. That stem elongation and flowering may be accelerated in several facultative long- or long-short-day plants, and induced in some having an obligatory long-day requirement has been reported (Bukovac and Wittwer, 1958; Bünsow and Harder, 1956a,b, 1957; Lang, 1956b, 1957; Langridge, 1957; Lona, 1956a,b; Wittwer and Bukovac, 1957a,b). Furthermore, flowering without a cold treatment has been induced with gibberellin in some cold-requiring biennials if they were exposed simultaneously, or subsequently, to long photoperiods (Carr *et al.*, 1957; Lang, 1956a,b, 1957); and in others irrespective of day length (Bukovac and Wittwer, 1957). By contrast, flowering has not been accelerated or induced with gibberellin in certain classical short-day plants grown under long days (Lang, 1956b, 1957), and gibberellin has retarded flower formation when some short-day plants were grown under inductive photoperiods (Harder and Bünsow, 1956, 1957; Lona, 1956b).

EXPERIMENTAL

The influence of foliar sprays of gibberellin on the time of flowering of photoperiodically sensitive plants was observed by growing them under both short (9 hr) and long (18 hr) day lengths. Photoperiods were maintained on a 24-hr cycle, and extended beyond the normal day length with incandescent lamps. Prior to treatment with gibberellin, long-day plants were held under a short photoperiod, and short-day plants under a long photoperiod, until they were of an age and

[1] Journal article No. 2165 of the Michigan Agricultural Experiment Station.

size capable of responding to photoinduction. The days from seeding to appearance of the first visible flower buds were selected as the criterion for measuring the modifying influence of gibberellin on photoperiodic responses.

Long-Day Plants

Flowering was accelerated in facultative long-day plants (*Brassica juncea* Coss., *Brassica pekinensis* Skeels, and *Centaurea cyanus* Linn.) grown under both long and short days (Table I and Fig. 1).

TABLE I. Modifying Effects of Foliar Sprays of Gibberellin on the Photoperiodic Responses of Several Facultative and Obligate Long-Day Plants

	9-hr Photoperiod Gibberellin, ppm			18-hr Photoperiod Gibberellin, ppm		
Plant	0[a]	100[a]	1000[a]	0[a]	100[a]	1000[a]
Facultative long-day						
Raphanus sativus Linn. (variety Comet)	70	—	60[b]	55	—	47[b]
Centaurea cyanus Linn. (variety Cyanus Double)	86	69[b]	68[b]	55	54	52
Brassica pekinensis Skeels (variety Michihli)	110	104	87[b]	88	81[b]	75[b]
Brassica juncea Coss. (variety Tendergreen)	116	95[b]	80[b]	92	84[b]	80[b]
Obligate long-day						
Spinacia oleracea Linn. (variety Bloomsdale)	No flowering	—	93	76	—	75
Cichorium endivia Linn. (variety Batavian)	No flowering	117	112	102	95[b]	94[b]
Chrysanthemum coccineum Willd. (Pyrethrum)	No flowering	214	137	—	—	—
Chrysanthemum parthènium Pers. (Feverfew)	No flowering	No flowering	No flowering	82	78[b]	77[b]

[a] Days from seeding to appearance of visible flower buds.
[b] Flowering in significantly fewer days than controls (P = 0.05).

The most pronounced differences were, however, at the 9-hr photoperiod. Furthermore, the acceleration in time of flowering under both day lengths was generally proportional to the amount (concentration) of gibberellin sprayed on the foliage.

Flowering in *Chrysanthemum parthènium* Pers. which had an

Fig. 1. Modifications of photoperiodic responses of (A) *Centaurea cyanus* Linn., (B) *Rudbeckia hirta* Linn., (C) *Spinacia oleracea* Linn., and (D) *Cosmos bipinnatus* Cav. with gibberellin. Left to right for each plant: 9-hr photoperiod, 9-hr photoperiod plus gibberellin, 18-hr photoperiod, 18-hr photoperiod plus gibberellin.

375

obligatory long-day requirement for flowering was significantly hastened under long days, but did not occur in short days even though
gibberellin was applied repeatedly. Stem elongation was promoted
after each treatment of gibberellin followed by the formation of an
aerial rosette between each application of gibberellin. *Spinacia oleracea*
Linn. (Fig. 1), *Chrysanthemum coccineum* Willd., and *Cichorium
endivia* Linn., obligatory long-day plants, flowered under short days
when treated with gibberellin (Table I) but only after a greater number of days than was required in a long photoperiod.

Flowering was also induced with gibberellin in *Rudbeckia hirta*
Linn. grown under short days. In this instance, however, stem elongation did not precede flower formation; and only single sessile flowers
were formed (Fig. 1), reminiscent of Murneek's observations (1937)
of flowering in *Rudbeckia* when grown near the critical photoperiod.
By contrast, gibberellin applied to *Rudbeckia* grown under long days
resulted in a "burning-out" of the growing tips, elongated leaves, and
greatly retarded flowering.

Thus flowering was accelerated by gibberellin in facultative long-
day plants grown under both long and short photoperiods. In plants
having an obligatory long-day requirement, and grown under short
days, flowering was induced in some but not all species. Acceleration
of flowering by gibberellin of obligate long-day plants in long days was
generally less pronounced than with facultative long-day plants.

Short-Day Plants

Of the short-day plants, only with *Cosmos bipinnatus* Cav. has gibberellin accelerated flowering in long days. While at least two papers in
this symposium (Greulach, p. 359; Salisbury, p. 381) have reported
an acceleration of flowering in *Xanthium pensylvanicum* Wallr. grown
under an inductive photoperiod (short days), there was no response in
long days.

Details of the flowering of *Cosmos* under short and long days as
modified by gibberellin are given in Tables II and III. Under a short
photoperiod all plants flowered simultaneously, and gibberellin had no
significant effect (Table II). At an 18-hr day length, however, gibberellin treatment hastened the appearance of visible flower buds—all
plants flowered as early as those under a short photoperiod. By con-

TABLE II. Modifying Effects of Gibberellin on the Photoperiodic Responses of Cosmos (*C. bipinnatus*, variety Sensation), a Facultative Short-Day Plant

	Control, No Treatment	Gibberellin, 100 ppm Foliar Spray
9-hr photoperiod		
Days to visible flower buds	47	46
Number of nodes	12	12
Final heights	94	114
Percent flowering	100	100
18-hr photoperiod		
Days to visible flower buds (of plants which flowered)	56	46[a]
Number of nodes	12	12
Final heights	101	121
Percent flowering	75	100

[a] Flowering in significantly fewer days than controls (P = 0.01).

trast, *Cosmos* that flowered under long days without gibberellin formed flower buds significantly later, and 25% remained vegetative (Fig. 1).

Cosmos bipinnatus Cav.[2] obviously does not have an obligatory short-day requirement for flowering, since most plants will eventually

TABLE III. Flowering of Cosmos (*C. bipinnatus*, variety Sensation) at an 18-hr Photoperiod Following Foliar Sprays of Gibberellin at Various Stages of Growth

Nodes at Time of Treatment	Gibberellin Concentration, ppm				
	0[a]	10[a]	100[a]	500[a]	1000[a]
2–3	64	68	64	53[b]	54[b]
3–4	65	60	53[b]	61[b]	49[b]
4–5	63	63	55[b]	54[b]	50[b]
5–6	78	64[b]	50[b]	50[b]	53[b]

[a] Days to visible flower buds.
[b] Flowering in significantly fewer days than controls (P = 0.05).

flower in long days. Accordingly a large number of plants maintained under long days were treated with several concentrations of gibberellin at various stages of growth as determined by node numbers (Table III). Plants which initiated flower buds under long days were eliminated at successively later growth stages. Only those which remained

[2] Variety Sensation, Ferry Morse Seed Co., Detroit, Michigan.

visibly vegetative were included in subsequent treatments. Flowering in *Cosmos* which were treated with gibberellin after the formation of 5 to 6 nodes, was accelerated as compared to no gibberellin, to a much greater extent than when sprayed at 2 to 3 nodes. It remains to be seen if flowering can be induced under long photoperiods in varieties of *Cosmos bipinnatus,* or in *C. sulphureus* Cav., which may have obligatory short-day requirements.

Two observations suggest that much work yet lies ahead before an accurate picture of the effects of gibberellin on the photoperiodic responses of short-day plants may be framed. These are the modifying effects of gibberellin on the flowering of *Cosmos bipinnatus* under a noninductive photoperiod, and the fact that only with a few classical short-day plants (Lang, 1957; Harder and Bünsow, 1957) has the response to gibberellin been subject to critical evaluation.

Stem Elongation and Flowering

In many long-day plants and in short-day *Cosmos,* stem elongation and flowering are induced and proceed simultaneously after photoperiodic induction. Similarly, both occur when gibberellin is used to replace the light requirement. With gibberellin, however, extensive stem elongation usually, but not always (see *Rudbeckia,* Fig. 1), precedes flower bud formation. Thus gibberellin provides a convenient means of separating the normally associated phenomena of stem elongation and flowering.

Pronounced stem elongation precedes flower initiation in gibberellin-treated plants, and accompanies flower bud development following photoperiodic induction. This suggests that the developing flower buds may form "gibberellin-like" substances capable of inducing both stem elongation and flowering. That this may be true has now been confirmed by reports in this symposium, wherein extracts from developing flower buds of *Brassica rapa* Linn. (Lona, p. 351) and immature seeds of *Echinocystis macrocarpa* Greene (Lang, p. 329) have broken the rosette habit of growth, and induced both stem elongation and flowering in certain biennials and long-day annuals. These reports recall those published by Wittwer (1943) and Mitchell *et al.* (1951) where crude extracts from developing plant reproductive organs induced stem elongation phenomena we now know are characteristic of gibberellin, but could not then be chemically identified when extraction and assay procedures for auxin were followed. A fruitful area for research should lie in a study of the comparative flower-inducing effects of the various gibberellins and "gibberellin-like" substances derived from the developing floral structures and immature seeds of higher plants (Phinney *et al.*, 1957). Emphasis on the extraction of the hypothetical flower-inducing hormone from the developing reproductive organs of plants may yet yield convincing evidence of its existence in these structures, whereas attempts to obtain a similar substance from photoinduced leaves have consistently failed.

REFERENCES

Bukovac, M. J., and S. H. Wittwer. 1957. Gibberellin and higher plants. II. Induction of flowering in biennials. *Mich. Agr. Expt. Sta. Quart. Bull., 39,* 650–60.

Bukovac, M. J., and S. H. Wittwer. 1958. Reproductive responses of lettuce (*Lactuca sativa,* variety Great Lakes) to gibberellin as influenced by seed vernalization, photoperiod and temperature. *Proc. Am. Soc. Hort. Sci., 71,* 407–11.

Bünsow, R., and R. Harder. 1956a. Blütenbildung von *Bryophyllum* durch Gibberellin. *Naturwissenschaften, 43,* 479–80.

———. 1956b. Blütenbildung von *Lampsana* durch Gibberellin. *Naturwissenschaften, 43,* 527.

———. 1957. Blütenbildung von *Adonis* und *Rudbeckia* durch Gibberellin. *Naturwissenschaften, 44,* 453–54.

Carr, D. J., A. J. McComb, and L. D. Osborne. 1957. Replacement of the requirement for vernalization in *Centaurium minus* (Moench) by gibberellic acid. *Naturwissenschaften, 44,* 428–29.

Harder, R., and R. Bünsow. 1956. Einfluss des Gibberellins auf die Blütenbildung bei *Kalanchoë blossfeldiana. Naturwissenschaften, 43,* 544.

———. 1957. Zusammenwirken von Gibberellin mit photoperiodisch bedingten blüfordernden und blühhemmenden Vorgängen bei *Kalanchoë blossfeldiana. Naturwissenschaften, 44,* 454.

Lang, A. 1956a. Induction of flower formation in biennial *Hyoscyamus* by treatment with gibberellin. *Naturwissenschaften, 43,* 284–85.

———. 1956b. Gibberellin and flower formation. *Naturwissenschaften, 43,* 544.

———. 1957. The effect of gibberellin upon flower formation. *Proc. Natl. Acad. Sci. U. S., 43,* 709–17.

Langridge, J. 1957. Effect of day-length and gibberellic acid on the flowering of *Arabidopsis. Nature, 180,* 36–37.

Lona, F. 1956a. L'azione dell'acido gibberellico sull'accrescimento caulinare di talune piante erbacee in condizioni esterne controllate. *Nuovo giorn. botan. italiano, 63,* 61–76.

――――. 1956b. Osservazioni orientative circa l'effetto dell'acido gibberellico sullo sviluppo riproduttivo di alcune longidiurne e brevidiurne. *Ateneo parmense, 27,* 867–75.

Mitchell, J. W., Dorothy P. Skaggs, and W. P. Anderson. 1951. Plant growth-stimulating hormones in immature bean seeds. *Science, 114,* 159–61.

Murneek, A. E. 1937. A separation of certain types of response of plants to photoperiod. *Proc. Am. Soc. Hort. Sci., 34,* 507–509.

Phinney, B. O., C. A. West, Mary Ritzel, and P. M. Neely. 1957. Evidence for "gibberellin-like" substances from flowering plants. *Proc. Natl. Acad. Sci. U. S., 43,* 398–404.

Wittwer, S. H. 1943. Growth hormone production during sexual reproduction of higher plants. *Missouri Agr. Expt. Sta. Research Bull., 371.*

Wittwer, S. H., and M. J. Bukovac. 1957a. Gibberellin effects on temperature and photoperiodic requirements for flowering of some plants. *Science, 126,* 30–31.

――――. 1957b. Gibberellin and higher plants. III. Induction of flowering in long-day annuals grown under short days. *Mich. Agr. Expt. Sta. Quart. Bull., 39,* 661–72.

INFLUENCE OF CERTAIN GROWTH REGULATORS ON FLOWERING OF THE COCKLEBUR

FRANK B. SALISBURY

Department of Botany and Plant Pathology, Colorado State University, Fort Collins

THE PARTIAL PROCESSES

The flowering process, especially as it applies to the cocklebur (*Xanthium pensylvanicum* Wall.), has been divided into a series of partial or component processes (Liverman, 1955; Salisbury, 1957b, 1958; Salisbury and Bonner, 1956). This division into steps has served as a framework of reference for evaluation of experiments done with short-day plants and has in some cases suggested new approaches to the problem of flowering. Since this system of partial processes has served as a foundation for the experimental work presented in this paper, it is summarized below as it applies to cocklebur.

High-Intensity Light Process

The experiments of Hamner (1940) and those of Liverman and Bonner (1953) indicated that the inductive dark period was ineffective unless sufficient photosynthates have been produced during the preceding light period. It is possible that the high-intensity light requirement involves more than photosynthesis (Lang, personal communication), but at present the more subtle aspects of this partial process remain vague.

Reactions of the Dark Period

1. *Pigment Conversion.* It has been suggested by Borthwick and co-workers (1952) that a reversible photoreceptor pigment exists in the leaf of plants sensitive to photoperiod, and that this pigment must be spontaneously converted from a far-red-receptive form to a red-receptive form before other reactions of the dark period may proceed. It has further been suggested (Salisbury and Bonner, 1956) that the

381

time interval required for this spontaneous conversion in the dark must be short (in the neighborhood of 2 to 3 hr).

2. *Preparatory Reaction(s).*   It is known that the minimum period of darkness required to produce the first perceptible signs of flowering in cocklebur always exceeds approximately 8.5 hr. This period so defined has been referred to as the critical night. Since pigment conversion accounts for only some 2 to 3 hr of this period, another time-measuring reaction has been postulated and referred to as preparatory reaction(s) (Salisbury and Bonner, 1956). Nothing is known about the biochemical nature of this reaction except that it is quite likely different from the reaction which follows (Salisbury, 1957b; Salisbury and Bonner, 1956).

3. *Hormone Synthesis.*   After the completion of the critical night, flowering hormone appears to be synthesized in the leaf, and the amount of hormone synthesized increases during the 4 to 8 hr which follow the critical night until a saturation point is reached.

An evidence in favor of this quantitative picture of hormone synthesis is that the rate of floral bud development, as measured by a series of floral stages observed a few days (usually 9) after induction, is proportional to the number of hours by which a single dark period exceeds the critical night (Salisbury, 1955). Many systems of floral stages have been proposed (Downs, 1956; Khadairi and Hamner, 1954; Mann, 1940), and one which has been used by the author (Salisbury, 1955) appears to be particularly well suited, not only to the study of the hormone synthesis phase of the dark period, but also to many other steps in the flowering process. This particular system of floral stages distinguishes small increments of change in rate of floral bud development. Furthermore, the numbers assigned to the stages are such that increase in floral stage is linear with time starting approximately 2.5 days after the beginning of induction (providing environmental conditions are optimal).

The conclusion drawn from the night length and floral stage experiment is based upon two assumptions. First, it is assumed that increasing amounts of flowering hormone cause an increased rate of bud development. Secondly, it is assumed that an increasing length of the dark period results in an increase in amount of flowering hormone produced. The truth of either assumption, in light of this experiment, implies the truth of the other. Thus evidence relating to either assumption would be valuable, and such evidence obtained from translocation experiments is presented below.

Second High-Intensity Light Process

Lockhart and Hamner (1954) have shown that flowering hormone produced during an inductive dark period may disappear unless this dark period is followed by a period of high-intensity light. Thus they have postulated a stabilization of flowering hormone by high-intensity light, and this has been referred to by Liverman (1955) as the second high-intensity light process.

Translocation

After the flowering hormone has been synthesized in the leaf it must be translocated to the bud where differentation of floral primordia will occur. The movement of flowering hormone can be measured by defoliating the plants at different times following a single inductive dark period (Khudairi and Hamner, 1954; Salisbury, 1955). It has been found that if plants are defoliated immediately after the dark period, the apical meristems remain vegetative. If, however, plants are defoliated a number of hours after the inductive dark period, the apical meristems develop into floral primordia at a rate comparable to that of plants which have not been defoliated. Intermediate times of defoliation result in intermediate rates of floral development. This observation is in harmony with the assumption mentioned above that the rate of floral development is a function of the amount of flowering hormone which reaches the bud, and thus it adds support to the assumption that the amount of hormone produced is a function of the length of the dark period.

Differentiation

The primary meristems respond to the flowering hormone by differentiating into floral primordia.

Development

The floral primordia develop into flowers and eventually into fruits. Of course a number of differentiation steps also take place during this period.

BASIC EXPERIMENTS WITH GROWTH REGULATORS

The effects of a series of growth regulators upon the flowering of *Xanthium* have been used as effective tools in the study of the partial processes. Three basic kinds of experiments have been done in the first phases of this study.

1. Prepared cocklebur plants (Salisbury, 1955, 1957b; Salisbury and Bonner, 1956) are treated just previous to induction by a single 14- (or 16-) hr dark period with a wide concentration range of the growth regulator in question. After 9 days the apical meristems are examined and floral stage is plotted as a function of growth regulator concentration. Vegetative condition of the plants is also noted. This appears to be an effective means of surveying for growth regulators which influence the flowering process, although it is conceivable that compounds which might influence flowering when applied at some time other than just before induction might be ineffective when applied at that time. It is also somewhat difficult to observe promotion of flowering by this method, although not impossible. In using this basic experiment, the following growth regulators have been found to inhibit flowering (Salisbury, 1957b): 2,4-dichlorophenoxyacetic acid (2,4-D), 2,2-dichloroproprionic acid (Dalapon), maleic hydrazide, indoleacetic acid, naphthaleneacetic acid, 2,4-dinitrophenol, and cobaltous chloride. Gibberellic acid has been found to promote flowering.

2. In the second kind of experiment, growth regulators are applied to plants at various times previous to, during, and following a single inductive dark period. With this technique, it is possible to determine which phase of the flowering mechanism might be influenced by a particular growth regulator. This is illustrated by Fig. 1, which is a composite of 13 experiments (Salisbury, 1957b) performed at Colorado State University. Data are shown as relative floral stage (usually measured 9 days after induction) plotted against the time of application of a particular chemical. The translocation experiment (defoliation) is carried out in conjunction with the time of application experiments, and this is plotted against the floral stage of plants at the time the apical buds are examined. The apical buds of some untreated plants are examined at various times after the inductive dark period to

determine the rate of floral bud development. This is shown as a solid line.

It can be seen from the composite curves of Fig. 1 that 2,4-D, maleic hydrazide, and Dalapon inhibit flowering even when they are applied only 1 or 2 days before buds are examined. Thus, it would appear that these compounds inhibit the development of floral buds.

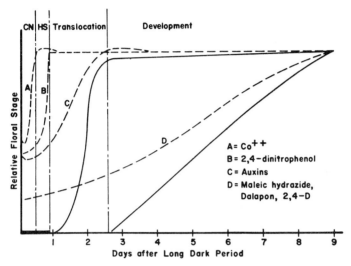

FIG. 1.   The inhibitory effect of various growth regulators upon flowering as a function of their time of application. The black bar at the left side of the abscissa represents the single inductive dark period. CN indicates the critical night portion of this period, and HS represents the hormone synthesis portion. The S-shaped solid line is typical of results obtained in translocation (defoliation) experiments, and the other slanted solid line indicates the relationship between floral stage of untreated control plants and days following the inductive dark period (development). The broken lines summarize 13 experiments using the indicated growth regulators at more than one concentration in each experiment (Salisbury, 1957b).

Indoleacetic acid and naphthaleneacetic acid (the auxins), however, inhibit flowering only when they are applied to plants before the flowering hormone has been translocated from the leaf. Thus, it would appear that these compounds influence flowering either by interfering in some way with the translocation of flowering hormone or by destroying flowering hormone in the leaf. Dinitrophenol appears to inhibit the synthesis of flowering hormone, since it is effective in floral inhibition only when applied before the dark period has ended. Cobaltous ion inhibits flowering when it is applied during the critical night and thus probably influences this phase of the flowering process.

Recently, gibberellic acid has been tested in this type of experiment. Figure 2 is typical of four such experiments with this compound. Al-

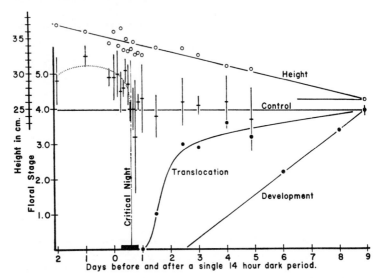

FIG. 2. The promotive effect of gibberellic acid upon flowering as a function of its time of application. The vertical lines through the points which represent the effects of gibberellic acid upon floral stage indicate standard error. All treatments applied previous to 8 hr after the beginning of the dark period except one are significantly above the control line, and all treatments applied after this time do not differ significantly from the control line. Plants were prepared and dipped in $1.0 \times 10^{-4}M$ gibberellic acid (6 drops Tween 20/liter) as explained in earlier publications (Salisbury, 1957b; Salisbury and Bonner, 1956). Inductive dark period was begun October 17, 1957. Ten plants per treatment; weather overcast.

though the data are quite variable, it is clear that gibberellic acid applied previous to the end of the critical night promotes flowering, while this substance applied just previous to and following this time has no significant effect upon flowering. It is interesting to note that gibberellic acid causes cocklebur stems to elongate regardless of when it is applied in relation to the inductive dark period.

3. In the third type of experiment, plants are induced with a single dark period of varying lengths. Control plants in such an experiment indicate the length of the critical night, and plants treated with growth regulators indicate whether or not a given substance influences the duration of the critical night. A number of experiments are summarized in Fig. 3. Of the above-mentioned growth regulators, only the

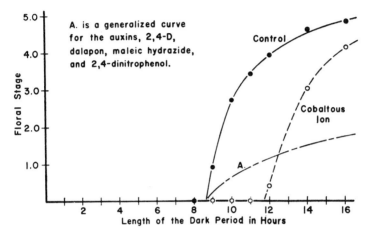

FIG. 3. The effect of cobaltous ion upon critical night. Points refer to an experiment in which the inductive dark period was begun August 11, 1956 (Salisbury, 1957b). Curve A summarizes approximately 6 other experiments.

cobaltous ion increases the minimum length of the dark period required for the first perceptible signs of flowering. This period may be increased as much as 2 to 3 hr depending upon cobaltous ion concentration. All other compounds except gibberellic acid inhibit the degree of flowering as measured 9 days after induction, but do not influence the critical dark period. Experiments in progress indicate that gibberellic acid promotes flowering somewhat with slight or no shortening effect upon the critical night.

FURTHER EXPERIMENTS WITH GROWTH REGULATORS

Each of the growth regulators mentioned above might be further investigated in relation to flowering. The general growth inhibitors might be studied as to their effect upon the morphological development of floral primordia. The auxins might be studied to see if their effect is upon translocation of flowering stimulus or some other process such as destruction of flowering hormone in the leaf. A start has been made with the auxins as shown in Fig. 4. Plants treated with auxin just fol-

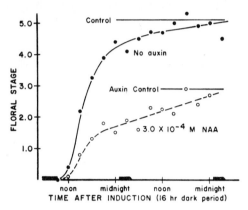

FIG. 4. The effect of naphthaleneacetic acid upon translocation of flowering hormone. Plants defoliated at various times following a single 16-hr inductive dark period, which was begun on July 30, 1957. Ten plants per treatment, buds examined after 9 days. Plants in this and subsequent figures were prepared as previously explained (Salisbury, 1957b).

lowing a single dark period were defoliated at various times. It is evident from the figure that the time relations of flowering hormone translocation are not influenced by auxin.

Dinitrophenol is being investigated further at Colorado State University to relate certain herbicidal effects of this compound to the effects upon flowering (Salisbury, 1957a). It is important to note that dinitrophenol will inhibit hormone synthesis but that it does not extend the critical night. This, along with other evidence (Salisbury and Bonner, 1956), would seem to separate these two reactions.

Since cobaltous ion influences the critical night (Salisbury, 1957a, b), it seemed pertinent to see whether this ion changed the amount of photoreceptor pigment or affected the preparatory reaction. Some idea of the amount of photoreceptor pigment present in the plant can be obtained by determining the amount of light required to saturate the photoreaction. This is done by exposing plants to various durations of

red light 5½ hr (or 4 to 5½ hr) after the beginning of a 16-hr inductive dark period. If plants are treated instead with saturating or even
subsaturating amounts of light near the *middle* of a 16-hr inductive
dark period, they remain vegetative, and thus the saturating amount of
light cannot be determined. After 5½ hr plants treated with a saturating amount of light still flower to some extent. Such an experiment is
shown in Fig. 5. Approximately 7 sec of light was sufficient to cause
the maximum degree of floral inhibition of control plants (curve A).
Plants treated with cobaltous ion at the beginning of the inductive
dark period and illuminated with the control plants are inhibited in

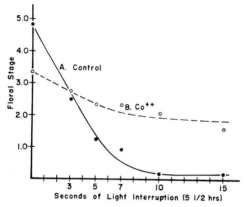

FIG. 5.   The effects of various durations of red light applied 5½ hr after
the beginning of a 16-hr dark period (Oct. 3, 1957). Treated plants were
dipped in 5.0 × $10^{-3}M$ CoCl$_2$ (6 drops Tween 20/liter) just previous to
induction. Twelve plants per treatment, buds examined after 9 days.

their flowering by the cobalt and also by the light interruption, but it
can be seen from curve B of Fig. 5, that light is less effective in inhibition of cobaltous-treated plants than untreated control plants. The
amount of light required to bring about the maximum inhibitory effect
has been quite difficult to determine, but two out of six experiments
seem to indicate that the amount of light required to saturate the
process is approximately the same whether the plants have been treated
with cobaltous ion or not (Fig. 6, for example). The other four experiments are inconclusive or perhaps suggest that more light is required
for cobaltous treated plants than untreated controls.

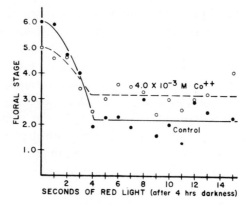

Fig. 6.   Red light interruptions of various duration applied 4 hr after the beginning of a 16-hr dark period (July 11, 1957). Eight plants per treatment, buds examined after 9 days.

Some insight into this "protective effect" of the cobaltous ion against light inhibition may be obtained from another kind of experiment. Cobaltous-treated and untreated plants are given an inductive dark period, and this dark period is interrupted at various times with a saturating amount of light. The results of such an experiment are shown in Fig. 7. The right half of the curves are approximately the same as those obtained in the critical night experiments shown in Fig.

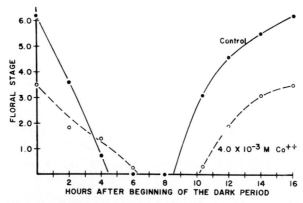

Fig. 7.   The effects of 15 sec of red light interruption given at various times during a 16-hr dark period upon flowering of control plants and plants treated with $4.0 \times 10^{-3}M$ CoCl$_2$ (6 drops Tween 20/liter). August 8, 1957; 16 plants per treatment; buds examined after 9 days.

3. That is, light interruption is approximately equivalent to returning plants to light (the critical night has been extended for cobaltous-treated plants). The processes that go on during the first part of the dark period, however, appear to be slowed down by the presence of cobaltous ion. Indeed, this would account for the increase in the critical night length and the inhibitory effect of cobaltous ion.

At this stage of the investigation, since the saturating quantity of light appears to be the same with or without cobaltous ion, it appears that pigment conversion is not influenced by the cobaltous ion, but that the preparatory reaction is in some manner decreased in velocity.

Work is also being carried on with gibberellic acid, although at this stage of the investigation, this work has all been of a preliminary nature.

In addition to the studies of growth regulators which are known to influence the flowering process, a continual effort is being made to discover new compounds which will influence the flowering process and allow us to gain further insight into the steps and mechanisms of this natural phenomenon.

REFERENCES

Borthwick, H. A., S. B. Hendricks, and M. W. Parker. 1952. The reaction controlling floral initiation. *Proc. Natl. Acad. Sci. U. S., 38,* 929–34.

Downs, R. J. 1956. Photoreversibility of flower initiation. *Plant Physiol., 31,* 279–83.

Hamner, K. C. 1940. Interrelation of light and darkness in photoperiodic induction. *Botan. Gaz., 101,* 658–87.

Khudairi, Abdul-Karim, and K. C. Hamner. 1954. The relative sensitivity of *Xanthium* leaves of different ages to photoperiodic induction. *Plant Physiol., 29,* 251–57.

Liverman, J. L. 1955. The physiology of flowering. *Ann. Rev. Plant Physiol., 6,* 177–210.

Liverman, J. L., and J. Bonner. 1953. Biochemistry of the photoperiodic response: The high-intensity-light reaction. *Botan. Gaz., 115,* 121–28.

Lockhart, James A., and Karl Hamner. 1954. Partial reactions in the formation of the floral stimulus in *Xanthium. Plant Physiol., 29,* 509–13.

Mann, Louis K. 1940. Effect of some environmental factors on floral initiation in *Xanthium. Botan. Gaz., 102,* 339–56.

Salisbury, F. B. 1955. The dual role of auxin in flowering. *Plant Physiol., 30,* 327–34.

———. 1957a. The mechanisms of action of cobaltous ion, 2,4-dinitrophenol, and auxins in flowering. Abstract of paper presented at AIBS meetings at Stanford, California. *Plant Physiol., 32,* x.

————. 1957b. Growth regulators and flowering. I. Survey methods. *Plant Physiol.,* 600–608.

————. 1958. The flowering process. *Sci. American, 198,* 108–117.

Salisbury, F. B., and James Bonner. 1956. The reactions of the photoinductive dark period. *Plant Physiol., 31,* 141–47.

SOME INTERRELATIONS OF COMPENSATORY GROWTH, FLOWERING, AUXIN, AND DAY LENGTH IN *Coleus blumei* Benth[1]

WILLIAM P. JACOBS, ROBERT V. DAVIS, JR.,
and BOB BULLWINKEL [2]
Department of Biology, Princeton University, Princeton, New Jersey

In a previous paper, compensatory growth[3] of *Coleus* shoots and leaves was described (Jacobs and Bullwinkel, 1953). Excising the axillary buds and branches induced compensatory growth in the main shoot; and excising, in addition, some of the leaves on the main shoot resulted in still further compensatory growth of the leaves that remained. Evidence was presented in support of the interpretations (1) that the compensatory growth of the main shoot was mainly due to greater growth of the young leaves on the main shoot; (2) that this compensatory growth of the young leaves, in turn, caused greater growth of the young internodes. When synthetic auxin in the form of indoleacetic acid (IAA) was substituted for the axillaries, the results were not absolutely clear-cut: the auxin-treated plants were typically intermediate between the untreated controls and the "axillaries-off" plants, although closer to the latter.

This paper investigates further the report in the previous paper that excising axillary buds and branches resulted in faster flowering as well

[1] Research supported by grants from the National Science Foundation and American Cancer Society and by funds of the Eugene Higgins Trust allocated to Princeton University. The aid of Dr. Roy Sachs, Miss I. B. Morrow, and Mrs. R. Speagle is gratefully acknowledged.

[2] The contributions of the junior authors were incorporated in their Princeton College Senior Theses (1955 and 1952, respectively).

[3] Compensatory growth was defined as the special type of regeneration characterized by greater than normal growth of an organ or organs of the same type as the one which has been lost. Regeneration was defined as the totality of phenomena of growth and differentiation which results from loss of a part of a living organism.

as in compensatory growth and attempts to elucidate the relation of auxin to these two effects of axillary excision.

MATERIALS AND METHODS

Material and methods were the same as in Jacobs and Bullwinkel (1953). Flowering was determined by checking the plants every day for the first appearance of a macroscopic inflorescence at the distal end of the main shoot. The inflorescences were recognizable while still very small. In the first experiments the plants were checked only until all the plants in one of the treatments had flowered—the data in Fig. 1 were

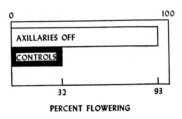

PERCENT FLOWERING

FIG. 1. Effect of excising all axillary shoots on the speed of flowering of *Coleus* plants which were small at the start of the experiment (pooled data from 5 experiments).

so recorded. For the later experiments, involving substitution of auxin for the axillary shoots, we used the more precise method of determining average days to flowering (Fig. 3). (The early method gives artificially large separation of the treatments.)

RESULTS

Confirmation was obtained of our previous reports that axillary excision causes compensatory growth and faster flowering of the main shoot. Synthetic auxin can substitute for the axillaries in inhibiting flowering, but has no detectable relation to the compensatory growth effect.

Excising Axillary Buds and Branches

Four more repetitions of this experiment confirmed the previous eight repetitions in showing that compensatory growth of the main shoot resulted from the treatment (details in Jacobs and Bullwinkel, 1953).

Faster Flowering Results from Excising Axillary Shoots

Accompanying the compensatory growth that resulted from this treatment was a striking and significant increase in the speed of flowering (Table I and Fig. 1). Similar results were obtained in each of the

TABLE I.   Effects of Photoperiod and Axillary Excision on Number of *Coleus blumei* Plants Which Show Flowering after Given Time[a]

	Controls			Axillaries-Off		
	SD	LD	Totals	SD	LD	Totals
			Experiment, B3, 54 days			
Flowering	2	2	4	7	9	16
Not flowering	7	6	13	1	0	1
			Experiment, B5, 40 days			
Flowering	3	4	7	7	6	13
Not flowering	4	3	7	0	0	0
	SD	"LD"[b]		SD	"LD"	

[a] Adjusted χ^2 test shows highly significant difference between controls and axillaries-off, no significant difference between short-day and long-day treatments.
[b] "LD" signifies interrupted-night treatments.

five experiments in which speed of flowering was compared in axillaries-off and control plants.

Under our usual greenhouse conditions, plants of our clone of *Coleus blumei* would flower fairly soon after they reached a stage of large-leaved, luxuriant growth which was recognizable by casual inspection. For the five experiments cited above, plants were selected which were obviously smaller than this ready-to-flower stage, i.e., the plants had been through fewer plastochrones. In four other experiments, however, we used only the larger plants. Results of a typical experiment are shown in Fig. 2. There is no significant difference in speed of flowering between axillaries-off plants and the intact controls, although the compensatory growth effect is as pronounced as ever. (Naturally, the time to flowering is much less than with plants which are initially smaller.)

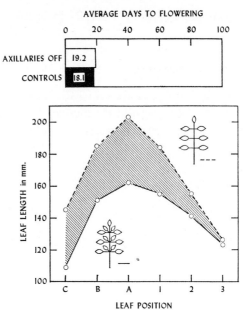

FIG. 2.   Effect of axillary excision on plants ready to flower at start.
The lack of effect on flowering is shown above; the compensatory growth
effect is shown below (leaf length after 28 days).

Indoleacetic Acid (IAA) Substituted for the Axillaries

To see if the two effects of axillary excision were a result of removing the axillaries as auxin sources, 1% IAA in lanolin was placed on
the axillary stumps in one set of plants, plain lanolin on the stumps in
another set. In the hope of increasing the precision of the experiments
over those reported in the earlier paper, particular care was taken to
match the sets of plants as exactly as possible. Results of a typical experiment starting with small plants are shown in Fig. 3 and Table II.
It is clear that auxin substituted for the axillaries has absolutely no
effect on the compensatory growth caused by axillary excision; however, at the same time it does cause slower flowering. These results
were confirmed in two repetitions of this experiment (see Fig. 5 also).
When large plants (of ready-to-flower size) were used in three experiments, otherwise comparable to the above, the auxin again had no
effect on the compensatory growth (Fig. 4), but also had no effect on

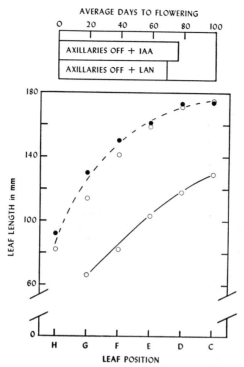

FIG. 3.   One percent indoleacetic acid in lanolin can substitute for the axillaries in causing slower flowering (above), but cannot substitute with respect to compensatory growth (below). (Data in Table II.)

speed of flowering (Table II). (Remember, too, that axillary excision did not speed flowering in such plants.)

How Complete Is the Compensation?

Small plants were divided into three matched groups and treated as shown in Fig. 5. After 86 days of treatment, all remaining leaves were excised and immediately weighed. Results are shown in Fig. 5. Despite the striking increase in the growth of those leaves that remain in the axillaries-off plants, the compensation is far from complete. Plants showing compensatory growth have leaf weights totaling 60% of the total leaf weight in the control plants with intact axillary shoots.

TABLE II. Average Leaf Lengths (in mm ± Standard Error) after 68 Days and Average Days to Flowering of *Coleus* Plants Treated as Shown

Leaf	Controls Length ± S.E. (n)	Axillaries-Off	Axillaries-Off + IAA
H	—	81.7 ± 5.4 (12)	91.8 ± 2.6 (20)
G	65.8[a] ± 1.6 (6)	114.1 ± 6.1 (14)	129.8[b] ± 3.1 (16)
F	81.6[a] ± 2.9 (19)	141.1 ± 4.5 (15)	149.8 ± 2.6 (19)
E	102.9[a] ± 2.1 (20)	159.3 ± 4.9 (15)	160.9 ± 2.3 (18)
D	117.7[a] ± 1.9 (18)	171.1 ± 4.9 (13)	173.4 ± 2.3 (20)
C	128.9[a] ± 2.4 (19)	174.9 ± 6.1 (14)	174.2 ± 1.6 (20)
Average days to flowering		68.8 ± 1.84 (9)	76.1[b] ± 1.98 (9)
Average days to flowering— ready-to-flower plants		41.2 ± 2.31 (10)	38.9 ± 1.52 (9)

[a] Signifies a statistically highly significant difference, by the t test, between the marked average and the average for the same leaf position in the central column.

[b] Signifies a statistically significant difference, as above.

Excising Very Young and Old Leaves on the Main Shoot

If, in addition to removing all axillaries, leaf pairs 1 and 2 are excised and leaf pairs A, B, C, etc., are excised as soon as they have unfolded from the apical bud and have reached the size of the original leaf pair 1, then additional compensatory growth is induced in leaf pairs 3 and 4 (Jacobs and Bullwinkel, 1953). Still greater compensatory growth results from excising the smaller leaves of original size A (ca. 15 mm) in addition to excising size 1 leaves (Jacobs and Bullwinkel, 1953). In other words, the more leaves removed, the greater was the growth in those leaves remaining, as one would expect from the concept of compensatory growth.

Does this statement hold for all other patterns of deblading? Further experiments showed it did not.

When the plant was completely stripped of its unfolded leaves (pairs 1–8), leaving only the small leaves in the apical bud (A-E), the young leaves did not show as much growth as when some of the older leaves were left on (Table III and Fig. 6; three repetitions). In other words, this pattern was an exception to the concept of compensatory growth. And, as with all the compensatory growth studied so far in *Coleus,* IAA which was substituted for the older leaves (5+) had no effect on the growth of the initially very young ones (Fig. 6 and Table III; also Jacobs, 1955, Table 4).

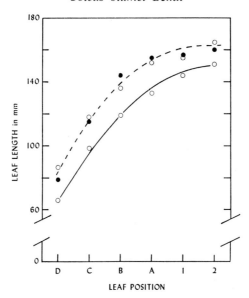

FIG. 4. One percent indoleacetic acid in lanolin cannot substitute for the axillaries of ready-to-flower plants with respect to compensatory growth (graph shows average leaf lengths after 39 days).

[The "reverse" experiment—excising *all* the young leaves and leaving on only the old ones (5+)—did give more growth of the remaining leaves. Leaves 5 and 6 grew somewhat more if the apical bud were removed than if it were on. Again, auxin could not substitute for the

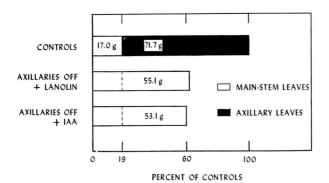

FIG. 5. Average wet weight in grams of all leaves on plants treated as shown (after 86 days).

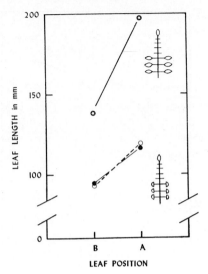

FIG. 6. Average lengths of leaf pairs A and B (the oldest, largest leaves in the apical bud at the start of the experiment) when leaf pairs 1–4 have been excised and petioles 5–8 have intact leaves, lanolin, or 1% indole-acetic acid in lanolin (after 21 days.) (Data in Table III.)

apical bud in reducing the compensatory growth of leaves 5 and 6 (experiment run twice).]

Day Length Effects

When plants were placed under long-day (LD) or short-day (SD) conditions, with axillaries either excised or left intact, results with respect to flowering were as shown in Table I. In B3 the natural day length was prolonged to 14 hr for long day, reduced to 8 hr for short

TABLE III. Average Lengths (in mm ± Standard Error) of Leaves A and B in Plants with All Leaves 1–4 Excised and with Indicated Treatments at Nodes 5–8 (after 21 days of treatment; $n = 14$ in each case)

Treatment on Petioles 5–8

Leaf Pairs	Intact Leaves	Lanolin	IAA + Lanolin
B	138.3[a] ± 3.7	94.1 ± 1.8	93.5 ± 3.2
A	197.5[a] ± 4.2	116.1 ± 2.8	119.4 ± 5.6

[a] Signifies a statistically highly significant difference, by the t test, between the marked average and the average for the same leaf position in the central column.

day; in B5, the long-day plants were given 4 hr during the middle of the night. Final leaf lengths for B3 are shown in Fig. 6 of Jacobs and Bullwinkel (1953). Although the plants in these two experiments were exposed to the photoperiods for 54 and 40 days, respectively, there was no detectable effect of photoperiod on the number of plants that formed flower buds during the experimental period. (The number of days to flowering averaged 5 days less in SD plants than in LD plants in both the axillaries-off treatments, but the difference was not statistically significant.)

An interesting differential appeared when growth was compared under "extended day" (B3) and "interrupted night" conditions (B5), the total hours of illumination being the same. Interrupted nights gave results in the control plants that showed no apparent differences from extended days. For instance, the ratio of LD/SD summated leaf lengths was 1.08 for extended days, 1.06 for interrupted nights [in both cases, reflecting the slightly larger leaf lengths in plants under LD when compared to plants under SD (see Fig. 6, Jacobs and Bullwinkel, 1953)]. The increased stem length in control plants likewise showed no differential as a result of the two different long-day treatments. However, interrupted nights had markedly different effects on the axillaries-off plants. Although compensatory growth of the leaves did occur under interrupted nights, it was only 24% greater than the controls, instead of 45 to 49% greater as under extended-day or short-day conditions. This difference is apparent from the ratio of LD/SD summated leaf lengths in the axillaries-off plants; the ratio was only 0.91 for interrupted nights, whereas it was 1.11 in the replication using extended days. Stem lengths, as would be expected from the relations between leaf and internode growth described by Jacobs and Bullwinkel (1953), also showed much less compensatory growth under interrupted nights (19% increase over controls, versus 52 to 56% for extended or short days). But, as one would also expect from the frequent use of interrupted nights as a substitute for extended days in research on flowering, we found no detectable differential effect of extended days versus interrupted night on the flowering rate.

Since there were the usual large number of uncontrolled variables in the greenhouse that we used for the above experiments, we were fortunate to get the aid of Dr. Roy Sachs, who generously ran an experiment for us in the California Institute of Technology phytotron. Our clone of *Coleus* was grown there, at a constant temperature of 23°C, under short-day, extended-day, and interrupted-night conditions (8 hr natural light, plus 8 hr artificial light as a supplement). The results confirmed the results above: interrupted nights gave less growth in axillaries-off plants than did extended-day treatments.

DISCUSSION

When lateral shoots of *Coleus* are cut off, the main shoot shows striking compensatory growth and much faster flowering. However, our experiments support the interpretation that the two responses are not causally related to each other. The faster flowering apparently results from releasing the main shoot from auxin inhibition by the laterals, whereas the compensatory growth is from some factor(s) other than auxin.

This relation of auxin to flowering in *Coleus* is particularly interesting because we are dealing with a naturally occurring inhibition of flowering in a day-neutral plant. This combination has been studied very little in the past. To summarize the evidence for *Coleus:* Excising axillaries results in significantly faster flowering (Table I and Fig. 1); axillaries have been shown in many plants to produce auxin (Went and Thimann, 1937) and the small, fast-growing leaves of this clone of *Coleus* produce large amounts (Jacobs, 1956, Fig. 1); synthetic IAA at 1% substituted for the axillaries significantly reduces the rate of flowering again, but it has no effect on the compensatory growth of the main shoot (Fig. 3). We conclude, therefore, that in the intact plant the axillary shoots are inhibiting flowering in the main shoot, and that all (or a significant part of) this effect is from the auxin produced by the axillaries. [Before we could say definitely that "all" the effect was from the auxin produced by the axillaries, we would need to determine the auxin production of the axillaries and then to match it *exactly* with that artificially supplied. Such exact replacement has not been done here—nor, we believe, in any other study of auxin's relations to flowering—although its feasibility has been demonstrated in studies of xylem regeneration in *Coleus* (Jacobs.

1956). But there is some reason to think that fairly exact matching is done by the plant, through the controlling action of the transport capacity of the stem for auxin (Jacobs, 1950a,b, 1954).]

There are already in the literature many reports of slower flowering following auxin application (review in Bonner and Liverman, 1952). This report differs from most in that (1) it concerns a day-neutral plant (as contrasted to SDP and LDP, which have been most thoroughly studied); (2) in being concerned with a *natural* flower-inhibiting effect of plant organs; (3) in *substituting* auxin for excised organs (instead of artificially increasing the natural auxin levels by spraying or immersing the intact organs); and (4) by providing more detailed evidence that the vegetative growth is unchanged by the auxin while flowering is being inhibited (cf. Figs. 3 and 5).

Leopold (1949) has observed in this clone of *Coleus* that more auxin diffuses from leaves kept under LD than under SD conditions. This result suggests that the somewhat slower flowering which we observed under LD conditions is also caused by auxin and is real (although not statistically significant in our experiments).

When interrupted night was used instead of extended day, an interesting effect appeared. Although the flowering rate was unchanged, much less compensatory growth occurred than under extended day, or even than under SD. There was no discernible effect on normal growth, i.e., when the axillary shoots were left intact, interrupted nights gave no differential effect in growth of the main shoot.

An inhibiting effect of interrupted nights on the "normal" growth of tomato plants has recently been described by Highkin and Hanson (1954). For growth at constant temperature, they found small but significant decreases in height and weight in plants treated with a 2-hr interruption of the night as contrasted to a 2-hr extension of the day. These differences could be increased if the plants were grown entirely under low-intensity artificial light (as contrasted to 8 hr of sunlight). By contrast, light during the night had no significant effect on sunflowers, and only a small effect on peas.

Can the inhibiting effects of interrupted night on growth of *Coleus* and tomato be basically similar, even though the inhibition has been found for normal growth in tomatoes but only for compensatory growth in *Coleus?* We think they are, but that tomato is much more sensitive. In 1930, Arthur *et al.* tested many plants under *constant* illumination as contrasted to various other day lengths. Tomatoes, *Coleus,* and geranium gave less growth under continuous artificial light than with some dark period every 24 hr—the growth inhibition was greatest in tomato, "not quite as severe" in *Coleus* and geranium. For all three plants, the inhibition was decreased by using sunlight for 12 of each 24 hr of continuous light. Under sunlight plus a 12-hr supplement of artificial light, tomato was still strongly inhibited, but *Coleus* showed little or no inhibition. [The decreased growth of *Coleus* under continuous artificial light was also found by Garner and Allard (1931).]

Thus, only a few of the plants tested showed inhibition of growth by light during the "night," and tomato was far more sensitive than *Coleus.*

Hillman (1956) has further investigated these photoperiodic effects in tomato, and among his interesting findings is the report that if older leaves are removed from intact plants, the plants show increased sensitivity to continuous light. He suggests that some substance from older tissues perhaps is destroyed by light. In view of our findings with *Coleus,* an alternative possibility is that excising some leaves caused compensatory growth in those which were left, with a concomitant increase in sensitivity.

In the light of these earlier papers, three aspects of our methods with *Coleus* would tend to obscure a growth-inhibiting effect on normal growth: (1) the use of sunlight for most of the daily illumination; (2) the use of a 2-hr interruption of the dark period (instead of continuous illumination); and (3) in measuring growth, the use of only leaves on the *main* shoot—thus [in contrast to Garner and Allard (1931), and Highkin and Hanson (1954)] eliminating 81% of the plant's leaf weight (Fig. 5).

Why should light during the middle of the night inhibit the vegetative growth of some plants but not of others? An intriguing answer is suggested by parallel studies on the developmental anatomy of *Coleus.* From round-the-clock collections we have found evidence that leaf initiation in our clone occurs between 11 P.M. and 1 A.M. (Jacobs and Morrow, 1957, Table 1, where leaf lengths of 1300± microns mark the plants which are initiating new leaf primordia at the shoot apex). Since the light interruption which we gave was during this period, our results suggest that interrupted night inhibits growth in those plants which are initiating leaves at the time of the interruption. This hypothesis is currently being tested.

Compensatory Growth

That auxin has no effect on compensatory growth has been shown for a number of new compensatory growth experiments as well as more precisely demonstrated for simple "axillaries-excised" treatments (e.g., Figs. 3, 5, 6). The absence of any detectable compensatory growth effect from auxin substituted for axillary shoots, old leaves, or the apical bud of the debudded main shoot is the more surprising in view of the widespread belief that auxin is the controlling factor for the "reverse" of our basic experiment; that is, that auxin *can* replace the apical bud in inhibiting the compensatory growth of the axillary shoots (Audus, 1953, p. 162). (We are currently investigating the role of auxin from the apical bud in our clone of *Coleus*.)

There are some interesting parallels between compensatory growth in *Coleus* and in animals. In many cases excision of one animal organ results in compensatory growth of the paired homologous organ (cf. Weiss, 1955). For kidney, ovary, and suprarenal glands, Addis and Lew (1940) reported approximately 70% restitution. Growth of leaves on *Coleus* shoots with bud axillaries excised was of the same order of magnitude, 60% of that on the controls (Fig. 5). How general these relations are, remains to be seen.

The greater growth of very young leaves when adult leaves were present (Fig. 6) is reminiscent of the greater growth of particular organs in chick embryos when a piece of the corresponding adult organ is grafted onto the chorio-allantoic membrane (Ebert, 1954; Weiss, 1955). The zoologists have found that greater growth of the embryonic organ is obtained only if the grafted organ is beyond a certain age. On this superficial level, at least, the phenomena are similar in animals and plants.

SUMMARY

Excising all the axillary shoots in *Coleus blumei* induces compensatory growth in the main shoot and significantly speeds flowering. One percent indoleacetic acid substituted for the excised axillaries significantly slows flowering again, but it has no effect on the compensatory growth.

The much greater growth of the leaves on the main shoot did not completely compensate for the loss of all leaves on the many axillary shoots—total leaf weight was 60% of that in the intact controls.

The small leaves of the apical bud showed greater compensatory growth when older leaves were present. IAA could not substitute for the older leaves in this effect.

The clone of *Coleus blumei* used in these experiments was apparently day neutral with respect to flowering: weeks of exposure to short-day and long-day conditions had no significant effect on speed of flowering. Long-day treatments given by extending the normal day gave equivalent results for flowering to those obtained by interrupting the night. But the compensatory growth induced by excising all axillary shoots was reduced by interrupted nights when compared to extended-day treatments.

REFERENCES

Addis, T., and W. Lew. 1940. The restoration of lost organ tissue. The rate and degree of restoration. *J. Exptl. Med., 71*, 325–33.

Arthur, J. M., J. D. Guthrie, and J. M. Newell. 1930. Some effects of artificial climates on the growth and chemical composition of plants. *Am. J. Botany, 17*, 416–82.

Audus, L. J. 1953. *Plant Growth Substances.* Interscience, New York.

Bonner, J., and J. Liverman. 1952. Hormonal control of flower initiation. *Growth and Differentiation in Plants,* W. E. Loomis, Editor. Iowa State College Press, Ames. Pp. 283–303.

Ebert, J. D. 1954. Some aspects of protein biosynthesis in development. *Aspects of Synthesis and Order in Growth,* Dorothea Rudnick, Editor. Princeton University Press, Princeton, N. J. Chapter IV.

Garner, W. W., and H. A. Allard. 1931. Effect of abnormally long and short alternations of light and darkness on growth and development of plants. *J. Agr. Research, 42*, 629–51.

Highkin, H. R., and J. B. Hanson. 1954. Possible interaction between light-dark cycles and endogenous daily rhythms on the growth of tomato plants. *Plant Physiol., 29*, 301–302.

Hillman, W. S., 1956. Injury of tomato plants by continuous light and unfavorable photoperiodic cycles. *Am. J. Botany, 43*, 89–96.

Jacobs, W. P. 1950a. Auxin-transport in the hypocotyl of *Phaseolus vulgaris* L. *Am. J. Botany, 37*, 248–54.

————. 1950b. Control of elongation in the bean hypocotyl by the ability of the hypocotyl tip to transport auxin. *Am. J. Botany, 37,* 551–55.

————, 1954. Acropetal auxin transport and xylem regeneration—a quantitative study. *Am. Naturalist, 88,* 327–37.

————. 1955. Studies on abscission: the physiological basis of the abscission—speeding effect of intact leaves. *Am. J. Botany, 42,* 594–604.

————. 1956. Internal factors controlling cell differentiation in the flowering plants. *Am. Naturalist, 90,* 163–69.

Jacobs, W. P., and B. Bullwinkel. 1953. Compensatory growth in *Coleus* shoots. *Am. J. Botany, 40,* 385–92.

Jacobs, W. P., and Ielene B. Morrow. 1957. A quantitative study of xylem development in the vegetative shoot apex of *Coleus. Am. J. Botany, 44,* 823–42.

Leopold, A. C. 1949. The control of tillering in grasses by auxin. *Am. J. Botany, 36,* 437–40.

Weiss, P. 1955. Specificity in growth control. *Biological Specificity and Growth,* E. G. Butler, Editor. Princeton University Press, Princeton, N. J. Chapter X.

Went, F. W., and K. V. Thimann. 1937. *Phytohormones.* Macmillan, New York.

SECTION VI

Analysis of Plant Photoperiodism

CHEMICAL NATURE OF THE INDUCTIVE PROCESSES

JAMES BONNER

Division of Biology, California Institute of Technology, Pasadena

This discussion will concern photoperiodic induction. By such induction we mean the changes which occur in a plant that enable it to continue to respond to an earlier photoperiodic treatment. Let us consider a specific case, photoperiodic treatment of the cocklebur, *Xanthium,* a short-day plant. We give to the cocklebur a photoperiodic treatment which we know to be effective in causing flowering. Such a treatment may consist, for example, of a single long dark period. The dark period may be 8½ to 16 hr or more in length. Approximately 48 to 60 hr after the beginning of the dark period, differentiation of the growing point begins. Obviously, chemical processes have gone on in the plant during this 48- to 60-hr period—chemical processes which result in a new and specific kind of differentiation. What are these chemical processes?

Our *Xanthium* plant, once given an inductive photoperiodic treatment, may continue to make flower primordia for many weeks or months. It "remembers" that it has once had a long dark period. This is induction. In a formal way induction resembles the transformation which has been studied so extensively by microbiologists. In both cases we give to our organism an agent. This agent permanently alters the receptor organism. In the case of transformation, we know what the transforming agent is, namely, a piece of DNA. This DNA is incorporated into the genetic complement of the cells of the receptor. But what are the chemical changes which result in induction in the case of photoperiodic treatment? We do not know. We can only discuss possibilities.

This discussion will be limited to photoperiodic induction of flowering phenomena. The limitation is necessary because (*a*) we know more about induction in the case of flowering than in any other case, and (*b*) vegetative responses are not in general inductive. They are

411

rather direct, nonpersistent after effects of appropriate photoperiodic treatment.

Let us summarize the events which occur in the course of photoperiodic treatment. We will again use the cocklebur as an example. We know, first of all, that the initial photoperiodic perception occurs in the leaf. The leaf to be responsive to a long night must first have been subjected to a light period of sufficiently high intensity and of sufficient duration (Hamner, 1940). In this preliminary high-light-intensity period we believe, on the basis of the work of Liverman and Bonner (1953) and others, that photosynthesis provides substrates necessary for the consummation of the subsequent dark steps. In addition, the light serves to maintain the pigment system in the far-red-absorbing form. Subsequent to the high-light-intensity treatment, the dark processes commence. We recognize today three separate processes that go on in the photoperiodic induction of a short-day plant. The first of these steps we may call "pigment decay" (Borthwick *et al.*, 1952). During the first 2½ to 3 hr of the dark period, the pigment system of the leaf is converted from a predominantly far-red-absorbing form to a predominantly red-absorbing form (Salisbury and Bonner, 1956). The presence of the red-absorbing form is essential, since the whole series of subsequent steps may be halted in their tracks by treatment of the plant with an appropriate energy dose of red light. The time-measuring reaction follows pigment decay. In the cocklebur this process takes about 6 hr to run its course. The time-measuring reaction is temperature insensitive, and this is all that we know about it. Once pigment decay and time measuring have together measured off 8.5 hr, the processes begin that lead to the formation of something within the leaf which is ultimately transported from it and which we call, for convenience, "flowering hormone." Hormone production is initially proportional to the amount by which the dark period exceeds 8.5 hr (Salisbury, 1955). The process declines in rate and saturates in cocklebur at dark lengths of about 16 hr. Hormone production we know to be inhibited by applied auxin (Bonner and Thurlow, 1949; Salisbury and Bonner, 1956), inhibited by high temperature, probably owing to hormone destruction, and inhibited by excessively low temperatures. After the dark period, the cocklebur is returned to light. In the light, however, a still further process takes place. The product of the dark reaction, the hormone that has been synthesized is readily destroyed by high temperature (Lockhart and Hamner, 1954). In the light, provided this is of sufficient intensity, these immediate products of the dark process are stabilized, converted to some material insensitive to high temperature. This process runs its course in a period of about 5 hr. Finally, translocation of the finished hormone from the leaf occurs. Translocation out of the leaf starts roughly 20 hr after the beginning of the dark period and completes its course perhaps 48 hr after the beginning of the dark period (Salisbury, 1955; Lockhart and Hamner, 1954). It is an interesting coincidence that the first visible signs of floral differentiation in the growing point occur at about the same time that translocation from the leaf is completed.

We have, then, an excellent and detailed description of the catenary series of events which lead to the ultimate manifestation of floral differentiation. All that we need to do is to put chemical names to the individual substances described in physiological terms above. This cannot be rigorously done. Let us see, however, what we can conclude about the chemistry of hormone production in the leaf. One might first ask: Is the floral hormone produced in the leaf identical with gibberellic acid? This is a sensible question since we know that applications of gibberellic acid will replace photoperiodic induction in certain long-day plants (Lang, 1956). Such applications will not, however, replace photoperiodic induction in short-day plants such as *Xanthium*. Gibberellic acid cannot therefore be the true flowering hormone since it is a criterion of this material that it must be effective both in long- and short-day forms. This follows from the fact that reciprocal grafting experiments have shown that long-day plants on long days produce material which causes flowering of short-day plants on long days, and vice versa (Lang, 1952). Similarly one might ask: Is the flowering hormone merely an antiauxin? Auxins inhibit flowering of short-day plants (Bonner and Thurlow, 1949). Antiauxins promote flowering of short-day plants, and in fact it has been shown to be possible to induce flowering in short-day plants, under conditions in which such flowering will not otherwise take place, by application of specific antiauxins (Bonner, 1949). The answer to this question is a clear-cut no. It has indeed been shown by Liverman and Lang (1956a) that antiauxins, as well as auxins, induce flowering in long-day plants under threshold conditions. The reason for this phenomenal behavior is unknown. Nonetheless antiauxin cannot be the actual floral hormone even of short-day plants because antiauxins are effective only if applied to the leaf and are ineffective if applied to the bud. It seems quite clear that the antiauxins must exert their effect on flowering by somehow promoting production of flowering hormone in the leaf.

The production of flowering stimulus during the dark period of a short-day leaf is not inhibited by anti-amino acids such as thionylalanine, methionine, and canavanine (Labouriau, 1956). Neither is it inhibited by materials which antidote the synthesis of nucleic acids such as thiouracil (Labouriau, 1956). It would appear, therefore, that the synthesis of flowering hormone does not specifically involve the synthesis of either proteins or nucleic acids or, by implication, nucleoprotein. Synthesis of flowering hormone is inhibited by cyanide, azide, fluoride, and dinitrophenol. The synthesis of the material would therefore appear to be an active process. Interestingly enough it has been shown by Nakayama et al. (1956) that synthesis of flowering hormone, i.e., processes taking place during the second half of a 16-hr dark period, are not inhibited by malonate. It seems probable that further investigations with specific metabolite antagonists might well define the pathways of metabolism involved in the production of flowering hormone. Such investigations should be carried out with clear understanding of the time intervals involved. If we are to inhibit synthesis of flowering hormone and to minimize effects on time measuring, etc., the inhibitors should be applied only during that part of the dark period which exceeds the critical night length. But for the time being it appears that we cannot as yet conclude from inhibitor studies anything positive about the nature of the flowering stimulus.

The flowering impulse, once formed in the leaf during a dark period of length longer than 8.5 hr, may be again destroyed by (a) high-temperature treatment (40°C, 2 hr) (Lockhart and Hamner, 1954) or (b) the presence of applied auxin. The leaf may be pasteurized, as it were, of the floral stimulus which it has accumulated. This process has been characterized in physiological detail by Lockhart (1955). The pasteurization process is not dependent upon the presence of oxygen; it is independent of light; antioxidants added to the leaf do not preserve the floral stimulus from destruction; and in general the reaction· appears to be determined by temperature alone and independent of other external factors. Useful as this finding has been for characterization of the physiology of induction, it has not helped us toward an understanding of the chemistry involved.

Auxin-induced destruction of the flowering hormone was first clearly recognized by Lockhart and Hamner (1954) and by Salisbury (1955). A plant is induced, say, with a 12-hr night. Auxin is now added to the leaf, and the plant is allowed to remain in darkness for a further 4 hr. It is now returned to light. It is found that those plants which have received auxin at the end of the 12-hr dark period not only flower more poorly than those to which auxin was not applied and which received a 16-hr night period but also more poorly than plants removed from dark at the end of 12 hr and returned to light. In the present terminology this represents destruction of flowering stimulus. It is a rapid effect since, as detailed above, the effect is readily detectable over a reaction period as short as 4 hr. The inhibition is a real auxin effect. Only compounds with the physiological effectiveness of auxin are active; antiauxins inhibit the auxin-induced destruction; and, as shown by Salisbury (1955), the auxin concentration dependence of destruction of floral stimulus resembles in its hyperbolic form the auxin concentration dependence of auxin-induced cell elongation. We ordinarily think of auxin-induced responses as positive ones. Auxin appears to bring about chemical effects which cause cell walls to become more plastic, for example. How can it cause a decrease in amount of floral stimulus in the leaf? Initiation of the auxin-induced metabolism within the tissue must apparently use up something which is needed for maintenance of the flowering stimulus. More specific we cannot be. Again, this phenomenon is not of great help to us in the elucidation of the chemistry of the inductive process.

The stabilization of the hormone during the first few hours in high-intensity light at the end of the dark period has been detected and established as a real phenomenon by Lockhart and Hamner (1954). The floral stimulus, once stabilized by the action of high-intensity light, is no longer subject to destruction either by high temperature or auxin. It should be possible to characterize the light stabilization process. Is it a photosynthesis-mediated process? Can the effect of high-intensity light be replaced by applied sugar? Does it require CO_2? What kinds of inhibitors inhibit light stabilization? Alas! it is easy to make suggestions for further experiments.

The transport of flowering stimulus from the leaf appears to a detectable extent approximately 2 to 4 hr after the end of the inductive dark period. In the experiments of Salisbury (1955) the half-time for transport, the time required to accomplish one-half of all translocation which will ultimately take place, is approximately 16 hr after the end of the inductive dark period. After a further 28 hr or so, or approximately 44 hr after the beginning of the dark period, the transport of flowering stimulus from the leaf asymptotically approaches completion. It is apparent at once that transport of the flowering stimulus from the leaf does not take place to a detectable extent until a fair proportion of the high-intensity light stabilization has been consummated. This process is apparently necessary for effective transport of the flowering stimulus from the leaf. It is not absolutely essential, however, since, as is well known, *Xanthium* flowers in response to an inductive dark period even if left in continuous dark. In the second place it appears probable that the transport of flowering stimulus from the leaf is slow as compared to the transport of other materials from leaves. Thus, for example, in the work of Burrows (1957), the translocation of labeled carbohydrates from leaves is found to be considerably more rapid. Leaves were allowed to label themselves with $C^{14}O_2$ for 8 min. At the end of the 8-min labeling period the plants were returned to unlabeled CO_2 and allowed to continue photosynthesis. The half-time for sweeping of the labeled sugar from the leaf was found to be approximately 1 hr. In similar experiments the half-time for removal of 2,4-D from the treated leaf was found to be approximately 3 hr. It is apparent therefore that the flowering stimulus is not rapidly transported or possibly is not rapidly absorbed into the transport system as compared to the usual readily transported metabolites.

From an operational point of view the property of transportability within the plant is the most accessible and most characteristic property of the flowering stimulus. It should perhaps be this property more than any other which might be expected to aid in identification of the material. Let us plan an experiment in which the property of transportability might be used to advantage. We might, for example, allow the leaves of a cocklebur plant to become labeled with $C^{14}O_2$ during the course of the high-intensity light period preceding the photoinductive dark period. We will cause the leaves to photosynthesize $C^{14}O_2$ for a short time only, say 10 or 20 min, in order to assure minimum labeling of cellulose and other structural components. We will now place our plant in a photoinductive dark period. During this dark period flowering stimulus will presumably be made. One may imagine that it will be made in part from C^{14}-labeled material. At the expiration of the photoinductive dark period we return the plant to light. The high-light intensity stabilization process now takes place and in addition photosynthesis, now with unlabeled CO_2, provides sugars which sweep all previously labeled sugars from the leaf and to the various receptor depots. Only after 4 or more hr in light will transport of the flowering stimulus from the leaf begin. We should now be able to detect in the petiole of the leaf, for example, the appearance of any new labeled compound—any compound which appears in the petiole at the appropriate time and which might be expected to be the flowering stimulus itself. This would appear to be a good and a straightforward experiment. Variations upon it are easy to envisage. One might, for example, label a leaf not with $C^{14}O_2$, but with more specific precursors. Experimental difficulties can be envisaged too. Nonetheless, this experiment has all the earmarks of a profitable one.

Let us now consider the events which occur in the bud itself after it receives the flowering impulse. I have drawn attention from time to time to the fact that the induced state is self-perpetuating and thus resembles a state of virus infection (Bonner and Liverman, 1953). The plant behaves as though by induction it catches the disease of flowering. Transmission of induction by grafting, lack of mechanical transmission of the induced state, self-perpetuation of the induced state, are all characteristics which would be expected if the flowering stimulus were a virus-like entity. We and others have therefore looked in leaves for any new macromolecule which might appear during induction. Such a material has been sought by electrophoresis, ultracentrifugation, and serology, and in all cases the answer has been a negative one (Campbell, 1951). It has been impossible to find a new and characteristic macromolecular entity in induced leaves. It might be, of course, that such an entity exists but that it is present merely in very low concentrations—concentrations so low as to be undetectable by our physical methods. We have already seen, however, that it is not possible to inhibit formation of the flowering impulse in leaves by amino acid antagonists or by antagonists of nucleic acid synthesis. Our conclusion must be, therefore, that the material produced in the leaf as a result of photoperiodic induction does not behave as though it were a specific new nucleic acid or specific new protein. The material produced in the leaf does not possess the properties of the more familiar self-perpetuating entities. Let us therefore consider a further possibility. This possibility is suggested by the experiment of Carr (1953) which has been repeated and extended by Lincoln (1954), Salisbury (1955), and others. The observation is that a plant such as *Xanthium* becomes photoperiodically induced only if an actively growing bud is present to receive the stimulus sent out from the leaf. If no actively growing bud is present, as for example, if buds are removed a day or two after the end of the inductive dark period so that previously dormant axillary buds must grow out, then these new shoots are not induced but remain vegetative. These results can be interpreted on the basis of the hypothesis that the leaf, as a result of photoperiodic induction, sends out a pulse of flowering stimulus. The stimulus must be dissipated within a few days after the end of a photoperiodic treatment since the treated leaf is no longer capable of causing flowering in buds which develop after this period of time. If, on the other hand, an actively growing bud is present during and after photoperiodic induction, then the plant as a whole becomes induced, and axillary buds, as they grow out, become reproductive. How can we interpret this phenomenon? It seems to me that one possibility is that the leaf, as the result of appropriate photoperiodic treatment, sends to the growing bud the material which brings about transformation of this bud into a reproductive one. The bud is induced. It is caused to start the production of what we may call "transformation product." From this transformed bud, materials can now go to other buds and bring about more transformation. The self-perpetuative aspect of induction is by this hypothesis referred completely to the actively dividing meristematic tissue. It is suggested that it is the material produced in transformed buds which is transported from one plant to another across graft unions, and so on.

This hypothesis suggests that there may be a real distinction between the flowering impulse sent out by a photoperiodically treated leaf and the material sent out by the bud which has been transformed as the result of the reception of such a flowering stimulus. It appears possible that the mature leaf, in *Xanthium* at least, may itself never become transformed in the sense of becoming permanently changed. The permanent change, the transformation which we associate with the induced state, may well take place only in buds in photoperiodic induction as it does in vernalization.

Difficulties stand in the way of the hypothesis presented above. Thus, a plant which has been photoperiodically induced may be removed from the photoperiodically inductive condition, disbudded, and may then continue to act as a donor of flowering stimulus in graft partnership. This fact has been interpreted by Carr (1953) to mean that active buds act to conserve, maintain, and stabilize the flowering stimulus of the mature leaf. But it could also mean alternatively that in disbudded donor plants, the buds, while they were present, became transformed, produced transforming principle, and then proceeded to fill the tissues of the donor plant with the material. The correct interpretation of these active bud experiments remains to be assigned. There are evident experiments to do. We should try to see whether we can distinguish physiologically between induction in the bud and perception in the leaf. We might try to make this distinction with the aid of metabolite antagonists. Preliminary experiments by Labouriau (1956) have in fact indicated that inhibitors of RNA synthesis, although they are inert in inhibition of the process of floral hormone synthesis in the leaf, do nonetheless act powerfully to inhibit differentiation of the vegetative bud into a floral bud.

This discussion has been remarkable by virtue of the paucity of chemical information which it contains. The chemical nature neither of the signal for flowering transmitted from the leaf nor of the factor responsible for transformation in the bud can be assigned. It has been noted, however, here, and by many earlier workers, that induction appears to be self-perpetuative. We are accustomed today to think of self-perpetuative processes of living things as being intimately associated with and referrable to nucleic acids or nucleoproteins. It is tempting, therefore, to wonder if the self-perpetuative aspects of photoperiodic induction may not also have their basis in phenomena associated with nucleic acid synthesis. The nucleic acid associated with photoperiodic induction—if indeed there be one—must be a special and specific nucleic acid. We know indeed that there are no gross changes in overall nucleic acid content in *Xanthium* during photoperiodic induction (Lockhart, 1955). We have seen that it is unlikely that nucleic acid synthesis is specifically associated with floral hormone synthesis in the leaves of *Xanthium,* although the participation of nucleic acid in the transformation process of the bud has not been excluded. Let us therefore consider for a moment a second kind of induction, that associated with vernalization. In the case of vernalization, as in photoperiodic induction, a particular treatment is applied to the plant which then "remembers" that it has once had this treatment and flowers forever afterward in response to it. In the case of vernalization the cold treatment, which is the effective environmental factor, must be perceived by the growing point itself. Aach and Melchers have shown (1957), in the case of vernalization, that just as in the case of photoperiodic induction, no new macromolecular entities can be detected even by delicate serological techniques during the course of the vernalization treatment. Inhibitors of nucleic acid synthesis similarly do not inhibit the progress of vernalization in cold-treated buds. There is nonetheless some basis for the supposition that the metabolism of compounds intimately associated with the nucleic acids may be related to vernalization. Highkin (1955) has shown, for example, that the effects of cold treatment on vernalizable pea seeds may be in part replaced by the nucleoside, guanosine. We have no quantitative estimate of the fate of the guanosine which is effective in this chemical vernalization. Although it may participate in the synthesis of a specific and unique type of nucleic acid, it has not been possible to show that this is the case. We are almost as much in the dark with regard to the chemical events of transformation in the vernalized growing point as we are in the case of transformation in the photoperiodically induced growing point. Clearly we are in need of new approaches, new techniques, new thoughts. And it is the hope of this reviewer that the thoughts and experiments outlined above may aid us in a final coming to grips with the chemical processes of the inductive process.

REFERENCES

Aach, H. G., and G. Melchers. 1957. Serologische Untersuchungen an kältebedürftigen Pflanzen. *Biol. Zentr., 76,* 466–75.

Bonner, J. 1949. Further experiments on flowering in *Xanthium. Botan. Gaz., 110,* 625–27.

Bonner, J., and J. Liverman. 1953. Hormonal control of flower initiation. *Growth and Development in Plants.* Iowa State University Press, Ames.

Bonner, J., and J. Thurlow. 1949. Inhibition of photoperiodic induction in *Xanthium* by applied auxin. *Botan. Gaz., 110,* 613–24.

Borthwick, H. A., S. B. Hendricks, and M. W. Parker. 1952. The reactions controlling floral initiation. *Proc. Natl. Acad. Sci. U. S., 38,* 929–34.

Burrows, V. 1957. Kinetics of transport processes. Thesis, California Institute of Technology, Pasadena.

Campbell, Jean M. 1951. Electrophoretic studies of leaf proteins. Thesis, California Institute of Technology, Pasadena.

Carr, D. J. 1953. On the nature of photoperiodic induction. II. *Physiol. Plantarum, 6,* 680–84.

Hamner, K. C. 1940. Interrelation of light and darkness in photoperiodic induction. *Botan. Gaz., 101,* 658–87.

Highkin, H. 1955. Unpublished experiments. California Institute of Technology, Pasadena.

Labouriau, L. G. 1956. Unpublished experiments. California Institute of Technology, Pasadena.

Lang, A. 1952. Physiology of flowering. *Ann. Rev. Plant Physiol., 3,* 265–306.

———. 1956. Stem elongation in a rosette plant induced by gibberellic acid. *Naturwissenschaften, 43,* 257–58.

Lincoln, R. 1954. Unpublished experiments. University of California, Los Angeles.

Liverman, J., and J. Bonner. 1953. Biochemistry of the photoperiodic response. The high intensity light reaction. *Botan. Gaz., 115,* 121–28.

Liverman, J., and A. Lang. 1956a. Induction of flowering in long day plants by applied indoleacetic acid. *Plant Physiol., 31,* 147-50.

———. 1956b. Unpublished experiments.

Lockhart, J. A. 1955. Unpublished experiments. California Institute of Technology, Pasadena.

Lockhart, J. A., and K. C. Hamner. 1954. Partial reactions in the formation of the floral stimulus in Xanthium. *Plant Physiol., 29,* 509–13.

Nakayama, S., O. Fukamizu, and Ikuo Sei. 1956. Experimental researches on photoperiodism. 6. *Mem. Fac. Liberal Arts and Ed., Myazaki Univ., 1,* 97–102.

Salisbury, F. B. 1955. Kinetic studies on the physiology of flowering. Thesis, California Institute of Technology, Pasadena.

Salisbury, F. B., and J. Bonner. 1955. Interaction of light and auxin in flowering. *Beitr. Biol. Pflanz., 31,* 419–30.

———. 1956. The reactions of the photoinductive dark period. *Plant Physiol.. 31,* 141–47.

THE PHOTOREACTION AND ASSOCIATED CHANGES OF PLANT PHOTOMORPHOGENESIS

STERLING B. HENDRICKS

Agricultural Research Service, United States Department
of Agriculture, Beltsville, Maryland

THE PHOTOREACTION

The photoreaction for plant photomorphogenesis can be written schematically as

$$(1) \qquad \text{Pigment R} \underset{\substack{7200\text{–}7400 \text{ A max} \\ \text{Darkness}}}{\overset{6500\text{–}6600 \text{ A max}}{\rightleftharpoons}} \text{Pigment FR}$$

where R and FR refer to absorption of red and far-red radiation, respectively. In writing the reaction in this way, emphasis is placed solely on the regions of absorption of two pigment forms and the ultimate reversible interconversion of the forms. With some uncertainty the reaction can be written more specifically as

$$(2) \qquad \text{Pigment RH}_2 + \text{A} \underset{\substack{7200\text{–}7400 \text{ A max} \\ \text{Darkness}}}{\overset{6500\text{–}6600 \text{ A max}}{\rightleftharpoons}} \text{Pigment FR} + \text{AH}_2$$

which is a photohydrogenation or dehydrogenation, with A as the hydrogen acceptor.

The term "associated changes" in the title refers to possible variations in the components of reaction (2), particularly A and AH_2. It also includes the fact that either one or both forms of the pigment enter into some type of reaction probably as a transferring agent, a more general term than "enzyme," either for electrons or atomic groupings including H. Physiological response is connected solely with this action as a transferring agent, or as a hormone.

423

PRINCIPLES OF STUDY

The features of the photoreaction are determined from measurements of physiological response. The methods are to be contrasted with the usual *in vitro* photochemistry. First, the functional relation of the response to the degree of pigment intraconversion in the photoreaction is not immediately known and need not be linear. This is like studying the photoreduction of methylene blue with ferrous iron by use of a buret, with a nonlinear and unknown marking for titration of the iron. An approach can be made, however, to finding the function, and considerable progress is possible without knowledge of its form. Second, each biological object—the plant to flower or the seed to germinate—varies in the stimulus required for the response, much as does each molecule in its reactivity *in vitro*. In the plant the essential result and the variable sensitivity affect the observations.

The several differences between *in vitro* and *in vivo* photochemistries increase the experimental labor. In work on lettuce and *Lepidium* seed, germination of over a million seeds of each kind were counted in lots of 100 and divided into more than a hundred experiments for each seed type. With photoperiodic control of flowering, a variance approximately equal to that of seed germination can be obtained with 1% as many plants. A given variance is attained with roughly equal areas of exposure to radiation—a square centimeter of leaf area on one plant or a square centimeter of seed (possibly 200 lettuce seed). This is probably a result of requiring equivalent volumes of reactant systems or equal numbers of responsive cells.

REVERSIBILITY

Before elaborating the details of the photoreaction as deduced from experiments, two simple but immense consequences of the photoreaction are to be emphasized. First, the responses potentiated by the photoreaction are photoreversible. This has been illustrated by Dr. Toole, Dr. Borthwick, and Dr. Downs in their discussions, and it is hardly necessary for me to give further examples in detail. This photoreversibility has the exceedingly important feature of establishing the equivalence of the control of many diverse and unrelated responses with a certainty rarely attained in physiological work. It also allows the photoreaction to be separated from the complexity of the response which serves as a basis for assay.

The second simple consequence is that the reaction can both control responses at exceedingly low irradiances by its great sensitivity to radiation as well as in full sunlight by the reversible balancing. Thus, etiolation phenomena of seedlings are controlled as well as leaf size and internode lengths at high light intensities. These were illustrated for bean seedlings by Dr. Downs.

The following phenomena have been shown by their photoreversibility and by their action spectra to be under the control of the photoreaction:

1. Flowering, photoperiodism: (*a*) *Xanthium*, short day; (*b*) *Hordeum vulgare,* long day
2. Seed germination, 20 species
3. Fern spore germination
4. Elongation (leaf, petiole, stem), 4 species, 14 varieties
5. Plumular hook unfolding
6. Pigment formation: (*a*) Anthocyanin (*Brassica oleracea* var. *rubra*), (*b*) Tomato cuticle

More limited information indicates that the reversible photocontrol also interacts with:

7. Epinasty
8. Leaf abscission
9. Bulb formation
10. Casparian strip formation
11. Rhizome production
12. Phylloidy of tracts
13. Succulency
14. Sex expression
15. Root development
16. Chromosome breakage following x-irradiation
17. Plastid generation
18. Protochlorophyll regeneration

Any of these responses, accordingly, can be used for study of the photoreaction.

The pigment system is possibly ubiquitous in seed plants as, to the extent of present testing, one or the other of the many responses is evident. A plant might fail to show obvious photoperiodic control of flowering but still respond in other ways. This is the case for the tomato, which responds to control of internode elongation and which sometimes has light-sensitive seed, but has no evident flowering control.

TEMPERATURE COEFFICIENT

The photoreaction for lettuce seed germination has been shown to have a temperature coefficient of 1.0 as shown by Table I. Here the

TABLE I. Photoreversibility of Lettuce Seed Germination
at Two Temperatures (Borthwick *et al.*, 1954)

	Irradiation		Germination, %, at 20°C with Irradiation at	
Red	Far Red	Last	26°C	6–8°C
1	0	R	70	72
1	1	FR	6	13
2	1	R	74	74
2	2	FR	6	8
3	2	R	76	75
3	3	FR	7	11
4	3	R	81	77
4	4	FR	7	12

importance is evident of separating the reaction from the confusion of the assay, as permitted by reversal before the response gets significantly under way. The implication of the upward creep in germination with the number of cycles is indicated in Fig. 1. According to the tempera-

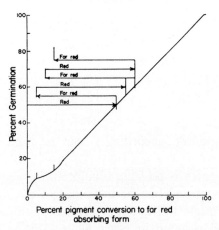

FIG. 1. A possible change in pigment conversion (schematic) and associated germination for several successive exposures to red (promotion) and far-red (inhibition) radiations.

ture coefficient of 1.0, the reaction rate is not limited by collision and is at least pseudo first order. This is compatible either with reaction (1) or (2), but if (2) holds, then A and AH_2 must be present in high concentrations relative to Pigment and Pigment FR.

DARK REACTION

The photoreaction is reversible in darkness—the change being from the far-red-absorbing form of the pigment to the red-absorbing form. This was shown for lettuce seed germination by Borthwick *et al.* (1954) as indicated in Fig. 2. Imbibed seed with the pigment shifted to the far-red-absorbing form by exposure to red radiation are held in darkness above 30°C which prevents germination otherwise promoted

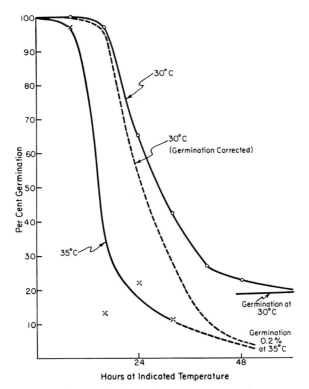

FIG. 2. Variation in germination of Grand Rapids lettuce seed at 20°C with time of holding imbibed seed in darkness at 30° and 35°. Seed initially irradiated with red radiation adequate for complete germination.

by the far-red-absorbing form of the pigment. As they are returned in darkness after various numbers of hours to 20°C, germination decreases but can again be promoted by exposure to red radiation.

In lettuce seed germination the half-time for pigment conversion at 30°C would be the order of 18 hr and not more than 10 hr at 35°C. Estimates of the half-time can also be made for photoperiodic control in flowering, as was suggested by Dr. Borthwick. These are of the order of magnitudes of 1 hr at 20° to 30°C. Such rates of pigment conversion are compatible with the conversion being an important factor, or the essential factor, measuring the duration of the dark period in photoperiodic systems.

ABSORPTION COEFFICIENT AND QUANTUM EFFICIENCY

The major features of the photoreaction can be found in an elegant way without assumption. A reversible first-order reaction allows calculation of F, the fraction of pigment conversion corresponding to a particular physiological response for a given irradiance, E. The method is equivalent to that used by Warburg and Negelein (1929) to find the absorption coefficient and quantum efficiencies for photodissociation of cytochrome oxidase-carbon monoxide. Its development in detail is given by Hendricks et al. (1956) and empirically illustrated by Downs et al. (1957).

After irradiation with energy E in the region $\lambda \pm \Delta\lambda$, the pigment conversion is given by the first order differential equation $dF/dE = k(1 - F)$. The solution of the equation is $kE = \log [1/(1 - F)]$. If the energies, E_1 and E_2, required for two physiological responses 1 and 2 have the ratio $\alpha = E_1 E_2$ then

$$\alpha \log [1/(1 - F_1)] = \log [1/(1 - F_2)]$$

The same response in the reverse direction will be obtained with energies having a different ratio, β, and

$$\beta \log (1/F_2) = (1/F_1)$$

if α and β are measured for any two arbitrary degrees of response, values of F_1 and F_2 can be calculated.

The dependence of the second internode length of pinto beans on

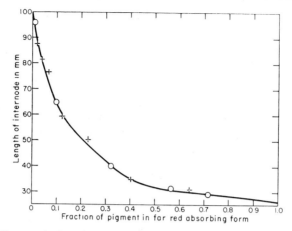

FIG. 3. Internode lengths of pinto beans as a function of pigment conversion. Circles and crosses are for irradiation in the red and far-red parts of the spectrum, respectively, with the pigment initially dominantly in one or the other form.

the fractional conversion of the pigment is shown in Fig. 3, the measurement being the one earlier discussed by Dr. Downs. The curve was obtained from four values, two for the reaction with red radiation and two for the reverse. All twelve values, however, fall on the same smooth curve. Similar functions for germination of pepper grass, *Lepidium virginicum,* and lettuce seed (var. Grand Rapids) are shown in Fig. 4.

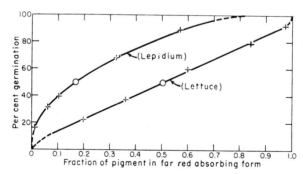

FIG. 4. Variation in germination of *Lepidium virginicum* seeds and of Grand Rapids lettuce seeds with pigment conversion. The circles represent interpolated values for 50% germination.

The fractional conversion F of the pigment is also:

$$F = \omega\phi X E$$

where ω is the absorption coefficient of the pigment (cm_2/gram mole weight), ϕ is the quantum efficiency for conversion (dimensionless), X is the fraction of the incident energy E (Einsteins/cm^2) reaching the site of the reaction. Thus, $\omega\phi X$ can be obtained from measured values of the incident energy giving a particular response. The molar extinction ϵ is

$$\epsilon = \omega:10^{-3}:\log_e 10$$

Values of $\epsilon\phi X$ at the absorption maxima are given in Table II.

TABLE II.   Values of Product $\epsilon\phi X$ for several responses

	Stem Elongation, Pinto Beans	Germination, *Lepidium virginicum*	Germination, *Lepidium sativum*
$\epsilon\phi X \times 10^5$			
Red absorbing	0.021	0.015	1.15
Far-red absorbing	0.025	0.44	0.025
Incident energy for 50% pigment conversion (10^{-7} Einsteins/cm^2)			
Red absorbing	5.6	9.2	0.1
Far-red absorbing	4.1	0.4	4.4

Again, it is to be emphasized that the values of $\epsilon\phi X$ at the absorption maxima as recorded in Table II do not depend upon assumptions. From these values a number of pertinent deductions can be made. These are that the values of the molecular absorption coefficients at the absorption maxima for both forms of the pigment are greater than 1.0 $\times 10^5$, that the quantum efficiencies for conversion are near 1.0, and that reaction (2), the photohydrogenation, is the correct one.

The extinction coefficients ϵ are molecular constants for the red-absorbing and far-red-absorbing forms of the pigment and accordingly are invariant for the three responses shown in Table II. Since X is necessarily less than 1.0 and ϕ is probably 1.0 or less, the minimum possible values of ϵ are:

ϵ_r at 6500 A (red-absorbing form) 1.15×10^5

ϵ_{fr} at 7300 A (far-red-absorbing form) 0.44×10^5

These values approach the maximum possible value, about 2.0×10^5, for an oscillator strength of unity.

ASSOCIATED REACTANTS

With constant ϵ_r and ϵ_{fr} the variations of $\epsilon\phi X$ must arise from variations in ϕX. In the absence of materials absorbing specifically at wavelengths greater than 6000 A, as is the case for seed germination, X changes monotonously inversely as the fourth power of the wavelength. Changes in X are not more than 1.5-fold for 6500 A compared with 7300 A for scattering, and are in the same direction for both *Lepidium* and lettuce seed. The approximately 70-fold greater value of $\epsilon\phi X$ (red absorbing) for lettuce seed compared with *Lepidium* and the 18-fold smaller value of $\epsilon\phi X$ (far red absorbing), giving a 1200 overall change, must chiefly be due to variations of the quantum efficiencies. The great changes in quantum efficiencies require the presence of other effective molecules than the pigment in the photoreaction which could only be quenching agents or reactants. The fact that $\epsilon_r\phi X$ (red absorbing) varies oppositely to $\epsilon_{fr}\phi X$ (far-red absorbing), as discussed in part by Dr. Toole, for the seed germination indicates that the change is due to another reactant. The high a priori probabilities for the reactions, which can approach a quantum efficiency of 1, indicate that either electrons or hydrogen atoms are transferred in the photoreaction, as is usual for photoreactions in condensed systems.

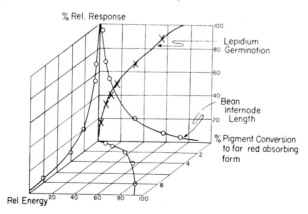

FIG. 5.   Relationships between the degree of response, the percent pigment conversion, and the relative energy.

Any of the several relations indicated in Fig. 5 can be found. This has not been possible for photoperiodic control of flowering, for the change from a small to a large percentage effect takes place over a twofold change in irradiance. There is some question in the flowering control, both of a threshold value of conversion for response and of saturation of response before complete pigment conversion.

PHYSIOLOGICAL ACTION

How does physiological action arise from the photoreaction, or simply, what is the next step after the photoreaction? Does the red-absorbing form of the pigment act as an inhibitor of a transferring agent, or does the far-red form act as a transferring agent? I know of no summary argument, but several favor the latter possibility. The most general statement is that the rapid rise of physiological response accompanying change of only a small amount of the pigment to the far-red-absorbing form, as displayed in control of elongation of pinto beans, indicates the appearance of a transferring agent. This is also evident for light-requiring seed that lie ungerminating in darkness for the order of a century, respiration being essentially absent. The releasing red radiation starts up the whole vital reaction system, which is an expression of a transferring agent being released (unblocked) or created. An inhibitor in the volume of action would likely have to reach concentrations of at least 10^{-6} molar for half effectiveness. The effective volume and concentrations of the pigment system are unknown, but the extremely low incident energies required suggest concentrations of the pigment system of the order of 10^{-8} molar or less in volumes of mitochondrial dimensions, which are in the concentration ranges of many functional enzymes.

The quantum efficiencies for photoconversion can be varied by temperature manipulations as indicated in Dr. Toole's discussion. These changes are evident as a change in one direction of the red irradiance required for a given germination and the simultaneous change in the opposite direction of the far-red irradiance for inhibition. Thus, in germination of *Lepidium virginicum* seed, the shift in sensitivity when attained is toward greater sensitivity to red radiation as would be expected from the low concentration of A relative to AH_2 as indicated by the low value of $\epsilon_r \phi X$ for the red-absorbing system (Table II). Moreover, many lots of lettuce seed that will germinate in darkness are readily induced to have a light requirement by holding for the order of 24 hr at 35°C. Despite this responsiveness of the physiological action to temperature changes, the photoreaction can be shown, as for lettuce seed, to have a constant rate independent of temperature.

RESPONSE TO HIGH RADIANT FLUX

Experiments on the photoreversible system in which the object is exposed to high radiant flux, such as sunlight, show that the pigment system is not destroyed by a process such as a photooxidation. In the case of internode elongation of the pinto bean, as discussed by Dr. Downs, and of photoperiodic control of flowering of millet, as indicated by Dr. Borthwick, the reversible photoresponsive system is present and operative immediately after the termination of a photoperiod of many hours with high light intensity. Growth features depend upon the relative amounts of red and far-red radiation during, and particularly at the close of, the photoperiod. Thus are to be explained the marked relative effects of incandescent and fluorescent sources on plant growth and maturation.

A newly recognized effect of radiation at high flux density that probably is important to growth of plants in sunlight, as well as to several other photobiological responses, is illustrated by results in Table III. The experiment was designed to test why *Lepidium virginicum* seeds germinate on exposure to direct or diffuse sunlight when the relatively greater sensitivity to far-red (inhibitory) than to red (promotive) radiation indicates that they should be inhibited. The answer was that during 1 sec in full sunlight the sensitivities were changed. By use of a water filter to remove radiation in the general region of wavelength >8000 A, it could be seen that the change was due to such radiation, i.e., heat, even though the rise in temperature was not more than the order of one degree after 8 sec exposure.

An explanation is that the high radiant flux is supplying activation energy that in the molecular surroundings of the point of absorption is not in equilibrium with the black-body radiation. This effects, to a

TABLE III. Effect of exposure to sunlight on germination of *Lepidium virginicum* seed. Seed were returned to darkness and shifted from 15° to 25° C after exposure to radiation. Average results from 4 lots of 100 seed each.

Duration of Exposure to Full Sunlight, sec	Germination with 4 min Prior Exposure to Red Radiation		Germination without Prior Exposure	
	Unfiltered Radiation, %	5 cm H_2O Filter, %	Unfiltered Radiation, %	5 cm H_2O Filter, %
0	64	78	0	0
1	42	53	21	
2	51	56	27	17
4	53	60	29	
8	85	53	30	25
16	87	60	36	
32	93	59	48	28
64	93	71	62	

degree dependent upon the radiant flux, the balance of those reactions having slow turnover rates in the vital system. The reversible photo-reaction samples this general condition through its dependence on the hydrogen-transferring systems. Upon removal to darkness, the pigment balance is fixed at the condition attained in the high radiant flux. In general, the systems seem to shift toward high amounts of A as shown in reaction 2—they become relatively more sensitive to red radiation.

SPECULATION ON POSSIBLE ISOLATION OF THE PIGMENT AND ON ITS NATURE

I can give only one precise bit of information bearing on the nature of the pigment, namely, curves showing variation of molecular absorption coefficients with wavelength (Fig. 6). These are obtained from the reversibility of the reaction, as previously explained, and from action spectra. Values of ϵ at the maxima are indicated as 2×10^5, which is probably correct to within the range of 1 to 3×10^5.

Perhaps you expect a discussion of the possible identification and isolation of the pigment. A short one is, "your guess is as good as mine." That such a strongly colored compound should be unobserved by the eye in plant tissue or not previously observed in preparations indicates that the average concentration must be very low. The physiological function would almost require it to be a protein with a strongly

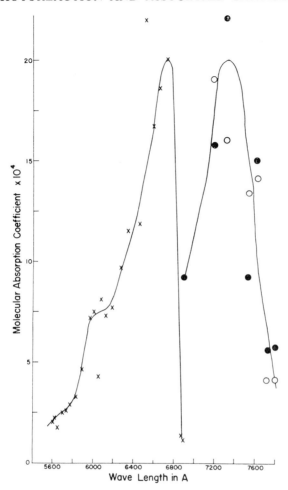

FIG. 6.   Molecular absorption coefficients of the red- and far-red-absorb-ing forms of the photomorphogenic pigment.

chromophoric grouping. We have traced down several indications of blue pigments but without any success.

The positions so far out in the visible spectrum of the absorption maxima, their high values of ϵ, and the low values of ϵ in the region between 4000 and 5200 A indicate that the pigments are largely conjugated systems. Porphyrins and close-ring tetrapyrroles are eliminated by the low absorptions in the blue. The most likely probabilities are linear polyenes—an unusual carotenoid—or open-chain tetrapyrroles such as the phycocyanins. C-Phycocyanin as isolated from the blue-green algae *Aphanizomen flos-aquae,* by Svedberg and Katsurai (1929) has an absorption maximum at 6150 with ϵ_{max} 2.76 × 10⁵. Allo-phycocyanin has an absorption maximum at 6500 A (Haxo *et al.,* 1955). The chemistry of these compounds has been very little studied, but they are thought to have biladiene prosthetic groups (Lemberg and Legge, 1949) with conjugation interrupted between rings 3 and 4. Oxidation to biliverdin would increase the conjugation by three double bonds, which could shift the absorption maxima by about 600 A as observed from the separation of the red and far-red absorption maxima for the photomorphogenic pigment.

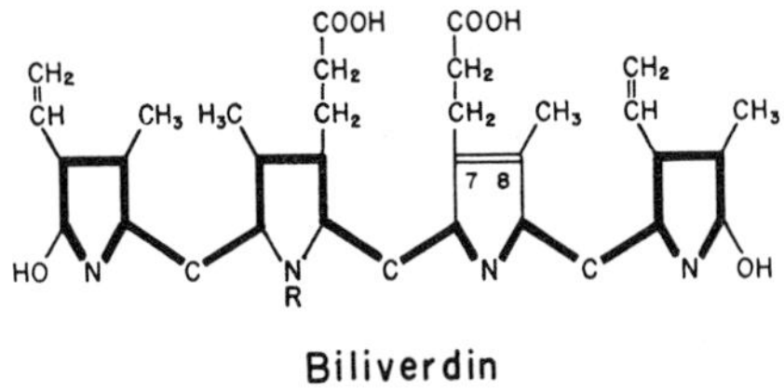

Biliverdin

FIG. 7.   Structural formula for biliverdin with indicated conjugation.

Physical methods of finding the pigment *in vivo,* in contradiction to physiological methods, might be based on a possible fluorescence at wavelengths greater than 7000 A, appearance of free radicals as might be examined by nuclear magnetic resonance, and on differential absorption at 6500 and 7300 A. Each would make use of the change accompanying the reaction being driven from one to the other pigment form. We have looked for fluorescence in this way from albino barley tissue and seed. None was observed that was as intense as 1×10^{-5} of that given by chlorophyll in green leaves. We are working on the differential absorption at 6500 and 7300 A and on the absolute absorption at 6500 A.

Even to specify the tissue in which the pigment is functional has not been possible. Nor are there sound reasons for associating the pigment with cellular fractions such as protoplasmic protein, mitochondria, or nuclei. The most localized reactions that have been demonstrated are in coloration of the tomato cuticle (Piringer and Heinze, 1954), anthocyanin formation in cotyledons and hypocotyls of red cabbage seedlings (Siegelman and Hendricks, 1957), the concave side of isolated plumular hooks (Klein *et al.*, 1956), sections of *Avena* coleoptiles (Liverman and Bonner, 1953), discs from primary leaves of bean plants (Miller, 1952; Liverman *et al.*, 1955), and the region near the micropile of germinating seed (Toole *et al.*, 1956; Koller, 1956). Translocation of some type-controlling response is clearly indicated by the absence of a phototropic response of dark-grown seedlings to unilateral irradiation with red light. We have repeatedly been enticed into looking for a phototropic response with red light and have been encouraged by initial indications which have always been eliminated by rigorous exclusion of blue light.

CONCLUSION

The reaction controlling photomorphogenic responses is photoreversible. It is probably a photohydrogenation with the quantum efficiencies being determined by the ratios of the oxidants and reductants. The molar absorption coefficients of the red- and far-red-absorbing forms of the responsive pigment are 2.0×10^5. Physiological response is associated with the far-red-absorbing form of the pigment. The reaction is probably ubiquitous for seed plants but need not be recognizable for all types of responses in a given plant.

REFERENCES

Borthwick, H. A., S. B. Hendricks, E. H. Toole, and V. K. Toole. 1954. Action of light on lettuce seed germination. *Botan. Gaz., 115,* 205–25.

Downs, R. J., S. B. Hendricks, and H. A. Borthwick. 1957. Photoreversible control of elongation of pinto beans and other plants under normal conditions of growth. *Botan. Gaz., 118,* 199–208.

Haxo, F., C. O'h Eocha, and P. Norris. 1955. Comparative studies of chromatographically separated phycoerythrins and phycocyanins. *Arch. Biochem., 54,* 162–73.

Hendricks, S. B., H. A. Borthwick, and R. J. Downs. 1956. Pigment conversion in formative reaction of plants to radiation. *Proc. Natl. Acad. Sci. U. S., 42,* 19–26.

Klein, W. H., R. B. Withrow, and V. B. Elstad. 1956. Response of the hypocotyl hook of bean seedlings to radiant energy and other factors. *Plant Physiol., 31,* 289–94.

Koller, D. 1956. Germination regulating mechanisms in some desert seeds: III. *Calligonum comosum* L'Her. *Ecology, 37,* 430–33.

Lemberg, R., and J. W. Legge. 1949. *Hematin Compounds and Bile Pigments.* Interscience, New York.

Liverman, J. L., and J. Bonner. 1953. Interaction of auxin and light in growth responses of plants. *Proc. Natl. Acad. Sci. U. S., 39,* 905–16.

Liverman, J. L., M. P. Johnson, and R. Starr. 1955. Reversible photoreaction controlling expansion of etiolated bean leaf disks. *Science, 121,* 440–41.

Miller, C. O. 1952. The relationship of the cobalt and light effects on expansion of etiolated bean leaf discs. *Plant Physiol., 27,* 408–12.

Piringer, A. A., and P. H. Heinze. 1954. Effect of light on the formation of a pigment in the tomato fruit cuticle. *Plant Physiol., 29,* 467–72.

Siegelman, H. W., and S. B. Hendricks. 1957. Photocontrol of anthocyanin formation in turnip and red cabbage seedlings. *Plant Physiol., 32,* 393–98.

Svedberg, T., and T. Katsurai. 1929. The molecular weights of phycocyanin and phycoerythrin from *Porphyra tenera* and of phycocyanin from *Aphanizomenon flos-aquae. J. Am. Chem. Soc., 57,* 3573–83.

Toole, E. H., S. B. Hendricks, H. A. Borthwick, and V. K. Toole. 1956. Physiology of seed germination. *Ann. Rev. Plant Physiol., 7,* 299–324.

Warburg, O., and E. Negelein. 1929. Über das absorptions spektrum des Atmengsferments. *Biochem. Z., 214,* 64–100.

A KINETIC ANALYSIS OF PHOTOPERIODISM[1]

R. B. WITHROW
Smithsonian Institution, Washington, D. C.

When a new physiological phenomenon is clearly delineated, the first information as to mechanism is nearly always based on kinetical experiments; i.e., one begins by measuring the rate of the biological response in relation to the intensity of physical and chemical factors. Although photoperiodism has been with us as a scientific phenomenon for nearly 40 years, the experimental research is still largely at the kinetic level. By this we infer that nearly all our quantitative information has been derived from observations on the effects of singly variant factors such as light, temperature, nutrients, and chemical growth-regulating agents. The next phase, which is just now beginning, will be biochemical, and the final phase will consist of an integration of our information to form a detailed physicochemical description of the overall process.

At the present time, we have not identified any pigment which can be assigned the role of the photoreceptor. We can only guess as to the biochemical reactions which are first mediated by light. Our knowledge of how growth is coupled to the endogenous rhythm is even less complete; we know little, if anything, as to the mechanism or cellular site of this low-frequency oscillatory phenomenon. While we have no direct proof that endogenous rhythms are closely related to photoperiodism, the evidence indicates that they probably are an integral part of it. We are about where photosynthesis would be if the only measurable criterion of the photoreaction were the rate of increase in dry weight of plant parts.

Ecologically one might define photoperiodism as a mechanism evolved by both plants and animals for measuring seasonal time. The need arose primarily because climatic conditions during certain seasons were unfavorable for growth, reproduction, or even survival, while

[1] Published with the approval of the Secretary of the Smithsonian Institution.

439

other seasons were suitable for such processes. This problem is typically characteristic of the Temperate Zone. For survival, it is necessary for Temperate Zone organisms to be able to predict the onset of unfavorable periods far enough ahead so as to get the year's growth and reproductive phases over with before the onset of cold or hot weather or drought.

The host of physical and chemical problems posed by biological photoperiodism in plants and animals might be resolved into four general questions:

1. What are the physical and chemical mechanisms by which light mediates growth and reproduction?

2. What is the nature of the internal time-measuring system or clock which is coupled to the photochemical stimulus?

3. How are the photochemical and thermal stimuli and their consequent growth-mediating systems coupled to the clock?

4. In the case of plant photoperiodism, how is it that the same photochemical stimulus is capable of invoking such a great variety of responses, often of opposite character in different species, at all stages of development from seed germination to maturity? Is there any evident pattern by which one might organize these apparently diverse responses?

The following discussion attempts to analyze the extent to which present kinetic information contributes toward answers to these questions. The discussion will be limited largely to plants, since it is here that we have the most complete information on the photochemical aspects, but many of the considerations may be applicable to animal photoperiodism as well.

THE RADIATION ENVIRONMENT

Before proceeding with an analysis of the biological responses, it is desirable to examine the natural environment for clues as to the precision required in the measurement of day length and the magnitudes of the spectral and intensity variables of sunlight. Throughout evolutionary development, living organisms have been exposed to three types of superposed celestial oscillations. The first is the diurnal cycle of 365 days per year caused by the rotation of the earth about its axis in the radiant energy field of the sun; the second is an annual cycle arising from the inclination of the earth's axis in its plane of rotation about the sun; the third is the lunar cycle.

The gravitational forces of the moon produce monthly tidal cycles which impose considerable environmental changes on coastal marine organisms. The moon also reflects some sunlight onto the earth during the night at certain parts of the lunar cycle. Although this intensity at the earth's surface is low, it cannot be ignored as a factor in growth. As will be shown later, the intensities of moonlight are well within the significant range of plant photomorphogenic responses.

The diurnal and annual cycles produce precisely changing sequences of day length and daily supply of energy which are largely responsible for the seasonal changes in weather. In most of the Temperate Zone, temperature and precipitation patterns approximately coincide with the day-length cycle. The coincidence is never precise, and neither temperature nor rainfall is a sufficiently reliable index of seasonal time for those organisms which must make drastic physiological adjustments in preparation for a period of adversity. It is the length of the natural photoperiod for which many plants and animals have evolved a seasonal time-measuring mechanism. However, it is not enough that the organism be able to elicit different responses to different day lengths; it must, in addition, have some means of comparing its day-length signals with an internal scale of time which is both precise and independent of wide variations in light intensity, temperature, water supply, and other environmental factors.

Cycle of Day Length

The time-sensing precision required of the biological clock can be estimated from standard tables of sunrise and sunset. The well-known monthly variation in day length is graphed in Fig. 1 for the latitudes from 30° to 60°, which include the major crop-producing areas of the Temperate Zone. It is probably in this general range that most of the photoperiodically sensitive plants have evolved. The refraction of the sun's rays by the earth's atmosphere and the finite diameter of the solar disk makes the day length constant at approximately 12 hr and 7 min · at the equator. In the Northern Hemisphere, at the solstices, the total day-length variation in hours and minutes from the winter solstice of

December 21 to the summer solstice of June 21 is zero at the equator; 1:47 at 15°; 3:52 at 30°; 6:50 at 45°; and 13:00 at 60°. At all latitudes, the day length is slightly over 12 hr at the spring and fall equinoxes of March 21 and September 21, respectively. It is this precisely repeating cycle of day length which organisms use for determining seasonal time.

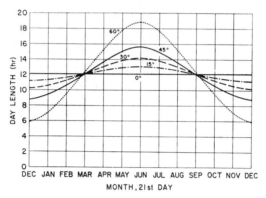

Fig. 1. Day length cycle at various latitudes. Data plotted from "Tables of Sunrise, Sunset and Twilight," U. S. Naval Observatory (1945).

The weekly rate of change in day length was calculated for each week centered about the twenty-first of each month. The rate of change is plotted in Fig. 2 as minutes change in day length per week and the percent change in day length for that week. The week was used as the basis for these estimations on the assumption that the plants and animals with the most precise timing mechanism can probably perceive yearly or seasonal time with an accuracy of one week during the spring and fall seasons. This seems to be a reasonable assumption, considering the soybean data presented by Borthwick and Parker (1939) and other observations on flowering of plants, bird migrations, and similar phenomena.

The rate of change in day length is minimal during the summer and winter solstices and maximal at the spring and fall equinoxes. The rate at the equinoxes for 30° latitude is 14 min/week or about 1%. For 45°, it is 26 min/week or 1.8%, and for 60°, 44 min/week or 3.1%, and the corresponding monthly rates are 3.5, 6.3, and 11%. The best opportunity for perceiving seasonal time is during the equinoxes. It is probably significant that reproductive cycles in both plants and animals are usually initiated in the spring and fall, when the rate of change in day length is maximal.

These data clearly demonstrate that organisms which are capable of perceiving seasons by the measurement of day length must have a clock that has a precision of the order of 1 to 3% if they are to meas-

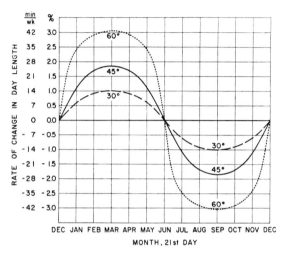

FIG. 2. Rate of change in day length. Values were calculated from data of Fig. 1 for latitudes of 30°, 45°, and 60° in minutes per week and percent. The rate is the average change for each week centered about the 21st of the month. The percent change is the ratio of the average weekly change to the length of a 24-hr day (1440 min). Multiply ordinate values by 4 for approximate monthly rates.

ure seasonal time to one week and 4 to 12% for an accuracy of one month. These are indeed high orders of precision for the poikilothermic organisms which have no means of controlling their body temperature.

There are few environments in which the temperature does not fluctuate in a somewhat random manner over at least ±5°C. Therefore, there should be a variation of several hundred percent in the reaction rate of the usual thermochemical reactions over this range in the poikilothermic organisms which would include the microorganisms, plants, and cold-blooded animals. In the case of the homoiothermic or warm-blooded animals, there is a high degree of temperature compensation and the problem of a temperature-compensated clock imposes a less severe requirement.

These data force us to conclude that the timing of photoperiodic responses cannot be of the chemical hourglass type which depends upon the accumulation of a photoproduct or a thermochemical reaction product that is initiated by the photoreaction. This type of postulate has been suggested by many workers in the field of plant photoperiodism. It seems to us that we are forced to consider two other possibilities; either the time-comparison system involves several chemical reactions having just the right differences in temperature coefficients so that they balance out to an overall coefficient of about one, or some physical process is involved, having an inherently low temperature coefficient.

The endogenous rhythm systems having periods of approximately 24 hr as reported by Bünning (1948, 1954) and Hamner (1940) in plants and Pittendrigh (1956) in animals have temperature coefficients of about 1.2. Since the seasonal temperature follows a fairly consistent pattern of average change in relation to the day-length cycle, a coefficient of 1.2 would appear to be adequate for perceiving time with a precision of a few weeks during most of the year. It seems that these considerations of the required precision of the biological clock are the basis for one of the most compelling arguments for accepting the endogenous 24-hr rhythm system as the actual clock which the organism uses for photoperiodically perceiving the seasons. When to these facts are added the observations of Bünning that the red is the most effective spectral region for phasing or "setting" the clock and that the phasing induction is reversible by the far red, the assumption appears to be a sound one.

Spectral Energy and Intensity Variables

The spectral energy distribution of sunlight is not greatly altered by either season or weather condition. At high solar angles on a clear day, the peak energy is in the green, but as the sun approaches the horizon and the mass of air through which the rays must pass increases, the blue is attenuated more rapidly than the red, and the peak shifts from the green toward the orange, and finally to the red

(Taylor and Kerr, 1941; Moon, 1940). At all times, however, the peak of energy of combined sun and sky radiation is in the visible.

Much more significant are the very great changes in intensity. The daily variation in light intensity with clear skies during the summer and winter solstices and spring and fall equinoxes are given in Fig. 3. It is seen that clear sky intensities do not vary by more than a 2:1 ratio between the summer and winter solstices. However, during the

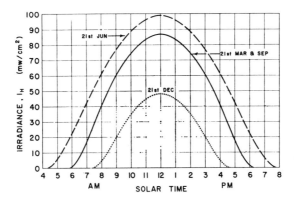

FIG. 3.   Sunlight intensity on a horizontal surface for clear days at latitude 42° N. for the 21st of December, March, June, and September. Data taken from that of I. F. Hand (1950) for the Blue Hill Observatory near Boston, Massachusetts. Multiply ordinate by 100 for approximate value in foot-candles.

winter, the average intensity is very much less than that indicated here because of the preponderance of cloudy weather in much of the Temperate Zone. The peak value of light intensity at the summer solstice is approximately 10,000 ft-c which is about 100 mw/cm². During periods of heavy overcast, the intensity may fall to a few percent of the maximal clear sky value. It is these extreme variations in intensity that must be smoothed out in the plant's response if they are not to introduce serious random variations in the biological measurement of day length. The photomorphogenic red-light responses such as anthocyanin synthesis, opening of the hypocotyl hook, inhibition of the hypocotyl and leaf expansion in bean, and inhibition of the first internode in *Avena,* all follow a response rate which is approximately proportional to the logarithm of the incident intensity. In other words, response-wise, the organism sees the logarithm of the intensity. This holds for the plants which we have studied at all values above 0.001% of noon sunlight.

The dashed curve of Fig. 4 is plotted as the logarithm of the sunlight intensity for values above 1 mw/cm² and therefore is proportional to the biological responses. When so plotted, it is evident that the response to full sunlight rises with extreme rapidity in the morn-

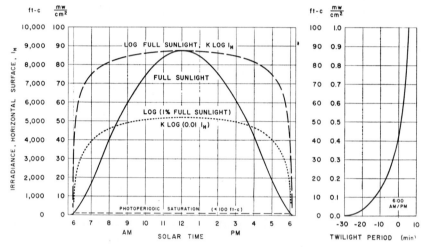

FIG. 4. Linear and log plots of sunlight intensity, I_H, on a horizontal surface for clear days at the spring and fall equinoxes. The solid curve is the same as in Fig. 3 for March and September. The dashed curve is the logarithm of the irradiance, log I_H, and the dotted curve is the logarithm of 0.01 I_H, which corresponds to a heavily overcast sky. The horizontal dashed line is the assumed upper limit of saturation of photoperiodically sensitive plants. The graph on the right is the time course for twilight intensity on an expanded scale from data of H. H. Kimball (1938). Zero is the time of appearance of the edge of the solar disk.

ing and falls quickly in the evening. The rate of change of intensity during the twilight period is very great, as shown in the right-hand portion of Fig. 4. The period extends for approximately 30 min beyond the time of actual disappearance of the solar disk. In a period of about 20 min at dawn, it rises from approximately 10 to 100 ft-c. The horizontal dashed line at 100 ft-c is the intensity below which the more photoperiodically sensitive plants saturate.

What the plant sees then is a very rapid rise in light intensity at sunrise, which within a few minutes reaches saturating values, and then as far as the plant is concerned, the intensity is above saturation until sundown when, within a matter of minutes, the intensity again swings back through the region of photoperiodic saturation and falls to zero. It is almost as if each day, a light is turned on in the morning and off at night as far as the photoperiodic mechanism of the plant is concerned. It is evident, then, that the kinetics of the photochemical reaction are such as to make extremely wide variations in intensity unimportant as far as the ability to measure the duration of the daily light period is concerned.

PHOTOPROCESSES IN HIGHER PLANTS

The growth and development patterns of higher plants are regulated in a large measure by the integrated activities of five photochemical reactions that supply the organic nutrient requirements and many control functions. There are undoubtedly many more photochemical reactions in higher plants still to be discovered. The general characteristics of these photochemical reactions are given in Table I and their action spectra in Fig. 5. Because of overlapping of the various action spectra and their very different kinetic properties in relation to growth, it is essential that we think in terms of these various processes as an integrated group when attempting to deal with any one process as a singly variant factor. This is especially true at the blue and red ends of the visible spectrum where the curves for photosynthesis, chlorophyll synthesis, and phototropism all overlap in the blue, and photosynthesis, chlorophyll synthesis, and photomorphogenesis in the red. With but few exceptions, it is practically impossible to excite one process without some significant excitation of the others.

The first two processes given at the top of Table I and Fig. 5 are chlorophyll synthesis and photosynthesis which are shown as related to energy conversion. Whereas chlorophyll synthesis is not directly involved in the conversion of radiant energy into chemical bond energy, it is a preparatory step for photosynthesis. The regulatory function of photosynthesis cannot be ignored. The classical work of Kraus and Kraybill (1918) demonstrated many years ago that the overall form

TABLE I. Principal Photochemical Reactions of Higher Plants

Photoprocess	Reaction or Response	Products	Photoreceptors	Action Spectra Peaks, mμ
		Energy Conversion		
Chlorophyll synthesis	Reduction of proto-chlorophyll	Chlorophyll *a* Chlorophyll *b*	Protochlorophyll	Blue: 445 Red: 640
Photosynthesis	Dissociation of H_2O into 2[H] and $\frac{1}{2}O_2$ and reduction of $[CO_2]$	Reductant [H] Phosphorylated compounds	Chlorophylls Carotenoids	Blue: 435 Red: 675
		Regulation of Growth		
Blue reactions	1. Phototropism 2. Protoplasmic viscosity 3. Photoreactivation	Oxidized auxin, auxin system and/or other components of the cell	1. Carotenoid and/or flavin 2. Unknown 3. Pyridine nucleotide, riboflavin, etc	1. Near UV: 370 Blue: 445 & 475 2. Uncertain 3. Uncertain
Red, far-red reactions	1. Seed germination 2. Seedling and vege-tative growth 3. Anthocyanin synthesis 4. Chloroplast responses 5. Heterotrophic growth 6. Photoperiodism 7. Chromosome response	Biochemistry completely unknown	Possibly tetrapyrrole	1–6. Induction by red: 660; reversal by far red: 710 & 730 7. Far-red induced, red reversed, spectral details uncertain

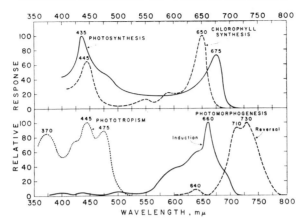

FIG. 5. Action spectra of the five principal plant photochemical reactions. Photosynthesis and chlorophyll synthesis are given in the upper graph. The photosynthesis curve is from data of Chen (1952) for the Hill reaction in spinach chloroplasts. The curve for chlorophyll synthesis is from corn leaf data of Koski, French, and Smith (1951). The lower graph contains the three action spectra of the regulatory photochemical reactions. The phototropic curve is from Shropshire and Withrow (1958) for *Avena*. The red induction and far-red reversal curves are from Withrow, Klein, and Elstad (1957) for the hypocotyl hook opening of the bean seedling. All the curves have been adjusted to an arbitrary value of 100 units response at the peak.

of the plant is, in part, determined by the balance between the carbohydrate supply on the one hand and the inorganic nutrients, especially nitrogen, on the other. However, photosynthesis often can be reduced to an insignificant level by the use of very low intensities. In terms of carbohydrate supply, photosynthesis is not significantly active at intensities below about 100 ft-c, whereas the regulatory photochemical reactions are excited to significant levels by many thousand-fold lower values of intensity.

The regulatory function of chlorophyll synthesis is likewise a possibility and cannot be excluded. Whereas we have shown by two experimental technics (Klein *et al.*, 1957), that photomorphogenesis in seedlings probably does not involve protochlorophyll activation, there is little doubt that chlorophyll synthesis or some closely related process is responsible for morphological changes in the chloroplast itself.

The regulatory photochemical reactions fall into two general classes: those in which the yellow pigments are activated by the blue to produce the so-called straight growth effects and bending responses in seedlings, and those activated by pigments having strong absorption bands only in the red end of the visible spectrum. The blue and red groups of reactions often produce very similar end results in terms of their effect on stimulation or inhibiting cell elongation, and this has led to confusion when white sources such as the incandescent or fluorescent lamp have been used in experimental work. Also, when monochromatic blue is used as the exciting radiant energy, it is important to realize that it is impossible to distinguish between the weak activity of the red-absorbing pigments in the blue, thus exciting photomorphogenesis, and activation of yellow pigments such as the flavins and carotenoids. The blue peaks of activity reported in this symposium by Meijer (p. 101) and Wassink, DeLint, and Bensink (p. 111), and elsewhere, may very well be the direct result of yellow pigment activation rather than any new photomorphogenic peak appearing in the blue, as has been implied.

The reversible red, far-red photomorphogenic reactions are capable of inducing a wide variety of seemingly different and oftentimes diametrically opposed responses in higher plants at all stages 'of development from seed germination to flowering. After a red induction, any one of these responses can be reversed by activation with the far red, as was first shown by the Beltsville group of Borthwick *et al.* (1952).

The red is capable of inducing germination in light-sensitive seeds of higher plants (Flint, 1936) and the germination of fern spores, (Mohr, 1956). In the seedling, the whole course of development is altered by very low intensities of red energy. In many dicotyledonous seedlings, the hypocotyl length growth is inhibited, whereas the epicotyl is stimulated; the hypocotyl hook, when present, is caused to straighten; and the rate of leaf development usually is greatly accelerated. In monocotyledonous plants, the first internode behaves much like the hypocotyl of the dicotyledon and is inhibited, whereas the coleoptile behaves like the epicotyl and is markedly stimulated. Leaf development likewise is accelerated in the monocotyledons. In the course of development of the seedlings of many, but by no means all plants, anthocyanin appears in certain portions of the stem and leaf. In certain varieties of bean and corn, Withrow *et al.* (1953) and Klein *et al.* (1957) showed that the rate of anthocyanin development is accelerated by very small amounts of red energy. However, synthesis does not appear to be a direct photochemical reaction in that the anthocyanin does not immediately appear after the exposure to red energy; there is a lag period which coincides with the growth lag phase. We concluded that it was in some way coupled to the growth reactions which are the end products of the photochemical stimulation. Siegelman and Hendricks (1957) have recently reported another anthocyanin-inducing photochemical reaction that requires relatively high energies and appears to be a direct photochemical conversion of a precursor. This process seems quite unrelated to the photomorphogenic red induction since the peak is in the far red and it is not reversible.

There is developing a considerable body of evidence that the change of proplastids into functioning chloroplasts involves more than simply the conversion of protochlorophyll to chlorophyll. At the Smithsonian we have been investigating this problem with the view that chloroplast development is, in part at least, controlled by the red, far-red photomorphogenic reactions (Withrow *et al.*, 1956).

Recent work by Hillman (1957) has demonstrated that the aquatic floating plant *Lemna minor* is unable to maintain continued growth in the presence of an adequate supply of sugar in complete darkness. A photochemical step is necessary for heterotrophic growth, which can be supplied only by very low intensities of red energy, and its red induction is reversible by the far red.

Photoperiodism is the other side of the red, far-red photoreaction coin. As a plant approaches maturity, many species exhibit marked sensitivity to day length in that their flower bud initiation processes can be controlled by the length of the photoperiod as long as the light intensity is above a very low threshold value. It was very early shown with light filters that it was the red end of the visible spectrum which induced the day-length responses, but the paradox of the phenomenon is that the same photochemical stimulus produces diametrically opposed responses in different types of plants. The existence of two major classes of plants, those which flower in days longer than a certain critical day length, and those which flower in days shorter than a certain critical day length, is difficult to reconcile on the basis of any simple mechanism. One of the principal kinetic problems presented by plant photoperiodism is the apparent absence of a sufficient number of parameters with which to explain the behavior of these classes of plants.

The chromosome response indicated as the last type of reaction induced by the red, far-red system is the one which we have been investigating at the Smithsonian (Withrow and Moh, 1957; Moh and Withrow, 1958.) This work shows that the so-called potentiating effect of infrared on chromosome damage in *Tradescantia* microspores and the root tips of *Vicia faba* actually involves a photoreaction that is limited to the far red in the range of 720 to 780 mμ, peaking at approximately 760 mμ, and that the red is capable of reversing the far-red induction. An interesting feature here is that this is a photoreaction in which a chromosome response is elicited. The nucleus of the cell is one of the most refractory sites, and the chromosomes are seldom directly affected by external agents, at least not to the degree that the cytoplasmic constituents are influenced.

Living organisms have developed a remarkable capacity for responding to a tremendous range of light intensity. This range is graphically presented in Fig. 6 on a logarithmic scale from 10^5 to 10^{-8} μw/cm^2, a range of 10^{13} in intensity. In foot-candles, the range is roughly 10^4 to 10^{-9} ft-c. The end of twilight occurs at about 0.4 ft-c, which is just slightly above the lowest limit of flower bud induction which has been shown to be in the range of 0.01 to 0.1 ft-c (Withrow and Biebel, 1936). Full moonlight has a maximum value of approximately 0.02 ft-c, which is well within the range inducing flower bud formation in the more sensitive plants. The limit of cone vision is an order of magnitude lower. The limit of rod vision for the dark-adapted eye is 10^{-5} μw/cm^2, but the bean or the oat seedling is still capable of "seeing" at three orders of magnitude lower. On an energy basis, of course, the situation is reversed between the dark-adapted eye and the seedling. The seedling "sees" these low intensities as a result of an accumulative photochemical process occurring in the cells in which 10^5 to 10^6 sec are required. The eye, on the other hand, is able to see its threshold energy in less than 1 sec, so that from the standpoint

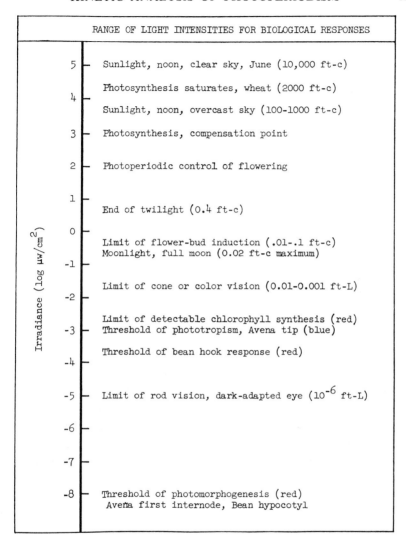

Fig. 6. Range of light intensities encompassed by the natural environment and biological photoresponses. Literature sources are: *Sunlight,* Moon (1940), Hand (1950), Kimball (1935); *Moonlight,* Kimball (1938); *Vision,* Committee on Colorimetry (1953); *Photosynthesis,* Hoover, Johnston, and Brackett (1933); *Chlorophyll Synthesis,* Koski, French, and Smith (1951); *Photoperiodism,* Withrow and Benedict (1936); and *Photomorphogenesis,* Klein, Withrow, and Elstad (1956).

of threshold energy requirement, the dark-adapted eye is a considerably more sensitive biological detector.

An intensity of 10^{-8} $\mu w/cm^2$ of red light represents approximately 3×10^4 quanta per cm^2/sec. If, for estimation purposes, one considers a cell as having an average cross-sectional area of 0.1×0.1 mm, the incident quantum intensity per cell is 3 per sec. Since it has not been possible to extract a pigment with absorption characteristics of the action spectrum, that is, a blue substance with a single strong absorption band in the red, and *in vivo* spectrophotometry has not revealed any strong red absorption band other than those of the chlorophylls and cytochromes, it is evident that the pigment must be present in an extremely low concentration. Therefore, only a very small portion of the incident quanta could be captured by the photomorphogenic pigment system. This means that the cellular quantum-absorption rate cannot be more than a few quanta per hour; yet the seedling is still capable of responding. These results clearly indicate that one must postulate some form of amplification in which the effect of the initial photoproduct is amplified many orders of magnitude by a secondary system.

The threshold energy requirements for the various red and blue light responses are given in Table II. The energy values in the last column are those obtained by extrapolating the log-response curve back to zero. This yields an arbitrary threshold; it is not the lowest value that can be detected, but it represents a convenient criterion of minimal excitation. It will be noted that the inhibition of the first internode in the oat seedling, the stimulation of leaf in pea, and inhibition of the hypocotyl in bean, all have approximately the same threshold energy requirement of 0.01 $\mu j/cm^2$, which is 0.1 erg/cm^2. Curvatures of the *Avena* coleoptile and the sporangiophore of the fungus *Phycomyces* are of the same general order of magnitude. The other responses have relatively higher threshold values.

RED LIGHT BIOLOGICAL RESPONSES

The biological consequences of the red, far-red photoreactions in higher plants are extremely varied. An analysis of the kinetics of the various responses reveals two broad classes of phenomena in which

TABLE II. Kinetic Classification of the Red, Far-Red Photoresponses

Class	Type of Response	Characteristics Common to Class
I. Graded growth responses: photomorphogenic	1. Cell elongation 2. Anthocyanin synthesis 3. Chloroplast development 4. Requirements for heterotropic growth	1. Action spectra of induction with maximum in the red (660 mμ) 2. Photoreversibility by far red 3. Low threshold energy requirement 4. Rate limited; radiant energy efficiency increases with time of exposure 5. Lack of reciprocity, It = f(t) – – – – – – – – – – – – – – – – 6. Graded response 7. Log energy response, no early saturation 8. Independent of time-phase
II. Time-phase controlled responses: photoperiodic	1. Photoperiodism 2. Photoperiodic chlorosis 3. Dormancy 4. Seed germination	1. Action spectra of induction with maximum in the red (660 mμ) 2. Photoreversibility by far red 3. Low threshold energy requirement 4. Rate limited; radiant energy efficiency increases with time of exposure 5. Lack of reciprocity, It = f(t) – – – – – – – – – – – – – – – – 6. Responses tend to be ungraded or threshold type 7. Energy response complex function of time, saturated at low irradiance 8. Highly dependent on time-phase of irradiation

the kinetic behavior for certain properties are the same in both classes, whereas in other respects they are quite different. However, each class is relatively homogeneous in regard to the complexities of the kinetic behavior. The two classes may be divided into: (1) the photomorphogenic responses in which the rate is some continuous, graded function of the radiant energy and relatively unrelated to any time phasing of the application of the light, and (2) the photoperiodic reactions which result in ungraded or threshold type responses in which, over a relatively narrow range of incident energy, one can proceed from no measurable response to a maximal response and the response level is a critical function of the time-phase of the light application to the environmental dark-light cycle. Typical responses of the first class are those of altered rates of cell growth in stems and leaves, and anthocyanin synthesis. The types of responses elicited by the second class are photoperiodic in nature and involve flower bud initiation, photoperiodic chlorosis, light-induced dormancy and probably light-stimulated seed germination.

It will be noted that there are eight kinetic characteristics listed for each class, the first five of which are the same. They involve the action spectra, photoreversibility, threshold requirements, the rate-limiting nature of the processes, and the general lack of reciprocity between intensity and time. The last three properties are characteristically different for the two classes. They include the graded versus ungraded nature of the response, the response to increasing energy, and the time-phasing requirements.

Before proceeding with the experimental evidence upon which the classification of the regulatory photoresponses are based, it is essential to specify precisely the implications involved in the distinction between graded and ungraded responses. In Fig. 7 are plotted hypothetical curves of the two classes. The graded response begins to develop at zero incident energy and increases in magnitude to a maximal or saturation value. The rate of increase may be linear or some complex

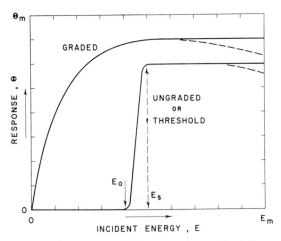

FIG. 7. Hypothetical curves of the fundamental difference between graded responses (open circles) and the ungraded, threshold or all-or-none responses (closed circles). E_0 is the threshold energy and E_s is the energy just capable of saturating a threshold system.

function of energy. In the case of the opening of the hypocotyl hook in bean and in the inhibition of hypocotyl growth, the first part of the curve is proportional to incident energy, after which the rate becomes proportional to the logarithm of the incident energy. In the ungraded or threshold type, no response is obtained until the intensity of the stimulus reaches a certain threshold value, E_0. Then the magnitude increases very rapidly to a saturating level, E_s, after which a further increase in stimulus elicits no further increase or appreciable change in response. This is frequently referred to as the all-or-none type. If the stimulus is less than E_0, nothing is obtained, and above E_s, the full magnitude of the reaction is induced. The responses to photoperiod are of the ungraded or threshold class.

TABLE III.   Extrapolated Threshold Energy Requirements

Plant Response	Growth Effect[a]	Exposure Time	Energy, $\mu j/cm^2$
Red Spectral Region			
Photomorphogenic systems			
Avena first internode	−	6 days continuous	0.01
Pea leaf	+	4 days continuous	0.01
Bean hypocotyl	−	6 days continuous	0.01
Bean epicotyl	+	6 days continuous	0.05
Bean leaf	+	6 days continuous	0.05
Bean hook (hypocotyl)	+	20 hr continuous	15.
Bean hook (hypocotyl)	+	2.8 hr	30.
Photoperiodic systems			
Seed germ. (lettuce)	+	8 min	1000.
Soybean, S. D.	−	2–4.5 min/night	3000.
Cocklebur, S. D.	−	4–9 min/night	4000.
Barley, L. D.	+	1–60 min/night	5000.
China aster, L. D.	+	Continuous	3000.
Spinach, L. D.	+	Continuous	3000.
Blue Spectral Region			
Avena coleoptile	Curv. (−)	15 sec	0.05
Phycomyces, sporangiophore	Curv. (+)	20 min	0.05

[a] Growth or flowering: stimulation +; inhibition −.

Table III shows a marked difference in energy requirement between the photomorphogenic and photoperiodic classes. If in photomorphogenesis, the organism is exposed to the energy for many days, the energy requirement ranges from 0.01 to 0.1 $\mu j/cm^2$, whereas a short-term irradiation results in lower sensitivities and a higher energy requirement which may extend to 50 $\mu j/cm^2$. On the other hand, the photoperiodic responses have a requirement of at least one to four orders of magnitude higher; the range is from 1000 to 5000 $\mu j/cm^2$. This is to be expected if one considers that the photomorphogenic group is graded and a significant effect is obtained at a very low energy level, and that there is a continuous range of effectiveness from a very low to a relatively high energy level. In photoperiodism, however, the ungraded nature makes it necessary to attain some threshold level which is capable of driving the system over an irreversible barrier, so to speak. Some relatively high energy level is required for this. Flowering behavior and the breaking of dormancy as well as seed germination phenomena are of this type. Seed germination has been included in the photoperiodic class for two reasons. The threshold energy requirement is of the same order of magnitude as that for photoperiodic flowering responses, and Wareing (p. 73) and others have shown that there appears to be some internal periodicity which must be phased with the irradiation to obtain the maximal response.

In the long-day plant, as the light intensity during the supplementary light period is increased, the plant remains vegetative until a critical level of intensity is reached at which flower bud initiation occurs. The magnitude of floral initiation as measured by the number of buds formed and rate of formation is then a function of intensity of energy up to a certain critical level. At this point the plant has reached its maximal capabilities of response and there is no further increase over a 1000-fold range of intensity. A short-day plant such as *Xanthium* also exhibits ungraded behavior. A light break during the dark period produces no effect on inhibiting flower bud initiation until a certain critical intensity is reached. Then flower bud initiation is progressively decreased in magnitude until a relatively low intensity of saturation is obtained, at which point the plant is vegetative; from then on, there is no further increase in activity. Undoubtedly, the differences between the graded and ungraded responses are not in any way correlated with the initial photochemical processes themselves, but are concerned wholly with the growth-response capability of the tissue systems involved.

We will now proceed with the various experimental evidences for the 8-point basis for classification given in Table II. There have been extensive investigations of the action spectra of all types of red induction responses in higher plants, and they all lead to the conclusion that this is a homogeneous group. Activation is either the same or is triggered by a very similar photoreceptor system. Withrow (1941) suggested that the photomorphogenic seedling reactions which had earlier been observed and studied extensively by Priestley and Ewing (1923) were due to the same photochemical stimulus as the photoperiodic reactions. These conclusions were based upon studies with light filters. More complete investigations with spectrographic technics by Parker *et al.* (1945, 1950) have greatly extended the range of observation to include both long- and short-day plants, light-induced seed germination (Borthwick *et al.*, 1952) and certain other photomorphogenic responses. A detailed spectral analysis of the induction of the opening of the hypocotyl hook in bean and the photoinactivation of the process reveals that the induction peak is at 660 mμ and that the reversal region has two peaks at 710 and 730 mμ. These curves are very similar to those reported by Mohr (1956) for fern spores. We can generally assume that the action spectra of all these processes have the same general characteristics and that these phenomena are capable of being photoreversed by the far red.

Reciprocity also completely fails for both classes of phenomena for all but the shortest of exposures. The efficiency of any given quantity of radiant energy in inducing various growth reactions is greatest when applied continuously over a long period of time. Any form of intermittent irradiation is less effective. This is clearly demonstrated in Fig. 8 for the hook-opening photomorphogenic response. In the solid line is plotted the angle of opening for various durations of the irradiation period, the intensity being inversely proportional to time. The total energy in each case was 250 mj/cm^2. It will be noted that as the time of exposure increases up to a total of the 20-hr period of the experiment, the effectiveness of the constant value of energy increases. If now the angle of hook opening is extrapolated over the log-response curve to give the equivalent energy required for a 20-hr exposure, the dashed curve is obtained. This curve is directly related to the photochemical effectiveness of the applied energy. It shows that the relative

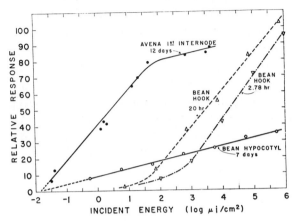

Fig. 8. Logarithmic-energy response of various photomorphogenic systems. Data for *Avena* were taken from Weintraub and Price (1947); bean seedling data, Klein *et al.* (1956, 1957).

effectiveness of the energy increases over 100-fold between 2.5 min of exposure and a 20-hr exposure. The same type of phenomenon is evidenced in the flowering response of the long-day plant Nobel spinach (Withrow and Withrow, 1944). The criterion of the effectiveness of the incident energy was taken as the time required for flower buds to appear. The most effective condition was continuous irradiation, and even 270 flashes per night were less effective. When the energy was distributed in the form of five equally spaced flashes per night, it was approximately equal to 225 ft-c-min, or about 50% efficiency.

In both the photomorphogenic and photoperiodic systems, then, it would appear that continuous irradiation is more efficient than any form of intermittancy and that the consequences of the photochemical reaction die out rather rapidly and require continuous renewal if the system is to be pushed at its maximum rate.

The photoperiodic systems have a second type of reciprocity failure which is related to the time-phase requirement for the system. This requirement is apparently superposed upon the need for continuously activating the system and considerably complicates the picture. A typical response is shown in Fig. 12 for a short-day plant, *Xanthium*, in which a single flash of incandescent lamp energy is applied at various times during a 16-hr night, which has followed an 8-hr photoperiod. The response was measured in terms of the floral stage attained at the end of the experiment as observed by microscopic dissection. A completely effective flash is one which prevented any development in the direction of a floral stage and the ordinant quantities would be zero. It is seen that the middle of the dark period is the time at which the flash has its maximum effectiveness. It is less effective either before or after this period. This is in contrast to the response of the hypocotyl hook of bean in which a single flash of energy has its maximum effectiveness at the beginning of a 20-hr dark period, and flashes applied at later times are decreasingly effective because there is less time available for a growth response to occur.

One of the most amazing features of the photomorphogenic system is the extreme range over which the response is proportional to the logarithm of the incident energy. This is graphically shown in Fig. 8 for oat and bean seedlings. The response is proportional to the logarithm of the incident energy above a certain low value, and below this point it is directly proportional to the incident energy. This is shown by the curving of the straight line in the case of the bean hook responses. In the hook response, which involves an inhibition of length growth in the hypocotyl as a result of a photochemical reaction by red energy, there is an extremely great range of linearity. In the graph, the data are plotted for six orders of magnitude from 1 to 1,000,000 μw/cm^2. However, we know that this curve continues for at least two more orders. This is an extremely wide range of stimulus value for any continuous function. This has many characteristics of the Weber-Fechner law, although here the logarithmic response seldom holds for more than two orders of magnitude in animals. The equation for the linear portion of these curves is given by:

$$\beta = M(\log)E/E_m \tag{1}$$

differentiating

$$D\beta = K\, de/e \tag{2}$$

where β is the response in terms of angle of hook opening or stimulation of the epicotyl or inhibition of the growth of the hypocotyl, M is the slope constant, E is the incident energy, and E_m is the minimum energy requirement which is the value of energy at zero response. This is often referred to as the threshold energy in discussions of the Weber-Fechner law, but it should not be confused with the threshold energy of an ungraded response. In no case do these responses have a crude threshold. The response is a linear function of energy up to some low value, which in the hook response amounts to about 10° opening, and from then on the response is proportional to the logarithm of the energy. Differentiating equation (1) yields $D\beta = K\, de/d$. This states that the incremental increase in response is proportional to the proportionate increase in energy. In the case of the hook opening, a 10-fold increase in energy results in approximately a 20° increase in angle of opening. The fundamental significance of this function is by no means clear. However, it does imply some type of feedback system which keeps reducing the response level and which decreases the rate of the response as the energy increases. It will be noted that in this type of function there is never true saturation. The curve always has a positive slope when plotted on a linear scale as shown in Fig. 9. In

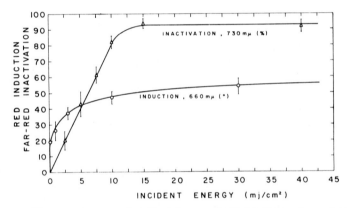

FIG. 9. Energy-response function for a photomorphogenic system; induction and reversal curves of the opening of the hypocotyl hook of bean. The incident energy is plotted on a linear scale. Data from Withrow, Klein, and Elstad (1957).

this figure the hook opening response is plotted on a linear scale showing the rapid rise in low energy levels and a gradual leveling off. We have not been able to get energies sufficiently high to produce true saturation although, undoubtedly, true saturation would occur at some very high value. This graph also presents the energy relationship for the reversal phenomenon. The interesting feature here is that reversal or inhibition of the induction response is directly proportional to energy, instead of proportional to the logarithm of the energy, and saturates at about 90% of complete reversal. One never seems to get complete reversal, which implies that the processes are so overlapping that complete spectral separation of the two cannot be attained.

THE CLOCK

Before presenting any integrated hypothesis of how these various phenomena are related to one another, it is important to consider

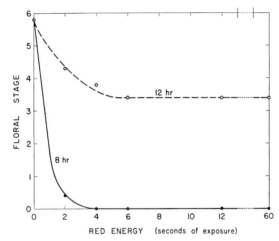

FIG. 10. Energy-response function for a photoperiodic system. The flowering response of a short-day plant, *Xanthium,* is shown when maintained on 8- and 12-hr photoperiods. A red exposure of the duration indicated was interposed in the middle of the dark period. The incident energy was varied by varying time; the irradiance was constant. The floral stage was observed by microscopic examination of the terminal bud and evaluation of its stage of floral development. Graph plotted from data of Salisbury and Bonner (1956).

certain essential characteristics of the clock. We have shown that the time precision required for the perception of seasonal time with an accuracy of one month requires a clock with an accuracy of the order of 10%. If the organism is exposed to a range of temperatures of

±10°, the temperature coefficient would have to have a value of about 1.1 in order to insure accurate precision. Since, as we have mentioned, average temperature cycles are probably more reproducible than this, it is likely that a temperature coefficient of 1.2 would be adequate.

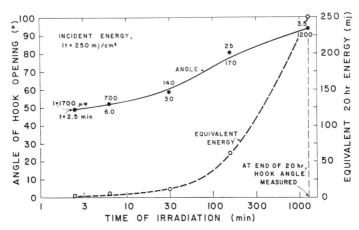

FIG. 11. Time-intensity response function for a photomorphogenic system, the hypocotyl hook of bean. The solid curve is the magnitude of hook opening as related to the time t, at various irradiances I. $I \times t =$ constant, 250 mj/cm^2. As the time varied from 2.5 min to 1200 min, the irradiances were decreased proportionately. In all cases, the irradiation began at zero time, i.e., excision. The dashed curve is a plot of the equivalent energy when the angle of opening is extrapolated over the log-curve of Fig. 9 to the equivalent energy value for a 20-hr exposure to give the same opening response. This is a measure of the true effectiveness of the applied energy. Data compiled from Withrow, Klein, and Elstad (1957) and unpublished data of these authors.

Not only must the period of the clock be relatively refractory and independent of the common environmental factors, but the phase must likewise be a refractory property and relatively uninfluenced by such factors. In fact, in order for photoperiod to be the sole control of the phasing of the clock, it should be the only factor which has the right key. The work of Buhnemann (1955a,b,c) and Bünning (1954) in this respect is quite significant. Both have shown that the period and the phase relationships of the clock are relatively unaffected by temperature and a great variety of chemicals, including auxin. The only

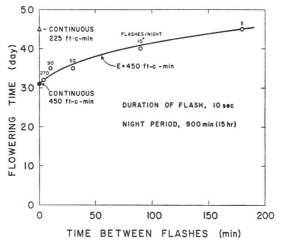

FIG. 12.   Time-intensity function for a photoperiodic system, flowering in the long-day plant Nobel spinach. The total energy had a constant value of 450 ft-c-min applied as a series of flashes of 10-sec duration for a 15-hr night (9-hr photoperiod). The number of flashes per night was varied from 5 to 270 and these were compared with continuous irradiation of 225 and 450 ft-c-min. Data taken from Withrow and Withrow (1944).

agents which appear to be capable of resetting the clock are those which can affect the nucleus, such as colchicine, urethane, BAL, more recently kinetin, and possibly gibberellin. In other words, the clock is much more refractory to chemical agents than the growth response

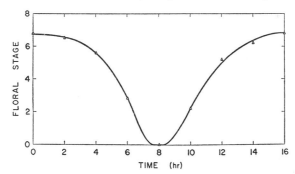

FIG. 13.   Time-phase requirement for a photoperiodic system. Flowering response of the short-day plant *Xanthium* to the time of application of a single flash during a 16-hr night following an 8-hr photoperiod. Data of Salisbury and Bonner (1956). A single flash was applied at various stages of the dark period. The response was measured in terms of the floral stage at the end of the experiment.

system since cell growth can be effected by a host of diverse chemical agents ranging from inorganic nutrients, water supply and sugars, to the more complex and subtle agents as the growth hormones. This great sensitivity does not appear to be true of the clock mechanism.

INTEGRATED ANALYSIS

We will now attempt to put all these facts together in a diagrammatic scheme (Fig. 14) of the relationship of the three principal

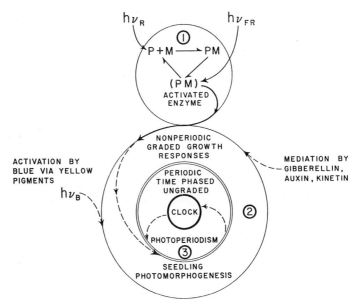

Fig. 14. Hypothetical scheme of the relationship between: (1) the photoreaction site, (2) the photomorphogenic response system, and (3) the photoperiodic response system. For details, see text.

spheres of activity: (1) site of the photochemical reaction, (2) the cell growth response of the photomorphogenic system, and (3) the photoperiodic system. Action spectra evidence indicates that the pigment system for induction has a single maximum at 660 mμ, with relatively little absorption in the blue. The only native pigments in the plant kingdom that have been observed to have this particular characteristic are the straight chain tetrapyrroles in which the four pyrrole rings are not closed into a major ring, such as biliverdin, and the algal pigment, phycocyanin. It would seem to be significant, also, that the most sensitive photoperiodic systems having this type of action spectrum are those including only the chlorophyllous plants, and the photoreceptors are always potentially green tissue. We are not aware of any photoperiodically red, far-red sensitive system that does not contain chloroplasts. Since the action spectrum appears to fit a tetra-pyrrolic type of structure, it is reasonable to assume, for the present at least, that the site of the photochemical reaction is most likely in the chloroplast and involves possibly either precursors to protochlorophyll or a chlorophyll analog. While much work has been done on the intermediate steps of chlorophyll synthesis in the algae by Granick *et al.* (1953) and others, there appears to be a considerable gap in knowledge of the steps between protoporphyrin 9 and its precursors. It is possible that these precursors are porphyrins which attain extremely low equilibria concentrations as would be indicated by the lack of *in vivo* absorption in this region and that, since the half-life of these compounds is very short, they have not been observed by direct chromatographic technics. The recent work of Krasnovskiĭ *et al.* (1957) which shows a photoreversible reduction of chlorophylls in the red and far red also is conducive to much speculation as to the involvement of a chlorophyll or one of its analogs as the photoreceptor.

Region 2 includes the complex cell growth systems that respond to the photoreactions and to all the other external physical and chemical factors of the environment. These include growth responsivity in stem length, leaf development, anthocyanin synthesis, and other activities of the organism. These systems are not refractory, their response is graded, and the magnitude of the response has little relationship to the phase of the applied energy.

It is System 3 which is closely coupled to the clock mechanism and which is relatively refractory as compared with the other systems. Flower bud initiation in plants is relatively uninfluenced by physiological levels of most physical and chemical factors except temperature in certain classes of plants and day length in others, or a combination of the two. Recent work has demonstrated that also in certain classes, especially the long-day plants, gibberellin is capable of inducing flower bud initiation in an unfavorable photoperiod. But the evidence of Lang (p. 329) certainly indicates that gibberellin is not a substitute for the photoreaction. Auxin has little influence on these processes unless extremely high levels are used. This is true of most other chemical factors such as inorganic and organic nutrient substances.

As has been mentioned previously, the clock itself is also a highly refractory system. It is the close coupling of these two refractory systems which makes possible the phenomenon of photoperiodism. In the environment, apparently day length and temperature are the only two factors that have the key for setting the clock. On the basis of this assumption, the diagram shows two-way arrows coupling the clock to the photoperiodic system. The work of Bünning (p. 507) has aptly demonstrated that photoperiod does not control the period of the clock. It merely controls the phase, and it is the phase relationships between the photoperiodic stimuli and the endogenous rhythmic system which appear to be the controlling factor in photoperiodism. This type of hypothesis has been presented many times by Bünning and his associates.

A hypothesis of the relationship between the photoperiodic stimulus

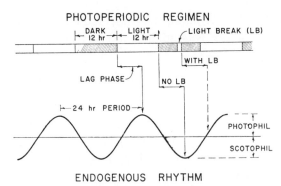

FIG. 15. Hypothetical relation of the photoperiodic stimulus to the endogenous rhythm. A. 12:12 hr dark-light cycle and a light-break (LB) are diagrammatically shown in relation to a 24-hr endogenous rhythm. See text for explanation.

and the endogenous rhythm is presented in Fig. 15. There is evidence that a lag period exists between the time of starting or stopping the photoreaction and the response of the endogenous rhythmic system (Bünning, p. 507). If the end of a light period occurs at such a point as to coincide with some suitable phase in the endogenous rhythm, and the beginning of the next photocycle coincides with the opposite phase of the rhythm after its suitable lag period, the stimulus and clock systems are in phase and will proceed with a given type of response; either the plant is vegetative, or it is thrown into the flowering stage. A light flash in the middle of the dark period, however, or an extension of the photoperiod through this phase so that the effective end of the photoperiod occurs in some other phase of the endogenous rhythm, introduces either the perturbations which have been observed by Bünning and Pittendrigh, or shifts the phase of the endogenous rhythm completely. As yet we do not have sufficient information to make any postulates as to the exact relationship between long- and short-day plants. The important point here is that such a hypothesis introduces the necessary extra parameters of lag-phase duration and photophil phases of the rhythmic system to make it possible to explain the existence of various classes of photoperiodic flowering responses in plants.

REFERENCES

Borthwick, H. A., and M. W. Parker. 1939. Photoperiodic responses of several varieties of soybeans. *Botan. Gaz., 101,* 341–65.

Borthwick, H. A., S. B. Hendricks, M. W. Parker, E. H. Toole, and Vivian K. Toole. 1952. A reversible photoreaction controlling seed germination. *Proc. Natl. Acad. Sci., U. S., 38,* 662–66.

Buhnemann, Fritz. 1955a. Das endodiurnale System der Oedogoniumzelle. II. Der Einfluss von Stoffwechselgiften und anderen Wirkstoffen. *Biol. Zentr., 74,* 691–705.

———. 1955b. Das endodiurnale System der Oedogoniumzelle. III. *Z. Naturforsch., 10b,* 305–10.

———. 1955c. Das endodiurnale System der Oedogoniumzelle. IV. Mitteilung. *Planta, 46,* 227–55.

Bünning, Erwin. 1948. Relationship between endogenic daily rhythm and photoperiodicity. *Z. Naturforsch., 3b,* 457–64.

———. 1954. The relationship of certain photoperiodic phenomena in *Soja* and *Xanthium* to endogenous daily rhythms. *Ber. deut. botan. Ges., 67,* 420–30.

Chen, S. L. 1952. The action spectrum for the photochemical evolution of oxygen by isolated chloroplasts. *Plant Physiol., 27,* 35–48.

Flint, Lewis H. 1936. The action of radiation of specific wavelengths in relation to the germination of light-sensitive lettuce seed. *Compt. rend. assoc. intern. essais semences, 1,* 1–4.

Granick, S., Lawrence Bogorad, and Herbert Jaffe. 1953. Hematoporphyrin IX, a probable precursor of protoporphyrin, in the biosynthetic chain of heme and chlorophyll. *J. Biol. Chem., 202,* 801–13.

Hamner, Karl C. 1940. Interrelation of light and darkness in photoperiodic induction. *Botan. Gaz., 101,* 658–87.

Hand, I. F. 1950. Insolation on clear days at the time of solstices and equinoxes for latitude 42°N. *Heating and Ventilating,* 3 pp.

Hillman, William S. 1957. Nonphotosynthetic light requirement in *Lemna minor* and its partial satisfaction by kinetin. *Science, 126,* 165–66.

Hoover, W. H., Earl S. Johnston, and F. S. Brackett. 1933. Carbon dioxide assimilation in a higher plant. *Smithsonian Inst. Publs., Misc. Collections, 87.*

Kimball, H. H. 1935. Intensity of solar radiation at the surface of the earth, and its variations with latitude, altitude, season and time of day. *Monthly Weather Rev., 63,* 1–4.

Kimball, H. H. 1938. Duration and intensity of twilight. *Monthly Weather Rev., 66,* 279–86.

Klein, W. H., R. B. Withrow, and V. B. Elstad. 1956. Response of the hypocotyl hook of bean seedlings to radiant energy and other factors. *Plant Physiol., 31,* 289–94.

Klein, W. H., R. B. Withrow, V. Elstad, and L. Price. 1957. Photocontrol of growth and pigment synthesis in the bean seedling as related to irradiance and wavelength. *Am. J. Botany, 44,* 15–19.

Koski, V. M., C. S. French, and J. H. C. Smith. 1951. The action spectrum for the transformation of protochlorophyll to chlorophyll a in normal and albino corn seedlings. *Arch. Biochem. Biophys., 31,* 1–17.

Krasnovskiĭ, A. A., and K. K. Voinovskaya. 1957. Reversible appearance of red and near infrared absorption bands with photoreduction of chlorophyll, protochlorophyll and their analogs. *Doklady Acad. Nauk S.S.S.R., 112,* 911–14.

Kraus, E. J., and H. R. Kraybill. 1918. Vegetation and reproduction with special reference to the tomato. *Oregon Agr. Expt. Sta. Bull., 149.*

Moh, C. C., and R. B. Withrow. 1958. Nonionizing radiant energy as an agent in altering the incidence of x-ray-induced chromatid aberrations. II. Reversal of the far-red potentiating effect in *Vicia* by red radiant energy. *Radiation Research* (in press).

Mohr, Hans. 1956. Die Beeinflussung der Keimung von Farnsporen durch Licht und andere Faktoren. *Planta, 46,* 534–51.

Moon, Parry. 1940. Proposed standard solar-radiation curves for engineering use. *J. Franklin Inst., 230,* 583–617.

Optical Society of America, Committee on Colorimetry. 1953. *The Science of Color.* Thomas Y. Crowell Co., New York.

Parker, M. W., S. B. Hendricks, and H. A. Borthwick. 1950. Action spectrum for the photoperiodic control of floral initiation of the long-day plant *Hyoscyamus niger. Botan. Gaz., 111,* 242–52.

Parker, M. W., S. B. Hendricks, H. A. Borthwick, and N. J. Scully. 1945. Action spectrum for the photoperiodic control of floral initiation in Biloxi soybean. *Science, 102,* 152–55.

Pittendrigh, Colin S. 1956. Perspectives in the study of biological clocks. *Per-*

spectives in Marine Biology, University of California Press, Berkeley. Pp. 1–47.

Priestley, J. H., and J. Ewing. 1923. Physiological studies in plant anatomy etiolation. *New Phytol., 22,* 30–44.

Salisbury, Frank B., and James Bonner. 1956. The reaction of the photoinductive dark period. *Plant Physiol., 31,* 141–47.

Shropshire, Walter, Jr., and Robert B. Withrow. 1958. Action spectrum of phototropic tip-curvature of *Avena. Plant Physiol., 33,* 360–65.

Siegelman, H. W., and S. B. Hendricks. 1957. Photocontrol of anthocyanin formation in turnip and red cabbage seedlings. *Plant Physiol., 32,* 393–98.

Taylor, A. H., and G. P. Kerr. 1941. The distribution of energy in the visible spectrum of daylight. *J. Opt. Soc. Am., 31,* 3–8.

U. S. Naval Observatory, Tables of sunrise, sunset and twilight. U. S. Government Printing Office, Washington, D. C., 1945.

Weintraub, Robert L., and Leonard Price. 1947. Developmental physiology of the grass seedling. II. Inhibition of mesocotyl elongation in various grasses by red and by violet light. *Smithsonian Inst. Publs., Misc. Collections, 106.*

Withrow, R. B. 1941. Response of seedlings to various wavebands of low intensity irradiation. *Plant Physiol., 16,* 241–56.

Withrow, R. B., and H. M. Benedict. 1936. Photoperiodic responses of certain greenhouse annuals as influenced by intensity and wavelength of artificial light used to lengthen the daylight period. *Plant Physiol., 11,* 225–49.

Withrow, R. B., and J. P. Biebel. 1936. Photoperiodic response of certain long and short day plants to filtered radiation applied as a supplement to daylight. *Plant Physiol., 11,* 807–19.

Withrow, R. B., W. H. Klein, and V. Elstad. 1957. Action spectra of photomorphogenic induction and its photoinactivation. *Plant Physiol., 32,* 453–62.

Withrow, R. B., W. H. Klein, L. Price, and V. Elstad. 1953. Influence of visible and near infrared radiant energy on organ development and pigment synthesis in bean and corn. *Plant Physiol., 28,* 1–14.

Withrow, R. B., and C. C. Moh. 1957. Nonionizing radiant energy as an agent in altering the incidence of x-ray-induced chromatid aberrations. I. Effects of far-red and infrared radiant energy on *Tradescantia* and *Vicia. Radiation Research, 6,* 491–500.

Withrow, R. B., and Alice P. Withrow. 1944. Effect of intermittent irradiation on photoperiodic responses. *Plant Physiol., 19,* 6–18.

Withrow, R. B., John B. Wolff, and L. Price. 1956. Elimination of the lag phase of chlorophyll synthesis in dark-grown bean leaves by a pretreatment with low irradiance of monochromatic energy. *Plant Physiol., 31* (Suppl.), xiii.

The Relation of Light to Rhythmic Phenomena in Plants and Animals

DAILY RHYTHMS AS COUPLED OSCILLATOR SYSTEMS AND THEIR RELATION TO THERMOPERIODISM AND PHOTOPERIODISM[1]

COLIN S. PITTENDRIGH AND VICTOR G. BRUCE
Biology Department, Princeton University, Princeton, New Jersey

CHRONOMETRY, RHYTHMS, AND PHOTOPERIODISM

For the last thirty years the fact that organisms can measure time has confronted biologists studying very diverse phenomena. The first clear and explicit demonstration of functional chronometry in organisms was that of Beling (1929) and Wahl (1932), who showed that the honeybee returns to a favorable feeding place for several days at precisely the same sun-hour at which it was initially discovered. A very definite instance of chronometry is implied—as later work has shown—in the photoperiodic effect initially discovered by Garner and Allard (1923); many plants and animals identify season by what amounts to a time measurement of night length. A third category of chronometry includes all the remarkable cases of celestial navigation recently uncovered by Kramer (1952), von Frisch (1950), Hoffman (1954), Pardi and Papi (1953), Lindauer (1957), Sauer (1957), and Birukow (1957). In these cases an endogenous timing system is utilized by vertebrates and arthropods in correcting for the shifting position of celestial direction-givers.

A fourth class of phenomena implying functional time measurement by organisms is that of persistent rhythms with a daily, tidal, or lunar period. Observations on persistent daily rhythms are, to be sure, much older than those in the other three categories. Bouvier (1922) cites observations in the nineteenth century, and the beginnings of essentially modern work on persistent rhythms go as far back as the classical researches of Pfeffer commenced in 1875 (see Bünning,

[1] Previously unpublished experimental data presented in this paper were obtained in studies supported by grants from the National Science Foundation and the Eugene Higgins Trust.

1956). Beling's (1935) review already discusses the possible relation of the bee's Zeitgedächtnis to persistent rhythms; but neither her discussion nor those of Kalmus in 1935 and 1938 appear to have impressed other workers on daily rhythms. In fact, frank use of the word "clock" has entered the biological literature only since 1950–1954 following the clear demonstration of chronometry in animal navigation. And only since then have students of persistent rhythms explicitly recognized and treated their problem as one of time measurement. Associated with this reorientation, and doubtless largely due to it, has been the discovery that persistent daily rhythms in protists, plants, and animals are temperature-independent in the sense that their period (measuring time) is nearly invariant over a wide range of temperatures (cf. the discussion in Pittendrigh and Bruce, 1957).

The evolutionary and physiological relationship of daily rhythms, on the one hand to the other, more elaborate cases of chronometry, and on the other hand to the diverse phenomena called photoperiodism is an attractive and many-sided problem.

The present authors (Bruce and Pittendrigh, 1957b; Pittendrigh and Bruce, 1957; Pittendrigh, 1958) have adopted the working hypothesis that a fundamentally similar time-measuring system, which they consider as a self-sustaining oscillation in cellular activity, underlies all cases of persistent daily rhythms as well as the bee's Zeitgedächtnis and the chronometry involved in animal navigation. Apart from its broad empirical support, this hypothesis was adopted for the unity and ultimate simplicity it implies; that living systems, having once evolved the seemingly difficult function of a temperature-independent time measurement, have exploited the basic oscillation involved—doubtless with modification—wherever time measurement has proved adaptively useful.

We have not, in the papers cited, considered photoperiodism in relation to this hypothesis. But it is clear that insofar as the photoperiodic control of flowering amounts to a relatively temperature-independent time measurement of night length (Long, 1939) we would seek to relate the phenomena, anticipating that a common cellular timepiece was again involved. Bünning (1937) has, of course, been the pioneer in this field and has urged for many years that endogenous daily rhythms are involved in the photoperiodic control of flowering. He was, however, surely led to his hypothesis for very different reasons: the temperature independence of the photoperiodic phenomena had not yet been discovered, and in spite of Grossenbacher's (1939) paper, it was almost twenty years before the period of endogenous plant rhythms was commonly taken to be temperature-independent (Ball and Dyke, 1954; Bünning and Leinweber, 1956; Leinweber, 1956); indeed Bünning himself has long held the explicit view that the period of plant rhythms was temperature-dependent (Bünning, 1935). Hamner demonstrated that a 24-hr rhythm is indeed involved in the flowering response of beans; but whether or not the relation of rhythms to photoperiodic effects is the one we would envisage—involvement of a common cellular clock—is a question still far from answered.

Use of the term photoperiodism has now been extended to cover a very different type of phenomenon from that discovered by Garner and Allard. Papers by Highkin and Hanson (1954) and Hillman (1956) show that the growth of tomatoes and other plants is sensitive to the light regime; damage ensues from continuous light or from light cycles in which the period differs markedly from 24 hr. The concept of photoperiodism is, in a sense, weakened by its extension to these cases. The original phenomenon, both in principle and in fact in the clear case of *Xanthium,* did not involve a periodicity as such: a single experience of long night is an adequate releaser of the flowering response in the cocklebur. But in the injurious effects of light on growth, just cited, significance does attach to the *period* (or *cycle length*) as such, vis-a-vis the length of a fraction (night) in one full cycle of fixed length (or period); 24 hr. Thus although it technically weakens the term, the new denotation of photoperiodism has more logical justification, and were it strictly followed the word would be properly juxtaposed with Went's (1944) thermoperiodism where again periodicity, as such, is a crucial issue.

The new model for daily rhythms developed in this paper has no special or new implications concerning the postulated bearing of rhythms to the night-length measurement involved in the flowering response. But it has, we believe, a substantial bearing on the relationship of daily rhythms to both Went's thermoperiodism (1957) and the newer photoperiodic phenomena described by Highkin and Hanson (1954) and Hillman (1956).

THE GENERALIZED OSCILLATOR MODEL
FOR CELLULAR CLOCKS

We have discussed elsewhere (Bruce and Pittendrigh, 1957b; Pittendrigh and Bruce, 1957; Pittendrigh, 1958) the general characteristics of daily rhythms considered as clocks. The skepticism voiced in some discussion at this symposium over use of the word "clock" prompts us to note again the salient facts which have led us to this usage. Persistent daily, tidal, and lunar rhythms stand sharply apart from all other biological rhythms, such as heartbeat, for instance, in two fundamental respects: (1) their natural period is an evolved approximation to the period of an ecologically significant cosmic period; (2) their period remains stable over a wide range of temperatures, thus satisfying the functional prerequisite of an efficient timegiver. In addition, it is noted that the feature of temperature independence of period is uniquely associated with rhythms which have a natural period matching a cosmic period and that all such rhythms are temperature-independent. Clearly the universal concurrence of these features is significant and implies that the systems they characterize owe their existence to natural selection and that they serve to measure time for the organism; in a word they are "clocks."

Earlier papers from this laboratory (see especially Pittendrigh and Bruce, 1957) have emphasized the fact that persistent daily rhythms in a very wide range of organisms, from single-celled systems to mammals, have many formal characteristics in common, and that these characteristics are those of *self-sustaining oscillators*. We have accordingly developed a generalized oscillator model for the discussion of cellular clocks embodying the following principal propositions:

1. The living cell possesses *either* as a distinct part *or* as a feature of its overall organization a system that can develop a self-sustaining oscillator, whose

2. Natural Period is an evolved approximation to that of the solar day, and

3. is temperature-independent, or nearly so, within wide ecological temperature limits.

4. This endogenous self-sustaining oscillation (ESSO) is an innate feature of cellular organization; it is not learned. [In addition to the discussion given on this point in Pittendrigh and Bruce (1957) and Pittendrigh (1958), see the excellent, more recent study of Hoffman (1957).]

5. The phase and period of ESSO (the cell's clock) are susceptible, like those of other self-sustaining oscillations, to entrainment by other systems to which it can be coupled. Specifically, the ESSO's of living cells can be coupled to a light cycle (and more indirectly to a temperature cycle) of the environment which establishes the appropriate phase of the living clock and corrects the error in its innate natural period. (Other environmental cycles—pressure, cosmic rays, air ionization, etc.—cannot be coupled to ESSO, and in a constant, or aperiodic, regime of light or temperature the oscillator is free-running, thus revealing its natural period.)

6. As with other self-sustaining oscillators, the phase of ESSO as a free-running system can be shifted by single, *nonperiodic* signals of light or temperature—the signals to which it can be coupled.

The working hypothesis of a fundamentally similar ESSO underlying all living clocks (Pittendrigh and Bruce, 1957) has only a general heuristic value until it is open to possible experimental rejection. In this connection two general points are noted.

First, fully acceptable tests must await *some* knowledge of the concrete physical nature of ESSO, and presently we have absolutely none. Moreover, as discussed fully in the writers' papers, there are difficulties in the way of discovering the physical nature of the cell's clock: in spite of increasing and highly interesting information on chemical periodicities in the cell and the organism (e.g., Barnum, Jardetzky, and Halberg, 1957) we still lack the necessary criterion for distinguishing primary (causative) cycles from those they control. Thus, it remains desirable in the present state of the problem to develop the formal oscillator model from physiological data to as explicit and restrictive a form as possible as a lead to its concrete nature.

Second, we are consequently limited in the meantime to using formal properties in testing the hypothesis of a common mechanism.

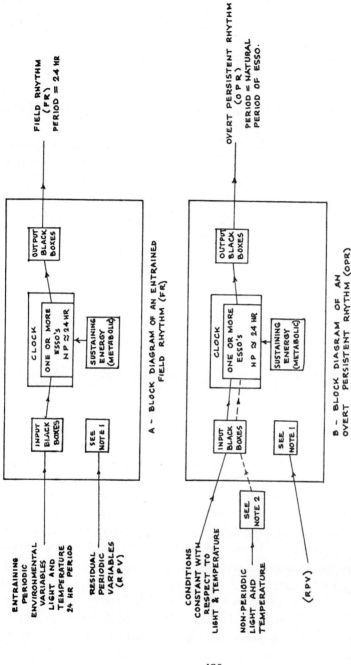

FIG. 1. Block diagrams of the generalized oscillator model for daily rhythms.

Notes. (1) All periodically fluctuating environmental variables other than light and temperature are called residual periodic variables (RPV). They are assumed never to be coupled to the oscillator. (2) Light shocks, temperature shocks, and nonperiodic treatment with light and temperature may affect the phase of OPR. (3) Detailed relations of light and temperature are further specified in the extension of this model given schematically in Fig. 9.

Again there are difficulties here which stem from the fact that diverse physical systems can be devised (or evolved) to behave in a formally similar way. In the comparison of living clock systems for instance, we can take neither temperature independence nor entrainability by light as evidence of a common mechanism; selection must have demanded both these features as functional prerequisites of clock systems and will, of course, have been indifferent to the particular physical mechanism by which the functional end is met. If we are to test the proposition of a common mechanism and use only formal properties, these must be of such a nature that selection can reasonably be dismissed as the agent responsible for their universal association with cellular clock systems; in short, the properties must lack adaptive value.

In the following sections of this paper we turn to a group of physiological effects that we have recently found to be widespread in living clocks. They have the two merits of (1) demanding a more explicit and restrictive form of the oscillator model than has previously been necessary and (2) of being apparently devoid of adaptive meaning.

PHASE SHIFTS WITH SINGLE SIGNALS

Definitions and Qualifications

It is necessary to establish provisional working definitions for the terms *period, phase,* and *transients* used in discussing the oscillator model. Figure 1 in an earlier paper (Pittendrigh and Bruce, 1957) summarizes the hypothesis of a fundamental endogenous self-sustaining oscillation (ESSO) underlying and controlling overt rhythms (OR). The type of experimental conditions which produce overt forced (or field) rhythms and overt persistent rhythms are summarized in the figure. Examples of overt forced rhythms and overt persistent rhythms are shown in Fig. 2 and 3, illustrating eclosion in *Drosophila* and running-wheel activity of small mammals.

We shall not attempt to do more than make operational definitions for the terms *period, phase,* and *transients* relative to overt rhythms. Ultimately we should like to relate these formal characteristics to equivalent ones for the underlying oscillatory clock mechanism, but at the present time these relationships must be inferential. We define the

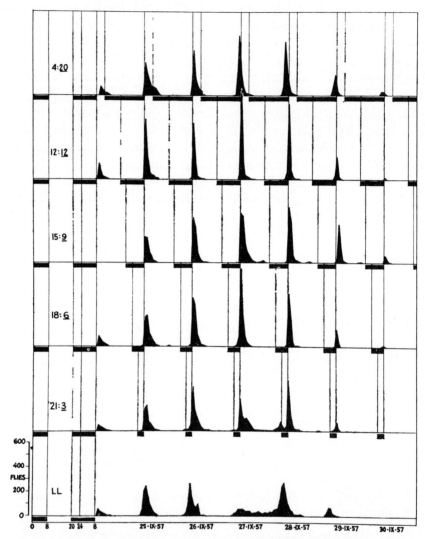

FIG. 2.   The eclosion of *Drosophila* in light-dark cycles of varying photoperiod is illustrated here. The phase of the eclosion rhythm remains fixed relative to the dark-light transition for all photoperiods greater than 4 hr. The light intensity was 75–100 ft-c.

period of an overt biological rhythm as the average time interval (in hours) between successive events in the periodic sequence. No biological rhythms are strictly periodic in the mathematical sense, and in practice one takes some arbitrary and well-defined statistic of the rhythm as a measure of the periodically repeated events. For example, in the case of *Drosophila* we take the median of the daily distribution of eclosion. For hamsters, mice, and many other organisms the time of onset of running-wheel activity is taken as the statistic which we use to discuss the formal properties of the rhythm. It is evident that the diverse assayed periodic events may occur at different clock hours in an alternating cycle of dark and light. For example, the median of the *Drosophila* eclosion peak occurs soon after dawn (Fig. 2), whereas the time of onset of running-wheel activity in a nocturnal animal may occur just after sunset (Fig. 3). Thus, the characterization of the *phase* of an overt rhythm with respect to an external entraining periodicity is arbitrary. For reasons given later on, we shall characterize the phase of an overt rhythm as the time interval from "dawn" to the arbitrary statistic defining the rhythm. For example, in a typical light-dark cycle of 12 hr of light and 12 hr of dark, the phase of the *Drosophila* rhythm would be about 1½ hr (Fig. 2), whereas the phase of the *Peromyscus* rhythm would be about 13 hr (Fig. 3). We extend the definition to the overt rhythm of the organism in constant conditions (such as DD) in the following way. *When the rhythm is in a steady state,* "dawn" comes 1½ hr before the median of the eclosion peak in *Drosophila* or 13 hr[2] before the time of onset of running-wheel activity in *Peromyscus.* Thus, when we discuss the phase of the rhythms of different organisms in constant conditions we have a common basis for comparison. In a steady-state condition, such as may happen in continuous light or darkness or in alternating cycles of light and dark, the actual intervals between successive events may not deviate much from the average interval. When the organism is subjected to nonrepeated disturbances (such as a single shock of light) the intervals between successive events may be systematically shortened or lengthened until a

[2] Strictly speaking this should be 13/24 times the natural period in constant conditions.

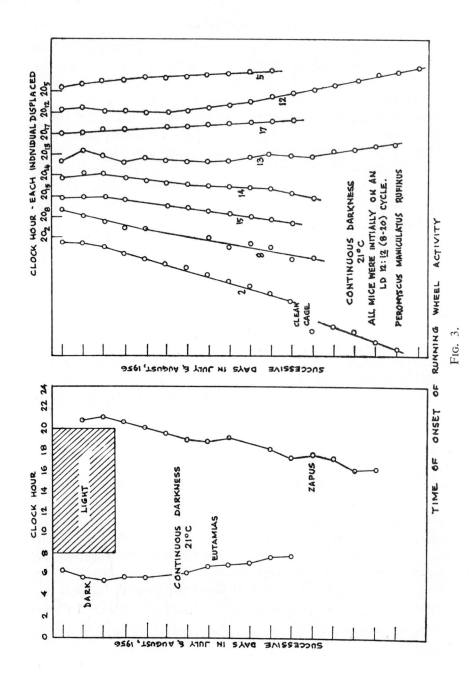

FIG. 3.

484

new steady state is reached. We call these lengthened or shortened intervals *transients*.

Some Generalizations about Phase Shifting

In earlier papers (Pittendrigh and Bruce, 1957; Pittendrigh, 1958) full descriptions have been given of the phase-shift experiments in *Drosophila* that have stimulated the present study. Figure 4 gives histograms illustrating the effects on the eclosion rhythms of a 12-hr light signal applied to 23 cultures of *Drosophila pseudoobscura*. Each culture receives a light signal beginning at the time marked by the line d_1. Three features are outstanding.

1. After 72 hr, at line d_3, all cultures have achieved a phase shift that is virtually complete; that is, the phase of the overt rhythm now bears the same relation to the d_1, d_2, and d_3 coordinates as it originally bore to those marked D_0, D_1, $D_2 \cdot \cdot \cdot D_5$. It is clear that the particular phase ultimately attained by each culture separately within the interval D_4–D_5 is, in some sense, fully determined by the single signal given three cycles earlier.

2. Attainment of new phase is not instantaneous; it proceeds gradually as the system moves through several transient cycles in which the "period" differs from the natural period of the steady-state system, which in this case is indistinguishably close to 24 hr and exemplified by culture 0 in Fig. 4.

3. The character of the transients is dependent on the time in the cycle when the phase-shifting signal is given. Signals beginning within the first 15 hr of the cycle generate transients whose "period" is greater than the natural period; those falling in the last 9 hr of the cycle generate transients with "periods" less than the natural period. This is well shown by the behavior of cultures 8 and 18, Fig. 5. In cultures 12, 13,

---

FIG. 3. Typical data of diurnal (*Eutamias*) and nocturnal (*Zapus* and *Peromyscus*) mammals. Circled points show the time of onset of running-wheel activity on successive days, at first in LD (light-dark) conditions and later in DD (constant dark) conditions. (*Left*) A typical long period in DD for the diurnal chipmunk (*Eutamias*) and short period for the nocturnal jumping-mouse (*Zapus*). (*Right*) Data for eight nocturnal deer mice (*Peromyscus*) numbered 2, 8, 15 . . . , etc. The time scale of each individual mouse is displaced 2 hr to the right; hr-20 is indicated for each mouse. Nocturnal mammals in general have periods less than 24 hr in DD, but it is evident that there are individual exceptions.

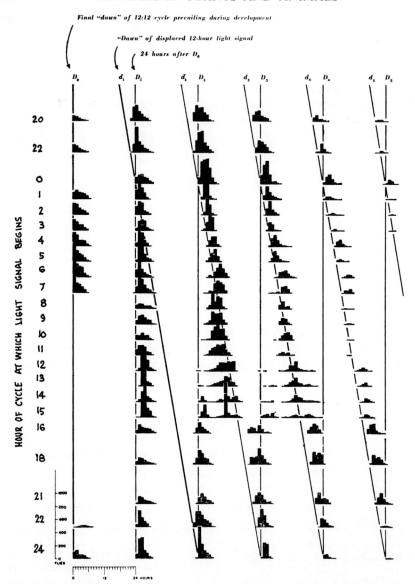

FIG. 4.   The effects on the *Drosophila* eclosion rhythm of single perturbations with light. The histograms show the number of flies eclosing in hourly intervals for 23 different cultures which have been exposed to a 12-hr light signal at different times of the cycle of the rhythm as described more fully in the text.

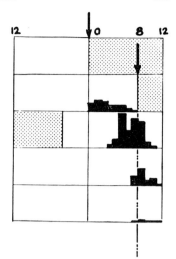

Fig. 5. The transient approach to a new steady state is illustrated for two of the *Drosophila* "Resets" shown in Fig. 4. The eclosion peaks on successive days are plotted underneath each other to illustrate the nature of the transients. The shaded area represents light; at all other times the cultures are in complete darkness. The first arrow corresponds to "dawn" (hour zero) of the previous light-dark cycle. The second arrow corresponds to the beginning of the resetting signal. The transients are lengthening ones for culture 8 (signal begins 8 hr after dawn), and shortening ones for culture 18. Compare with Fig. 9.

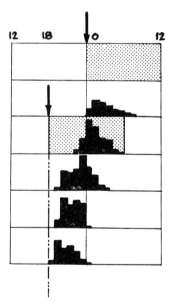

14, and 15 (Fig. 4) there are small "subsidiary" peaks at lines D_2 and D_3, which probably represent a fraction of the fly population in which no phase reset was accomplished.

Two previous papers from this laboratory (Pittendrigh and Bruce, 1957; and Pittendrigh, 1958) have discussed these data in a different context. It was, however, noted (1) that a transient motion was to be expected of perturbed oscillations achieving a new steady state and (2) that transients were a promising tool for further formal analysis of daily rhythms generally. We have now extended their study in *Drosophila* and have detected them also in the hamster (Burchard, 1957), *Euglena, Mus, Sceloporus,* and the cockroach *Leucophaea* (Roberts, 1957). In all these organisms there is evidence—clearest in the hamster and *Euglena*—of a phase-shifting behavior sufficiently similar to

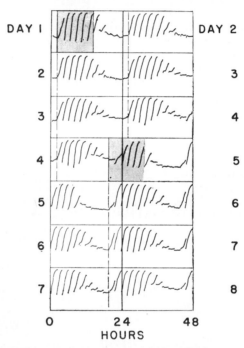

FIG. 6.   A typical reset of the rhythm of phototactic response in *Euglena* is illustrated. Seven successive days are shown, one under another, and for clarity days 2 through 8 are repeated at the right so that the reset can be more easily visualized. As described elsewhere (Bruce and Pittendrigh, 1956) each of the 12 lines per 24-hr interval represents the phototactic response to a "test-light" measured turbidimetrically every 2 hr. The first day shown is the last of several in LD 12:*12*, where the shaded portion represents 12 hr of light. Starting at hr 18 in the cycle (middle of night phase) a 12-hr light signal is given on the fourth day resulting in an immediate advance of the typically daytime responses.

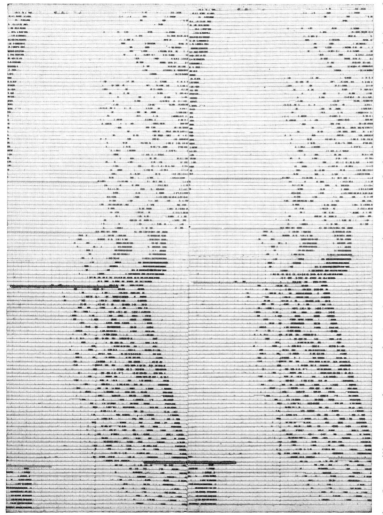

Fɪɢ. 7. The figure illustrates the actual record on successive days of the running-wheel activity of a hamster. Except for the two 12-hr periods of light indicated on the 13th and 59th days the animal is in continuous darkness. The resetting effect of the light on the time of onset of activity is clearly evident. In one case, the time is advanced, and in the other, the time is delayed as discussed in the text. The experimental record has been duplicated and each 24-hr period is thus shown twice resulting in a horizontal time scale of 48 hr.

that in *Drosophila* to suggest that we are confronted with a very general feature of daily rhythms.

Figure 6 shows a phase shift in *Euglena* attained by an advance (short transients) following a 12-hr light signal that began in the night phase; similar signals beginning in the day phase cause phase shifts attained by delays. There is evidence in Fig. 6 that two transient cycles precede the new steady state, but there is no doubt that in this organism the reset is more nearly complete in one cycle than is the case in *Drosophila* and the hamster (Bruce and Pittendrigh, 1958).

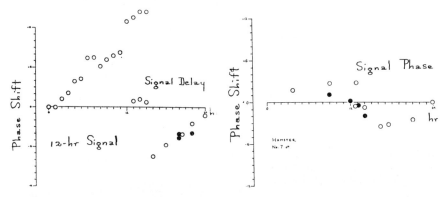

FIG. 8.   Steady-state phase shifts in (*left*) *Drosophila* and (*right*) the hamster (*Mesocricetus auratus*). The abscissa represents the hour of the original cycle at which the phase-shifting 12-hr light signal was begun. Hour zero on the abscissa corresponds to "dawn" of the previous steady state. The ordinate represents the total phase shift in hours after a new steady state is attained. Positive phase shifts (points above the line) correspond to delays of the eclosion peaks or activity onsets and negative phase shifts correspond to advances.

Figure 7 shows two phase shifts in the hamster caused by single 12-hr light signals. The new steady-state phase is always preceded by many clear transients, more even than in *Drosophila*. Perhaps associated with this prolonged duration of transients is the failure of any signal so far used to cause a "saturation" phase shift in the hamster: a signal falling at hour 12 fails to shift phase a full 12 hr. Figure 8 compares the steady-state phase shift in *Drosophila* and hamster following 12-hr light signals given at various times throughout the cycle. In *Drosophila* the shifts (all saturated) are achieved by delays up to hour

15 and by advances thereafter. In the hamster the switchover from delays to advances occurs at about hour 13; and in no case is the steady-state shift saturated.

A COUPLED OSCILLATOR MODEL FOR DAILY RHYTHMS

We can now be more explicit about the interest attaching to the pattern of phase shifts. First, it lacks any obvious adaptive meaning; and we take it, therefore, with some caution, as evidence of a common feature in the mechanism of the diverse daily rhythms it characterizes. Second, its analysis leads to a more restrictive and explicit form of the oscillator model for rhythms.

The *Drosophila* case, for which fullest data are available, is considered first. Any model based on a single oscillator seems unable to explain the concurrence of the three features that strongly characterize resetting in the fly: (1) ultimate determination of phase by a signal seen three cycles previous to the new steady state, (2) the presence of transients, and (3) the dependence of transient length on the time of the cycle at which the signal fell. These features are, on the other hand, all explained by a model for the system based on two coupled oscillators.

Essential features of the two-oscillator scheme are given in Fig. 9. The principal departure from an earlier model (Fig. 1) is addition of a second oscillator, *B*. The *A* oscillator is self-sustaining; it can be coupled with and entrained by the light regime of the environment; when free running in aperiodic conditions its phase can be shifted by single light signals; it is temperature-independent; and it is coupled with and drives a second (*B*) oscillation. The *B* oscillator is the system whose rhythmic behavior is more immediately reflected in the fly's overt rhythm; in some sense the fly reads phase (hence time) from the motion of *B*.

The peculiarities of phase shifting are represented schematically in the lower part of the figure: (1) the light signal immediately resets the phase of the *A* oscillator; the new phase, which is expressed by the fly much later, is instantaneously registered by the *A* oscillator; (2) the transients observed in the fly reflect the gradual reentrainment of the *B* oscillator (which the fly follows) by the *A* oscillator; (3) the transients

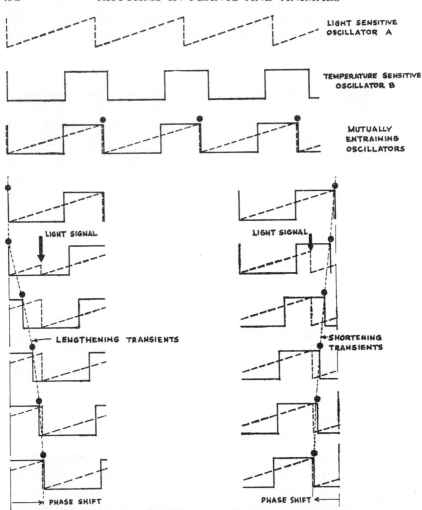

Fig. 9. The figure illustrates schematically the two-oscillator model described more fully in the text. The *A* and *B* oscillators are shown "free-running" and "mutually entraining" each other, with a period close to 24 hr, at the top of the figure. The black dots represent an arbitrary point in the cycle of the *B* oscillator, which represents the assayed rhythm in a particular organism. The two lower figures, representing six successive days, illustrate what is to be expected if a signal of light completely and immediately resets the *A* oscillator and if the *B* oscillator is gradually re-entrained by the *A* oscillator. For simplicity no feedback of *B* on *A* has been shown.

are longer or shorter than the natural period of A depending on the phase of B when A is reset. A mathematical formulation of the model has been developed (Pittendrigh, Bruce, and Kaus, 1958).

To explain the fly-resetting data it is unnecessary to assume that B feeds back on A; we may, that is, assume B to be completely driven by A. Nor do we need any special assumptions concerning its temperature sensitivity. However, it soon became evident that the coupled-oscillator model would also explain several additional types of *Drosophila* data if we allowed two further broad assumptions: (1) that there is some slight feedback of B on A; and (2) that B is temperature-sensitive in the senses that it can be entrained by an external temperature cycle, and its period (unlike A's) is temperature-dependent.

Temperature Dependence of the B Oscillator

One of the most challenging features of the *Drosophila* data has been the strange mixture of temperature dependence and independence they have revealed. Pittendrigh (1954) showed that immediately following a temperature drop the overt rhythm of the fly was strongly affected: the period lengthened (Fig. 10). However, it immediately and spontaneously reverted to its natural period and to nearly its original phase. A special temperature-dependent terminal clock, operative only in the last day of pupal life, was adduced to explain these facts. This hypothesis has subsequently been withdrawn (Pittendrigh and Bruce, 1957), and explanation of the behavior has been sought in terms of an oscillator's transients. Perplexing features have nevertheless remained. As noted in our previous paper (Pittendrigh and Bruce, 1957, p. 98): "There are . . . great differences in the response of the *Drosophila* clock to light and temperature stimulation; . . . sharp temperature perturbations produce spectacular transients with relatively little phase shift in the ultimate steady state; light perturbations have, on the other hand, spectacular effects on the steady-state phase shift."

The coupled oscillator model offers the most promising interpretation of these facts so far available if the B oscillator is taken to be temperature-dependent. The transients produced by temperature drops reflect temporary lengthening of the period of the B oscillator, which is promptly reentrained by the temperature-independent A oscillator.

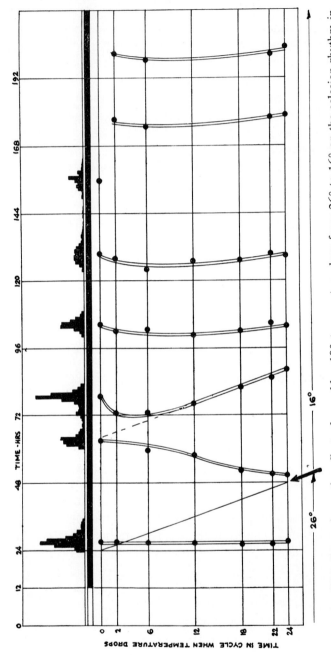

FIG. 10. The figure shows the effect of a sudden 10° temperature drop from 26° to 16° on the eclosion rhythm in *Drosophila*. Seven cultures were synchronized by light-dark cycles and after hour 12 were put in continuous darkness. At different times of the cycle, as indicated on the figure, the temperature was lowered 10°. The top histogram relates to the culture in which the temperature drop comes at hour 24, and the solid points are calculated medians of the peaks. The total number of eclosed flies in the second eclosion peak of culture 6 (hour of cycle at which temperature is dropped) and the third eclosion peaks of cultures 12, 18, 22, and 24 is relatively small.

494

The peculiar combination of large transients and little ultimate phase shift (Fig. 10) is explained by the temperature insensitivity of the *A* component. The fact that *some* phase shift is ultimately attained is taken to imply a slight feedback of *B* on *A* that is demonstrable by other types of experiment briefly described below.

Figure 11 summarizes experiments with the *Drosophila* eclosion rhythm in which the flies are subjected to simultaneous light and temperature periodicities. The phase relations of the light and temperature cycles are systematically varied in the twelve experiments. On hypothesis, the light cycle entrains the *A* oscillator and the temperature

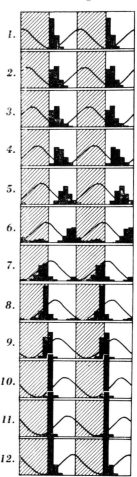

FIG. 11. The figure shows the effect on the *Drosophila* eclosion rhythm of simultaneous periodic cycles of temperature and light. Two successive days are shown for twelve separate cultures. The graphs are arranged so that the phase of the light-dark (shaded) cycles are synchronized, and the phase of the temperature cycle of each culture is displaced 2 hr from the phase of the culture shown just above. The temperature curve is approximately sinusoidal with a mean of 18°C and an amplitude of ±8°C.

cycle entrains the *B* oscillator. Only when the phase relations of light and temperature are those found in nature (low point of the temperature curve near dawn) can we expect the *B* oscillator, and hence the fly's overt rhythm, to exhibit its typical phase. Displacement of the temperature curve relative to dawn should lead to conflicting entrainment forces on the *B* oscillator: the light regime will pull in one direction via its control of *A*, which in turn entrains *B*; and the temperature regime will pull in the other direction via its direct entrainment of *B*. Figure 11 shows that the phase of the fly rhythm is indeed some compromise between the light and temperature cycles until the peak of activity is moved to 15 hr after dawn; there is then a clear phase jump over to the next dawn. (This phase jump from hour 15 to hour 24 is a striking phenomenon we are not yet ready to discuss; it implies a zone of forbidden phase relations between *B* and its driving oscillator *A* that is evident in other unpublished data.)

The interpretation of these effects in terms of the coupled oscillator scheme can be to some extent tested in the experiments summarized by Fig. 12 which involve replications of conditions applying to cultures 5,6,7, and 8 in Fig. 11. These are the cultures subjected to the most drastic disturbance of normal light and temperature phase relations. In Fig. 12A the system, initially in steady state, dictated by the conflicting light and temperature signals, is transferred to constant dark and a steady 21°C. Within 3 days all the cultures revert to a phase corresponding with that of the previous light cycle, thus confirming the conclusion that *A* drives *B* with very little feedback. Figure 12B, however, demonstrates that some feedback is surely present. When the cultures are released from control by the external light cycle, but maintained under the temperature cycle, they all assume a phase determined wholly by the temperature. The phase of *B*, still being forced by the temperature oscillation, ultimately entrains *A*, which is no longer held by a light cycle. It is unnecessary to emphasize that the experiments summarized in Figs. 10, 11, and 12 reveal strong details we have not attempted to explain. It is simply our current opinion that the complex interaction of light and temperature in *Drosophila* and mixture of temperature-dependent and temperature-independent features are all best approached and will ultimately be explained by the coupled oscil-

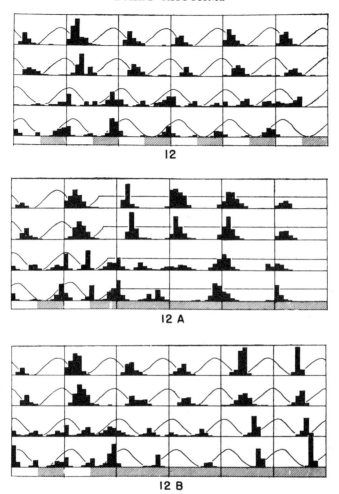

FIG. 12. As in Fig. 11 the result of conflicting light and temperature
cycles on the eclosion rhythm in *Drosophila* is illustrated. The top four
histograms (12) are results of experiments similar to those shown in
cultures 5, 6, 7, and 8 of Fig. 11 except that the temperature cycle had a
mean of 18°C and an amplitude of ±6°C. The next four histograms
(12A) show what happens if cultures on these conflicting cycles of light
and temperature are put into DD and constant temperature (21°C). The
eclosion rhythm settles down to a phase determined primarily by the
previous light-dark cycle. The bottom set of histograms (12B) show
what happens if cultures on these conflicting cycles of light and temperature are put into DD. The eclosion rhythm becomes entrained by the
temperature cycle.

lator model we adduced initially for the peculiarities of light-induced phase shifts.

Some Qualifications: Phase Control versus Phase Shift

Data already available on phase shifting in *Drosophila, Euglena,* hamster, deer-mouse, and cockroach reveal complications whose full discussion is postponed but which must be noted.

Failure of a 12-hr light signal to give a saturation phase shift in the mammals (like the hamster) is open to more than one interpretation, including the likelihood that the B oscillations in this case feed back strongly on A, thus conferring an inertia, so to speak, on the system which a single signal cannot overcome.

Some signals even in *Drosophila* and *Euglena* fail to give saturation shifts (cf. Fig. 6, p. 97, in Pittendrigh and Bruce, 1957). There is evidently some dependence of the extent of phase shift on the "magnitude" of the resetting signals; weaker signals (lower intensity, shorter duration) may give smaller shifts. But there is already enough evidence to dismiss a simple duration-intensity reciprocity. Signals shorter than 12 hr (8 hr, 4 hr, and 1/2000 sec) can all cause phase shifts if they fall within the night (Bünning's scotophil) phase, but they apparently fail to reset very much, or even at all, if they fall entirely in the photophil phase. If this proves to be generally true, it would imply that the efficacy of our 12-hr signals that *begin* in the photophil is due largely or wholly to the tail end of the signal that extends into the scotophil. The surprising fact that extremely short (1/2000 sec) high-intensity flashes can reset the hamster (Burchard, 1957) and *Drosophila* (Bruce and Pittendrigh, 1957a) rhythms makes possible a detailed analysis of the resettability of the A oscillator in which the issue of time in the cycle is unconfounded by duration of signal.

Our provisional view that dawn (or any dark-light transition) is the efficient phase-giver in *Drosophila* has strong support in spite of its apparent contradiction by these indications of nonresettability in the photophil. Figure 2 summarizes this support, but indicates, again, that there are complications. The phase of the *Drosophila* eclosion rhythm remains fixed relative to dawn (and independent of the light-dark transition) over a wide range of photoperiods. Nevertheless this rule breaks down when the photoperiod is reduced to 4 hr; the phase of the rhythm now shifts back—activity anticipates dawn. Aschoff and Meyer-Lohmann (1955) and Übelmesser (1954) have published similar data demonstrating some dependence of phase on photoperiod in mammals and the fungus *Pilobolus*. Finally, it is noted that contrary to strong expectations based on Fig. 2, when periodic cultures in constant light are transferred to constant dark, the single light-dark transition completely resets the system; after two transient cycles a new steady-state phase is established with eclosion peaks occurring at $n \times 24 + 12$ hr after the single light-dark step that is evidently taken, in some sense, as "sunset."

Obviously the problem of *phase control* in LD conditions is still far from understood. This does not, however, preclude a meaningful discussion of *phase shifts* imposed on the free-running (LL or DD conditions) rhythm by discrete light and temperature signals. It is the strongly characterized pattern of such phase shifts that leads to the coupled oscillator model; the further development of this model will have to accommodate the problems of phase control.

THE CELL AS OSCILLATOR; PHOTOPERIODISM, THERMOPERIODISM, AND DAILY RHYTHMS

There is no way at present of further characterizing the A and B oscillators nor of localizing them to cellular parts. The coupled-oscillator model attributes to the A component nearly all those major clock features that in the single-oscillator scheme (Fig. 1) were considered inherent in what we called ESSO; the A oscillator must be self-sustaining, temperature-independent, and receptive to light signals. The coupling of the whole rhythmic system to temperature cycles is now considered a function of the distinct B component.

Clearly, as long as it is driven by A, we have no way of knowing whether B is truly self-sustaining. It seems unlikely that the B oscillation will prove a single, discrete, and identical entity in the fly and the hamster; or for that matter, that there should be only one B oscillator even in a single organism in which several persistent rhythms run side by side. A more plausible guess is that much of the whole cell's activity is innately rhythmic with a period—surely both temperature-sensitive and temperature-dependent—that approximates 24 hr in the optimal temperature range. The cell, in this view, comprises a whole class of *B* oscillators coupled to and entrained by a master *A* oscillator that alone imposes that temperature independence of period universally characteristic of the steady-state rhythm.

Further discussion of detail in our scheme must await more experimental data; but its relevance to thermoperiodism and photoperiodism needs comment. The photoperiodism we here have in mind is that discussed in Highkin and Hanson's (1954) and Hillman's (1956) papers. Highkin and Hanson showed that tomato plants exposed to light-*dark* cycles with periods of 12 (6:6), 24 (12:*12*), and 48 (24:*24*) hr differed markedly in their growth although they received equal total light per 48 hr. Only those plants grown on a light regime with a *period* of 24 hr escaped a radically stunted growth. In a separate experiment a 2-hr light supplement was given to greenhouse plants either at the end of the day (photophil fraction of the cycle) or in the middle of the night (scotophil); in the latter case growth was measurably depressed. The authors relate their findings to Bünning's (1937) hypothesis that endogenous daily rhythms are involved in "photoperiodic" responses. The essential feature of this hypothesis, which Highkin and Hanson seize, is the division of the plant's daily cycle into photophil and scotophil fractions; light falling in the scotophil fraction is operative either in affecting flowering or, in this case, inhibiting growth.

Hillman also found that tomatoes could be injured by an abnormal light regime. They developed necrotic or chlorotic spots in continuous light or in light-dark cycles with periods of 8, 10, 12, 15, or 16 hr. No injury resulted, however, from light-dark cycles with periods closer to 24 hr (viz., 20, 24, 30 hr). Hillman's most remarkable result was demonstration that the injury caused by continuous light in a constant-temperature regime of either 30°C or 17°C was avoided when the continuous light was accompanied by a cycle of temperature with a "daily" (24-hr) period (30° day, 17° night). Hillman also considers his results in terms of the Bünning hypothesis: ". . . it is possible that all the results with tomato are due to the existence in the plant of a rhythm whose period of 24 hours must be in phase with environmental changes for normal development." This comes much closer to the present writers' view than does the Highkin and Hanson paper where damage is considered simply in terms of the light having fallen in the scotophil fraction of the cycle.

It seems to the present writers that photoperiodic and thermo-periodic effects on growth efficiency are indeed related, as their dis-coverers suggest, to the distinct phenomenon of endogenous daily rhythms. We feel, however, that this relationship cannot be properly elucidated as long as the discussion is restricted to the special terms of Bünning's view that the endogenous cycle comprises distinct photophil and scotophil fractions. The most fruitful insights and suggestions for new experiments arise, we believe, from the broader picture given by the generalized oscillator model and the particular coupled-oscillator scheme outlined above. A strong feature of the model is its general prediction of *entrainment* effects (Pittendrigh and Bruce, 1957). An oscillating system is entrained, or driven, when it is energetically coupled to another oscillating or periodic system. Pittendrigh (1958) has described three types of entrainment that might relate to biological cases; two are pertinent here: (1) in unilateral entrainment one system completely drives the other which is unable to feed back on the driving periodicity that, accordingly, exclusively determines the phase and period of the coupled system; (2) in mutual entrainment there is feed-back, and the coupled oscillators share a frequency (with determinate phase relations) that is some intermediate between the natural periods of the separate components. All entrainment involves control of phase and period in the entrained oscillation, and in general it can only be effected within a restricted range of periods close to the natural period of the entrained system. Tribukait (1954) has illustrated this rule in a biological case: the natural period of mouse locomotory activity is about 22½ hr, and while it can be entrained by light cycles to other periods, such entrainment fails below 19 hr and above 26 hr.

Entrainment enters into the operation of daily rhythms in at least two major ways. First, the proper functioning of the overall endoge-nous oscillation depends on its strictly unilateral entrainment by the environment; the periodicity of dawns entrains the A oscillation and thus controls the slight innate error of its period and establishes its adaptively appropriate phase. The B oscillations in the cell are them-selves directly affected by the environmental temperature cycle (which, in general, bears a unique phase relation to the light cycle); but it seems likely that the effective control of *B*'s phase and period is usually due more to its entrainment by *A* than to direct entrainment by the external temperature regime. This second instance of entrainment (that between *A* and *B*) is again predominantly unilateral; at any rate this is clearly the case in *Drosophila*. But even in the fly there is evidence of some feedback of *B* on *A*, and it may well be that *A*-*B* entrainment is more nearly mutual elsewhere, especially in plants.

It is through entrainment phenomena that the theory of the cell as a self-sustaining oscillatory system bears on the photoperiodic and thermoperiodic control of growth. It seems to us that interpretation of deleterious effects due to the light and temperature regime should not be sought in terms of their direct action as such even when this is coupled to the Bünning hypothesis of a scotophil phase; it should be sought in terms of the success or failure of the light and temperature regimes as entraining agents that maintain: (1) appropriate *synchrony* of cellular oscillations; and, perhaps, (2) a *period* sufficiently close to the natural period of the system at which overall metabolic efficiency is likely maximal.

There can be little doubt that the general coordination of activity between cells which must underlie normal tissue function will include the synchronization of the innate oscillations in the constituent cells; and conversely that failure of cells to be synchronized will lead to tissue and organ disfunction. This is how we would interpret the Highkin and Hanson and Hillman results. The issue does not seem to hinge on the *phase* relation of the plant's rhythm to environment, as Hillman suggests, but rather on the synchronization of constituent cells. There is good reason to believe that continuous light will induce an asynchrony between cells. Constant light usually has one of two effects in organisms: either (1) the period changes, lengthening in some cases, shortening in others (see summary and examples in Pittendrigh and Bruce, 1957); or (2) it is, more commonly, lost (Bruce and Pittendrigh, 1957b, for summary of insect and microorganism cases). We have suggested earlier that the loss of an assayable rhythm in a multicellular organism may reflect only a loss of cell synchrony, perhaps due to a differential light-induced period change in the individual cells. And certainly Hillman's remarkable demonstration that a

24-hr temperature cycle obviates the damage otherwise induced by constant light is strong evidence for the interpretation offered here. In terms of the coupled-oscillator model synchrony is achieved in Hillman's case through direct temperature entrainment of the cells' B oscillations. Went (1957) has already suggested that the beneficial effect of a thermoperiod on a growing shoot is due to its synchronization of cell division which he considers essential for normal organogenesis. We would only add that the need for synchronization probably goes well beyond the geometrical consequences of cell division to the coordination of the whole biochemical activity of adjacent cells.

The coupled oscillator model appears to offer a unique explanation of Went's (1957; and this symposium) description of the interactive effects of light and temperature on the African violet. These plants die when grown on a 24-hr light cycle at $10°C$ but not $23°C$; on the other hand they grow well at $10°C$ when the light cycle is lengthened to a period of 32 hr. This implies to us that at $10°C$ the period of the temperature-dependent B oscillations have lengthened to such an extent that they are out of the range within which the A oscillator (itself entrained to 24 hr by the light cycle) can entrain and thus synchronize them. When, however, the A oscillator is entrained by the light regime to a 32-hr period, it is able, once again, to entrain the long-period B oscillations and thus establish the essential synchrony of cell processes. In discussing the entrainment relations of A and B it is pertinent to note the peculiarities of temperature independence described by Bruce and Pittendrigh (1956) for the *Euglena* phototaxis rhythm. Temperature independence is good between $30°C$ and $18°C$, but it breaks down quite sharply at lower temperatures. This relatively abrupt transition to temperature dependence in the overt rhythm suggests that the B oscillation's free-running period had extended beyond the range where the A oscillator (with a $23\frac{3}{4}$-hr period) could hold it by entrainment.

Damage induced by cycles with a period too far from 24 hr can also be interpreted as due to failure of entrainment and, hence, cell asynchrony. But an intriguing possibility, also suggested by the oscillator model, is not excluded, and merits the experimental tests to which it is open. It seems plausible to us that the efficiency of the cell, the overall activity of which pursues an oscillatory course, should fall when it is driven by external cycles too far removed from its evolved natural period. These external cycles might be close enough to the natural period to insure entrainment and hence synchrony of adjacent cells, but nevertheless sufficiently different from the natural period to impair coordination of the constituent intracellular processes that are involved in the B oscillations.

REFERENCES

Aschoff, J., and J. Meyer-Lohmann. 1955. Die Aktivitätsperiodik von Nagern im künstlichen 24-Stunden-Tag mit 6–20 Stunden Lichtzeit. Z. vergleich. Physiol., 37, 107–17.

Ball, N. G., and J. J. Dyke. 1954. An endogenous 24-hour rhythm in the growth rate of the Avena coleoptile. J. Exptl. Botany, 5, 421–33.

Barnum, C. P., C. D. Jardetzky, and F. Halberg. 1957. Nucleic acid synthesis in regenerating liver. Texas Repts. Biol. Med., 15, 134–47.

Beling, I. 1929. Zeitgedächtnis der Bienen. Z vergleich. Physiol., 9, 259–338.

———. 1935. Über das Zeitgedächtnis bei Tieren. Biol. Revs., 10, 18–41.

Birukow, G. 1957. Tages-und jahreszeitliche orientierungsrhythmik beim Wasserläufer Velia currens F. (Heteroptera). Naturwissenschaften, 44, 358.

Bouvier, E. L. 1922. The Psychic Life of Insects. The Century Co., New York.

Bruce, V. G., and C. S. Pittendrigh. 1956. Temperature independence in a unicellular "clock." Proc. Natl. Acad. Sci. U. S., 42, 676–82.

———. 1957a. Unpublished observations.

———. 1957b. Endogenous rhythms in insects and microorganisms. Am. Naturalist, 91, 179–95.

———. 1958. Resetting the Euglena clock with a single light stimulus. Am. Naturalist, 92, 295–306.

Bünning, E. 1935. Zur Kenntnis der endogenen Tagesrhythmik bei Insekten und bei Pflanzen. Ber. deut. botan. Ges., 53, 594–623.

———. 1937. Die endonome Tagesrhythmik als Grundlage der photoperiodischen Reaktion. Ber. deut. botan. Ges., 54, 590–607.

———. 1956. Die physiologische Uhr. Naturw. Rundschau, 9, 351–57.

Bünning, E., and F. J. Leinweber. 1956. Die Korrektion des Temperaturfehlers der endogenen Tagesrhythmik. Naturwissenschaften, 43, 42–43.

Burchard, J. E. 1957. Unpublished observations.

von Frisch, K. 1950. Die Sonne als Kompass im Leben der Bienen. Experientia, 6, 210–21.

Garner, W. W., and H. A. Allard. 1923. Further studies in photoperiodism, the response of the plant to relative length of day and night. J. Agr. Research, 23, 871–920.

Grossenbacker, K. A. 1939. Autonomic cycle of rate of exudation of plants. Am. J. Botany, 26, 107.

Hamner, K. C., and J. Bonner. 1938. Photoperiodism in relation to hormones as factors in floral initiation and development. Botan. Gaz., 100, 388–431.

Highkin, H. R., and J. B. Hanson. 1954. Possible interaction between light-dark cycles and endogenous daily rhythms on the growth of tomato plants. *Plant Physiol., 29,* 301–302.

Hillman, W. S. 1956. Injury of tomato plants by continuous light and unfavorable photoperiodic cycles. *Am. J. Botany, 43,* 89–96.

Hoffmann, K. 1954. Versuche zu der im Richtungsfinden der Vögel enthaltenen Zeitschätzung. *Z. Tierpsychol., 11,* 453–75.

———. 1957. Angeborene Tagesperiodik bei Eidechsen. *Naturwissenschaften, 44,* 359–60.

Kalmus, H. 1935. Periodizität und Autochronie als zeitregelnde Eigenschaften der Organismen. *Biol. Generalis, 11,* 93–114.

———. 1938. Periodizität und Autochronie als Zeitregelnde Eigenschaften bei Mensch und Tier. *Tabulae Biologicae, 26,* 60–109.

Kramer, G. 1952. Experiments on bird orientation. *Ibis, 94,* 265–85.

Long, E. M. 1939. Photoperiodic induction as influenced by environmental factors. *Botan. Gaz., 101,* 168.

Leinweber, F. J. 1956. Über die Temperaturabhängigkeit der Periodenlänge bei der endogenen Tagesrhythmik von *Phaseolus. Z. Botan., 44,* 337–64.

Lindauer, M. 1957. Sonnenorientierung der Bienen unter der äquatorsonne und zur Nachtseit. *Naturwissenschaften, 44,* 1–6.

Pardi, L., and F. Papi. 1953. Ricerche sull'orientamenta di *Talitrus saltator* (Montagu) (Crustacea-Amphipoda). *Z. vergleich. Physiol., 35,* 459–89, 490–518.

Pittendrigh, C. S. 1954. On temperature independence in the clock-system controlling emergence time in *Drosophila. Proc. Natl. Acad. Sci. U. S., 40,* 1018–29.

———. 1958. Perspectives in the study of biological clocks. *Symposium on Perspectives in Marine Biology.* University of California Press, Berkeley. Pp. 239–268.

Pittendrigh, C. S., and V. G. Bruce. 1957. An oscillator model for biological clocks. *Rhythmic and Synthetic Processes in Growth.* Princeton University Press, Princeton, N. J. Pp. 75–109.

Pittendrigh, C. S., V. G. Bruce, and P. Kaus. 1958. On the significance of transients in daily rhythms. *Proc. Natl. Acad. Sci. U. S., 44,* 965–73.

Sauer, F. 1957. Astronavigatorische Orientierung einer unte Künstlichen Sternenhimmel verfrachteten Klappergrasmücke, *Sylvia c. curruca* (L). *Naturwissenschaften, 44,* 71.

Tribukait, B. 1954. Aktivitätsperiodik der Maus im Künstlichen verkürtzen Tag. *Naturwisseschaften, 41,* 92–93.

Übelmesser, E. R. 1954. Über den endonomen Rhythmus der Sporangientrager bildung von *Pilobolus. Arch. Mikrobiol., 20,* 1–33.

Wahl, O. 1932. Neue Untersuchungen über das Zeitgedächtnis der Bienen. *Z. vergleich. Physiol., 16,* 529–89.

Went, F. W. 1944. Plant growth under controlled conditions. II. Thermoperiodicity in growth and fruiting of the tomato. *Am. J. Botany, 31,* 135–140.

———. 1957. Some theoretical aspects of effects of temperature on plants. *Influence of Temperature on Biological Systems.* American Physiological Society. Pp. 163–74.

PHYSIOLOGICAL MECHANISM AND BIOLOGICAL IMPORTANCE OF THE ENDOGENOUS DIURNAL PERIODICITY IN PLANTS AND ANIMALS

ERWIN BÜNNING

Department of Botany, University of Tübingen, Germany

Observation of many physiological phenomena establish that organisms are able endogenously to measure the course of the time of day. As far as man and other animals are concerned we call this ability a sense of time, or time memory. Man can estimate the time without a clock, without seeing the sun, in fact, without the use of any external means. Even during sleep, this sense of time continues to function. Many observations establish that lower animals also have such a sense of time. Bees, for instance, can be trained to certain feeding times (Beling, 1929; Kalmus, 1934; Renner, 1957; Wahl, 1932; Fig. 1).

Plants, also, are able to measure the course of time. With their photoperiodic reactions, the organisms compare the actual lengths of day and night with a measuring stick called the critical day length. The study of these "measures," or in other words, of the light- and dark-induced processes of a specific duration, is one of the principal subjects of photoperiodic research.

There are reasons for assuming that plants, animals, and man all measure the course of the time of day with the same type of cellular clock system. This physiological clock operates on 24-hr cycles.

MEASUREMENT OF ENDOGENOUS DiURNAL PERIODICITY

The physiological clock can regulate several processes and we, therefore, may select different physiological rhythms in order to study the responsible timing mechanism. With constant external conditions, we can, for instance, observe: diurnal fluctuations in turgor-pressure of leaf pulvini, in the growth rate (Ball and Dyke, 1954; Fig. 2), in root pressure, in the activity of several enzymes, in metabolism, in

507

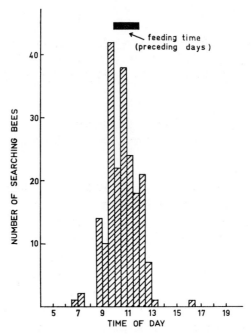

FIG. 1. Time memory in bees. The animals were offered food for 7 days between 10 and 12 A.M. They continue to search for food at that time of day. (After Beling, 1929.)

spore discharge (Bühnemann, 1955; Schmidle, 1951; Fig. 3), in bioluminescence (Hastings *et al.*, 1956; Haxo and Sweeney, 1955), in the activity of movements (Figs. 4–6), in the emergence of insects, and in the quantity and quality of light influences on certain processes

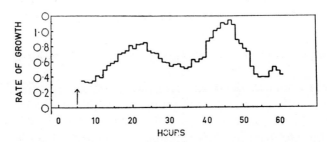

FIG. 2. Diurnal changes of growth rate in *Avena* coleoptiles. The seedlings were transferred from red light to darkness at the moment indicated by an arrow. (After Ball and Dyke, 1954.)

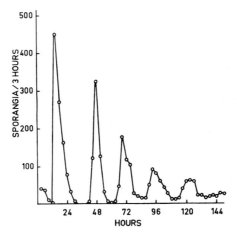

FIG. 3. *Pilobolus sphaerosporus*. Periodic discharge of sporangia in continuous darkness (after 12:12-hr light-dark cycles). Abscissas 0 = beginning of continuous darkness. (After Schmidle, 1951.)

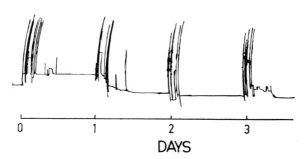

FIG. 4. *Periplaneta americana*. Rhythm of activity in continuous dim light.

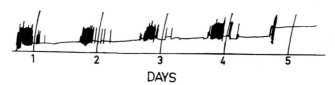

FIG. 5. *Mesocricetus auratus*. Rhythm of activity in continuous dim light.

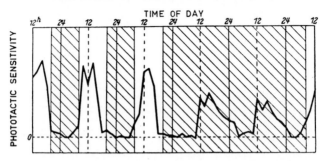

FIG. 6. *Euglena gracilis.* Diurnal changes of phototactic activity in 12:12-hr light-dark cycles and in continuous darkness. Dark period cross-hatched. (After Pohl, 1948.)

(Clauss and Rau, 1956; Melchers, 1956). Reviews on these several phenomena have been published by Aschoff (1955b), Bruce and Pittendrigh (1957), Harker (1958), and Bünning (1956b, 1957b, 1958b,c).

HEREDITY AND LENGTH OF PERIODS

The endogenous rhythm is established in the individual plant or animal through heredity and is not induced in early stages of the individual's development. If the young plants or animals are exposed to constant external conditions, they will nevertheless show the endogenous rhythm later on. If they are exposed to external conditions with rhythms deviating from the normal 24-hr cycles, their internal clocks will, in spite of this, operate on cycles of 24 hr thereafter.

This has been established for plants as well as for animals. Klein-hoonte (1932) tried in vain to influence the cycle by such a pretreatment beginning with seed germination. Influences on the mother plant during the embryonal development are also ineffective (Bünning, 1932). Bees show the normal cycle after having developed under constant conditions (Wahl, 1932). The eggs of chickens and of lizards may develop under constant conditions, but nevertheless the animals later on show the diurnal cycle (Aschoff and Meyer-Lohmann, 1954; Hoffmann, 1957b). An abnormal cycle does not influence the rhythm of the next generation of rats (Hemmingsen and Krarup, 1937). Mice may live for several generations without an external

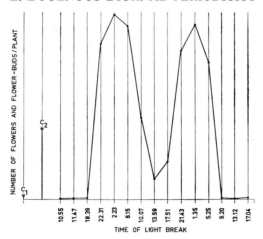

FIG. 7. *Kalanchoë blossfeldiana.* The plants were offered cycles of 10-hr light and 62-hr darkness. Light period from 20ʰ to 7ʰ. The dark period was interrupted by light breaks of 1 hr. Time of light break on abscissas. Controls with continuous light (C_1) or without light breaks in the dark period (C_2). (After Melchers, 1956.)

cycle and yet continue to show the endogenous periodicity (Aschoff, 1955a,b). The same holds true for *Drosophila* after 15 generations without external cycles (Bünning, 1935b).

There are genetic differences in the length of the periods which

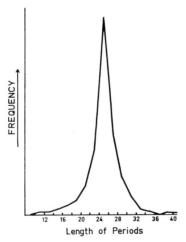

FIG. 8. *Phaseolus multiflorus,* leaf movements in continuous darkness. Frequency distribution of length of periods. (After Bünning, 1952.)

proved to be constant for many generations (Aschoff, 1955a,b; Bünning, 1932; 1935a). The average values are between 22 and 28 hr. Within a population we shall find a certain variability due to modifications and to genetic differences (Bünning, 1932; Fig. 8).

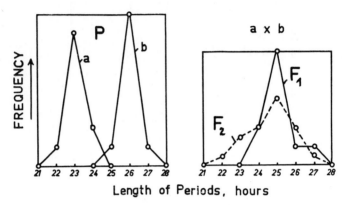

FIG. 9. *Phaseolus multiflorus*. Variability of periods in strain a and b (left), and in F_1 and F_2 after crossing a x b (right). (After Bünning, 1935a,b.)

After crossing individuals that differ in the length of their genetically fixed periods, we shall observe in the next generation average values. It is not yet clear whether or not the splitting in the F_2-generation occurs according to Mendelian laws (Bünning, 1935a; Fig. 9).

INFLUENCE OF TEMPERATURE ON LENGTH OF PERIOD

Immediately after a sudden increase or decrease of temperature which had previously remained constant, we may observe the expected increase or decrease of the length of the periods (Bünning, 1931, Kalmus, 1935; Table I). The first experiments of Kalmus, published in 1935, showed the astonishing result that in bees this temperature influence apparently can be nullified by some process of compensation.

The same conclusion can be drawn from experiments of longer duration. Several days after the influence of a low-temperature period,

TABLE I. *Phaseolus multiflorus*, Leaf Movements.
Temperature before Recording, 20° C (Bünning, 1931)

Temperature, °C	Length of Periods, hr
15	29.7
20	27.0
25	23.7
30	22.0
35	19.0

or even while this low temperature is still prevailing, the delay of the clock is compensated (Tables II, III). The cycles may even, for several days, become shorter than they are normally (Bünning and Leinweber, 1956; Leinweber, 1956). It would appear that the processes of compensation are working too actively during this period. (For explanation see Addendum.)

TABLE II. *Phaseolus*, Leaf Movements at 15° C;
Temperature for Several Hours 1° C; Length of
Periods (After Leinweber, 1956)

Day before first treatment	28.4
Day of first treatment	32.1
Days after first treatment	
1	24.4
2	24.7
3	20.8

Extending these experiments for a still longer period of time enables plants and animals to become adapted to the new temperature: temperature dependence can no longer be observed. This phenomenon has been described by several research workers. I may mention the experiments of Pittendrigh (1954) on *Drosophila,* of Bruce and Pit-

TABLE III. *Periplaneta americana*, Rhythm of Activity;
Length of Periods, hr, at 22° C after Chilling 12 hr to 5° C
(Bünning, unpublished data)

Days before chilling	24.5
Period after chilling	
First	21.5
Second	23
Third	23.5
Fourth	24.5

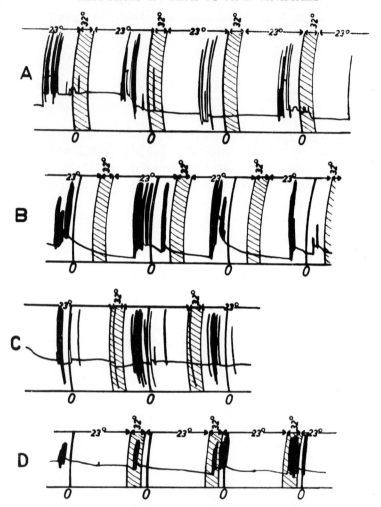

FIG. 10. *Periplaneta americana.* Rhythms of activity. A period of increased temperature (crosshatched, 4 hr from 23° to 32°C) does not shift the phases of the rhythm. Increased temperature from 0–4 (A), 6–10 (B), 12–16 (C), or 18–22 (D) hr. 0 = midnight. (Unpublished data.)

tendrigh (1956) on *Euglena,* Brown and Webb (1948) on the fiddler crab, of Ball and Dyke (1954) on *Avena* coleoptiles, of Leinweber (1956) on *Phaseolus,* and of Hoffmann (1957a) on lizards.

Dr. Pittendrigh will doubtless report on his own experiments. Here

TABLE IV. *Phaseolus*, Leaf Movements; Plants at
Experimental Temperatures since Germination
(After Leinweber)

Temperature, °C	Length of Periods, hr
15	28.3±0.4
20	28.0±0.4
25	28.0±1.0

I will present two examples from my own laboratory (see Tables IV, V).

We do not yet know how to interpret this temperature independence. I have mentioned some evidence for the induction of compensating processes, but also there are in both plants and animals indications of a different sensitivity to temperature of the several phases within one cycle (Bünning and Tazawa, 1957; Stephens, 1957). But this is

TABLE V. *Periplaneta americana*, Rhythm of Activity
(Bünning, 1958a)

Temperature, °C	Length of Periods, hr
19–20	24.4–0.1
22–23	24.5–0.1
27–28	24.0–0.3
29	25.8–0.7

only a differing effect of temperature on the shifting of the phases. Experiments on *Periplaneta* showed no difference in temperature effects on the speed of the clock when increased temperature was offered during the several phases of its cycles (Figs. 10, 11; Bünning, 1958a).

Though there is no temperature dependence in the length of the periods, some medium temperature is always the optimum condition

TABLE VI. *Phaseolus*, Leaf Movements; Percentage of
Measurable Periods as Influenced by Temperature;
Second Day of Observation (After Leinweber, 1956)

Temperature, °C	Measurable Periods, %
10	30
15	55
20	95
25	65
30	20

for the functioning of the endogenous periodicity. The more the constant temperature deviates from the optimum, the more often we shall find that the clock system fails to work; this means that no diurnal cycles can be observed (Table VI).

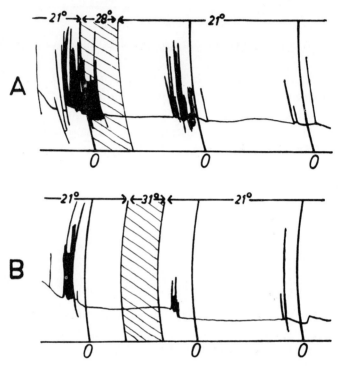

FIG. 11.   As in Fig. 10, but increased temperature for 8 hr, from 0–8 (A), 8–16 hr (B). (Unpublished data.)

With extreme values of temperature the clock fails completely. In that case, for instance in *Phaseolus* exposed to a temperature of about 10°C, the diurnal cycles stop suddenly, and a very irregular periodicity occurs, in many cases showing cycles of 8, 10, or 14 hr (Fig. 12; Bünning and Tazawa, 1957). There is no gradual shifting from the diurnal cycles to these very short ones. Either the clock operates on the 24-hr cycle or it fails completely (Fig. 12A). This seems to be true also with respect to animals. Brown and Webb (1948), in their experiments on the diurnal rhythmic color change in the fiddler crab,

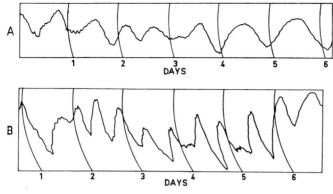

FIG. 12. *Phaseolus multiflorus,* leaf movements in continuous light. Irregular periodicity with temperatures of 10°C. In A, two cycles with normal length. (After Bünning and Tazawa, 1957.)

found no modification in the length of periods between 6° and 29°C. Temperatures of 0° to 3°C, however, prevented the functioning of the clock completely, that is, the rhythm became out of phase afterward for the time of chilling to this temperature. The same holds true for insects (Kalmus, 1934; Renner, 1957; cf. Addendum).

INFLUENCE OF LIGHT ON LENGTH OF PERIOD

With constant external conditions, the length of the period is different in continuous dark and in continuous light of different qualities (Table VII). Moreover, with higher plants, far red inhibits the opera-

TABLE VII.   Light and the Length of Periods

Object	Light Condition (Continuous)	Length of Periods, hr	Reference
Bullfinch (*Pyrrula*), activity	Dark	24	Aschoff, 1955₁,b
	Light (white)	22	
Mice, activity	Dark	23–23.5	Aschoff, 1955₁,b
	Light (white)	25–26	Meyer-Lohmann, 1955
Beans (*Phaseolus*), leaf movements	Dark	26.5	Bünning and Lörcher, 1957
	340–450 mμ	26.5	
	450–610 mμ	26.5	
	610–690 mμ	28.0	
	690–850 mμ	24.3	
	850 mμ	26.5	

tion of the clock within a few days. Orange light, however, is very favorable for the functioning of the clock (Bünning and Lörcher, 1957).

INFLUENCE OF CHEMICAL FACTORS

Several attempts have been made to discover the mechanism of the endogenous periodicity by influencing it with chemical factors (Bünning, 1935a, 1956a; Grabensberger, 1934; Kalmus, 1934, 1935, 1938; Renner, 1957). Kalmus in 1934 and 1935 produced a delay of the clock in bees and in *Drosophila* by applying CO_2 and by

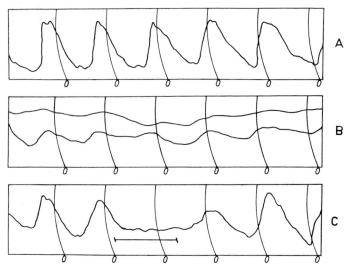

Fig. 13. *Phaseolus multiflorus,* leaf movements in continuous light. A, controls; B, 10^{-4} mole dinitrophenole, offered via the transpiration stream during the whole experiment; C, 10^{-3} mole dinitrophenol offered for the period marked by horizontal line; the rhythm comes back without a shifting of the phases. 0 = midnight.

removing O_2. Similar results with plants had been published by that time (Bünning, 1935b).

However, things appear very different if we check the influence of chemicals for more than one period. In experiments of several days duration we shall quite often find that the clock returns to the normal length of period. It seems that most of the metabolic poisons inhibit only the special process which depends on the clock, but do not inhibit the clock itself. This becomes especially clear from experiments of Bühenemann (1955) with *Oedogonium*. He applied poisons like NaCN, arsenate, 2,4-dinitrophenol, and NaF. Spore discharge in all these cases remains a cyclic process as long as it continues. Moreover, there is no shifting of the phases and no increase in the length of the periods. Our results with *Phaseolus* are similar (Fig. 13A,B).

If these poisons have been active for several days and are then removed, the rhythmical process starts once again. And, most interesting, there is no shifting of the phases. Maxima and minima occur at the same time that the controls occur (Fig. 13C). That means the clock system is still functioning while the physiological process, normally governed by it, is fully inhibited by poisons.

I may just mention that we tried in vain to find specific influences of varying ratios of Ca and K or of different pH values. Influences of these factors are always combined with visible injury to the plant (Bünning, 1956a).

There are, as we found in *Phaseolus*, distinct influences of colchicine and urethane. Alcohol, ether, and especially digitonine can also cause irregularities of the internal clock (Fig. 14). Many other substances,

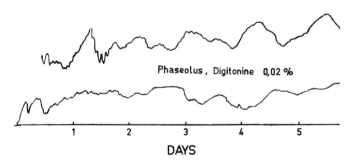

FIG. 14. *Phaseolus multiflorus,* leaf movements in continuous light. Effect of 0.02% digitonine, offered via the transpiration stream.

such as all the different plant hormones (Ball and Dyke, 1956) and alkaloids, have no specific influence (Bünning, unpublished data).

By applying a poison like urethane it is possible to observe a phenomenon which reminds us of what happens after a period of

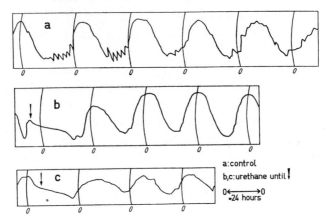

FIG. 15. *Phaseolus multiflorus.* Decreased length of periods after replacing urethane (ca. 0.02%) by water. 0 = midnight. (After Bünning, 1957a,b.)

chilling. The delay observed at first is later on replaced by an acceleration; this means that the periods become even shorter than they are normally. This compensation becomes especially clear after removing the poison Fig. 15, Table VIII; Bünning 1957a; cf. Addendum).

TABLE VIII.   Influence of Urethane on Leaf
Movements of *Phaseolus* (Bünning, 1957a)

Treatment	Length of Periods, hr
Water	25.3–0.2
Urethane, ca. 1%	33.3–1.3
From urethane into water	23.4–0.3

ROLE OF NUCLEI

Within different kinds of plant tissues we have observed endogenous diurnal fluctuations in the volume of the nuclei (Fig. 16; Bünning and Schöne-Schneiderhöhn, 1957). Poisons like urethane, which disturb the physiological clock, are also effective in this case.

We should check whether the structural changes within the nuclei, which are responsible for those volume changes, are connected with the mechanism of the physiological clock. According to this working

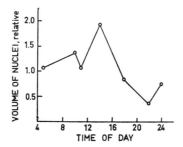

FIG. 16. *Phaseolus multiflorus,* epidermal cells of leaf blade. Diurnal changes of volume of nuclei during the first day of continuous light after normal light-dark cycles. (After Bünning and Schöne-Schneiderhöhn, 1957.)

hypothesis, the primary processes in the clock are structural changes in the nuclei. Secondary processes are diurnal fluctuations, such as in metabolism, in enzyme activities and growth. Also the well-known diurnal periodicity of mitosis may be one of those secondary processes. But the diurnal structural changes in the nuclei are still going on while mitosis, owing to the aging of the cells, is no longer possible.

At any rate this would mean that the internal clock has a cellular mechanism, which actually was almost self-evident for plants, but not for animals.

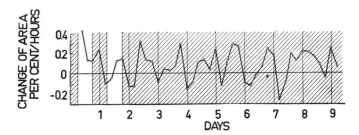

FIG. 17. *Daucus carota.* Diurnal fluctuations in the area of a tissue culture. (After Enderle, 1951.)

The cellular nature of the internal clock is also confirmed by the possibility of endogenous diurnal processes in tissue cultures of plants (Enderle, 1951; Fig. 17).

EVOCATION OF RHYTHMS BY SINGLE STIMULI

Plants or animals, grown under constant temperature and light conditions sometimes show no diurnal processes, but a single stimulus can evoke the periodicity. This single stimulus may be a light break within continuous darkness. Also the shifting from continuous dark to continuous light, or from continuous light to continuous dark, is sometimes sufficient (Fig. 18; Ball and Dyke, 1954; Bünning, 1931, 1935b; Hastings *et al.*, 1956).

How can we explain this evocation of a periodic process by a single stimulus? It seems that even prior to this evocation, diurnal processes are going on within the cells, although they are not yet synchronous

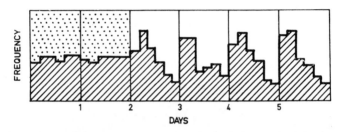

FIG. 18.   *Drosophila* emergence. Evocation of the periodicity by shifting from continuous darkness to continuous light. (After Bünning, 1935a,b.)

within the several cells. The external stimulus would have the function of synchronizing the processes within the several cells. There is evidence in favor of this explanation. We can bring about a desynchronization by certain light stimuli. The periodicity is now subdivided into several processes, each of which has periods of about 24 hr. A single strong light stimulus offered later on may cause a new synchronization (Bünning, 1931).

Pittendrigh's experiments on *Drosophila* have demonstrated this synchronization within a population; there is still another evidence for the single individual plant. Without this synchronization we shall observe at any time of the day a great variability of the nucleic volumes. After the synchronization, however, the variability at a certain moment is much lower. In this case, the diurnal fluctuations within the cell population of the individual plant become evident. But in other cases the single stimulus actually starts the oscillation in the individual cells (unpublished data).

With *Phaseolus* we found only wavelengths between 610 and 690 mμ to be effective for this synchronization (Bünning and Lörcher, 1957). Far red has an antagonistic effect. With cycles of red and far

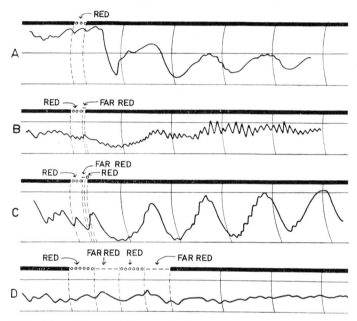

Fig. 19. *Phaseolus multiflorus,* leaf movements; A, evocation of the rhythm by red light; B–D, antagonistic effects of red and far red in evocation and prevention of the periodicity. Broad black lines indicate darkness. (Lörcher, unpublished experiments.)

red, it is always the latter that determines whether or not the evocation is established (Fig. 19). There is also evidence, both for plants and animals, that the decline in amplitudes which customarily occurs after 1 or 2 weeks of constant conditions is due to asynchrony in the population of individuals or of cells inside the single individual.

MODIFICATION BY LIGHT-DARK CYCLES

The synchronization mentioned before means, of course, for the majority of the cells a shifting of the phases. It is self-evident that this shifting is also possible after the synchronization. Even short light periods of a few minutes, offered during the normal dark period of diurnal light-dark cycles, are effective. By exposing the plant or animal to a reversed 12:12-hr light-dark cycle, the phases are shifted by 12 hr. In both plants and animals, about 2 to 8 days are necessary for the complete inversion (Aschoff, 1955b; Brown and Webb, 1949; Hemingsen and Krarup, 1937; Kleinhoonte, 1929).

The regulating influence of light-dark cycles is also made evident by the fact that under normal conditions the length of the periods is regulated to exactly 24 hr, whereas under constant conditions the periods may be between some 22 and 28 hr. But this modification works only within certain limits. In higher and lower animals, as well as in many plants, the internal clock will not follow external cycles of less than about 16 to 20 hr. If for instance, we offer cycles of 6 hr of light and 6 hr of darkness, the organism will show only its specific cycles of approximately 24 hr (Aschoff, 1954; Hemmingsen and Krarup, 1937; Kleinhoonte, 1929; Tribukait, 1956).

In certain green plants this regulation works only with orange and far-red light. In a fungus we could establish only a blue light efficiency. In certain animals all the qualities of visible light are effective (Remmert, 1955).

We may also mention that other factors, such as cycles of high and low temperature, have a regulating effect.

PROCESSES CONTROLLED BY ENDOGENOUS PERIODICITY

The internal clocks may, as we mentioned before, control processes such as mitosis, growth, turgor pressure, spore discharge, motility, and luminescence. Of special importance is the influence of the internal clock on quantity and quality of the sensitivity to light and temperature. Because of this influence, the internal rhythm becomes important for photoperiodism and thermoperiodicity.

Photoperiodic reactions enable plants and animals to get the essential information on the course of the seasons. This means that the organisms have inherited a measure which they compare with the actual length of day or night.

Our first conception of this measure was rather simple. With the beginning of the light or the dark period the plant was supposed to start a single process with a specific duration of, for instance, 10, 12, or 14 hr. If light is offered while the dark-induced process, or darkness while the light-induced process is still going on, there will be a specific reaction of the plant. With respect to short-day plants, for example, the light-induced timing process coincides approximately with a light-liking or "photophil," the dark-induced timing process with dark-liking or "scotophil" status.

But this explanation had to be improved. In experiments with longer dark periods of about 40 hr, a light break will have different effects, revealing that the alternation of photophil and scotophil phases is going on (Figs. 20, 21). Claes and Lang (1947), Wareing (1954), and others tried to explain this without the concept of endogenous periodicity by assuming some interaction between the light break and the preceding or ensuing main light period. Of course they had to postulate in addition that this interaction requires a certain time relation. The main light period and the light break are cooperating only as long as they, together with the interrupting dark period, fit into a duration of about 24 hr (Figs. 20, 21). It would be strange indeed if this had nothing to do with the endogenous periodicity.

Experiments with still longer dark periods in certain cases showed a continual alternation of photophil and scotophil phases for about 3 days (Fig. 7). In other cases there was at least a continuation of cycles with higher and lower photophil character. In yet other cases even this was missing. To summarize: Sometimes one light period induces several consecutive cycles of different photoperiodic sensitivity; in other cases it induces only one or two of these cycles. This is exactly the same situation as with the light-regulated diurnal cycles in turgor pressure, growth rate, and spore discharge.

Therefore, the best and simplest way to combine the known facts is to assume that the light- and dark-induced timing processes in photoperiodism are phases of the endogenous diurnal rhythm, regulated by the light-dark alternation. I cannot see any reason why these facts should be complicated by postulating quite different timing processes in the diurnal change of sensitivity to light and darkness on the one hand, and in diurnal physiological capacities on the other hand.

We do not yet know how the diurnal change of light sensitivity is

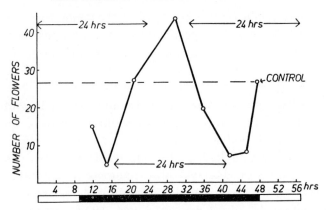

Fig. 20. Biloxi soybean (short-day plant). Effects of light breaks (30 min) given at various intervals during long dark period. "Interaction" of light break with main light period (reduction of flower formation) only if both light periods fit into one period of 24 hr. Times of maximum reduction a little more than 24 hr apart. (After Wareing, 1954.) Arrows added by author of this paper.

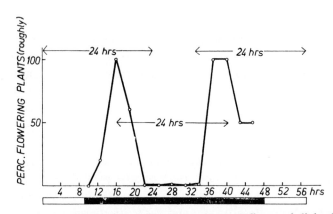

Fig. 21. *Hyoscyamus niger* (long-day plant). Effects of light breaks (2 hr) at various intervals during long dark period. "Interaction" of light break with main light period (promotion of flower formation) only if both light periods fit into one period of 24 hr. Times of maximum promotion 24 hr apart. Controls (without light break) are not flowering. (After experiments of Claes and Lang, 1947.)

controlled by the internal clock. It seems, however, that this clock may have an influence on diurnal changes in the well-known red far-red pigment system. In photoperiodic experiments, we may establish antagonistic diurnal changes in the sensitivity to red and far red (Bünning and Könitz, 1957).

Time memory is a further phenomenon in which the endogenous periodicity definitely is involved. Bees use the clock as an alarm clock. They fix the time of day on this clock because the search for honey at a certain distant place proved to be successful on preceding days. They are even able to mark several points that mean different spots on their alarm clock.

Several animals use the clock in a more striking way. It is known that certain birds, bees, and crabs use a solar compass for their homing movements. This solar compass could possibly mislead them in case they neglect the movement of the sun during their absence from their homes. The animals, however, do not neglect this; instead they correct the angle needed between the direction of the sun and the direction of their way home. They use their internal clocks to decipher this (Hoffmann, 1954; Kramer, 1953; Papi, 1955).

In summary, we may state that apparently for very different phenomena, such as photoperiodism in plants and animals, sense of time in lower and higher animals, and regulation of the diurnal sleeping and activity rhythm, the same cellular clock system is used.

Addendum

Further experiments in plants and animals (Bünning, 1958a,b) suggest that the cycles of the endogenous periodicity are periods of a relaxation oscillator. This is confirmed by offering low temperature or poisons in different phases of the cycle. There is, in both plants and animals, one phase of several hours which cannot be delayed very much by chilling; but low-temperature treatment of the other phase makes the oscillator drop to its zero value, thus causing the delay mentioned in the paper. The former is the relaxation, the latter the tension phase. If chilling is less extreme, the system still may oscillate, but the tension is interrupted by relaxation earlier than normally. This explains the extreme short cycles with these temperatures (for instance, 10°C) mentioned in the paper (Fig. 12).

The fact, mentioned in the paper, that the first cycles after transition to lower temperature or after the application of a poison are even longer than the normal ones found an explanation too: These treatments make the oscillator drop to a lower level of energy, i.e., the first relaxation is continuing for a longer time than the normal ones. But the ensuing tensions are very small, thus causing shorter cycles. This looks like a delay, followed by processes of compensation.

REFERENCES

Aschoff, J. 1953. Aktivitätsperiodik bei Gimpeln unter natürlichen und künstlichen Belichtungsverhältnissen. *Z. vergleich. Physiol., 35,* 159–66.

———. 1954. Aktivitätsperiodik der Maus im künstlich verkürzten Tag. *Naturwissenschaften, 41,* 92–93.

———. 1955a. Tagesperiodik bei Mäusestämmen unter konstanten Umgebungsbedingungen. *Pflügers Arch., 262,* 51–59.

———. 1955b. Exogene und endogene Komponente der 24-Stunden-Periodik bei Tier und Mensch. *Naturwissenschaften, 42,* 569–75.

Aschoff, J., and J. Meyer-Lohmann. 1954. Angeborene 24-Stunden-Periodik beim Kücken. *Pflügers Arch., 260,* 170–76.

Ball, N. G., and I. J. Dyke. 1954. An endogenous 24-hour rhythm in the growth rate of the *Avena* coleoptile. *J. Exptl. Botany, 5,* 421–33.

———. 1956. The effects of indole-3-acetic acid and 2,4-dichlorphenoxyacetic acid on the growth rate and endogenous rhythm of intact *Avena* coleoptiles. *J. Exptl. Botany, 7,* 25–41.

Beling, I. 1929. Über das Zeitgedächtnis der Bienen. *Z. vergleich. Physiol., 9,* 259–338.

Brown, F. A., R. O. Freeland, and C. L. Ralph. 1955. Persistent rhythms of O_2-consumption in potatoes, carrots, and the seaweed, *Fucus, Plant Physiol., 30,* 280–92.

Brown, F. A., and H. M. Webb. 1948. Temperature relations of an endogenous daily rhythmicity in the fiddler crab, *Uca. Physiol. Zoöl., 21,* 371–81.

———. 1949. Studies on the daily rhythmicity of the fiddler crab, *Uca.* Modifications by light. *Physiol. Zoöl., 22,* 136–48.

Bruce, V. G., and C. S. Pittendrigh. 1956. Temperature independence in a unicellular "clock." *Proc. Natl. Acad. Sci. U. S., 42,* 676–82.

———. 1957. Endogenous rhythms in insects and microorganisms. *Am. Naturalist, 91,* 179–95.

Bühnemann, F. 1955. Das endodiurnale System der Oedogonium-Zelle. II. Der Einfluss von Stoffwechselgiften und anderen Wirkstoffen. *Biol. Zentr., 74,* 691–705.

Bünning, E. 1931. Untersuchungen über die autonomen tagesperiodischen Bewegungen der Primärblätter von *Phaseolus multiflorus. Jahrb. wiss. Botan., 75,* 439–80.

———. 1932. Über die Erblichkeit der Tagesperiodizität bei den *Phaseolus*-Blättern. *Jahrb. wiss. Botan., 77,* 283–320.

————. 1935a. Zur Kenntnis der erblichen Tagesperiodizität bei den Primär-blättern von *Phaseolus multiflorus*. *Jahrb. wiss. Botan.*, *81*, 411–18.

————. 1935b. Zur Kenntnis der endogenen Tagesrhythmik bei Insekten und bei Pflanzen. *Ber. deut. botan. Ges.*, *53*, 594–623.

————. 1956a. Versuche zur Beeinflussung der endogenen Tagesrhythmik durch chemische Faktoren. *Z. Botan.*, *44*, 515–29.

————. 1956b. Endogenous rhythms in plants. *Ann. Rev. Plant Physiol.*, *7*, 71–90.

————. 1957a. Über die Urethan-Vergiftung der endogenen Tagesrhythmik. *Planta*, *48*, 453–58.

————. 1957b. Endogenous diurnal cycles of activity in plants. 15th Symposium Soc. for the Study of Development and Growth, Princeton.

————. 1958a. Über den Temperatureinfluß auf die endogene Tagesrhythmik, besonders bei *Periplaneta americana*. *Biol. Zentr.*, *77*, 141–52.

————. 1958b. *Die Physiologische Uhr*. Springer-Verlag, Berlin.

————. 1958c. Cellular clocks. *Nature, 181*, 1169–71.

Bünning, E., and W. Könitz. 1957. Diurnale antagonistische Schwankungen von Hell- und Dunkelrot-Empfindlichkeit einer Kurztagpflanze. *Naturwissenschaften, 44*, 568.

Bünning, E., and F. J. Leinweber. 1956. Die Korrektion des Temperaturfehlers der endogenen Tagesrhythmik. *Naturwissenschaften, 43*, 42.

Bünning, E., and L. Lörcher. 1957. Regulierung und Auslösung endogentagesperiodischer Blattbewegungen durch verschiedene Lichtqualitäten. *Naturwissenschaften, 44*, 472.

Bünning, E., and G. Schöne-Schneiderhöhn. 1957. Die Bedeutung der Zellkerne im Mechanismus der endogenen Tagesrhythmik. *Planta, 48*, 459–67.

Bünning, E., and M. Tazawa. 1957. Über den Temperatureinfluss auf die endogene Tagesrhythmik bei *Phaseolus*. *Planta, 50*, 107–27.

Claes, H., and A. Lang. 1947. Die Blütenbildung von *Hyoscyamus niger* in 48-stündigen Licht-Dunkel-Zyklen und in Zyklen mit aufgeteilten Lichtphasen. *Z. Naturforsch., 2b*, 56–63.

Clauss, H., and W. Rau. 1956. Über die Blütenbildung von *Hyoscyamus niger* und *Arabidopsis thaliana* in 72-Std.-Zyklen. *Z. Botan., 44*, 437–54.

Enderle, W. 1951. Tagesperiodische Wachstums- und Turgorschwankungen an Gewebekulturen. *Planta, 39*, 530–88.

Grabensberger, W. 1934. Experimentelle Untersuchungen über das Zeitgedächtnis von Bienen und Wespen nach Verfütterung von Euchinin und Jodthyreoglobulin. *Z. vergleich. Physiol., 20*, 338–42.

Harker, J. E. 1958. Diurnal rhythms in the animal kingdom. *Biol. Revs. Cambridge Phil. Soc., 33*, 1–52.

Hastings, J. W., M. Wiesner, J. Owens, and B. Sweeney. 1956. The rhythm of luminescence in a marine dinoflagellate. *Anat. Record, 125*, 611.

Haxo, F. T., and B. M. Sweeney. 1955. Bioluminescence in *Gonyaulax polyedra*. *The Luminescence of Biological Systems*, F. H. Johnson, Editor. American Association for the Advancement of Science, Washington, D. C.

Hemmingsen, A. M., and N. B. Krarup. 1937. Rhythmic diurnal variations in the oestrous phenomena of the rat and their susceptibility to light and dark. *Kgl. Danske Videnskab. Selskab, Biol. Medd., 13* (7), 1–61.

Hoffmann, K. 1954. Versuche zu der im Richtungsempfinden der Vögel euthaltenen Zeitschätzung. *Z. Tierpsychol., 11,* 453–75.

————. 1957a. Über den Einfluss der Temperatur auf die Tagesperiodik bei einem Poikilothermen. *Naturwissenschaften, 44,* 358.

————. 1957b. Angeborene Tagesperiodik bei Eidechsen. *Naturwissenschaften, 44,* 359–60.

Kalmus, H. 1934. Über die Natur des Zeitgedächtnisses der Bienen. *Z. vergleich. Physiol., 20,* 405–19.

————. 1935. Periodizität und Autochronie (Ideochronie) als zeitregelnde Eigenschaften bei Organismen. *Biol. Generalis, 11,* 93–114.

————. 1938. Tagesperiodisch verlaufende Vorgänge an der Stabheuschrecke (*Dixippus morosus*) und ihre experimentelle Beeinflussung. *Z. vergleich. Physiol., 25,* 494–508.

Kleinhoonte, A. 1929. Über die durch das Licht regulierten autonomen Bewegungen der *Canavalia-Blätter*. *Arch. néerl. sci.,* III B 5, 1–110.

————. 1932. Untersuchungen über die autonomen Bewegungen der Primärblätter von *Canavalia ensiformia*. *Jahrb. wiss. Botan., 75,* 679–725.

Kramer, G. 1952, 1953. Die Sonnenorientierung der Vögel. *Verhandl. Zool. Ges. Freiburg,* Leipzig. 72–84.

Leinweber, F. J. 1956. Über die Temperaturabhängigkeit der Periodenlänge bei der endogenen Tagesrhythmik von *Phaseolus. Z. Botan., 44,* 337–64.

Melchers, G. 1956. Die Beteiligung der endonomen Tagesrhythmik am Zustandekommen der photoperiodischen Reaktion der Kurztagpflanze *Kalanchoe blossfeldiana. Z. Naturforsch., 11b,* 544–48.

Papi, F. 1955. Experiments on the sense of time in *Talitrus saltator* (Montagu) (Crustacea-Amphipoda). *Experientia, 11,* 201–202.

Pittendrigh, C. S. 1954. On temperature emergence-time in *Drosophila. Proc. Natl. Acad. Sci. U. S., 40,* 1018–29.

Pohl, R. 1948. Tagesrhythmus im phototaktischen Verhalten der *Euglena gracilis. Z. Naturforsch., 3b,* 367–74.

Ralph, Ch. L. 1957. Persistent rhythms of activity and O_2-consumption in the earthworm. *Physiol. Zoöl., 30,* 41–55.

Remmert, H. 1955. Untersuchungen über das tageszeitlich gebundene Schlüpfen von *Pseudosmittia arenaria* (Dipt. Chironomidae). *Z. vergleich. Physiol., 37,* 338–54.

Renner, O. 1957. Neue Versuche über den Zeitsinn der Honigbiene. *Z. vergleich. Physiol., 40,* 85–118.

Schmidle, A. 1951. Die Tagesperiodizität der asexuellen Reproduktion von *Pilobolus sphaerosporus. Arch. Mikrobiol., 16,* 80–100.

Schwabe, W. W. 1955. Photoperiodic cycles of length differing from 24 hours in relation to endogenous rhythms. *Physiol. Plantarum, 8,* 263–78.

Stephens, G. C. 1957. Influence of temperature fluctuations on the diurnal melanophore rhythm of the fiddler crab, *Uca. Physiol. Zoöl., 30,* 55–69.

Tribukait, B. 1956. Die Aktivitätsperiodik der weissen Maus im Kunsttag von 16–29 Stunden Länge. *Z. vergleich. Physiol., 38,* 479–90.

Wahl, O. 1932. Neue Untersuchungen über das Zeitgedächtnis der Bienen. *Z. vergleich. Physiol., 16,* 529–89.

Wareing, P. F. 1954. Experiments on the "light-break" effect in short-day plants. *Physiol. Plantarum, 7,* 157–72.

ADDITIONAL REMARKS ON THE ROLE OF THE ENDOGENOUS DIURNAL PERIODICITY IN PHOTOPERIODISM

ERWIN BÜNNING

Department of Botany, University of Tübingen, Germany

In the discussion following my paper, I stressed several facts which may be summarized as follows.

1. *Definitions.* The term photophil means "light liking," not "light induced" nor "during light period." The term scotophil means "dark liking," not "dark induced" nor "during dark period."

2. *Light breaks in normal dark periods.* The strongest inhibition by light breaks offered to short-day plants during long nights is not necessarily in the middle of the night. The exact time of this maximum scotophil stage depends more or less on the beginning of the dark period, but also on the beginning of the preceding light period. If, for instance, this maximum sensitivity in light-dark cycles of 10:14 hr is reached 7 hr after the beginning of the dark period, it may be reached 12 hr (or between about 7 and 12 hr) after the beginning of this dark period in 5:19-hr light-dark cycles. Thus not the splitting of the dark period into its smallest possible parts is decisive; decisive are processes requiring a certain time. With the beginning of the light period a timing reaction starts which requires more than 12 hr (in our example 17 hr) to reach a certain extreme physiological status. Within this timing process a qualitative change also occurs, since light breaks offered earlier than, for instance, 12 hr after the beginning of the light period do not inhibit flower formation but promote it. A certain time (for instance, 12 hr) after the beginning of a light period, the photophil status is followed by a scotophil status, both with long-day and with short-day conditions. This scotophil status reaches the maximum about 6 hr after its beginning. Consequently the timing reaction is a cyclic one; it is not of the "hourglass type." The cycles are not only characterized by increasing and decreasing scotophil

character in their second half. Experiments with interrupted light periods reveal the increase and decrease of photophil character in the first half-cycle. In *Kalanchoë,* in soybeans, and in *Chenopodium,* for example, the maximum of the photophil character is reached 5 to 6 hr after the beginning of the light period (Bünning, 1950; Bünning and Könitz, 1957).

The reactions of long-day plants lead to the same conclusion. Owing to the concept of induced cycles (instead of hourglass processes), it was postulated that flower formation in this type should be possible even under short-day conditions, that is, if after starting the cycle by a short light period, the plants were offered some additional light at the right moment (the photophil stage) of the induced cycle. The assumption was that only a certain length of time (for example, 12 hr) after the beginning of a light period, the long-day plants become photophil, both with long-day and with short-day conditions. This has been confirmed, as is well known. Again, the maximum sensitivity is not necessarily in the middle of the dark period, but at a time on which the beginning of the light period can have a decisive influence. This point may be reached, for instance, 16 hr after the beginning of the light period.

Moreover, by determining the action spectra, it became evident that the light-induced process in the first part of the cycle differs from that prevailing in the second half of the cycle. This again shows the endogenous change from one status to another. These facts once more show the cyclic nature of the timing process.

Also, experiments of Takimoto (1955) on the long-day plant *Silene armeria* show that it is not the splitting of the dark period into its smallest possible parts that is decisive: With long light periods of 14 hr or more, flowering is possible even if the dark periods are extended up to 24 hr or more. This again shows that the light period initiates a timing reaction, which after some 12 to 14 hr brings the plant to a photophil status.

It is known that in certain species the onset of the light period is more effective in setting the phases of these cycles, while in other species it is the onset of the dark period.

3. *Light breaks in 48-hr cycles.* If light breaks are offered in a prolonged dark period of, for example, 40 hr, alternating with short

days within 48-hr cycles, long-day plants and short-day plants continue to change from the photophil to scotophil stage. The results of these experiments were just as predicted by assuming the role of the endogenous diurnal periodicity. This was described in my paper. (Further experiments like these have been published by Bünsow, 1953a,b.) Thus one short day is able to induce at least two full cycles of 24 hr each, i.e., two photophil phases alternating with two scotophil phases.

4. *Light breaks in extremely long dark periods.* For more than fifty years it has been known that the endogenous diurnal periodicity of normal plants grown in diurnal light-dark periods may fade away within 2 to 3 days after bringing the plants into continuous darkness. Therefore, most research workers preferred etiolated plants for studying the endogenous periodicity. In view of these facts, no one expected a continuation of the diurnal change from the photophil to scotophil phase for more than about two days in any case (Bünning, 1954). But in certain species, in which the conditions controlling the rhythms are favorable, the endogenous diurnal periodicity, as detected by recording the leaf movements, continues for more than two days in a prolonged dark period, though the plants are adapted to normal light conditions. In such instances the diurnal changes from photophil to scotophil stage are going on too. One of these experiments was mentioned in my paper, and others have been published (for example, Clauss and Rau, 1956). Thus one light period can sometimes induce three consecutive cycles of 24 hr each. To expect the same result in every experiment with extremely long dark periods means to neglect the long-known facts mentioned above.

Thus it is not significant that, as Dr. Wareing has stated, the direct evidence for such endogenous rhythms in photoperiodism is rather slight. The situation with respect to diurnal changes of sensitivity to light and darkness is exactly the same as with other processes governed by the endogenous rhythm. If we record leaf movements of a normal greenhouse plant in continuous light of high intensity or in continuous darkness, the evidence for an endogenous rhythm will be very slight too. This tenuous evidence, however, stimulated experiments with more suitable conditions, resulting in excellent evidence. Thus, both with diurnal leaf movements and with diurnal changes in the sensitivity to light and darkness, the endogenous cycles may continue for one or two periods only in certain cases, for a longer time in others.

5. *Long-day and short-day plants.*   I agree with Dr. Wareing that I have changed my original opinion on several points. The most essential change is the following. The regulation of the endogenous cycles by the light-dark periods, as is well known, makes the short-day plants scotophil in the second half of the day, the long-day plants photophil. But now we understand that this is not due to a 12-hr phase difference of the basic cycle in the two types. All our experiments with different species of both types show that in long-day and short-day plants the same biochemical features prevail in parts of the cycle which are comparable with respect to their time position within the light-dark periods. For instance, in the first half-cycle, i.e., during about the 12 hr following the beginning of a light period, synthetic capacities are predominant. Even the maximum sensitivity to red light in the second half-cycle, about 16 to 18 hr after the beginning of the light period, is common to many species of both types. Thus the question now is: Why do short-day and long-day plants show antagonistic reactions to red light offered in the same phase of the basic cycle, i.e., why do long-day plants show a photophil character about 16 to 18 hr after the onset of the light period while short-day plants have a scotophil character during the same phase of the basic cycle? This is not as strange as it seemed previously. Sachs has reported on dual day length requirements. Thus the light, offered during that highly red-sensitive phase, may be involved in two different reactions, both of which are necessary for flower formation. But the light sensitivity of these reactions is different in long-day and in short-day plants. In case each of these reactions shows a light sensitivity, the plant needs at first long days, afterward short days (long-short-day plants). In other cases, one or the other (even both in day-neutral plants) of these two reactions are sufficiently independent of light.

REFERENCES

Bünning, E. 1950. Über die photophile und skotophile Phase der endogenen Tagesrhythmik. *Planta, 38,* 521–40.

————. 1954. Der Verlauf der endogenen Tagesrhythmik bei photoperiodischen Störlichtversuchen mit Soja. *Physiol. Plantarum, 7*, 538–47.

Bünning, E., and W. Könitz. 1957. Diurnale antagonistische Schwankungen von Hellrot- und Dunkelrot-Empfindlichkeit bei einer Kurztagpflanze. *Naturwissenschaften, 44*, 568.

Bünsow, R. 1953a. Endogene Tagesrhythmik und Photoperiodismus bei *Kalanchoe blossfeldiana. Planta, 42*, 220–52.

————. 1953b. Über tages- und jahresrhythmische Änderungen der photoperiodischen Lichtempfindlichkeit bei *Kalanchoe blossfeldiana* und ihre Beziehungen zur endogenen Tagesrhythmik. *Z. Botan., 41*, 257–76.

Clauss, H., and W. Rau. 1956. Über die Blütenbildung von *Hyoscyamus niger* und *Arabidopsis thaliana* in 72-Stunden-Zyklen. *Z. Botan., 44*, 437–54.

Takimoto, A. (1955) Flowering response to various combination of light and dark periods in *Silene armeria. Botan. Mag. (Tokyo), 68*, 308–14.

DIURNAL CHANGES IN PIGMENT CONTENT AND IN THE PHOTOPERIODIC EFFICIENCY OF RED AND FAR RED

ERWIN BÜNNING
Department of Botany, University of Tübingen, Germany

With *Hyoscyamus* we observed some time ago a remarkable effect of light on chlorophyll formation. If the plant is offered a 3-hr light break within a prolonged dark period, the effect of this light break on the chlorophyll content depends on the time of day at which it is offered (Fig. 1). Within a 63-hr dark period, there are two periods

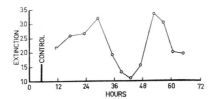

FIG. 1. *Hyoscyamus niger.* Chlorophyll production in 9:63-hr light-dark cycles. During the dark period, 3 hr light breaks. Controls without light breaks. Abscissas, time of light break (Clauss and Rau, 1956).

of time with an optimum effect of the light which are 24 hr apart. Between these maxima the light break even makes the chlorophyll content decrease (Clauss and Rau, 1956).

Continuing these experiments, we found that significant diurnal fluctuations in the chlorophyll content of seedlings can interfere with those effects. This reminds us of observations published by Sironval (1957), Wendel (1957), and others. In addition, our experiments with *Perilla* demonstrated the continuation of these changes for at least 4 days (Fig. 2).

Of course, chlorophyll itself is not the light-absorbing pigment in photoperiodism. But what about those substances which must increase or decrease in quantity along with the changes in chlorophyll content?

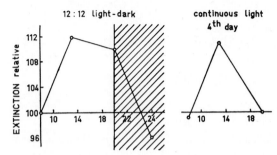

FIG. 2. *Perilla*. Diurnal changes in quantity of chlorophyll *b* during light-dark cycle and in continuous light. (Bünning, Mitrakos, and Eberhardt, unpublished data.)

At any rate, if there are diurnal changes in chlorophyll content, it might well be possible that other pigments are involved too. With these aspects in mind, experiments with *Chenopodium amaranticolor* may be of some interest (Fig. 3).

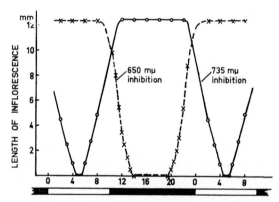

FIG. 3. *Chenopodium amaranticolor*. Influence of light breaks during light and dark period on length of inflorescence. The plants were offered 10 short-day cycles (10 hr light, 14 hr dark). Length of the inflorescence in the controls 12 mm. Light breaks in light period 200,000 kiloerg/cm², in dark period 20,000 kiloerg/cm². Determination of inflorescence length 15 days after beginning the experiment. (After Bünning and Könitz, 1957.)

Offering 10:14-hr light-dark cycles, again we found the well-known inhibiting effect of breaks with red light (10 or 15 min). This effect was strongest 7 hr after the beginning of the dark period, but in order to abolish this inhibition at any time of the dark period, the same energy of far red was necessary.

If on the other hand, the 10 hr light period (white light) is interrupted by light breaks (2–3 hr), it is only far red that causes an inhibition of flower formation. The highest sensitivity was found 5 hr after the beginning of the main light period. This inhibition may be cancelled by red light, and again in any part of the main light period the same energy is necessary to remove the inhibition.

These facts show that some diurnal antagonistic change in the sensitivity to red and far red is involved in photoperiodism. This also is made clear by measuring the energy of light breaks required to prevent flower formation under suitable experimental conditions (Fig. 4). Perhaps these antagonistic changes in the light sensitivity

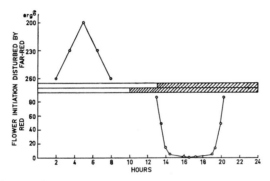

FIG. 4. *Chenopodium amaranticolor.* Required energy of light breaks for complete suppression of flowering impulse. The light breaks were offered in the 13-hr light period of 13:11-hr light-dark cycles or in the 14-hr dark period of 10:14-hr light-dark cycles. (Unpublished experiments, Könitz.)

are to be explained by diurnal changes in the responsible pigments, but other explanations are also possible.

REFERENCES

Bünning, E., and W. Könitz. 1957. Diurnale antagonistische Schwankungen von Hell- und Dunkelrot-Empfindlichkeit einer Kurztagpflanze. *Naturwissenschaften, 44,* 568.

Clauss, H., and W. Rau. 1956. Über die Blütenbildung von *Hyoscyamus niger* und *Arabidopsis thaliana* in 72-Stunden-Zyklen. *Z. Botan., 44,* 437–54.

Könitz, W. 1958. Blühhemmung bei Kurztagpflanzen durch Hellrot- und Dunkelrotlicht in der photo- und skotophilen Phase. *Planta, 5,* 1–29.

Sironval, C. 1953. A propos du métabolism de la chlorophylle dans la feuille (ses rapports avec la floraison). *Bull. Soc. Roy. Botan. Belg., 85,* 285.

———. 1957. La photopériode et la sexualisation du fraisier des quatre-saisons à fruits rouges. (Métabolism chlorophyllien et hormone florigène.) *Compt. rend. rech. I.R.S.I.A. (Bruxelles)* No. 18, 1–229.

Wendel, K. 1957. Über die Veränderlichkeit des Chlorophyllgehaltes einiger Pflanzen im Ablauf eines Tages. *Protoplasma, 48,* 382–97.

INDUCTION OF PHASE SHIFT IN CELLULAR RHYTHMICITY BY FAR ULTRAVIOLET AND ITS RESTORATION BY VISIBLE RADIANT ENERGY[1]

CHARLES F. EHRET
**Division of Biological and Medical Research,
Argonne National Laboratory, Lemont, Illinois**

When nondividing cells of *Paramecium bursaria* of complementary mating types are mixed together during a sexually reactive phase, a mass agglutination occurs that is known as the mating reaction. This is normally followed by pairing of cells and conjugation of the complementary types. In nature, the reactive phase occurs in the daytime and the nonreactive, or weakly reactive phase, at night. In the laboratory it has been demonstrated that phase shifts can be induced by visible radiant energy (Ehret, 1953, 1955a), that under constant conditions of darkness and temperature an endogenous diurnal rhythm persists (Ehret, 1953, 1955b), and that these relationships hold equally for cells freed of the symbiotic algae that normally inhabit the cytoplasm of this species (Ehret, 1953).

In the course of an investigation of the dose-response relationships for the determination of phase-shift action spectra, it became obvious that radiant energy of the far ultraviolet region of the spectrum was not only highly efficient in inducing phase shifts, but that the efficiency was directly related to the phase stage during which the stimulus was applied. It was further observed that the UV effect was almost entirely photoreversible with visible radiant energy. This paper describes the results of such an experiment.

METHODS

Culture methods were essentially similar to those previously described (Ehret, 1953). *Chlorella*-less cell populations of *P. bursaria*

[1] Work performed under the auspices of the U. S. Atomic Energy Commission.

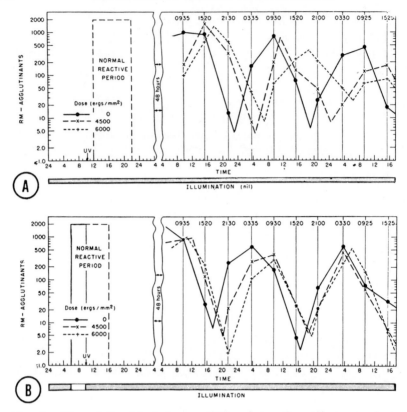

FIG. 1. The relationship between ability of experimental paramecia to mate, and the time of day at which the mixture with competent cells of complementary mating type was made. Reaction magnitude of agglutination (RM) was measured 10 min after mixing. Four categories were irradiated at each of four different phases during a reactive-nonreactive diurnal cycle: A in the late scotophilic phase; B just before the middle of the reactive phase; C at the end of the reactive phase; D just before the middle of the scotophilic phase.

stock Wu-5, mating type D, in 250-ml Erlenmeyer flasks were transferred at the end of the exponential period of growth into four different light-dark compartments. The flask within each compartment received 150 ft-c illumination from a 15-w daylight fluorescent lamp. Each compartment was scheduled according to a photoperiodic cycle consisting of 10 hr of light and 14 hr of darkness. From one compartment to the next, each cycle was unique, with 6-hr spacings between

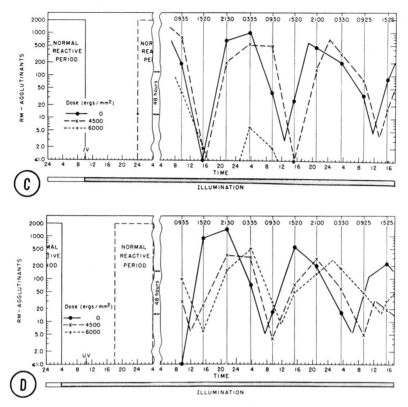

FIG. 1   (*Continued*)

the starts of the photoperiods. By the third day, the mid-reactive phases of each of the four populations was either 6 or 12 hr removed from the other three. This starting condition is represented diagrammatically by the rectangles at the left of each of the graphs in Figs. 1 and 2. Thus at midnight (2400 hr, left end of the abscissas) population A was in the early nonreactive or scotophilic phase, population B was in the middle to late scotophilic phase, population C was in the early reactive phase, and population D was in the middle to late reactive phase.

At 0945, each of the four populations was removed from its compartment, and aliquots were transferred to 10-cm petri dishes that served as exposure vessels. A germicidal lamp (15-w Westinghouse Sterilamp G15T8) was employed as source, the irradiance at 254 mμ

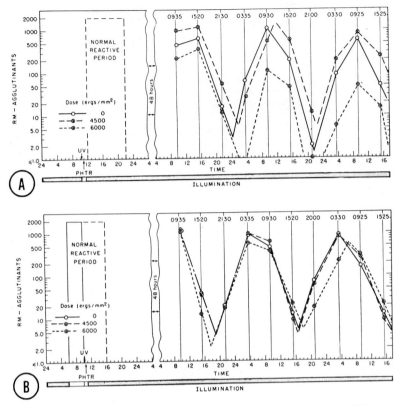

FIG. 2. Like Fig. 1, except that 420 ft-c of photoreactivating light was applied 15 min after UV dose for 1 hr.

was 50 ergs sec^{-1} mm^{-2}, and the exposure times were zero, 90, and 120 sec. These operations were performed under dim red light, and UV exposures were completed by 1015. After irradiation the populations were retained in the dark or exposed to photoreactivating (PHTR) light (420 ft-c, "daylight" fluorescent illumination for 1 hr. One milliliter aliquots of the twenty-four respective cell populations were transferred under dim red light from the exposure vessels into 240 storage vials. These vials were placed in black envelopes within copper cannisters suspended in a water bath held at 25°C. The first counts (24 vials, 3 on each graph) were made 71 hr after UV exposure (0935), and counts were made at six hourly intervals for three consecutive days until all ten sets of the vials were counted. The

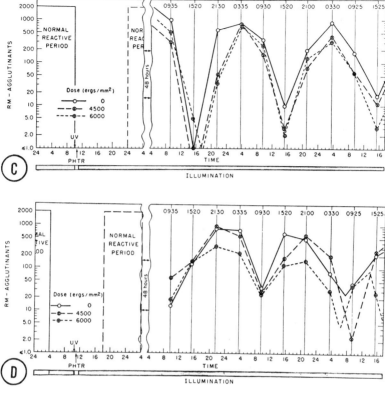

FIG. 2 (*Continued*)

counts included two measures: (1) the number of experimental cells that participate in the initial agglutination masses formed between the cells in the vials and known *reactive* test cells (Ehret, 1953) of complementary mating type 10 min after mixing; this measure is the *reaction magnitude* (RM) *of agglutination;* (2) the number of conjugant pairs formed as a consequence of this mixture, 6 hr after mixing. In each measure it was possible to distinguish between the experimental animals and the testers, because the former were colorless, whereas the latter were green (*Chlorella*-containing cells of mating type A). The contribution of the second measure was to assign an ascending or descending direction to a curve from a given point: this is valid because many conjugants are formed from early reactive period mixtures, whereas few conjugants are formed from late reactive period mixtures. (By this method each intersection of lines that occur at some place other than at a measured point on the plotted curves was inferred.)

RESULTS

The effects of exposure to far ultraviolet are shown in Fig. 1. Three general effects are obvious. (1) In each category there is an endogenous rhythmicity of reactivity with cycles of approximately 23 hr duration. (2) There is apparent phase shift to the right (delay) that is UV dose-dependent. (3) The amplitudes (RM) of the response curves are only slightly affected by low doses of UV. (Higher doses, correlated with some cell death, cause an extreme depression of maxima and a slight elevation of minima (Ehret, 1955b).)

The results of subsequent exposure of ultraviolet-irradiated cells to visible irradiances are shown in Fig. 2. (1) The approximately diurnal rhythmicity (23 hr) is again evident. (2) There are no conspicuous phase shifts experienced by treated groups independently of the controls. (3) The response curves are either not at all, or only slightly depressed, and there is a slight elevation of minima in curve D.

A further analysis of these results shows that there are three rather general superimposing effects that can be distinguished from the more specific UV + dark and UV + light effects on the cellular mechanism. The superimposing effects are (1) an endogenous 23-hr rhythm, (2) the initial exposure of all categories to dim light, and (3) the effect of photoreactivating light itself on controls. In Table I such an analysis is summarized, and the consequent minimum and maximum sensitivity phases are inferred from it. It should be noted in the table that in categories 1A and 1B the controls are 2.5 hr earlier than expected. This is compatible both in direction and degree with the shift expectations that ensue from foreshortening of the photoperiod (Ehret, 1953) in 1B, and from a dim light stimulus applied during the late scotophilic phase in 1A (Ehret, 1955a). It is probable that the stimulus in this case was the dim red light to which the cultures were exposed at the start of the experiment. However, in both 1A and 1B the irradiated categories are late whether compared with the

TABLE I. Analysis of UV-Induced Phase Shift to Distinguish between Normal Light Effect, UV Effect, and Photoreversing Effect[a]

Code			Nonirradiated Controls					Irradiated	
			Time of Reaction Peak			Shift (from 3)		UV-Induced Shift (from 4)	
(1)			(2) Last	(3)	(4)	(5)	(6)	(7) 4500 ergs mm^{-2}	(8) 6000 ergs mm^{-2}
Fig.	Graph	PHTR[b]	Photoperiod	Expected	Observed	(hr)	(Direction)	(hr)	(hr)
1	A	−	1700	1300	1030	2.5	Early	3.8	7.1
2	A	+	1700	→	1130	1.5	Early	0.8	0.0
1	B	−	1100	0700	0430	2.5	Early	2.5	3.5
2	B	+	1100	→	0530	1.5	Early	0.0	0.7
1	C	−	0500	0100	0100	0	On time	3.0	4.0
2	C	+	0500	→	0350	2.8	Late	0.0	0.0
1	D	−	2300	1900	1900	0	On time	5.0	8.5
2	D	+	2300	→	2200	3.0	Late	1.0	1.0

[a] The figures are extrapolated from the data of UV categories A-D and corresponding dark controls (Fig. 1) and UV + light categories A-D and corresponding light controls (Fig. 2). The expected time of the reaction peak (column 3) is calculated for each category on the basis of a 23-hr cycle, four days after the last photoperiod experienced before the start of the experiment. Observed time (column 4) refers to the actual peak closest to the expected one. The difference in hours between these values is entered as an early or late shift in columns 5 and 6. The average shifts induced by UV are entered in columns 7 and 8 as hours later than the observed peak (column 4).
[b] Exposed (+) or not exposed (−) to 1 hr "photoreactivating" (PHTR) light.

547

controls as they are (early, column 4) or as they should have been without phase shift ("on time," column 3). Therefore, UV-induced phase delay is not entirely (if at all) due to failure of the cells to respond to a phase-shifting stimulus.

In 1C the controls are on time, indicating no response to a short dim light stimulus in the very early scotophilic phase; the irradiated group is late and clearly sensitive to phase delay by UV. In 1D the controls are on time, which is compatible with an interruption of the mid-scotophilic phase by dim light (Ehret, 1955a) (before this time, the shift is late; after it the shift is early). The irradiated categories are conspicuously late; however, even here the magnitude of the delay is possibly influenced by pretreatment with dim red light, since the subsequent exposure to white light at this time (2D below) produces an unexpected synergism.

The photoreactivated categories can similarly be compared. It appears that the control and UV-irradiated populations that have been illuminated post-UV each reacts synchronously. Was this because the UV delays were prevented or because illumination maximized delays in each instance? In three cases this distinction is possible. In 2A and 2B, light applied before or at the beginning of the normal photoperiod induces the reaction to occur ahead of schedule. These are not so early as 1A and 1B controls above because the stronger stimulus occurred 1 hr later. Nevertheless, the UV-irradiated categories in 2A and 2B are just as early as their light controls, although they should have been at least 1.0 to 4.5 hr later than even the 1A and 1B dark controls had photoreactivation not occurred.

In 2D the controls are late, which is unexpected since illumination in the late scotophilic phase usually shortens the phase; however, when added to red-light mid-scotophilic interruption (1D above) the effect appears to be that of an early or prolonged scotophil interruption, and the phase shift is delayed. Compatible with this interpretation is the broadening effect of a slightly heterogeneous cell population. However, the UV-irradiated categories show only 1 hr greater delay, whereas they would have been at least 2 to 5.5 hr later had photoreactivation *not* occurred.

These distinctions cannot be made in 2C in which the UV-irradiated categories are no later than the controls, but which were as late as they would have been without light, although possibly more synchronous. It is conceivable that the UV-induced phase delay was photoreversed and a photoinduced phase delay substituted for it, but this experiment cannot decide that issue.

DISCUSSION

This demonstration that phase shifts in cellular rhythmicity can be induced by ultraviolet irradiation should prove encouraging to the investigator who hopes to find clock escapements for the rhythm-controlling timepieces at the cellular level. It is of further interest that the UV-induced damage is photoreversible. This brings the phenomenon into line with a large number of diverse biological mechanisms, none of which in the past has been directly associated with rhythms. The high efficiency of ultraviolet both in absolute energy and in time for induction must ultimately be compared with induction efficiencies of the longer wavelengths that are generally associated with phase shift, but are not usually associated with either nucleic acid absorption nor with photoreactivation. Separate avenues of phase-shift induction may thus be employed by visible and by far ultraviolet radiant energy within the cell. In the preliminary speculations, the conspicuous intranuclear and nucleolar (Kimball and Gaither, 1951; Ehret, 1955b) effects of far ultraviolet should not go unnoticed.

While there is little known about the chemistry of mating substance or its biosynthesis, the present results can be described within the framework of the heuristic scheme previously adopted for *Paramecium* (Ehret, 1953). In that terminology, the times at which cells are *most* sensitive to phase shift are those at the middle and end of the scotophilic phase, when mating-substance precursor is being synthesized and during the time just prior to the conversion of such precursors to mating substance.

SUMMARY

1. Phase shifts in cellular rhythmicity in *Paramecium* can be induced by low doses of far ultraviolet irradiation.

2. Stages most sensitive to induction are the middle and late portions of the scotophilic phase.

3. Phase-shift induction by UV is photoreversible by radiant energy from the visible region of the spectrum.

Acknowledgment

I am grateful to Mrs. Janet Fraembs for her very capable assistance.

REFERENCES

Ehret, C. F. 1953. An analysis of the role of electromagnetic radiations in the mating reaction of *Paramecium bursaria*. *Physiol. Zoöl., 26,* 274–300.

Ehret, C. F. 1955a. The effects of pre- and post-illumination on the scotophilic recovery phase of the *Paramecium bursaria* mating reaction. *Anat. Record, 122,* 465–57.

————. 1955b. The photoreactivability of sexual activity and rhythmicity in *Paramecium bursaria*. *Rad. Research, 3,* 222–23.

Kimball, R. F., and N. Gaither. 1951. The influence of light upon the action of ultraviolet in *Paramecium aurelia*. *J. Cellular Comp. Physiol., 37,* 211–33.

THE PERIODIC ASPECT OF PHOTOPERIODISM AND THERMOPERIODICITY

FRITS W. WENT
Missouri Botanical Garden, St. Louis, Missouri

This symposium has heralded the twilight of the chemical approach and marked the coming of age of the physical approach to the problem of photoperiodism, just half a century after Klebs started his work with *Sempervivum,* which led him in 1913 to suggest that its flowering was apparently controlled by the day length. In a clear and frank appraisal Bonner has shown earlier in this symposium that evidence for the chemical nature of the intermediary steps between perception of the photoperiodic stimulus and its manifestation is almost completely lacking in spite of diligent and prolonged research. The most definite evidence he saw was in the grafting experiments in which a photoperiodically induced scion can make the stock plant flower, indicating transfer of something material from scion to stock. Also the first high-energy light process seemed of a chemical nature, although Professor Bünning (p. 507) pointed out that even this process might be largely connected with the internal clock mechanism basic for flowering.

Fortunately, the discarding of so many of the seemingly fundamental concepts of the chemical control of flowering need not bother the theoretically inclined biologists so much, since the recognition of the periodic aspects of the problem can at least partly substitute for the discarded ideas, and it is most encouraging that at this symposium so much new material has been presented relating to this periodic aspect.

The light reactions discussed during this symposium can be divided into three groups. First are the morphogenetic processes in general, without special reference to a red-sensitive process with a peak in its action spectrum at 667 mμ, usually reversible by far-red radiation of 710–730 mμ wavelength. It was clear that these processes, nonperiodic in nature, were mediated by a fairly large number of light-sensitive absorption processes, each with a different action spectrum and presumably depending on different pigments. These morphogenetic processes, including growth responses of stems and leaves of many plants, seem to be completely separate from the problem of photoperiodism as discussed in this symposium. The second group of light processes depends for its response on the red, far-red pigment system, but also is nonperiodic in nature. Many germination processes fall into this group. And finally the third group of light processes comprises the truly photoperiodic processes, which are periodic in nature, that is to say, which depend on the Bünning cycle, and which seem to be controlled by the red, far-red pigment system. Flower initiation and leaf and stem growth processes belong to this group. The analysis of their behavior can be expressed by Galston's P-I-G abbreviation (p. 137) indicating Photoreceptor-Intermediate processes-Growth responses.

There exists another set of periodic responses that can be induced by temperature cycles and that have been termed thermoperiodic phenomena. They can be of a daily or a yearly nature; in the following discussion only the daily thermoperiodic phenomena will be treated. Their analysis can be succinctly expressed by another reference to our sister science as T-I-C, meaning Thermoreceptor-Intermediate process-Cellular responses. Before going into greater detail in a comparison between T-I-C and P-I-G, some pertinent thermoperiodic phenomena will be discussed. Since most of these thermoperiodic responses relate to vegetative processes, it is perhaps well to point out that photoperiodic responses in plants are by no means restricted to flowering, but that almost any vegetative or biochemical process may be involved, such as those discussed by Dr. Galston and Professor Bünning. The action spectra of several of these vegetative photoperiodic processes have been determined; they were found to agree very closely with the action spectra of the photoperiodic flowering responses (e.g., leaf expansion of etiolated pea plants and straightening of the plumular hook in bean seedlings).

The flowering of a tomato plant is not affected at all by the length of daily exposure to light, but many of its vegetative responses are strongly influenced. Their daily rhythms can easily be demonstrated by experiments in which the daily 8-hr light exposure is interrupted by dark periods (see Fig. 1). When in this way the second exposure extends into the scotophil phase of Bünning, i.e., the sum of the light and dark periods is more than 12 hr, growth is strongly inhibited, and

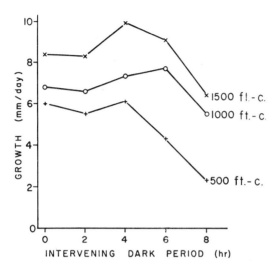

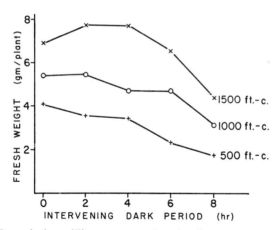

FIG. 1. Growth in millimeters per day (ordinate, upper curve) and fresh weight production in grams per plant (ordinate, lower curve) for tomato plants grown at three light intensities with 8 hr of light per 24 hr. The 8 hr of light was given in two 4-hr periods with zero, 2-, 4-, 6-, or 8-hr dark periods, intervening (abscissa).

also dry weight production is much less. That we are here dealing with the Bünning phenomenon is clearly indicated by the leaf angle, which is small in the scotophil and large in the photophil phase. When this angle is small at the beginning of the light exposure, light is little effective (Went, 1957).

The basic 24-hr cycle in growth of the tomato plant can be demonstrated in a different way. When groups of plants are exposed to 22-, 24-, 27-, and 30-hr cycles of equal periods of light and darkness at 20°C, these plants do not grow at the same rate. The 24-hr cycle of 12 hr light and 12 hr darkness produces the heaviest and fastest growing plants. In the 22- and 27-hr cycles, in which in the long run the plants are exposed to exactly the same total amount of light, they grew less, and in the 30-hr cycle, growth was much less. Therefore, light exposure at 20°C is most effective if presented with a 24-hr period. At 14°, optimal growth occurred on a 27-hr cycle and less on 24-, 30-, and 33-hr cycles, indicating that at a lower temperature the endogenous cycle is slightly longer.

It seems to me that this type of experiment is very significant in connection with the question of the existence of innate cycles or rhythms. For we do not depend here on a demonstration that under presumably constant external conditions the organism continues to respond rhythmically. In such experiments the question remains open whether we are perhaps still confronted with an unsuspected periodicity in the environment. But here we determine the degree to which the tomato plant adjusts itself to different rhythms, and the conclusion seems warranted that maximal growth and dry matter production indicates the greatest degree of adjustment of the internal Bünning cycle with the externally applied light-dark periodicity.

The necessity of light-dark cycles in the environment for normal growth of tomato plants is most clearly demonstrated by their abnormal growth under continuous light. This phenomenon, first studied by Arthur and Harvill (1937) and the Withrows (1949), is now under investigation in the Earhart Plant Research Laboratory by both Hillman (1956) and Kristoffersen (unpublished). When young tomato plants are grown in continuous light, in a constant temperature, the newly developing leaves become light green, mottled, and especially at higher temperatures such new leaves may be completely chlorotic, and ultimately the plants may die. A more quantitative measure of this effect of continuous illumination is the wet and dry weight production, which is strongly reduced even when no serious chlorosis develops. A few hours of darkness in a 24-hr cycle greatly increases dry matter production, with an optimum at about 6 hr darkness.

When the darkness is given at any cycle differing very much from 24 hr, the effect is just as severe or even more severe than in continuous light (Hanson and Highkin, 1954; Hillman, 1956). Therefore darkness is effective only if it comes at exactly 24-hr intervals, or, to a lesser extent at 48- and 72-hr intervals. There is also a temperature effect, inasmuch as a high temperature causes much more severe injury in continuous illumination than a low temperature (23° against 14°; at 10° constant there is very little growth at all). Kristoffersen has found that injury will occur only under conditions of maximal growth with daily applications of nutrient solution.

It is not necessary to fluctuate light over a 24-hr cycle to prevent injury. Hillman found that a 24-hr temperature cycle in continuous light produces perfectly normal tomato plants. Kristoffersen has now studied the quantitative aspects of the effect of temperature fluctuation, and has found that temperature and darkness are practically equivalent: in both cases a 6–8 hr interval of darkness or lower temperature is required to get normal plants, and in both cases this causes about the same absolute increase in weight compared with continuous light at constant temperature. There is one additional fact: to prevent injury the temperature fluctuation must occur above and below 14°C; a 23–17° change is hardly effective, but a 17–10°, or 23–10° sequence is fully effective. The greatly increased weight due to a daily exposure to 10° (i.e., during the photoperiod) indicates that at that temperature photosynthesis must take place, and also when the 10° is given for 16 hr out of every 24 hr.

We have seen that for normal development a tomato plant must have periodic changes in its environment, and that this periodicity must have a 24-hr rhythm. The most remarkable aspect of this essential periodicity is that temperature fluctuations are just as effective as light-dark sequences; in this case, periods of lower or higher temperature can fully substitute for periods of darkness.

To tie this tomato behavior up with photoperiodism as affecting flowering we should point out that both operate under a 24-hr cycle and that morphological development of the tomato in the absence of cycles in the environment is slowed down. The growing point is slower in forming nodes, and it becomes much smaller when not subjected to a 24-hr cycle of either temperature or light. Therefore the cycle of cell division requires also an external cyclic change to continue normally.

The requirement of adequate cycles in the environment also is clearly indicated in the case of peas. When these are grown in continuous light at a constant temperature, they start to grow very fast, at least as long as the food reserves in the cotyledons last, and then their growth rate drops rapidly to a very low value. This drop in growth rate can be prevented either by a dark period or by a temperature fluctuation. The latter two conditions are apparently equivalent again; by changing both at the same time there is no further change in response, and therefore ultimately both must control the same growth mechanism. This is also indicated by the coefficient of variability[1] in these peas (see Table I). It is quite obvious that a 24-hr cycle regulates growth, which it may well do through a regulating effect on mitosis.

TABLE I. Periodicity in Plant Development

Light	Temperature	Coefficient of Variability	Number of Separate Measurements on 16 Plants Each
Continuous	Constant	21.2	18
Continuous	Varying	12.7	18
Varying (8-hr + 16-hr photoperiod)	Constant	12.6	27
Varying (8-hr + 16-hr photoperiod)	Varying	12.6	49

Bünning (1952) has found a very clear-cut 24-hr cycle in mitosis in the growing points of a number of plants (see Fig. 2). We know that neither light nor temperature as such causes mitosis, but cell divisions can become synchronized by changes in light or temperature. This has been found in a number of organisms (bacteria, *Para-*

[1] Mean value of a set of measurements divided by the standard deviation of the mean.

mecium), and the main requirement is that cell division had been inhibited by some means prior to the light or temperature change. Such inhibition can then be overcome by the change in the environment. And a periodic change in the environment might then result in a

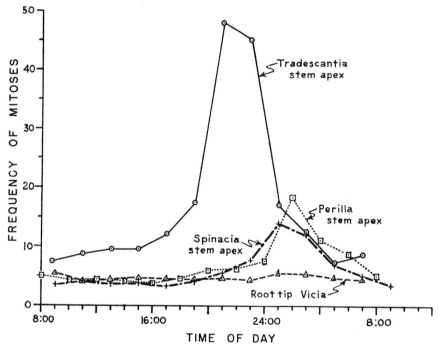

FIG. 2.   Frequency of mitoses (ordinate) for different tissues as a function of time of day (abscissa) for a number of different plants. (Data from Bünning, 1952.)

periodic sequence in mitosis. We can even imagine that the synchronization in development between all cells in the growing point, which is necessary to insure the proper sequence of node formation, is actually produced by this cycle in the environment. This is all the more attractive as a working hypothesis, since thus far no concrete evidence has been found for the existence or activity of hormones which control these processes within the growing point of the higher plants.

That in the photocontrol of vegetative growth we are dealing with the same basic phenomenon as in flowering is indicated by the action spectra of both flowering and stem elongation of peas, and even in seed germination the same pigment is involved (Hendricks, 1956).

The most disturbing new fact in photoperiodism is that temperature can substitute for light. De Zeeuw (1957) and also Nitsch (p. 225) found that *Xanthium* grown in a 16-hr photoperiod at 23 °C would not flower, as is well known. But when the first 8 hr of the photoperiod were spent at 4°, the plants were induced. A very similar effect was found by Paton (unpublished) for peas. These are (at least the variety Green-feast) long-day plants; in short days flowering is retarded for as much as several weeks. When there is a 7–14° temperature drop or rise in the middle of the dark period, they flower as early as the same plants on a long photoperiod. We are only just starting to collect facts on the effects of thermoperiod on flowering; we already know other cases where temperature alters the flowering response to photoperiod (straw-berries, *Bidens*). A good analysis of the effects of thermoperiod as compared with photoperiod has been carried out only for vegetative growth.

Is there any further evidence of the reality of the Bünning cycle in plant development? For this we have to return to some of the earliest papers of Bünning (1932) in which he shows the existence of an autonomous cycle in the nyctinastic movements of leaves of *Phaseolus*. When he kept his plants in darkness at different temperatures, the autonomous cycle was slightly different, and he found a Q_{10} of 1.21–1.25 for the temperature effect on the rate of the cycle. These experi-ments were not very convincing because of the relatively poor re-sponses of the plants, so that the results of Leinweber (1956), claim-ing that there was no temperature coefficient for the Bünning cycle, are apparently generally accepted, even by Bünning himself, of whom Leinweber was a student. In the meantime, however, I had set up a lapse-time movie camera with which plants could be photographed in extremely weak infrared light. This setup was placed in different dark-rooms at different constant temperatures. Preliminary results show that at 23° the nyctinastic movements of *Phaseolus* have a period of 23.1 ± 0.5 hr (see Fig. 3). At 14° the period is 30.5 hr. These points lie exactly on Bünning's original curve (1932). Therefore I assume that Bünning was correct and that Leinweber introduced in his experiments an external factor which changed with the 24-hr cycle of the solar day. I assume that this was air pollution, which easily penetrates into physiological darkrooms unless carbon filters have been installed. In addition, there seems to be an autonomous cycle of 10-hr duration,

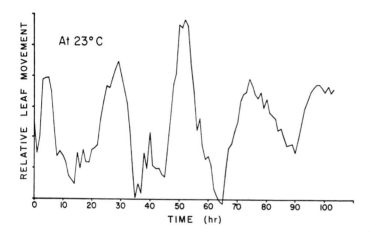

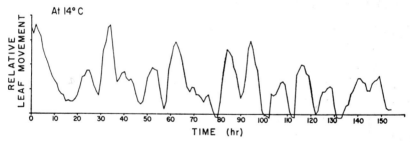

FIG. 3. Leaf movements of the primary leaves of *Phaseolus* in complete darkness and in constant temperature. Abscissa, time in hours after initial light exposure of 1 hr.

which may be independent of temperature, but this is definitely a secondary cycle.

Recently Hamner and Nanda (unpublished) have found excellent evidence of the existence of the Bünning cycle in the photoperiodic induction of the soybean. When they carried out experiments in the Earhart Laboratory at different temperatures, they found that whereas at 23° the cycle length was 24 hr, at 17° it was 30 hr and at 10° it was 36 hr. These points coincide with Bünning's and my own data (see

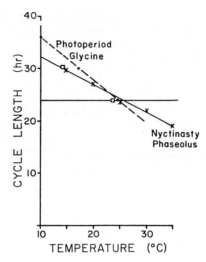

FIG. 4. Relationship between autonomous cycle lengths (the ordinate in hours) as a function of temperature. Crosses, data of Bünning (1932) for nyctinastic movements of *Phaseolus* leaves. Squares, similar data for *Phaseolus* leaf movements from Fig. 3. Circles, length of internal photoperiodic cycle for soybean, after Hamner and Nanda (unpublished).

Fig. 4). Therefore I think that we can conclude that in higher plants in general the Bünning cycle has a temperature coefficient of 1.2–1.25.

From the preceding it must be obvious that plants from a warm climate will not have synchronization of their internal cycle with the solar cycle at relatively low temperatures. We actually find that such plants grow very poorly and often die within a few months when grown at 4°, 7°, or 10°. Perhaps most significant is the fact that the first symptoms of abnormal growth are lack of chlorophyll formation in the newly formed leaves and ultimately complete cessation of growth in the growing point. Tomatoes turn yellow at 4°, tobacco and *Begonia* at 4° and 7°, *Saintpaulia* and *Coleus* at 10°.

To test whether death of warm-climate plants in cool temperatures can be attributed to a lack of synchronization between internal and external daily cycles, *Saintpaulias* and *Begonias* were grown at 10° in both a 24- and a 32-hr light-dark cycle, getting during one-third of the cycle artificial light at 1000 ft-c. Very soon the *Begonias,* and after several months, the *Saintpaulias,* died in the 24-hr cycle, but growth was very healthy in the 32-hr cycle (see Fig. 5).

FIG. 5. *Saintpaulia* plants grown at 10°C at different cycle lengths of 24 and 32 hr, for 5 months.

We know that in a number of cases (strawberry, *Poinsettia*, etc.) temperature strongly modifies the photoperiodic response. It is possible that this must be attributed to interference with the changed internal cycle.

Now I want to come back to photoperiodism. I have stressed the importance of the periodicity aspect of this phenomenon. We know that the periods of light and darkness have to alternate with a 24-hr cycle, and that it is not a question of a certain amount of light or a certain total length of darkness. Only in the exceptional case of *Xanthium* is a single long dark period sufficient to cause a certain degree of induction. Therefore the extensive work with *Xanthium* has perhaps made us overlook the significance of the periodicity aspect of photoperiodicity. When we look at the process with this new information at hand, then we must come to the conclusion that in some way a synchronization has to be achieved between some internal process and the external conditions.

As a further point we can state that it is not primarily a photochemical process we are looking for, since a temperature cycle can achieve the same effects as a light-dark cycle. Although we might be tempted to think of the primary effect as a release mechanism, a stimulus in Pfeffer's sense, a shock effect, it must become clear that this is not the case. For the darkness or the differing temperature has to act for a definite length of time, indicating that there is a definite energy level which will interfere with the photoperiodic induction. It seems very significant that both the lower temperature and the darkness have to last for the same length of time to prevent continuous-light injury in tomatoes.

The previous analysis has turned up as the principal conclusion, to which I feel most of the participants at this symposium had come already, that one of the major attributes of the photoperiodic response is its periodic nature. Remarkably enough, this had been recognized right from the beginning by Garner and Allard, when they coined the term photoperiodism, but it was largely neglected by investigators in the following years. I also want to stress the second major attribute of the photoperiodic response, namely its 24-hr period, which is only slightly temperature-dependent. And in the third place, I want to record my conclusion, that the photoperiodic response need not be solely based on a photoreceptor, but can proceed also with a thermoreceptor, in which not temperature as such, but a 24-hr alternation of temperatures is effective.

How do these three attributes affect our theoretical considerations about the mechanism of the photoperiodic process? None of these is at present incorporated in a general theory of the process, parts of which were presented by Bonner (p. 245) and Hendricks (p. 423). Let us first consider Galston's P-I-G scheme. In this the photoreceptor part is not changed at all and Dr. Hendricks' discussion stands unaltered, with the suggestion that even more stress be laid on the natural decay of the far-red modification of the pigment which can make it an effective oscillating system with a 24-hr cycle. The growth response end of the scheme is very definitely periodic in nature as the experiments with the tomato have shown. These experiments have also shown that when the endogenous period of the growth response end of the system does not mesh with the externally induced period of the photoreceptor pigment, growth is reduced, and when no periodic signal comes from the photoreceptor, growth is equally reduced.

An analysis of the parallel T-I-C scheme leads to approximately the same picture. The thermoreceptor must also be an oscillating system, and it would be very attractive if the red, far-red pigment could be sufficiently affected by temperature to serve the perception of temperature fluctuations. The cellular response at the other end of the scheme can be considered in terms of mitotic activity in the stem meristem, which according to Bünning (1952) has a clear-cut 24-hr rhythm. On the basis of Wetmore's anatomical analysis (p. 255) of the major events in the stem tip as it changes from vegetative to generative, we can assume that properly timed cyclic stimuli could activate one or the other group of cells, benefiting leaf primordia or axillary structures.

Upon closer analysis the P-I-G and T-I-C systems have shown a remarkable similarity; in both, the receptor responds to periodic stimuli and is periodic itself with the rhythm impressed upon it by the environmental stimuli, and in both, the reactor has an endogenous periodicity, which must be synchronous with the period of the receptor to respond properly. We can only envisage such synchronization when the intervening processes, I, are rhythmic, probably with the period imposed upon them by the receptor. The synchronization of the complete system could then be expected to occur at the I-C or I-G transfer point.

If the previous analysis is correct, we should expect not a *specific* substance to mediate between perception in the leaf and response in the growing parts of the plant, but the intermediary processes would be of the nature of a pulse, perhaps in the form of *rhythmic concentration changes* in some chemical constituent.

Now I leave these thoughts with you. I want to stress that I do not reject a single fact in the extensive photoperiodic lore; I claim only that they give a one-sided picture of the problem because all experiments were slanted toward the photoside of it, neglecting the periodicity and the temperature aspects. Whether I have overemphasized them, will have to be seen in the future when a proper balance between these views has been achieved.

REFERENCES

Arthur, J. M., and E. K. Harvill. 1937. Plant growth under continuous illumination from sodium vapor lamps supplemented by mercury arc lamps. *Contribs. Boyce Thompson Inst.,* 8, 433–43.

Bünning, E. 1932. Untersuchungen über die autonomen tagesperiodischen Bewegungen der Primärblätter von *Phaseolus multiflorus. Jahrb. wiss. Botan.,* 75, 439–80.

————. 1952. Über den Tagesrhythmus der Mitosehäufigkeit in Pflanzen. *Z. Botan.*, *40*, 193–99.

Carr, D. J. 1953. On the nature of photoperiodic induction. I and II. *Plant Physiol.*, *6*, 672, 680.

Hanson, J. B., and H. R. Highkin. 1954. Possible interaction between light-dark cycles and endogenous daily rhythms on the growth of tomato plants. *Plant Physiol.*, *29*, 301–302.

Hendricks, S. B. 1956. Control of growth and reproduction by light and darkness. *Am. Scientist*, *44*, 229–47.

Hillman, W. S. 1956. Injury of tomato plants by continuous light and unfavorable photoperiodic cycles. *Am. J. Botany*, *43*, 89–96.

Leinweber, F. J. 1956. Über die Temperaturabhängigkeit der Periodenlänge bei der endogenen Tagesrhythmik von *Phaseolus*. *Z. Botan.*, *44*, 337–64.

Went, F. W. 1957. *The Experimental Control of Plant Growth*. Chronica Botanica Co., Waltham, Mass.

Withrow, Alice P., and Robert B. Withrow. 1949. Photoperiodic chlorosis in tomato. *Plant Physiol.*, *24*, 657–63.

de Zeeuw, D. 1957. Flowering of *Xanthium* under long-day conditions. *Nature*, *180*, 588.

SECTION VIII

Photoperiodism in the Invertebrates

THE GONYAULAX CLOCK[1]

J. WOODLAND HASTINGS

**Division of Biochemistry, Noyes Laboratory of Chemistry,
University of Illinois, Urbana, Illinois**

BEATRICE M. SWEENEY

**Division of Marine Biology, Scripps Institution of Oceanography,
La Jolla, California**

Gonyaulax polyedra is an armored marine dinoflagellate that is both photosynthetic and luminescent. It is one of several unicellular forms that are responsible for the brilliant displays of luminescence seen in the ocean at night when the water is disturbed. Luminescence in dinoflagellates is considered in detail in Harvey's (1952) monograph. The organism was isolated from a net sample taken off Scripps Pier in La Jolla and has been grown in a supplemented sea water medium (Haxo and Sweeney, 1955; Sweeney and Hastings, 1957a). It has retained its brilliant blue luminosity in culture for more than five years. The wavelength of maximum emission is about 475 mμ (Hastings and Sweeney, 1957a).

The studies of Zacharias (1905), Moore (1909), Kofoid and Swezy (1921), and Harvey (1952) indicated that the bioluminescence of sea water containing dinoflagellates exhibited diurnal rhythmicity. Moreover, a rhythm of cell division in the dinoflagellate *Ceratium* had been demonstrated by the studies of Gough (1905), and Jörgensen (1911). A similar rhythm of cell division in cultures of *Peridinium triquetrum* was reported by Braarud and Pappas (1951). These observations suggested that *Gonyaulax* might be expected to have a diurnal rhythmicity.

Our studies have demonstrated the existence of a persistent endogenous diurnal rhythmicity, i.e., a "clock" system, in *Gonyaulax,* and this paper will serve to review its essential features. All our observations

[1] The previously unpublished studies cited in this paper were supported in part by a grant from the National Science Foundation.

567

concerning the nature of the clock system are consistent with the idea, outlined and discussed in considerable detail (Bruce and Pittendrigh, 1957; Pittendrigh and Bruce, 1957; Bünning, 1956) that clocks result from an endogenous self-sustained oscillation (ESSO) of cellular components.

Four overt manifestations of rhythmicity have been observed in *Gonyaulax,* and the question arises as to whether the organism possesses a single "master oscillating system" by which the overt rhythms are governed, or whether these are several independent, or quasi independent, oscillating systems. Evidence from earlier studies (Hastings and Sweeney, 1957b) led us to suggest the possibility of several independent oscillating systems. Our more recent evidence, presented here, makes the "master clock" proposal (Pittendrigh, 1958) seem more likely. The question still awaits a more definitive study, however.

THE RHYTHM OF LUMINESCENCE

This is a rhythm of induced luminescent flashing. *Gonyaulax* characteristically emits light (as a discrete flash; see Fig. 1) only when it is

FIG. 1. Flash of *Gonyaulax* in response to stimulation. Ordinate, light intensity; abscissa, time. Sweep time, 0.25 sec. Cells in the phase of maximum luminescence were placed in a test tube in front of the photo-tube and the table was tapped lightly. Temperature, 24°C.

stimulated. Luminescence in this instance is assayed in terms of the total amount of light emitted when the cells are stimulated to exhaustion. Stimulation is accomplished by bubbling air through a cell suspension in a test tube for a period of 1 min (Sweeney and Hastings, 1957a). When cultures are grown in conditions of alternating light and dark periods of 12 hr each (=LD), the luminescence during the dark period is greater by 40 to 60 times than the luminescence during the

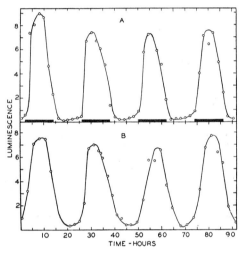

FIG. 2.   The curves illustrate the nature of the rhythm of luminescence in *Gonyaulax*. (A) The cells were exposed to alternating light and dark (black bars) periods of 12 hr each. (B) The cells were maintained at constant temperature (21°C) and at a constant light intensity of 120 ft-c subsequent to treatment with 12-hr light and dark periods as in (A). Note that in (A) the period is exactly 24 hr; in (B) the *natural period* is about 24.4 hr.

light period, as shown in Fig. 2A. As shown in Fig. 2B, these fluctuations will then continue as a persistent endogenous diurnal rhythm if the cultures are transferred to conditions of constant dim light (100–200 ft-c) at constant temperature (Hastings *et al.*, 1956). If the LD cultures are, instead, transferred to darkness, the rhythm will continue for several days, but with a decreasing amplitude (see Fig. 7). This amplitude decrease occurs because the nutrition of the organism requires light.

FLASHING AND GLOW RHYTHMS

Gonyaulax cultures have been found to emit light even if they are not stimulated. If a cell suspension is left undisturbed in front of the sensitive photomultiplier tube and the output is recorded on a chart, a record such as that shown in Fig. 3 is obtained. The closely spaced

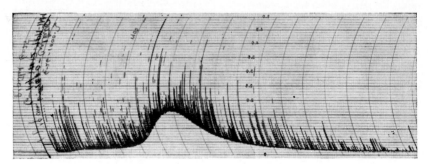

Fig. 3.   Photograph of a tracing from the automatic graphic chart, recording luminescence from undisturbed cultures. Ordinate, light intensity; abscissa, time, each division being equal to 1 hr. The changes in the baseline level represent the course of a steady dim light emission. The vertical traces result from flashes similar to the one illustrated in Fig. 1. Temperature, about 23 °C.

vertical lines represent flashing, which we think may result from cells bumping into one another or into the side of the tube. It is not due to external stimulation, i.e., vibration of the building, etc. Since the pattern shown, covering 18 hr (Fig. 3), is essentially repeated with approximately a 24-hr period, there is an evident rhythm in the flashing of undisturbed cell suspensions. It is our opinion that this rhythm of flashing is another manifestation of the rhythm of luminescence as measured by deliberate stimulation (described in the previous section), rather than a distinct and separate clock-controlled process. We have not made extensive studies of this flashing rhythm, but the records obtained serve to indicate that the important factors in the rhythm of luminescence include both (1) a variation in the sensitivity of the cell to stimulation—the frequency of flashing is always much greater during the night phase than during the day phase; and (2) a variation in the concentrations of the chemical components of the luminescent system—the flashes are much brighter during the night phase. The latter notion is also supported by the fact that the activities of the components of the luminescent system (*Gonyaulax* luciferin and luciferase) extractable from the cells during the night phase have much higher activities than those extractable during the day phase (Hastings and Sweeney, 1957a).

The gradual rise and fall of the baseline on the record (Fig. 3) results from a steady light emission, or glow. It is so dim that we have not been able to see it even after several hours of dark adaptation. This glow also recurs at approximately 24-hr intervals. Since the cells are kept in darkness during the recording, the glow rhythm does not persist for a long time, owing to the necessity of light for nutrition, as previously mentioned.

The glow rhythm appears to have the characteristics of an endogenous rhythm even though it is not possible to demonstrate its persistence for more than three days (Sweeney and Hastings, 1958). It has, however, provided a useful technique for the study of phase shifting.

THE RHYTHM OF CELL DIVISION

When *Gonyaulax* cultures were observed under the microscope, it was found that a large proportion of the cells were in the process of cell division at about the time when the glow was taking place, and that there was very little cell division at other times during the day (Sweeney and Hastings, 1957b; Sweeney and Hastings, 1958). Since recently divided daughter cells remain attached as "pairs" for about 30 min after cell division, the most convenient index of cell division is the number of these pairs. In LD cultures, a very sharp maximum in the number of pairs occurs every 24 hr, just at the end of the dark period. This peak occurs an hour or so after the maximum of the luminescent glow, so it is thought that the glow occurs during, and perhaps results from, a stage or stages of mitosis. If cell division occurs at only one time of day, then the growth curve should have a staircase shape. Direct cell counts made on LD cultures confirmed that this was indeed the case (Fig. 4).

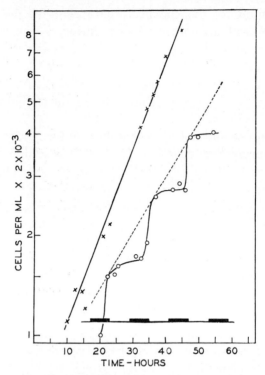

Fig. 4. Growth curves for *Gonyaulax*. Under conditions of constant bright light (X) the logarithm of the cell number increased linearly with time and the average generation time was 1 day. Under conditions of alternating light and dark periods (O) the growth curve had a staircase shape, and the average generation time was 1.5 days. Dark periods indicated by black bars. Light intensity in both cases was 900 ft-c; temperature, 21.5°C.

The rhythm of cell division has all the properties of an endogenous rhythm. It will persist for long periods under conditions of constant dim light and constant temperature, as shown in Fig. 5.

The average growth rates measured in phased or rhythmic cultures have always been found to be less than one division per day. In experiments such as those shown in Figs. 4 and 5, therefore, the generation time for some cells must have been approximately 24 hr, while for others it was 48 hr, or a higher integral multiple of 24 hr. This indicates that the population is heterogeneous with respect to life cycle and mitotic events.

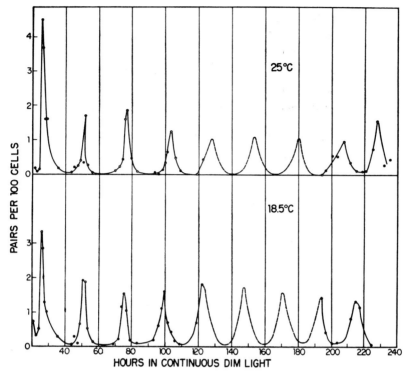

FIG. 5. The curves illustrate the diurnal rhythm of cell division at 18.5°C (lower curve) and at 25°C (upper curve), as measured by the percent of paired cells present in a cell suspension. The *average* generation time was 4.2 days at 18.5°C and 3.8 days at 25°C. Period as related to temperature, see Table I.

CHARACTERISTICS OF THE RHYTHM

The period of each of the rhythms under constant conditions (= the natural period) is always close to, but not necessarily exactly, 24 hr. Moreover the phase, under constant conditions, may bear any desired relation to solar time. As pointed out by Pittendrigh (1958) and Pittendrigh and Bruce (1957), these are compelling reasons for the assertion that diurnal rhythms are endogenous self-sustaining oscillations. The phase and period are clearly not related to phase and period of uncontrolled periodic variables in the environment.

The period of each of the three overt rhythms which we have studied is essentially temperature-independent (Hastings and Sweeney, 1957b; Sweeney and Hastings, 1958). Table I summarizes our data with respect to this question. It is of interest to find *some* temperature dependence, even though it is not great. The unusual temperature coefficient (period is longer at higher temperatures) suggests that the clock has a temperature compensation mechanism which, however, is not pre-

TABLE I. Effect of Temperature and Light Intensity upon Natural Period of *Gonyaulax* Rhythms[a]

Rhythm Measured	Temperature, °C	Light Intensity, ft-c	Average Period, hr	Number of Periods Measured to Get Average
Luminescence	11.5 (and below)	100	Rhythm is lost	—
"	15.9	100	22.5	2
"	16	100	22.8	6
"	19	100	23.0	6
"	21	120	24.4	5
"	21	100	24.4	5
"	21	380	22.8	5
"	21	680	22.0	4[b]
"	22	100	25.3	6
"	23.6	100	25.7	6
"	23.7	100	25.7	3
"	26.6	100	26.8	2
"	26.7	100	26.5	6
"	32	100	25.5	4
"	21	Dark	23.0	1
"	21	Dark	24.4	3
"	21.3	Dark	23.5	2
"	21.3	Dark	24.2	4
"	22.8	Dark	24.5	2
Glow	18	Dark	22.9	2
"	20	Dark	23.3	2
"	25	Dark	24.7	2
Cell division	18.5	200	23.9	8
"	25	200	25.4	8
"	18	Dark	22.8	1
"	25	Dark	24.8	1

[a] The table gives all the data thus far obtained in our laboratories with reference to the natural period in *Gonyaulax*. Many of the data were taken from experiments not specifically designed to study the effect of temperature. Only those in which the temperature did not vary by more than ±1.0°C were used. In most cases the temperature fluctuation was much less than this.

[b] Overt rhythmicity in luminescence is inhibited at this light intensity and is no longer measurable after four periods.

cisely balanced. Each of the three overt rhythms shows this same relationship to temperature. Bruce and Pittendrigh (1956) had also concluded that compensation was the most likely mechanism for temperature-independent periods in the *Euglena* clock.

The natural period is also a function of the light intensity. We have studied this only with respect to the rhythm of luminescence, where at higher light intensities the period is shorter than at lower intensities (see Table I).

Since the rhythmic mechanism in *Gonyaulax* is capable of marking off 24-hr periods with a fair degree of accuracy, irrespective of temperature and light intensity (within limits), the use of the word "clock" seems justified. Although the term "clock" carries with it a functional connotation, the fact that the functional importance of the clock in *Gonyaulax* is not apparent to us does not seem to be a basis for excluding the use of the word. The overt rhythms which we have observed may, in fact, have a clock significance which we do not understand. Also, it is clearly possible that the overt rhythms may be incidental results of another, but as yet unidentified, cellular rhythmicity, which *does* have an important clock function. As Pittendrigh (1958) and Pittendrigh and Bruce (1957) have pointed out, a "master" clock mechanism might necessarily result in a rhythmic aspect to a whole variety of physiological processes.

Under "natural" conditions, the alternating light and dark periods serve to hold the periods at precisely 24 hr and to determine the phase so that maximum luminescence occurs during the middle of the dark period. But it seems adequately clear from a variety of experiments that the endogenous rhythmicity in *Gonyaulax* does not require, and is not the result of, previous treatment with alternating light and dark periods.

After the cells have been kept in bright light (800 to 1600 ft-c), the rhythm of luminescence, and also of cell division, is lost. In bright light, the amount of luminescence which can be evoked from the cells, and also the number of pairs observed, does not vary with time of day. As would be expected, the growth curve is then perfectly straight (Fig. 4). If such cells are then placed in darkness, or if the light intensity is reduced to 100 to 200 ft-c, a pronounced diurnal rhythm of luminescence is initiated (Sweeney and Hastings, 1957a; Hastings and

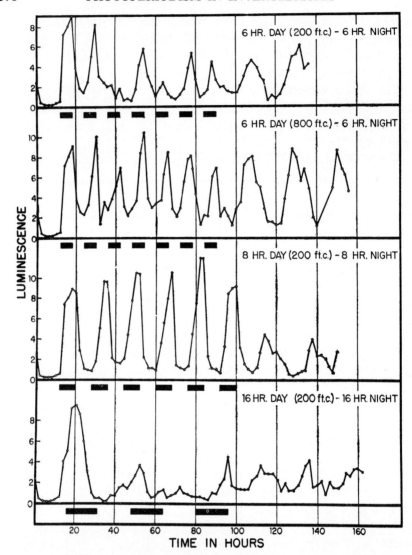

FIG. 6. Entrainment of the luminescence rhythm by periods of alternating light and dark which differ from 24 hr. Black bars show dark periods. In subsequent experiments of this type a more uniform illumination system has been used, and most of the apparent irregularities are no longer observed. Note that when the cultures are placed in continuous dim light (200 ft-c) subsequent to the entrainment, the rhythm reverts to its natural period of approximately 24 hr. The importance of the light intensity to the response observed in a particular entrainment schedule may be

(*Continued on p. 577*)

Sweeney, 1958). The amplitude of the rhythm progressively diminishes when the cells are in the dark, but it remains undamped when they are in dim light. The phase of the initiated rhythm is dependent only upon the time at which the light intensity was changed. Experiments of this nature have been carried out with cells from cultures grown in bright light for a year or more (200 to 400 generations). There is, therefore, no recent history of exposure to day-night conditions, or of information from light or temperature concerning a 24-hr period.

The converse type of experiment, namely, attempting to "train" cells to periods which differ greatly from their natural period, is illustrated in Fig. 6. The cells were grown under conditions of alternating light and dark periods, as illustrated in the figure, for about 90 hr. In most instances, the luminescence changes showed a period of the same length as the imposed light-dark cycle. Subsequent to this "nondiurnal" alternating light-dark treatment the cells were left in constant dim light. In each case it is evident that a rhythm with a period of approximately 24 hr is resumed. The same result was obtained when the cells were left in darkness after the "nondiurnal" alternating light-dark treatment. Preliminary studies indicate that the rhythm of cell division behaves identically. It may therefore be concluded that a diurnal fluctuation in environmental factors is not obligatory for the functioning of the *Gonyaulax* clock. It will be of interest to see the results of an experiment, now in progress, in which the cells are maintained on a 16-hr cycle for several months or years.

An important point, demonstrated and discussed in detail in the work of Pittendrigh and Bruce (Pittendrigh, 1954; Bruce and Pittendrigh, 1957; Pittendrigh and Bruce, 1957; Pittendrigh, 1958), is that the phase of an endogenous rhythm may be shifted (= resetting the clock) by a nonrepeated, relatively brief exposure to changed environmental conditions, such as light. Such a treatment was appropriately called a perturbation. As the above authors have noted, this feature

---

FIG. 6 (*Continued*).
    noted from the results with 12-hr cycles at 200 ft-c and 800 ft-c. With the dim light, a type of frequency demultiplication is observed (maxima every 24 hr); with the bright light, entrainment or repetitive resetting occurs, with maxima every 12 hr. The distinction between these phenomena is discussed by Bruce and Pittendrigh (1957) and by Pittendrigh (1958). It appears that little consideration has been given to the effect of varying the energy input to the system in experiments such as these.

might well have been expected, since an endogenous rhythm quite evidently has the inherent property of a *natural period*. Light and dark periods serve, in essence, only to give information concerning phase. It is therefore logical that a phase shift may be accomplished by a treatment which is not accompanied by any information concerning period.

The *Gonyaulax* clock illustrates this principle well. It was mentioned previously that with aperiodic cultures that have been grown in bright light, a change in the light intensity (to dim light or dark) not only initiates overt rhythmicity, but also determines phase. It is also apparent that in the experiments shown in Fig. 6, repetitive resetting is achieved by the alternating light and dark periods, and that the phase of the endogenous rhythm under the subsequent constant conditions is determined by the last dark to light transition.

Resetting of the *Gonyaulax* clock by a single perturbation has been found to occur irrespective of the particular way in which the experiment is performed. For example, the phase of the luminescent rhythm in cultures in constant dim light (which exhibit rhythmicity similar to that shown in Fig. 2b) may be shifted either by an exposure to bright light or by a sojourn in darkness. Alternatively, if cultures otherwise in constant darkness are given an appropriate exposure to light, a phase shift occurs. Some results of experiments of the latter type are shown in Fig. 7. As pointed out by Pittendrigh (1958), the effectiveness of phase shift in a model oscillator should be a function of the time during the cycle when the exposure is made, the duration of the exposure, and the intensity of the exposure. This has indeed been found to be the case in *Gonyaulax*.

Exposure to light, i.e., a perturbation, given within 6 hr of the maximum in luminescence is more effective in shifting the phase than a perturbation during the other 12 hr of the cycle. Moreover the *direction* of the phase shift varies with the time of the cycle, as illustrated in Fig. 7. A perturbation before the maximum in luminescence results in a phase delay, whereas a similar treatment at or after the maximum causes the phase to advance. Our results indicate that the initial phase shift is a stable one, no transients being involved. This point must be investigated with *Gonyaulax* in greater detail, however.

A longer exposure to light is more effective in phase shifting than

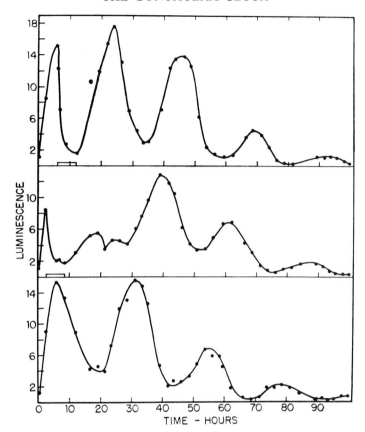

FIG. 7.   Phase shift of the luminescence rhythm by single light perturbations. The lower curve is the control left in the dark all the while. Previous to the time shown all cultures were in LD conditions. Zero time was
the end of the last light period. The upper two curves show the response
of cells kept under identical conditions, with the exception of a 6-hr light
exposure (1400 ft-c) given at the times indicated by the bars on the time
axis (middle, from 2½ to 8½ hr; upper, from 6 to 12 hr). Temperature,
21.2°C.

shorter exposures of the same intensity. In this system the amount of
phase shift increases linearly with time up to a maximum, which is obtained with a 2½-hr exposure to bright light (> 1000 ft-c). This
response is evidently somewhat complicated by the differences in sensitivity with time in the old cycle, as noted above.

High light intensities are more effective in shifting the phase than are lower ones. When both the time at which the exposure is made and its duration are held constant, the resetting is an approximately linear function of intensity, up to a saturation value of about 800 ft-c.

The last-noted feature has permitted a determination of the action spectrum for resetting. Measurements were made of the effectiveness of monochromatic light (from 325 mμ to 750 mμ, in 25-mμ steps) in shifting the phase. The results obtained show relatively sharp maxima in effectiveness at 475 mμ and at 650 mμ. Although these peaks do not correspond exactly with the absorption spectrum for the cellular pigments, it is probable that the chlorophylls are the primary photoreceptive pigments involved.

Several aspects of phase shifting have also been studied with the glow rhythm, yielding results essentially identical with those obtained with the rhythm of luminescence. A detailed analysis of the data should be of use in constructing and evaluating models such as the one presented to us at this symposium by Drs. Pittendrigh and Bruce.

DISCUSSION

The fact that the several overt rhythms in *Gonyaulax* have similar properties supports the idea of a single "master clock." The similarities include a loss of overt rhythmicity when the organism is subjected to constant bright light, but a retention of rhythmicity in constant dim light; the manifestation of natural periods in constant dim light or darkness which are close to but not exactly 24 hr; an entrainment to light and dark cycles which differ from 24 hr; and a phase shift of the endogenous rhythm upon changes in illumination, the light perturbations yielding no information concerning the period. In addition, the period of each rhythm is essentially temperature-independent, but in each case the temperature sensitivity that does exist has a Q_{10} of less than 1.0. An unusual temperature relationship of this type has also been reported by Bühnemann (1955) for the clock system in *Oedogonium,* suggesting that a common mechanism is involved. The idea of a temperature compensation mechanism carries with it the distinct possibility of imprecision, within the limits of adaptive selection pressure. The cases with a Q_{10} of slightly less than 1.0, therefore, need not fall into a separate class from those with a Q_{10} of slightly greater than 1.0.

If indeed there were several independently oscillating systems in *Gonyaulax,* one might suppose that the luminescent system was such an oscillator. Our interest in this possibility was discussed earlier (Hastings and Sweeney, 1957b) in connection with the finding that the effect of temperature upon period was similar to its effect upon the amplitude of luminescence. This implied that an inhibitor system, presumed to be specific for the luminescent system, was involved, and that its action was directly upon the luminescent system rather than via a master clock.

More recent experiments appear to exclude the luminescent system as an independently oscillating system. If cells are stimulated to exhaustion at a time when they are sensitive to resetting by light (refer to Fig. 7), their luminescent response falls to a low value. The effect of stimulation is thus overtly similar to the perturbation by light, both presumably resulting in an exhaustion of a component(s) of the luminescent system. If the luminescent system were itself a clock, then perturbation by stimulation should be an effective way by which phase shifting could be accomplished. When the luminescence of aliquots was assayed at times subsequent to stimulation, it was found that the rhythmicity persisted, but that no phase shift whatsoever occurred. This tells us not only that the luminescent system is not a clock; it also tells us that its precise chemical status has no effect upon the clock. In other words, there is no feedback from the luminescent system to the clock. These experiments may be of significance in directing our approach toward finding the essential components of the clock, since feedback is a critical property to be expected in any biological clock mechanism.

If we look for a single biological element or class of elements which may function to regulate a variety of physiological processes, our attention is drawn to the nucleus since it does have a "master" role in the control of cellular processes. Is there any known aspect of nuclear metabolism which might be involved in the clock mechanism? From a variety of experiments it seems clear that cell division and the mitotic cycle may be excluded as a possibility. In the absence of cell division the clock continues to run. When cell division does occur, the population may be heterogeneous with respect to the mitotic cycle, with no evident change in clock activity. It is therefore not possible to identify the clock with processes involved in the mitotic cycle, although it is clear that the mitotic cycle may be clock controlled.

From what we know of clock systems on the one hand, and from our knowledge of nuclear metabolism on the other, it seems that a detailed study of the ribose nucleic acid (RNA) metabolism in clock systems would be of value. Its known metabolic role suggests it as a likely candidate for a "master" oscillator, and a model for the way in which it might oscillate is not difficult to envision. From the studies of Mazia (1956) we know that RNA is formed in the nucleus and moves unidirectionally into the cytoplasm. Specific enzymes, formed in response to RNA, could decrease the level of substrates specific for new RNA synthesis, thereby decreasing the rate of RNA production. Via an appropriate turnover of the components involved, a rhythmic RNA production could occur, giving rise to a rhythmic aspect to all RNA-coupled systems, which we might measure as overt physiological rhythms. Such a system has the possibility of controlling many diverse cellular reactions, and at the same time the feedback in the system might be rather specific.

This model is essentially a prey-predator type, in the general class considered by Lotka (1920). In the simple case that he considers, the period is inversely proportional to the square root of the product of the velocity constants. All that would be necessary to expect temperature independence is that the period be, instead, a function of the ratio of the velocity constants. Additional assumptions concerning the nature of the mechanism might result in this. Since very little is known concerning the chemical events involved in a clock system under constant conditions, a great variety of specific models is possible.

The need for biochemical information is evident; what does RNA metabolism look like in such a system, for example? We certainly are not suggesting that RNA is the only component which could be supposed to function as the "master" oscillator. We merely point to it as a likely example, in order to illustrate the fact that additional information concerning the nature of the key compounds involved in the clock system will be of indispensable value in understanding the mechanism.

REFERENCES

Braarud, T., and I. Pappas. 1951. Experimental studies on the dinoflagellate *Peridinium triquetrum* (Ehrb.) Lebour. *Avhandl. Norske Videnskaps-Akad. Oslo. I. Mat.-Natury. Kl.* No. 2, 1–23.

Bruce, V. G., and C. S. Pittendrigh. 1956. Temperature independence in a unicellular "clock." *Proc. Natl. Acad. Sci. U. S., 42,* 676–82.

———. 1957. Endogenous rhythms in insects and microorganisms. *Am. Naturalist, 91,* 179–95.

Bühnemann, F. 1955. Das endodiurnale System der *Oedogonium* Zelle, III. Über den Temperatureinfluss. *Z. Naturforsch., 10b,* 305–10.

Bünning, E. 1956. Endogenous rhythms in plants. *Ann. Rev. Plant Physiol., 7,* 71–90.

Gough, L. H. 1905. Report on the plankton of the English Channel in 1903. *Mar. Biol. Assoc. U. K. International Fishery Investigation. First Report on Fishery and Hygrographical Investigations in the North Sea and Adjacent Waters (Southern Area),* 1902–1903, 325–77. London.

Harvey, E. N. 1952. *Bioluminescence.* Academic Press, New York.

Hastings, J. W., Marlene Wiesner, Jean Owens, and B. M. Sweeney. 1956. The rhythm of luminescence in a marine dinoflagellate. *Anat. Record, 125,* 611.

Hastings, J. W., and B. M. Sweeney. 1957a. The luminescent reaction in extracts of the marine dinoflagellate *Gonyaulax polyedra. J. Cellular Comp. Physiol., 49,* 209–25.

———. 1957b. On the mechanism of temperature independence in a biological clock. *Proc. Natl. Acad. Sci. U. S., 43,* 804–11.

———. 1958. A persistent diurnal rhythm of luminescence in *Gonyaulax polyedra. Biol. Bull., 115* (3).

Haxo, F. T., and B. M. Sweeney. 1955. Bioluminescence in *Gonyaulax polyedra. Luminescence of Biological Systems.* F. H. Johnson, Editor. American Association for the Advancement of Science, Washington, D. C. Pp. 415–20.

Jörgensen, E. 1911. Die *Ceratien.* Eine kurze Monographie der Gattung *Ceratium* Schrank. *Intern. Rev. ges. Hydrobiol. Hydrog., Biol. Suppl.* Ser. II, 1–124.

Kofoid, C. A., and O. Swezy. 1921. The free unarmoured dinoflagellata, *Mem. Univ. Calif., 5,* 1–562.

Lotka, A. J. 1920. Analytical note on certain rhythms in organic systems. *Proc. Natl. Acad. Sci. U. S., 6,* 410–15.

Mazia, Dan. 1956. Nuclear products and nuclear reproduction, *Enzymes: Units of Biological Structure and Function.* O. H. Gaebler, Editor. Academic Press, New York. Pp. 261–78.

Moore, Benjamin. 1909. Observations on certain organisms of (*a*) variations in reaction to light and (*b*) a diurnal periodicity of phosphorescence. *Biochem. J., 4,* 1–29.

Pittendrigh, C. S. 1954. On temperature independence in the clock-system controlling emergence time in *Drosophila. Proc. Natl. Acad. Sci. U. S., 40,* 1018–29.

————. 1958. Perspectives in the study of biological clocks. *Perspectives in Marine Biology*. University of California Press, Berkeley, Calif.

Pittendrigh, C. S., and V. G. Bruce. 1957. An oscillator model for biological clocks. *Rhythmic and Synthetic Processes in Growth*. Dorothea Rudnick, Editor. Princeton University Press, Princeton, N. J. Pp. 75–109.

Sweeney, B. M., and J. W. Hastings. 1957a. Characteristics of the diurnal rhythm of luminescence in *Gonyaulax polyedra*. *J. Cellular Comp. Physiol., 49*, 115–28.

————. 1957b. A persistent rhythm of cell division in populations of *Gonyaulax polyedra*. *Plant Physiol., 32* (Suppl.), XXV.

————. 1958. Rhythmic cell division in populations of *Gonyaulax polyedra*. *J. Protozool., 5*, 217–24.

Zacharias, O. 1905. Beobachtungen über das Leuchtvermögen von *Ceratium tripos* (Müll). *Biol. Zentr., 25*, 20–30.

PHOTOPERIODISM IN INSECTS AND MITES

A. D. LEES

**Agricultural Research Council, Unit of Insect Physiology,
Cambridge, England**

The effects of day length on an aphid were reported by Marcovitch (1924) only four years after the announcement of the fundamental discoveries by Garner and Allard. Nevertheless, despite this encouraging beginning, little more was accomplished in the field of arthropod photoperiodism until the postwar years, which have witnessed a considerable revival of interest. It is perhaps for this reason that physiological analysis of this phenomenon is still at an early stage of development. Sufficient species have now been examined to show that photoperiodism is widespread, although certainly less ubiquitous than in plants; and the adaptive significance of the response has come to be appreciated. In the course of such studies useful information has been accumulated which will have eventual utility in interpreting the photoperiodic mechanism. However, it must be emphasized that the insect physiologist is not yet in a position to present a satisfactory working hypothesis of the controlling mechanisms in any one species.

No "endogenous" annual rhythms, akin to the persistent diurnal or tidal rhythms of Crustacea, have yet been described in insects. When such seasonal rhythms occur, it has invariably been possible to relate them to some component of the environment, the day or night length being particularly pertinent in this respect. In general, the processes so determined fall into two categories: the control of growth in species that hibernate or estivate; and the control of differentiation in species that show seasonal differences of form. The two are sometimes interconnected. In the following account some of the salient features of arthropod photoperiodism are surveyed, with the emphasis on recent work.

PHOTOPERIOD AND DIAPAUSE

The total cessation of growth or reproduction (diapause) is one of the most striking characteristics of dormant insects. It is now clear that photoperiod is one of the most important factors in the environment concerned in the induction of diapause (Lees, 1955, 1956). Although low temperature is often the sole agency responsible for terminating dormancy, this is not always true. In the moth *Dendrolimus,* for example, the hibernating larvae remain photosensitive and resume feeding and growth at any time in response to the appropriate photoperiod (Geyspitz, 1949). The many species of arthropods known to have a photoinduced diapause include many Lepidoptera, the Colorado beetle *Leptinotarsa* (de Wilde, 1954; Goryshin, 1956) and the red mite *Metatetranychus* (Lees, 1953a). It is worth noting that all these species feed on plants; it is perhaps for this reason that they require a particularly accurate and repeatable seasonal "timetable."

The direction of the response is the same in nearly all species: long days (or permanent light) cause uninterrupted development while short days of 8 or 12 hr initiate diapause (Fig. 1A). This uniformity in the response is hardly surprising since the usual ecological require-

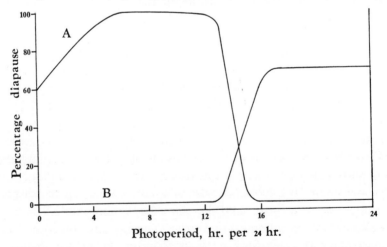

Fig. 1. The induction of diapause by photoperiod. A, the mite *Metatetranychus ulmi* (from Lees, 1953a); B, the silkworm *Bombyx mori* (from Kogure, 1933).

ment is for dormancy to set in at one particular time of year, namely autumn. The insect may pass through two or more generations in late spring and summer when long days permit uninterrupted growth; and it is held in diapause in winter and early spring, thus escaping the effect of short days at this time. The mulberry silkworm *Bombyx mori* is exceptional in this respect, the overwintered eggs becoming photosensitive almost immediately development is resumed in early spring. Associated with this circumstance is a reversal in the response, long days during early development causing the moths to lay diapause eggs, and short days, developing eggs (Fig. B) (Kogure, 1933). Such a short-day response is well suited to the two-generation pattern of bivoltine races of silkworms, but it is obviously incompatible with the production of more than two generations.

An interesting variant has recently been described by Masaki (1956) in some geographical strains of the cabbage moth (*Barathra brassicae*. It seems that the same insect may exhibit alternative forms of arrest: a transient "summer" diapause and a long-enduring "winter" diapause. The summer type is induced by a long photoperiod, the winter type by a short one. The essential difference between these forms of diapause is underlined by the finding that summer dormancy can be completed at higher temperatures than the winter.

The photoresponse in insects and mites is often modified by other environmental factors. Temperature independence is not noted to the same extent as in similar reactions in plants or in light-controlled diurnal rhythms. Indeed, temperature dependence is frequently an adaptive mechanism in itself, whereby a rapidly breeding species can take advantage of year to year variations in weather. In most long-day species, high temperatures tend to suppress diapause, while low temperatures have the opposite effect. In *Bombyx,* however, the response is reversed and therefore remains in harmony with the reversal of the photoreaction.

The mode of action of temperature requires further study. According to Goryshin (1955) the photoperiod critical for the induction of diapause in the moth *Acronycta* falls with successive increments of temperature to the extent of almost 1.5 hr per 5°C. Short exposures to temperatures below the threshold of development exert no influence when they are made coincident with the dark phase, but low-temperature periods in light are rendered equivalent to darkness. That the light reaction has such a marked temperature coefficient had not previously been suspected. Indeed, preliminary results with *Metatetranychus* suggested that temperature sensitivity was confined to the dark period in this species (Lees, 1955a).

The quantity or quality of the food is also sometimes a modifying influence. In *Metatetranychus* nutritional deficiency due to leaf senescence or to damage by the feeding punctures of other mites causes the female to lay diapause eggs even when exposed to a long photoperiod and high temperature. The codling moth *Carpocapsa pomonella* provides a further example (Gambaro, 1954). Although it was previously thought that the larvae were influenced only by photoperiod, acting through the semitransparent flesh of the apple, it now seems that some quality connected with the maturity of the fruit is important: thus ripeness is conducive to diapause, and immaturity to diapause-free development.

PHOTOPERIODIC ADAPTATION IN GEOGRAPHICAL RACES

It is well known that populations of arthropods with a wide geographical range often show local differences in the character of their diapause. In general, diapause tends to be obligatory in populations from high latitudes and the life cycle is univoltine; in contrast, populations from lower temperate latitudes often pass through two or more generations a year, this facultative diapause being controlled by photoperiod and other environmental factors (Andrewartha, 1952; Lees, 1955). These different forms of arrest are also known to be inherited. The recent work of Harvey (1957) on the spruce budworm *Choristoneura* illustrates the point afresh. In eastern Canada this insect is essentially univoltine although 3–4% of the larvae were found to develop without diapause when placed on long days. After selecting this phenotype for six generations a strain was produced which was almost diapause-free in long days but which entered diapause uniformly in short days.

Even if the species exhibits a facultative diapause consistently throughout the area of distribution, there is every reason to expect that the light response will show local adaptations to photoperiod. Thus it has been noted that the photoperiod critical for diapause initiation in a Cambridge (England) population of red mites (*Tetranychus telarius*) was about 2 hr less than in a Leningrad population 8° of latitude to the north (Bondarenko, 1950; Lees, 1953a). A systematic study of these variations has recently been made by Danilyevsky (1957) in the moth *Acronycta*. Insects from the Leningrad (60°N.) region were found to have a critical photoperiod of nearly 20 hr; whereas in insects from Vitebsk (55°N.), Byelgorod (51°N.), and Sukhumi on the Black Sea coast (43°N.) the values were 18, 17, and 14½ hr respectively. There is a further difference in that high temperatures are more effective in preventing diapause in the more southerly strains. Since the pupae are released from diapause much earlier in the south than in the north (a further adaptation in the diapause mechanism) the net result is that long-day conditions persist for more than four months in the south, and three generations can develop. On the other hand, short-day conditions prevail almost throughout the summer for Leningrad insects which are invariably univoltine despite the latent capacity to respond to photoperiod. As is suggested by Danilyevsky, local variations in the diapause characteristics will undoubtedly operate as important isolating mechanisms.

The mode of adaptation to the environment of the Japanese races of *Barathra* investigated by Masaki (1956) is entirely different. This species is adjusted to a two-generation pattern almost throughout its range. Strains from northern Japan show the usual response to photoperiod, a short day inducing an intense diapause and a long day preventing diapause completely. But insects taken from populations in the south respond to the long photoperiods of summer by aestivating. This short-term "summer" diapause delays development just sufficiently for the second generation to develop in autumn. Pupae of the latter generation, having been acted upon by short days, then enter an intense "winter" diapause.

The three examples detailed in this section show that there is considerable plasticity in the photoperiodic behavior, even within a single order (Lepidoptera). Clearly, there may well be still other types of response awaiting discovery.

MODE OF ACTION OF CYCLES OF LIGHT AND DARKNESS

There seems little doubt that the majority of arthropods respond to the length of the light-dark cycle as such and not to gradual changes in either component. For example, this statement is certainly applicable to the moth *Grapholitha* (Dickson, 1949) and the mite *Metatetranychus* (Lees, 1953a,b). The critical role of the dark period in the measurement of time provides a further parallel with the photoperiodic mechanism in plants. Several Lepidoptera including *Acronycta* (Danilyevsky and Glinyanaya, 1949, 1950), *Antheraea* (Tanaka, 1950) and *Grapholitha* as well as *Metatetranychus,* are now known to have a long night requirement for diapause induction. But besides an adequate dark period *Grapholitha* also requires a light period of appropriate length. Indeed the larva will enter diapause only with days of 7 to 15 hr duration and nights of 11 to 16 hr; all other cycles are inoperative. Failure to initiate diapause in permanent darkness (a common feature in arthropods) is a special case of this response.

Some differences are apparent in the behavior of *Metatetranychus*. Although long dark periods are always strongly inductive and long light periods noninductive, the former are far more potent. Thus a 12-hr dark period can completely annul an accompanying light period of nearly 36 hr. It follows that the combinations of light and dark capable of inducing diapause are much wider than in *Grapholitha*.

There are also obvious contrasts with the mechanism in plants. The failure of light "breaks," even of several hours duration, to reduce the effect of inductive dark periods is a noteworthy feature of the response in arthropods. Moreover, the interruption of long light periods by fairly protracted intervals of darkness is also inoperative. The impression conveyed is of the light and dark reactions increasing in rate with time. Nevertheless, it may well be that their products must reach a threshold before becoming active. A further point is that some reactant in the system must be accumulated, since one or two inductive cycles are usually without effect. Indeed, some twenty or thirty cycles are required by the larvae of some Lepidoptera.

In all cases yet examined photoperiodic induction has proved to be independent of light intensity, provided the latter is adequate for stimulation. Unlike plants, all such reactions require only low intensities: 1–2 ft-c of white light in *Metatetranychus;* less than 1.0 ft-c in several Lepidoptera; and approximately 0.01 ft-c in the embryos of *Bombyx.* The important question of the wavelength dependence of the reaction requires further attention, but it is known that the violet, blue, and blue-green regions of the spectrum are especially effective in *Bombyx, Grapholitha,* and *Metatetranychus,* all these genera being nearly or totally insensitive to red. There appears nevertheless to be some variation between species. In a recent investigation by Geyspitz (1957) the following descending order of sensitivity was established for two genera of Lepidoptera: violet, green in *Dendrolimus;* green, violet, red in *Pieris.* A third genus, *Acronycta,* appeared to be equally sensitive to violet, green, and red, although this may have been a consequence of the high intensities used. Unfortunately, no response curves so far obtained have sufficient accuracy for any firm conclusions to be drawn as the nature of the photosensitive pigment. It is worth noting in this context that there is as yet no evidence that the photo-response can be reversed by other wavelengths in the manner of the red, far-red reaction in plants.

Although it has been repeatedly demonstrated that photoperiod acts directly on arthropods, and not indirectly through the food plant, information is still lacking as to the precise location of the photoreceptor. The receptors in the larvae of *Dendrolimus* are certainly in the anterior region of the body, for it is possible to place the head in a light-tight hood for 12 hr a day while exposing the thorax and abdomen to permanent light—a treatment that invariably results in diapause initiation (Geyspitz, 1957). *Dendrolimus, Pieris,* and *Acronycta* also show a well-defined locomotor response to light which is mediated by the eyes. Since a comparison of the wavelength dependence of the behavioral and photoperiodic reactions revealed certain similarities, Geyspitz concluded that the eyes were also responsive to photoperiod. This argument must, however, be treated with some reserve in view of the earlier experiments by Tanaka (1950) on the larvae of the silkworm *Antheraea pernyi.* In this species photoperiodic induction remains unimpaired after the lateral ocelli have been destroyed by cauterization.

ENDOCRINE CONTROL OF DIAPAUSE

Future work on photoperiodism will undoubtedly profit from recent research on the regulation of insect diapause by hormones. It now seems probable that humoral controlling mechanisms participate in all forms of diapause whether embryonic, larval, pupal, or adult. But it is equally clear that the mechanism of control, indeed the endocrine systems themselves, differ according to the stage of arrest.

Diapause in the silkworm *Bombyx* is controlled maternally, the type of egg laid by the moth being decided by a secretion from the sub-oesophageal ganglion (Fukuda, 1951; Hasegawa, 1952, 1957). If this hormone is liberated into the blood, diapause eggs are formed in the ovaries; if it is not secreted, they become nondiapause eggs. But there is also a further element in the system of control: the suboesophageal ganglion is in turn controlled by the brain, which inhibits the liberation of the "diapause hormone" in moths previously determined by photoperiod and temperature as nondiapause egg producers, while permitting or stimulating its liberation in diapause egg producers. This influence is exerted through the circumoesophageal commissures; when these connectives are cut during the pupal stage, the moth will lay diapause eggs regardless of the direction of the initial determination. It is not yet certain whether this controlling system also operates in other insects with diapause eggs.

It is well known from the researches of Williams that the pupal diapause in the silkworm *Platysamia* is due to the failure of the neurosecretory cells in the brain to supply the hormone necessary for the tropic activation of the prothoracic glands. Without the secretion from these glands, moulting and metamorphosis remain permanently in abeyance. In this instance the brain controls the prothoracic glands through a diffusible hormone.

After the brain has become inactive at the onset of diapause, prolonged exposure to moderately low temperatures (ca. 6–15°C) is required before the competence of the neurosecretory cells to secrete hormone is restored (Williams, 1956). Recent work by van der Kloot (1955) has shown that the dormant condition of these cells in the diapausing insect is associated with the inactivation of the entire brain. All spontaneous electrical activity ceases (in other ganglia of the ventral chain such activity remains normal); and cholinergic material vanishes, reappearing only as the period of chilling is extended. The implication is that the neurosecretory cells are accessible to stimulation by other nervous connections, in the same manner as the neurosecretory cells of the vertebrate hypothalamus. The temporary depolarization of these neurones may well be necessary to prevent neurosecretion.

The humoral control of larval and adult (reproductive) diapause is less well understood. However, there seems little doubt that the same endocrine system, namely the brain and prothoracic glands, regulate both pupal and larval diapause. But in the case of reproductive dormancy the corpora allata and probably the brain are involved (de Wilde, 1954).

It will be readily apparent from these examples that the brain plays a key role in the control of diapause. Unfortunately, although we have valuable information as to the kind of mechanisms involved in "triggering" the neurosecretory cells, we do not know how the brain is "switched off," even in those species with an obligatory diapause. There are several possibilities. One is that the mechanism is intrinsic, the brain being committed from the outset to a certain "program" of activity. A second is that the brain is influenced by afferent (perhaps proprioceptive) nerve impulses which occur uniquely at the appropriate point in ontogeny. However, it is not easy to visualize the steps by which this input could result in the inhibition of nervous activity. A third possibility is that the brain responds to a humoral stimulus, linked in turn with the state of nutrition (Andrewartha, 1952; Monro, 1956).

The problem is even more challenging when diapause is photoperiodically determined, since the action of this factor is often exerted many instars before growth is arrested. One or more normal cycles of neurosecretion (each corresponding to an instar) may therefore intervene between the period of photosensitivity and the more immediate events in the brain by which the endocrine control of diapause is established. The most striking example is in the silkworm *Bombyx,* where the egg type is decided by the conditions of photoperiod and temperature prevailing during late embryonic and early larval life (Kogure, 1933).

PHOTOPERIODIC CONTROL OF FORM DETERMINATION

A number of multivoltine insects exhibit such striking seasonal changes in form that considerable confusion has arisen over their taxonomy. It is now known that these changes are often governed by photoperiod. A classical example is provided by the nymphalid butterfly *Araschnia*. The differentiation of the characteristic wing pattern is connected with the occurrence of a photoperiodically induced diapause in the preceding pupal stage. Such diapausing pupae always yield the spring (*levana*) form of the butterfly. The nondiapause pupae of the first annual generation (resulting from the operation of long photoperiods on the larvae) always give the summer (*prorsa*) form under natural conditions of temperature (Danilyevsky, 1948; Müller, 1954).

This connection between diapause and form determination can also be observed in several dimorphic Homoptera. In the pear sucker *Psylla pyri* the individuals composing the overwintering generation are larger and darker and have longer wings than the summer generation insects. Moreover, the winter generation always exhibits reproductive diapause. These alternative paths of development are controlled by the photoperiod experienced by the early nymphal instars. But it seems that the progeny of the winter and summer forms are not strictly equivalent in their response to photoperiod. For under short-day conditions the progeny of winter forms include a fair proportion of the summer phenotype, whereas these are entirely wanting in the offspring of summer forms (Bonnemaison and Missonnier, 1955).

A further instance of photodetermination is met with in the jassid *Euscelis* where the spring (*incisus*) and summer (*plebejus*) generations differ conspicuously in size, pigmentation, and penis shape (Müller, 1954). In the leafhopper *Delphacodes* the development of long- or short-winged forms is controlled principally by the density of larvae on the food plant; but photoperiod again exerts some effect, for nymphs induced to enter diapause by exposure to short days yield a relatively high proportion of brachypterous adults in comparison with nymphs that have not experienced dormancy (Kisimoto, 1956).

These problems have been most extensively studied in aphids. Although it has been claimed that day length is responsible for the determination of winged and wingless parthenogenetic forms (virginoparae) (Shull, 1928), most authors have concluded that this factor controls the production of parthenogenetic and sexual individuals. Relevant species include the black bean aphis *Aphis fabae* (Davidson, 1929; de Fluiter, 1950), the cabbage aphis *Brevicoryne brassicae,* the peach aphis *Myzus persicae* (Bonnemaison, 1951), and the pea aphis *Acythosiphon pisum* (Kenten, 1955).

The sequence of events that leads to the appearance of sexual forms (this is, the winged males and the wingless egg-laying females or oviparae) differs according to species. In a species with host alternation such as *A. fabae* the first result of a shortened day length upon the summer generations of virginoparae is the production of winged offspring (gynoparae), which migrate from the summer host (broad bean) to the winter host (the spindle tree). These gynoparae differ slightly from the alate virginoparae in their sensory equipment and also show differences in behavior (Kennedy and Booth, 1954). Their progeny become the oviparae which in turn lay diapause eggs on the winter host. It may be seen therefore that the connection with diapause is in this case entirely indirect.

Preliminary studies on the aphid *Megoura viciae* have revealed a different pattern of development (Lees, unpublished work). For example, there are no gynoparae in this "one host" species, the absence of this form being clearly correlated with the absence of host alternation. The oviparae (and males) arise directly from a virginoparous generation. When this aphid is reared in long days in uncrowded conditions and at moderate temperatures, a succession of virginoparous generations is produced. On the other hand, when young parent virginoparae are put on short days they give birth to oviparae (and males) exclusively.

Experiment shows that the oviparae are determined long before birth; indeed determination is actively proceeding when the parent aphid is passing through the early nymphal instars. This is scarcely surprising in view of the fact that embryogenesis is known to be highly precocious in parthenogenetic aphids. In *Megoura,* as in other species, each ovariole in the first instar aphid already contains two embryos, and by the final moult the number has risen to seven. It is therefore of interest to inquire how the fate of the embryos within the mother is decided by photoperiod. There are two possibilities: either the embryos are influenced directly, the light passing through the rather transparent body wall and blood, or their determination is controlled in some way by the physiology of the mother.

Some information on this point can be gained by studying the response to photoperiods of critical length. A photoperiod of 14½ hr or permanent darkness both provide conditions of "intermediate" stimulation. Figure 2 shows that under these circumstances a small proportion of the mothers produce virginoparae only or oviparae only. Many more produce both types of progeny, but when these are collected serially at birth (as an indication of the order of determination), it is soon evident that the two types are not intermingled randomly but are produced in uniform batches of varying size. In some instances there is an obvious oscillation between the production of oviparous and virginoparous offspring. These findings suggest strongly that the determination is under maternal control and is perhaps mediated by an endocrine mechanism. The curve shown in Fig. 2 has been constructed on this basis and traces the proportion of mothers which produce oviparae only when reared at different photo-

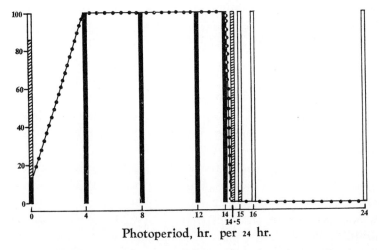

Photoperiod, hr. per 24 hr.

FIG. 2.   The photoperiodic determination of virginoparous and oviparous female progeny in the aphid *Megoura viciae*. Black histograms and beaded curve indicate the percentages of mothers that produced oviparae only; white histograms, the percentages producing virginoparae only; shaded histograms, those producing female offspring of both types.

periods. The resemblance of this curve to those relating photoperiod and diapause needs no emphasis (cf. Fig. 1A).

The question of male determination in aphids is instructive for various reasons. In the first place it provides an example of sex determination by external factors, including photoperiod. Secondly, this system of control is unusual in that the operation of an alternative stimulus (long or short photoperiods) controls the production of three morphological types. It is well known that parthenogenesis in aphids is of the diploid type so that both virginopara and ovipara may be expected to preserve the full complement of chromosomes. Their determination is therefore entirely "physiological." On the other hand, the immediate cause of maleness is genetical, sex determination being of the usual XX-XO type with the male egg losing one X chromosome during the single nonreductional meiotic division. Since it is also clear that in many aphids (e.g., *A. pisum*) the production of males is entirely suppressed in long days (Kenten, 1955), this chromosomal change must be under physiological and ultimately environmental control. The second problem is met in such species as *A. pisum* and *Megoura viciae* where, under inductive conditions, males and oviparae both arise from the same parent. Why is the sex of the offspring not uniform? Records show that it is rare for the male progeny of one mother to exceed one-quarter of the total. Further, serial collections of the offspring indicate that the probability of a given egg becoming a male embryo depends on its time of release from the germarium, the chances being greatest near the middle of the sequence in *Megoura* and at the end in *Acyrthosiphon*. The eggs must therefore differ in their proneness toward chromosome loss, although this is only expressed if the physiological conditions favor the production of sexual forms. Whether these conditions are the same that induce female embryos to become oviparae is at present uncertain.

From this brief survey of arthropod photoperiodism it will at least be apparent that a wealth of material is available for study by the insect physiologist. Although some regularities in the pattern of response are becoming evident, new variations are still being discovered as the list of examined species grows. Moreover, with regard to one of the central problems, namely the photoperiodic measurement of time, little more than a beginning has been made at the physiological level. Nevertheless, the investigator is offered many practical advantages. The possibility of obtaining abundant and uniform material is one. The ease with which many insects are reared and their high intrinsic rate of development are others. These considerations may suggest that this field will continue to attract the attention of the student of photoperiodism.

REFERENCES

Andrewartha, H. G. 1952. Diapause in relation to the ecology of insects. *Biol. Revs., 27,* 50–107.

Bondarenko, N. V. 1950. The influence of short days on the annual cycle of development of the common spider mite (in Russian). *Compt. rend. acad. sci. U.R.S.S., 70,* 1077–80.

Bonnemaison, L. 1951. Contribution a l'étude des facteurs provoquant l'apparition des formes ailées et sexuées chez les Aphidinae. *Ann. épiphyt., 2,* 1–380.

Bonnemaison, L., and J. Missonnier. 1955. Recherches sur le déterminisme des formes estivales ou hivernales et de la diapause chez le psylle du poirier (*Psylla pyri* L.) *Ann. épiphyt., 4,* 417–528.

Danilyevsky, A. S. 1948. Photoperiodic reactions of insects in conditions of artificial illumination (in Russian). *Compt. rend. acad. sci. U.R.S.S., 60,* 481–84.

———. A. S. 1957. Photoperiodism as a factor in the formation of geographical races in insects (in Russian, English summary). *Ent. Oboz., 36,* 5–27.

Danilyevsky, A. S., and Y. I. Glinyanaya. 1949. On the relationships of the dark and light periods of day in the development of insects (in Russian). *Compt. rend. acad. sci. U.R.S.S., 68,* 785–88.

———. 1950. On the influence of the rhythm of illumination and temperature on the origin of diapause in insects (in Russian). *Compt. rend. acad. sci. U.R.S.S., 71,* 963–66.

Davidson, J. 1929. On the occurrence of the parthenogenetic and sexual form in *Aphis rumicis* L., with special reference to the influence of environmental factors. *Ann. Appl. Biol., 16,* 104–34.

Dickson, R. C. 1949. Factors governing the induction of diapause in the oriental fruit moth. *Ann. Entomol. Soc. Am., 42,* 511–37.

de Fluiter, H. J. 1950. De invloed van daglengte en temperatuur op het optreden van de geslachtsdieren bij *Aphis fabae* Scop., de zwarte bonenluis. *Tijdschr. Plantenziekten, 56,* 265–85.

Fukuda, S. 1951. The production of the diapause eggs by transplanting the suboesophageal ganglion in the silkworm. *Proc. Jap. Acad., 27,* 672–77.

Gambaro, P. 1954. L'importanza del fattore "alimentazione" nella determinazione della diapausa di *Carpocapsa pomonella* L. *Boll. Zool., 21,* 163–69.

Geyspitz, K. F. 1949. Light as a factor regulating the cycle of development of the pine Lasiocampid *Dendrolimus pini* L. (in Russian). *Compt. rend. acad. sci., U.R.S.S., 68,* 781–84.

―――. 1957. On the mechanism of light stimuli perception during the photoperiodic reaction in caterpillars of Lepidoptera (in Russian, English summary). *Zool. Zhur., 36,* 548–60.

Goryshin, N. I. 1955. The relationship of light and temperature factors in the photoperiodic reactions of insects. (in Russian). *Ent. Oboz., 34,* 9–13.

―――. 1956. On the photoperiodic reaction in the Colorado bettle *Leptinotarsa decemlineata* (Say) (in Russian). *Compt. rend. acad. sci. U.R.S.S., 109,* 205–208.

Harvey, G. T. 1957. The occurrence and nature of diapause-free development in the spruce budworm *Choristoneura fumiferana* (Clem). (Lepidoptera: Tortricidae). *Can. J. Zool., 35,* 549–72.

Hasegawa, K. 1952. Studies on the voltinism of the silkworm *Bombyx mori* L. with special reference to the organs concerning determination of voltinism. *J. Fac. Agr. Tottori Univ., 1,* 83–124.

―――. 1957. The diapause hormone of the silkworm, *Bombyx mori. Nature, 179,* 1300–1301.

Kennedy, J. S., and C. O. Booth. 1954. Host alternation in *Aphis fabae* Scop. II. Changes in the aphids. *Ann. Appl. Biol., 41,* 88–106.

Kenten, J. 1955. The effect of photoperiod and temperature on reproduction in *Acyrthosiphon pisum* (Harris) and on the forms produced. *Bull. Entomol. Research, 46,* 599–624.

Kisimoto, R. 1956. Effect of diapause in the fourth larval instar on the determination of wing-form in the adult of the small brown planthopper, *Delphacodes striatella* Fallen (in Japanese, English summary). *Ōyō-Kontyū, 12,* 202–10.

Kogure, M. 1933. The influence of light and temperature on certain characters of the silkworm *Bombyx mori. J. Dept. Agr. Kyushu Univ., 4,* 1–93.

Lees, A. D. 1953a. Environmental factors controlling the evocation and termination of diapause in the fruit tree red spider mite *Metatetranychus ulmi* Koch(Acarina: Tetranychidae). *Ann. Appl. Biol., 40,* 449–86.

―――. 1953b. The significance of the light and dark phases in the photoperiodic control of diapause in *Metatetranychus ulmi* Koch. *Ann. Appl. Biol., 40,* 487–97.

―――. 1955. *The Physiology of Diapause in Arthropods.* Cambridge Univ. Press, Cambridge, England.

―――. 1956. The physiology and biochemistry of diapause. *Ann. Rev. Entomol., 1,* 1–16.

Marcovitch, S. 1924. The migration of the aphididae and the appearance of the sexual forms as affected by the relative length of daily light exposure. *J. Agr. Research, 27,* 513–22.

Masaki, S. 1956. The local variation in the diapause pattern of the cabbage moth, *Barathra brassicae* Linné, with particular reference to the aestival diapause (Lepidoptera: Noctuidae). *Bull. Fac. Agr. Mie Univ. No. 13,* 29–46.

Monro, J. 1956. A humoral stimulus to the secretion of the brain-hormone in Lepidoptera. *Nature, 178,* 213–14.

Müller, H. J. 1954. Der Saisondimorphismus bei Zikaden der Gattung *Euscelis* Brullé. *Beitr. Ent., 4,* 1–56.

————. 1955. Die Saisonformenbildung von *Araschnia levana,* ein photoperiodisch gesteuerter Diapause-effekt. *Naturwissenschaften, 5,* 134–35.

Shull, A. F. 1928. Duration of light and the wings of *Macrosiphum solanifolii. Roux Archiv, 113,* 210–39.

Tanaka, Y. 1950. Studies on hibernation with special reference to photoperiodicity and breeding of the Chinese Tussar silkworm. III. *Jap. J. Seric. Sci., 19,* 580–90.

van der Kloot, W. G. 1955. The control of neurosecretion and diapause by physiological changes in the brain of the cecropia silkworm. *Biol. Bull., 109,* 276–94.

de Wilde, J. 1954. Aspects of diapause in adult insects with special reference to the Colorado beetle, *Leptinotarsa decemlineata* Say. *Arch. néerl. zool., 10,* 375–85.

Williams, C. M. 1956. Physiology of insect diapause. X. An endocrine mechanism for the influence of temperature on the diapausing pupa of the cecropia silkworm. *Biol. Bull., 110,* 201–18.

PHOTOPERIODIC CONTROL OF DIAPAUSE IN THE PITCHER-PLANT MIDGE, *Metriocnemus knabi*[1]

OSCAR H. PARIS, JR.[2], AND CHARLES E. JENNER

Department of Zoology, University of North Carolina, Chapel Hill, North Carolina

The widespread occurrence of the phenomenon of photoperiodism among both plants and animals makes its study a matter of considerable biological importance. Thus far knowledge has advanced most rapidly in the case of plants, perhaps owing in part to the more suitable nature of plants for experimentation. A search among animals, therefore, for favorable experimental material for the investigation of photoperiodism seems particularly desirable at this time. The present paper reports our progress in the study of the photoperiodic response of the pitcher-plant midge, *Metriocnemus knabi*, a species offering many advantages as an experimental animal for photoperiodic research.

Surprisingly few photoperiodic studies, and none of a comprehensive nature, have been made on dipterous insects, despite the fact that one of the earlier reports on insect photoperiodism concerned this group (Baker, 1935). The photoperiodic control of the termination of diapause (i.e., developmental arrest) has been reported for the winter eggs of *Aedes triseriatus* (in Canada, Baker, 1935); for the hibernating larvae of the mosquitoes *Aedes triseriatus* (in Georgia, Love and Whelchel, 1955), *Anopheles barberi* (Baker, 1935), *Anopheles claviger* (Kennedy, cited by Andrewartha, 1952), and *Wyeomyia smithii* (Jenner, 1951); and for the hibernating larvae of the ceratopogonid midge, *Culicoides guttipennis* (Baker, 1935), the phantom larva *Chaoborus* sp. and the pitcher-plant midge *Metriocnemus knabi* (Jenner, 1951). Normal autumnal hibernation was

[1] This investigation was supported by a research grant (E-356) from the National Institute of Allergy and Infectious Diseases, Public Health Service.

[2] Present address: Department of Zoology, University of California, Berkeley 4, California.

prevented in adults of the mosquito *Culex pipiens* by exposure to continuous light (Tate and Vincent, 1936).

A general account of insect photoperiodism as related to diapause was published recently by Lees (1955). Lees' timely review has been especially helpful to the present authors since it summarizes important papers in Japanese and Russian, translations of which were not available to them. Additional investigations, apart from those related specifically to diapause, have shown day length to be important in the control of the seasonal pattern of wing production and reproductive types in aphids (Marcovitch, 1923, 1924; Shull, 1928, 1929; Bonnemaison, 1949, 1950; and others) and in the control of morphological types in leaf hoppers (Bonnemaison and Missonnier, 1955; Müller, 1954) and butterflies (Müller, 1955). A summary of insect photoperiodism shows that the phenomenon has been demonstrated in the Odonata, Orthoptera, Homoptera, Lepidoptera, Diptera, Coleoptera, and Hymenoptera (references given by Lees, 1955, and above). It is becoming apparent that day length is a major environmental factor in controlling seasonal activity in insects.

MATERIALS AND METHODS

The larvae of *M. knabi* develop in the water contained in the leaves of *Sarracenia purpurea* and feed on the remains of small animals which fall into these pitchers. Pupation occurs just above the surface of the water in a secreted gelatinous mass, and is completed in about three days at 23°C. Winter is passed in the larval stage; mature larvae fail to pupate as winter approaches and do not resume development until environmental conditions are again favorable. Presumably several generations are passed during the summer without interruption, and thus diapause is of the facultative type. Experiments reported in this paper were conducted primarily to study the factors controlling the termination of diapause.

Larvae employed in experiments were collected from *S. purpurea* growing either in Suitland Bog, Prince Georges County, Maryland, or at various places in North Carolina. The specific sites of the latter are named only when it seems relevant to the interpretation of the results.

An attempt was made to use only fully grown diapausing larvae (except for Experiment 9 described below). Larvae collected during the nondiapause period were held on a diapause-inducing photoperiod (11 hr) until at least a week after all pupations had stopped, which generally occurred within one month. Larvae collected during the diapause period were available immediately for experimentation.

Mass cultures were held on an 11-hr photoperiod in loosely covered 20-cm finger bowls. Larvae in experiments were cultured in covered stender dishes (6 cm) containing water from pitcher plants 0.5 cm deep; ten larvae were placed in each container, and unless otherwise indicated, twenty larvae constituted an experimental group. Experimental larvae were distributed at random to the culture dishes, and dishes were assigned to groups by turning cards. In all experiments a record was made of every pupation and of the day on which it occurred; pupae were removed from the dishes after being counted. Results are given as percent pupation of survivors. A few individuals died in nearly every experiment, but fatalities were apparently at random and usually few in number. Commercially available dried daphnia proved to be satisfactory as food. A thick mixture of ground daphnia was made with pitcher-plant water, and the capacity of one medicine dropper of this mixture was given once a week to each mass culture bowl. One drop of the food mixture was added weekly to each container of experimental larvae (except in Experiment 8 described below). Mass cultures and most experimental groups were maintained in lightproof cabinets located in a controlled temperature room at about 23°C; when closed, air from the room was circulated through the cabinets by means of a centrifugal fan and a system of lightproof ducts, thus preventing a significant rise in temperature even when lights in the chambers were turned on. Maximum variation between groups was generally within ±1°C. The results of temperature studies described in this paper make it clear that these small temperature variations were insignificant in accounting for results obtained at different photoperiods. Light intensity at the level of the dishes in the cabinets was 35–45 ft-c, supplied by two 30-watt daylight fluorescent lamps operated by automatic time switches; ballasts for the lamps were mounted outside the cabinets to minimize heating further.

Experiments to determine critical photoperiods were conducted in a cabinet containing boxes into each of which a different day length group was placed. The cabinet was maintained on a long day, and after the appropriate number of hours of illumination for each group had passed, a lightproof cover was placed over the box containing that group. In the evening, in total darkness, all covers were removed so that the photoperiod for all groups began when the lights later turned on automatically.

Photoperiods in temperature experiments were given as described for critical day length experiments, with three temperature levels employed. Intermediate temperature levels were those obtained in the photoperiod cabinets described above. Low-temperature conditions were provided by walk-in cold rooms, and those for high temperature by a small inside room where temperatures were normally elevated and rather constant. Occasionally an infrared lamp was turned on in this high-temperature room as a supplementary heating unit; it was placed on the floor and directed against a wall opposite the animals. Results at high temperature were the same whether or not the infrared lamp was employed, and it is therefore assumed that its use did not add an important variable to the experiment. Temperatures for all levels were recorded daily from thermometers whose bulbs were immersed in a volume of water approximating that in each culture dish.

Light-intensity experiments were conducted in a large lightproof room located in a frame annex to the main laboratory building. A steam heater and circulating fan controlled by thermostat maintained a mean temperature of approximately 20°C. Temperatures remained fairly constant, but extremes of 18.5°C and 24°C were recorded by a monitoring thermograph. The effectiveness of experimental low intensities could be determined by extending a noninductive photoperiod of 12 hr to an inductive photoperiod of 13½ hr. Mirrors, placed on tables at varying distances from a 15-watt clear incandescent lamp, were angled so as to reflect light from the lamp onto the table top. Mounted on the lower side of the mirror frame was a 15-watt fluorescent lamp which provided light for the basic 12-hr photoperiod (40 ft-c intensity). Four stations were employed: A, B, C, and D. Cultures at station B were located so that the distance from the incandescent lamp to the culture dishes (via the mirror surface) was twice that from the lamp to dishes at station A. The same relation held for stations C and B and also for D and C. The experimental intensity at station A was measured with a Model 756 Weston illumination meter; intensities for the remaining stations were calculated by the inverse-square law. The incandescent lamp was shrouded by black cloth in order to minimize scattered light from the walls of the room. The fluorescent lamps and the incandescent lamp were operated by two different timers; the latter light source was turned on 1 min before the fluorescent lamps were turned off.

EXPERIMENTS AND RESULTS

Critical Photoperiods (Experiments 1, 2, and 3)

The results of three critical day length experiments are given in Fig. 1 and Table I. Only photoperiods near the previously determined

TABLE I.   Day Length and Pupation: North Carolina Midges

Experiment 2

	Results after 40 Days		Results after 60 Days	
Photoperiod, hr	No. Pupations of Total Survivors	Percent Pupation	No. Pupations of Total Survivors	Percent Pupation
$11\frac{1}{2}$	0 of 20	0	0 of 20	0
12	0 of 20	0	0 of 20	0
$12\frac{1}{2}$	0 of 19	0	0 of 19	0
13	0 of 20	0	6 of 20	30
$13\frac{1}{2}$	7 of 19	37	17 of 19	89
14	11 of 19	58	19 of 19	100

Experiment 3

Results after 40 Days

Photoperiod, hr	No. Pupations of Total Survivors	Percent Pupation
12	0 of 20	0
$12\frac{1}{2}$	1 of 20	5
13	14 of 19	74
$13\frac{1}{2}$	11 of 19	58

critical range were employed. Experiment 1 used Maryland midges collected March 5, 1954; the experiment started May 6, 1954, and continued for 78 days. Results, given after 40 and 78 days, show the entire critical range to lie between a 12-hr photoperiod, which gave no pupations (noninductive), and a 13-hr photoperiod, which was just as effective as the longer day lengths employed in terminating diapause. In other experiments not reported here it was shown that still longer photoperiods, including continuous light, were all essentially of equal effectiveness. Midge larvae collected in North Carolina were used in Experiments 2 and 3. Those for Experiment 2 were collected on October 1, 1955, and the experiment ran 60 days beginning October 12. Larvae for Experiment 3 were collected December

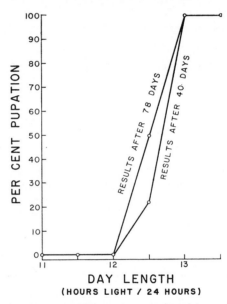

FIG. 1.   Day length and pupation: Maryland midges. (Experiment 1.)

26, 1955; the experiment started January 12, 1956, and continued 40 days. The results of these two experiments (Table I) did not demonstrate a clear difference between the response of North Carolina and Maryland midges. Indeed, the results of Experiment 3 were more similar to those of Experiment 1 than they were to Experiment 2. In Experiment 2 fewer larvae had responded at long and intermediate photoperiods than at corresponding day lengths after the same length of time in Experiment 3. A possible explanation for this difference will be considered in the discussion.

Light Intensity (Experiment 4)

The duration of the effective photoperiod experienced by *Metriocnemus knabi* in nature depends, of course, upon the minimum light intensity to which the larvae are sensitive. Experiment 4 was conducted to test the effectiveness of intensities from 0.64 to 0.01 ft-c (see section on Methods above). Four groups of 30 larvae each, at stations A, B, C, and D, were given 12 hr of light at an intensity of about 40 ft-c followed by 1½ hr at the lower experimental intensities. A fifth group, E, received the basic 12 hr of light (40 ft-c) plus 1½ hr of the very low intensity of light which scattered from the walls and ceiling of the room where the experimental intensities were being administered. This group was placed in a small uncovered box at station B, but did not receive light directly from the mirror at that station. A short-day control group in the same room received only the basic photoperiod of 12 hr at 40 ft-c. Results of this experiment (Table II)

TABLE II.   Effect of Low Light Intensities:[a]
Experiment 4, Results after 40 Days

Group	Intensity, ft-c	No. Pupations of Total Survivors	Percent Pupation
A	0.64	26 of 30	87
B	0.16	25 of 28	89
C	0.04	28 of 30	93
D	0.01	24 of 26	92
E	Scattered light < 0.01	7 of 30	23
Short-day controls	0	0 of 30	0

[a] 13½-hr photoperiod given: 12 hr at 40 ft-c plus 1½ hr at experimental intensities.

show that all experimental intensities were equally effective and that pupations were obtained even in the scattered-light controls. Similar experiments, data for which are not given, show intensities from 35 to 0.0025 ft-c to be equally effective. It is remarkable that some pupations were obtained in the scattered-light controls, E, in Experiment 4, the very low intensity of which we were unable to measure. Apparently the intensity threshold below which no response is obtained is extremely low and was approximated to some degree in the scattered light received by group E.

Temperature (Experiments 5 and 6)

Experiments were conducted to determine critical photoperiods at high, intermediate, and low temperatures. In one such experiment (Experiment 5) the temperatures employed were 30.6 ± 1°C, 25.6 ± 1°C, and 12.0 ± 0.5°C. Photoperiods were 11½, 12, 12⅓, 12⅔, 13, and 13½ hr in duration. The experiment, started June 15, 1955, employed Maryland midges collected April 7, 1955. Results after 40 days (Fig. 2) showed little difference between the photoperiodic

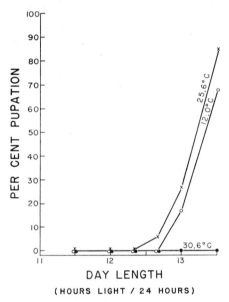

FIG. 2. Temperature, day length, and pupation. Results after 40 days. (Experiment 5.)

response of the midges at an intermediate temperature (25.6°C) and those at a low temperature (12.0°C). No pupations, however, occurred at the high temperature (30.6°C).

In a similar experiment (Experiment 6) the low temperature was dropped to 8.3 ± 1°C, the intermediate temperature was 23.5 ± 1°C and the high temperature was 29.5 ± 1°C. Maryland midges, collected on June 19, 1955, were employed; the experiment started

TABLE III. Temperature and the Photoperiodic Response:
Experiment 6, Results after 40 Days

Photoperiods, hr	8.3°C		23.5°C		29.5°C	
	No. Pupations of Total Survivors	Percent Pupation	No. Pupations of Total Survivors	Percent Pupation	No. Pupations of Total Survivors	Percent Pupation
11½	0 of 14	0	0 of 16	0	0 of 6	0
12	0 of 16	0	0 of 13	0	0 of 9	0
12½	0 of 17	0	0 of 14	0	0 of 10	0
13	0 of 17	0	3 of 8	38	0 of 2	0
13½	0 of 14	0	8 of 9	89	0 of 1	0
14	0 of 18	0	11 of 18	61	0 of 8	0
16	—	—	14 of 15	93	0 of 15	0

October 19, 1955. Table III gives the photoperiods used and the results after 40 days. The low-temperature portion of the experimen was continued until 75 days had elapsed. The first pupations at this low temperature occurred as follows: the 14-hr group on the 47th day, 13½-hr group on the 61st day, and the 13-hr group on the 75th day.

These temperature experiments showed that long photoperiods were most effective in terminating diapause at intermediate temperatures. Constant low temperature reduced the rate at which the larvae responded, and constant high temperature prevented the response completely, at least for 47 days. In both experiments mortality was relatively high, particularly at the upper temperatures, perhaps indicating that these temperatures were sufficiently high to have a general adverse physiological effect.

The possibility that failure to pupate at high temperatures resulted from partial starvation due to increased metabolic rate was considered, and for this reason a test was conducted to determine the effect of starvation on the photoperiodic response. Two groups of 10 animals each in dechlorinated tap water were placed on a 13½-hr photoperiod; one group was fed regularly and the other received no food. Similar groups were maintained on photoperiods of 12½ and 11 hr. Of the survivors on the 13½ hr photoperiod 9 of 9 fed larvae and 6 of 10 starved larvae had pupated by the 40th day; in the same period 2 of 10 fed larvae and 1 of 9 starved larvae pupated on the 12½-hr photoperiod; no pupations, fed or starved, occurred on the 11-hr photoperiod. Starvation apparently reduced slightly the response to inductive photoperiods, but did not prevent pupations altogether.

Photoperiod and Larval Growth (Experiment 7)

Experiments described thus far employed fully grown larvae in diapause. In order to determine whether diapause could occur at some earlier stage in larval development, several of the smallest larvae (about 2 mm in length) that could be found in a collection made in North Carolina on October 1, 1955, were isolated individually. On October 11, 1955, 7 of these were placed on a 13½-hr photoperiod and 8 on an 11-hr photoperiod (Experiment 7). Examinations made at about 10-day intervals indicated that growth rate was essentially equal under both conditions. No exuviae were seen, probably because of their delicate nature. After about one month larvae under both conditions were of a size of those normally used in experiments (about 6 to 7 mm in length). After 48 days one larva on a 13½-hr photoperiod pupated, as did the remaining 6 by the 72nd day. After 81 days, during which time no pupations had occurred on the 11-hr photoperiod, 4 short-day larvae were placed on a 13½-hr photoperiod; all of these pupated within 34 days after transfer. On the 11-hr day one pupated 152 days after the beginning of the experiment while three still remained as larvae 190 days from the beginning of the experiment. These results indicate that diapause induced by short photoperiods must occur only in the last larval instar. Larvae grown at favorable temperatures and photoperiods develop directly without the intervention of diapause.

Inductive Cycle Requirement (Experiments 8, 9, and 10)

Two experiments were conducted to determine the number of consecutive inductive cycles required to initiate pupation in diapausing larvae. In one experiment (Experiment 8) groups of 10 larvae each were exposed to an inductive photoperiod of 13 hr from 0 to 28 days, depending on the group, and then were placed on a noninductive photoperiod of 11½ hr. Results (Table IV) show that at least 10 inductive cycles were required to induce pupation, and maximum response was approached only in groups receiving 19 or more induc-

TABLE IV.   Inductive Cycle Requirement[a]

Experiment 8 Results after 35 Days		Experiment 9 Results after 53 Days	
No. of Cycles	No. Pupations of Total Survivors	No. of Cycles	No. Pupations of Total Survivors
0	0 of 7	0	0 of 10
2	0 of 3	1	0 of 8
4	0 of 6	3	0 of 6
6	0 of 2	3	0 of 7
8	0 of 3	6	0 of 10
10	1 of 6	6	0 of 8
12	0 of 4	6	0 of 10
14	0 of 5	7	0 of 7
16	2 of 6	8	0 of 10
19	5 of 5	9	0 of 5
20	3 of 4	10	0 of 9
22	4 of 6	11	0 of 7
24	4 of 4	12	0 of 6
26	3 of 4	13	0 of 10
28	2 of 2	14	1 of 10
		15	0 of 9
		16	2 of 10
		17	1 of 9
		18	0 of 8
		19	1 of 9
		20	5 of 10

[a] Experiment 8: number of cycles indicates consecutive 13-hr photoperiods given, followed by 11½-hr photoperiods for remainder of experiment.

Experiment 9: 13½-hr inductive photoperiods followed by 11-hr photoperiods for remainder of experiment.

tive cycles. Fatalities were high in Experiment 8, but the results of another experiment (Experiment 9) were confirmatory. From 0 to 20 consecutive inductive cycles (13½-hr photoperiod) were given, and then the midges were returned to noninductive conditions (11-hr photoperiod). Results in Table IV show that in this case no pupations occurred until 14 cycles had been given; 14 to 19 such cycles result in only a few pupations, while 50% pupation was obtained in the 20-cycle group.

In these experiments, the response once triggered went to completion in spite of subsequent short days; if an insufficient number of cycles was given, diapause was maintained. Pupation occurred up to

8 days after groups had been changed from an inductive to a non-inductive regime. Apparently, however, the effect of inductive day lengths may carry over a much longer period than this, for when collections were brought into the laboratory from nature during the summer, pupations occurred for several weeks in spite of the short day on which they were placed.

Experiment 10 tested the effectiveness of the alternation of various combinations of long day, inductive cycles (13½-hr photoperiods) with short-day, noninductive cycles (11-hr photoperiods). The larvae used were collected in North Carolina on December 26, 1955, and the experiment began January 19, 1956. Experimental group A was given a treatment of consecutive long days, group B received a long day alternated with one short day, group C a long day alternated with two consecutive short days, group D a long day alternated with three consecutive short days, and group E a long day alternated with four consecutive short days. After 42 days 65% of group A had pupated, and no pupations had occurred in any of the other groups. At this time the larvae in groups C, D, and E, apparently still in diapause, were placed under different experimental conditions. One dish of larvae from group C and one from group E were used to make up group F, which was placed on a regime of one short day alternated with two consecutive long days. The two dishes from group D were used for group G, which received one short day alternated with three consecutive long days. Finally, the remaining dishes from groups C and E (one from each) were used to make up group H, which was given one short day alternated with four consecutive long days. Results after 72 days under these regimes are given in Table V; also

TABLE V.   Experiment 10, Results after 72 Days

Group	Photoperiod Schedule[a]	No. Pupations of Total Survivors	Percent Pupation
A	L only	18 of 18	100
B	LSLS	1 of 20	5
F	SLLSLLS	10 of 13	77
G	SLLLSLLLS	16 of 19	84
H	SLLLLSLLLLS	20 of 20	100

[a] L, long day; S, short day.

given in this table are the results obtained after 72 days with groups A and B, which had been continued on their original schedule.

When a short day length occurred only every fifth day in a schedule of otherwise inductive day lengths, the results obtained were similar to those obtained with consecutive long days. It appears that a more frequent occurrence of noninductive photoperiods reduced the response. Only one larvae pupated in group B (after 72 days), thus indicating a near absence of effectiveness of a regime of long photoperiods alternated with short.

Dark Period Interruption (Experiments 11 and 12)

In the experiments described thus far, all larvae were exposed to cycles consisting of a light phase, followed by a dark period, one being complementary to the other and together totaling 24 hr. An insight into the relative importance of each phase—light and dark—can be obtained by departing from cycles having this simple complementary relationship. Two experiments involving night interruption will be described.

Experiment 11 was conducted to determine whether the period of light making up the difference between a 12- and a 13½-hr photoperiod need be continuous with the short photoperiod to be effective, or whether it would be so if given at different times during the dark period. The light regimes and results are given in Table VI. The experiment ran 49 days, beginning January 13, 1956, and utilized larvae collected in North Carolina on December 26, 1955. A 12-hr photoperiod cabinet was not available for the experiment, so an 11-hr day group served as a short-day control. Ample evidence in other experiments indicated, however, that 11-hr and 12-hr photoperiods were equally noninductive. Pupations occurred in every group except the 11-hr day controls, indicating the effectiveness of the added light when given so as to interrupt the dark period.

Another experiment (12) tested the effectiveness of night interruptions when the total amount of light given during 24 hr was less than that required in a normal day-night sequence for induction of pupation. The larvae used were collected December 26, 1955, in North Carolina, and the experiment, begun March 8, 1956, ran for 65 days.

TABLE VI. Dark-Period Interruption

Group	Light Regime[a]	No. Pupations of Total Survivors	Percent Pupation
	Experiment 11		
	Results after 49 Days		
A	$13\frac{1}{2}$ L, $10\frac{1}{2}$ D	20 of 27	74
B	12 L, 2 D, $1\frac{1}{2}$ L, $8\frac{1}{2}$ D	27 of 28	96
C	12 L, $5\frac{1}{2}$ D, $1\frac{1}{2}$ L, 5 D	18 of 29	62
D	12 L, 9 D, $1\frac{1}{2}$ L, $1\frac{1}{2}$ D	26 of 30	87
Control	11 L, 13 D	0 of 30	0
	Experiment 12		
	Results after 65 Days		
A	$10\frac{1}{2}$ L, $2\frac{1}{4}$ D, $1\frac{1}{2}$ L, $9\frac{3}{4}$ D	15 of 17	88
B	$10\frac{1}{2}$ L, 6 D, $1\frac{1}{2}$ L, 6 D	9 of 15	60
C	$10\frac{1}{2}$ L, $9\frac{3}{4}$ D, $1\frac{1}{2}$ L, $2\frac{1}{4}$ D	19 of 19	100
Control	11 L, 13 D	0 of 19	0

[a] L, hours of light; D, hours of dark.

Table VI gives the light regimes used and the results obtained. It will be seen that interrupting the dark period produced pupation even though the total amount of light was without effect when given as a continuous short day. (See Discussion.)

Continuous Darkness (Experiment 13)

Several workers have demonstrated that photoperiodic arthropods respond to very short day lengths and continuous darkness in more or less the same way that they respond to long photoperiod and continuous light. Experiment 13 was designed to test this phenomenon in *Metriocnemus knabi*. A group of 20 individuals was held in complete darkness for 43 days, interrupted twice weekly for 1 or 2 min while the larvae were fed and checked. A control group of 10 individuals was maintained on an 11-hr day. The experiment commenced February 22, 1956, utilizing larvae collected in North Carolina on December 26, 1955. At the end of the experiment 11 of 19 surviving larvae in continuous darkness had pupated, whereas none of the 10 on an 11-hr day had done so. In this response to continuous darkness, *M. knabi* is similar to most other arthropods in which it has been tested.

DISCUSSION

The life cycle of *Metriocnemus knabi,* like that of most organisms, is attuned to a seasonally changing environment; such adjustment is required for survival. During the spring, summer, and early autumn, the population appears to pass through several generations, but with the approach of winter the full-grown larvae enter diapause, a period of developmental arrest. This physiological state is maintained throughout the winter, until, in the spring, development is resumed and pupation and emergence of adults occur.

The most obvious environmental factors that might control the timing of such a seasonal cycle are temperature, quality or quantity of food, and day length. The present study indicates that temperature and food are probably of secondary consequence as effective agents in the seasonal adjustment of this species. Day length, on the other hand, offers the perfect indicator of season, repeating the same cycle year after year with a minimum of variation. For those species capable of responding to it, unerring attunement to season is guaranteed. The present investigation has established that it is day length which is of primary importance in controlling seasonal diapause in *Metriocnemus knabi.*

This analysis of the response of *M. knabi* to day length shows that photoperiods of 8 to 12 hr are diapause-maintaining, while those longer than this are diapause-terminating. The location of the critical day length range is, of course, important in determining when diapause will be terminated in the spring and when it will be initiated in the fall. As will be shown below, the 12- to 13-hr critical range established experimentally for *M. knabi* correlates closely with the length of daily illumination at that time in the spring and fall when the transition is made by the organisms from the diapause to the nondiapause condition, and vice versa.

In nature, the daily photoperiod to which *M. knabi* will respond depends upon the minimum light intensity to which the larvae are sensitive, which for this species was found to be below 0.0025 ft-c. This appears to be the lowest threshold sensitivity yet recorded for a photoperiodic animal (Lees, 1955). This extreme sensitivity brings up the question as to why moonlight is not effective in inducing development during the diapause period in nature, since the intensity of direct moonlight falls within the range 0.01–0.05 ft-c. An answer can be seen, at least in part, from the fact that a relatively large number of successive inductive cycles are required—10 to 14 at 23°C (Experiments 8 and 9)—to induce development and that low temperature (Experiments 5 and 6) slows the rate of response. It must be remembered also that the light intensity reaching the larvae in nature is reduced through shading, since the larvae live in the leaves of the pitcher plant.

To make possible a correlation between these experimental results and events in nature, collections, each consisting of many hundred larvae, were made in the spring and fall to determine when pupations begin and cease in midge populations in North Carolina. In the spring of 1955 collections were made near Spout Springs, Harnett County, North Carolina (about 35° 15′ N. Lat.). Larvae taken February 19 and returned to the laboratory, where they were placed on a 11-hr day, started pupating on February 28. A second collection made on March 7 produced pupations the following day. It is concluded that those larvae collected February 19 had been induced to pupate by natural day lengths, which had just become long enough to be inductive, but that the response was so newly set in progress that several days were required in the laboratory before it was expressed. Fall collections were made at two locations. On August 30, 1955, larvae in Horse Cove, near Highlands, Macon County, North Carolina (about 35° 2′ N. Lat.) were pupating, as were larvae collected on September 9 at Mulkey Gap, near Cashiers, Jackson County (also about 35° 2′ N. Lat., and approximately 6½ miles from Horse Cove). No pupations, however, occurred from a collection made at Mulkey Gap on October 1. Diapause had been induced sometime between September 9 and October 1. A winter collection made December 26, 1955, in Duncan Valley, near Cedar Mountain, Transylvania County (about 35° 5′ N. Lat.) yielded no pupations. No midsummer collections were made in North Carolina, but many pupations were observed in pitcher plants at Suitland, Maryland, on June 19, 1955.

The correlation between dates for initiation and termination of diapause and natural photoperiods at 35° 0′ N. Lat. is shown in Fig. 3. Three day length curves are given, one for the period between sunrise

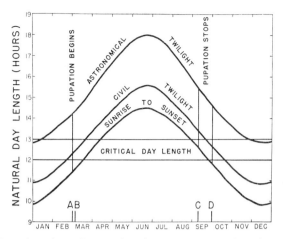

Fig. 3. Day length and pupation in nature. Day length curves were drawn from data taken from *Tables of Sunrise, Sunset, and Twilight,* issued by the Nautical Almanac Office, U. S. Naval Observatory, 1946. A, larvae collected 9 days earlier began pupating; B, larvae pupated day after collection; C, larvae pupating in nature; D, larvae no longer pupating in nature.

and sunset, a second for this period plus civil twilight, and a third for this period plus astronomical twilight. Light intensity at the end of civil twilight (sun 6° below horizon) on a clear evening is about 0.4 ft-c; when the sun is 10° below the horizon, it is slightly less than 0.01 ft-c (at end of astronomical twilight the sun is 18° below the horizon) (Kimball, 1916). Because of the very low threshold intensity for the response of *Metriocnemus knabi,* it seems apparent that a part of astronomical twilight must be effective. In Fig. 3 horizontal lines have been drawn at 12- and 13-hr photoperiods to mark the critical range for the midge's response, and vertical lines mark the approximate time pupation was found to begin in the spring and the period within which it ceased in the fall. Although there appears to be a close correlation between the timing of events in nature and the occurrence of effective day lengths of critical duration, it is interesting that pupation began in the spring on photoperiods that were perhaps 1 hr shorter than those on which it ceased in the fall, a point which will be considered later in the discussion.

Temperature plays only a modifying role in the control of diapause in *Metriocnemus knabi*. Photoperiodic induction was optimal at intermediate temperatures (23° to 25°C); high temperatures prevented the response, while low temperatures (12° to 8°C) retarded the rate of response on inductive photoperiods. The threshold temperature for the response was not determined, but it was found to be below 8°C. Most workers have found that long photoperiods and high temperature both act toward the same effect, while short photoperiods and low temperature also work in concert. Such is the case in *Macrosiphum* (Shull, 1929), *Bombyx* (Kogure, 1933), *Diataraxia* (Way and Hopkins, 1950), and *Metatetranychus* (Lees, 1953a). In *Grapholitha,* however, both high and low temperatures tended to prevent diapause, which was initiated on short photoperiods only at intermediate temperatures. *Antheraea* (Tanaka, cited by Lees, 1955) responded to photoperiod almost independently of temperature. It would appear that a critical evaluation of the significance of these different patterns of day length-temperature interaction must await a better understanding of the processes involved.

The critical day length range has been determined for a number of arthropods—the aphid *Macrosiphum* (Schull, 1929), the lepidopterous insects *Bombyx* (Kogure, 1933), *Grapholitha* (Dickson, 1949), *Diataraxia* (Way and Hopkins, 1950), *Acronycta* (Danilyevsky, cited by Lees, 1955), *Antheraea* (Tanaka, cited by Lees, 1955), and *Barathra* (Otuka and Santa, 1955); and the red-spider mite *Metatetranychus* (Lees, 1953a). All these organisms live in temperate regions of the world, and the critical photoperiod ranges, which separate effective short photoperiods from long, lie somewhere between 12 and 16 hr. However, for species from high latitudes there is a clear tendency for the range to be shifted to longer photoperiods (Lees, 1954).

Little information is available in this regard concerning the possibility of subspecific variation. Apparently only one case is described in the literature for photoperiodic animals.[3] Lees (1953a, 1955) found the critical day length range for mites at Cambridge, England, to be about 2 hr shorter than that reported by Bondarenko (cited by

[3] See the recent paper by Bondarenko and Hai-Yüan, in *Doklady Akad. Nauk S.S.S.R., 119* (6), 1247 (1958), and others cited by Lees in his contribution to this symposium.

Lees, 1955) for the same species at Leningrad, U.S.S.R., 8° farther north. It was pointed out that this should mean that mites at Leningrad would enter diapause about 2 weeks earlier than those at Cambridge.

Metriocnemus knabi has a wide latitudinal distribution, and one might expect to find evidence of similar geographic variation. The present study involved experiments employing midges collected in Maryland (ca. 38° 55′ N. Lat.) and in North Carolina (ca. 35° 2′ N. Lat.); there appeared to be little difference, if any, in the responses of animals from these two latitudes, but the results of an earlier experiment by Jenner (1951) suggest that geographical differences do occur. Midge larvae collected on May 8, 1950, at Petersham, Massachusetts, were employed in an experiment started May 30. Five larvae in separate culture dishes were placed on each of the following photoperiods at room temperature: 6¾, 11, 13½, and 16½. After 46 days only the 5 larvae on the 16½-hr photoperiod had pupated; the failure of the 13½-hr larvae to pupate would appear to demonstrate a difference in response from that obtained with Maryland or North Carolina midges. Efforts to substantiate this difference have not yet resulted in a satisfactory experimental test; thus, an intriguing question remains for further research.

The difference in rate of response on inductive photoperiods in Experiments 2 and 3, both employing North Carolina larvae, offers another interesting problem (Table I). In Experiment 2, 50% pupation on the 14-hr photoperiod occurred in 40 days and for the 13½-hr group in 45 days, while in Experiment 3, this percent was realized in 30 days and 36 days on the 13½-hr and 13-hr groups respectively. Of the several possible alternative explanations to account for this difference, two seem most worthy of consideration. First, the difference might have been genetic, since the collections were made at different places—Experiment 2 from Mulky Gap and Experiment 3 from Duncan Valley, about 30 miles apart. Since *Sarracenia purpurea* occurs only locally in the North Carolina mountains, this distance might constitute an effective geographical barrier for these two midge populations. A more probable explanation relates to the time when the midges were collected and the experiments conducted. Experiment 2 employed larvae collected October 1 and was started October 12, while the larvae for Experiment 3 were collected December 26 and the experiment began January 12. Thus the larvae used in Experiment 3 had been in diapause over three months before the start of the experiment, as contrasted with Experiment 2 where the larvae were just recently in diapause. Perhaps during the period of diapause there occurs a physiological development which enables the larvae collected late in diapause to respond more readily to inductive daylengths.

Additional evidence for the latter hypothesis comes from the fact that a few larvae eventually pupate after being maintained for a very long time on an 11-hr photoperiod at 23°C. In Experiment 7, for example, an individual larva which was reared and maintained on an 11-hr day length finally pupated after 152 days. Similar examples came from mass cultures kept in the laboratory on an 11-hr day length for several months. In a culture collected July 16, 1953, several pupations occurred on and following February 26, 1954, more than 7 months later, and in another culture collected October 10, 1954, 3 larvae pupated April 4, 1955, about five months later. These facts suggest a gradual development toward a readiness to pupate, so that eventually a few pupations occurred even on an 11-hr photoperiod.

It will be recalled that observations in nature indicated that pupations began in the spring on day lengths that were almost 1 hour shorter than those in the fall when pupations ceased. Perhaps this was the result of such a physiological development by the larvae during the winter, enabling them to pupate on shorter photoperiods in the spring than in the fall. It is planned that this will be a matter for future research.

When larvae received 12 hr of light per day plus an additional 1½ hr given either continuously with the 12-hr light interval or at different times during the dark period (Experiment 11), diapause was terminated. Night interruption also effectively induced pupation even when the total amount of light given daily was only 12 hr (10½ hr plus 1½ hr night interruption), an ineffective amount when given as a single continuous photoperiod. The greatest proportion of pupations in both night-interruption experiments occurred when the 1½-hr interruption was given either soon after the long light period ended or shortly before it began. This could be indicative of a carry-over effect of the light phase during the short intervening period of darkness, but the evidence is adequate for only a suggestion.

Lees (1954, 1955, 1956) has reviewed the literature on the role of the periods of light and dark in the photoperiodic responses of arthropods and points out that knowledge is insufficient to permit a detailed interpretation of results that have been obtained thus far. Further, our own data are too few to allow a critical comparison with the findings of others; however, one point does deserve mention. In other photoperiodic arthropods, in which night-interruption experiments have been conducted, a relatively long period of light is needed to effectively "break" the night. For example, in *Metatetranychus* an 8-hr photoperiod (16 hr of dark) produced 100% diapause, but when an 8-hr light interruption was introduced into the dark period, reducing total dark to 8 hr, diapause dropped only to 62% (Lees, 1953b). The effectiveness of a 1½-hr interruption in *Metriocnemus* appears to represent an exception to the pattern that has been established for other arthropods.

It has been reported in several arthropods that very short photoperiods (with corresponding very long dark periods) and continuous darkness tend to have an effect more or less like that of a long day. This is true in *Macrosiphum* (Shull, 1929), *Diataraxia* (Way and Hopkins, 1950), *Grapholitha* (Dickson, 1949), *Metatetranychus* (Lees, 1953a), *Acronycta* (Danilyevsky, cited by Lees, 1955), *Antheraea* (Tanaka, cited by Lees, 1955), and *Barathra* (Otuka and Santa, 1955). It appears to hold for every arthropod in which it has been tested except *Bombyx* (Kogure, 1933). When *Metriocnemus knabi* larvae were given continuous darkness for 43 days, more than 50% pupated, as compared to 0% in a control group on a 11-hr day. This effect appears to be characteristic of most arthropods. Its approach to universality in this group of animals suggests the desirability of investigating the matter in other photoperiodic animals. In birds, for example, Rowan (1938) claims to have obtained complete spermatogenic stimulation through enforced wakefulness in total darkness, apparently overlooking the possibility that the response obtained might have resulted directly from the action of continuous darkness.

The present study has attempted to correlate day length changes with seasonal diapause in *Metriocnemus knabi* and to determine some of the characteristics of the photoperiodic response. It will serve as a basis for research planned for the future.

SUMMARY

1. Both the initiation and termination of larval diapause in *Metriocnemus knabi* were shown to be under the control of day length. Long days prevent and short days induce diapause; the entire critical range separating long and short photoperiods was between 12 and 13 hr.

2. Larvae were sensitive to light intensities below 0.0025 ft-c and intensities from 0.0025 ft-c to 35 ft-c were equally effective. Such extreme sensitivity indicates that larvae in nature respond to a portion of the daily twilight period.

3. The timing of events in nature correlated well with the occurrence of the experimentally determined effective photoperiods of critical duration; however, in nature, diapause was terminated in the spring when day lengths were shorter than those which prevailed when diapause was initiated in the fall, indicating a physiological conditioning.

4. Temperature modified the photoperiodic response. Inductive photoperiods were most effective at intermediate temperatures (23° to 25°C). Constant low temperatures (12° to 8°C) reduced the rate at which larvae responded; constant high temperature (ca. 30°C) prevented pupation.

5. Diapause occurred only in fully grown larvae.

6. Ten to fourteen successive inductive cycles were required to produce any pupations in diapausing larvae. Short photoperiods introduced into a regime of inductive day lengths reduced the effectiveness of the long photoperiods when given as often as every fourth day; short photoperiods alternated with long were almost completely ineffective in inducing pupation.

7. When larvae on a diapause-inducing day length had the corresponding long night period interrupted by 1½ hr of light, pupations occurred even though the total amount of light given per 24 hr was less than the normal threshold duration when given as a single period during each 24 hr.

8. The effect of continuous darkness was similar to that produced by long photoperiods, a feature shared with many other photoperiodic arthropods.

REFERENCES

Andrewartha, H. G. 1952. Diapause in relation to the ecology of insects. *Biol. Revs., 27,* 50–107.

Baker, F. C. 1935. The effect of photoperiodism on resting, treehole, mosquito larvae. *Can. Entomologist, 67,* 149–53.

Bonnemaison, L. 1949. Sur l'existence d'un facteur inhibant l'apparition des formes sexuées chez les Aphidinae. *Compt. rend. 229,* 386–88.

———. 1950. Influence de l'alimentation et de la lumière sur la réproduction sexuée de *Myzus persicae* (Hem. Aphidinae). *Compt. rend. 230,* 136–37.

Bonnemaison, L., and J. Missonnier. 1955. Influence du photopériodisme sur le déterminisme des formes estivales ou hivernales et de la diapause chez *Psylla pyri* L. (Homoptères). *Compt. rend., 240,* 1277–79.

Dickson, R. C. 1949. Factors governing the induction of diapause in the oriental fruit moth. *Ann. Entomol. Soc. Am., 42,* 511–37.

Jenner, C. E. 1951. Photoperiodism in the fresh-water snail, *Lymnaea palustris.* Ph.D. thesis, Harvard University, Cambridge, Mass.

Kimball, H. H. 1916. The duration and intensity of twilight. *Monthly Weather Rev., 44,* 614–20.

Kogure, M. 1933. The influence of light and temperature on certain characteristics of the silk worm, *Bombyx mori. J. Dept. Agr. Kyushu Imp. Univ., 4,* 1–93.

Lees, A. D. 1953a. Environmental factors controlling the evocation and termination of diapause in the fruit tree red spider mite, *Metatetranychus ulmi* Koch. *Ann. Appl. Biol., 40,* 449–86.

———. 1953b. The significance of the light and dark phase in the photoperiodic control of diapause in *Metatetranychus ulmi* Koch. *Ann. Appl. Biol., 40,* 487–97.

———. 1954. Photoperiodism in arthropods. *Proc. 1st Intern. Photobiol. Congr., Amsterdam 1954,* 36–45.

———. 1955. *The Physiology of Diapause in Arthropods.* Cambridge University Press, Cambridge, England.

———. 1956. The physiology and biochemistry of diapause. *Ann. Rev. Entomol., 1,* 1–16.

Love, G. J., and J. G. Whelchel, 1955. Photoperiodism and the development of *Aedes triseriatus. Ecology, 36,* 340–42.

Marcovitch, S. 1923. Plant lice and light exposure. *Science, 58,* 537–38.

———. 1924. The migration of the Aphididae and the appearance of the sexual forms as affected by the relative length of daily light exposure. *J. Agr. Research, 27,* 513–22.

Müller, H. J. 1954. Der Saisondimorphismus bei Zikaden der Gattung *Euscelis* Brullé. *Beitr. Entomol., 4,* 1–56.

———. 1955. Die Saisonformenbildung von *Arachnia levana,* ein photoperiodisch gesteuerter Diapause-Effekt. *Naturwissenschaften, 42,* 134–35.

Otuka, M., and H. Santa. 1955. Studies on the diapause in the cabbage armyworm, *Barathra brassicae* L. III. The effect of the rhythm of light and darkness on the induction of diapause. *Bull. Natl. Inst. Agr. Sci. (Japan), Ser. C, 1955:* 49–56.

Rowan, W. 1938. Light and seasonal reproduction in animals. *Biol. Revs., 13,* 374–402.

Shull, A. F. 1928. Duration of light and the wings of the aphis *Macrosiphum solanifolii. Arch. Entwicklungsmech. Organ., 113,* 210–39.

———. 1929. The effect of intensity and duration of light and of duration of darkness, partly modified by temperature, upon wing-production in aphids. *Arch. Entwicklungsmech. Organ., 115,* 825–51.

Tate, P., and M. Vincent. 1936. The biology of autogenous and anautogenous races of *Culex pipiens* L. *Parasitology, 28,* 115–43.

Way, M. J., and B. A. Hopkins. 1950. The influence of photoperiod and temperature on the induction of diapause in *Diataraxia oleracea* L. (Lepidoptera). *J. Exptl. Biol., 27,* 365–76.

REPRODUCTIVE CYCLES OF SOME WEST COAST INVERTEBRATES [1]

ARTHUR C. GIESE
Hopkins Marine Station of Stanford University, Pacific Grove, California

That many marine animals breed in a restricted part of the year (MacGinitie and MacGinitie, 1949) as do many fresh-water and terrestrial forms (Bullough, 1951), is evident to all who have collected them for use in the laboratory. Sometimes the spawning is timed by phases of the moon to a remarkable degree, as in the case of the grunion which spawns during the spring months (Thompson and Thompson, 1919), or the palolo worm which will spawn only after a certain phase of the moon, in two months of the year (Clark, 1941). In most marine invertebrates spawning is less spectacular and, in fact, seldom seen, yet the breeding season is marked. Furthermore, spawning may be triggered by factors, such as the phases of the moon, which may have little to do with the overall growth of the gonads and the annual gonadal cycle. The latter may be the result of the operation of one or more of a number of possible factors, e.g., supply of food, temperature, or photoperiod.

It is the purpose of the program outlined below to survey the breeding cycles in as many of the invertebrates of the central California coast as is feasible with the following objectives in mind: (1) to determine for each species whether an annual breeding cycle occurs, (2) to obtain a quantitative measure of the cycle, with the aim of finding some very clearly demarcated ones, (3) to ascertain with which

[1] This paper covers work done in collaboration with a group of associates: John Bennett, Richard Boolootian, Allahverdi Farmanfarmaian, Leonard Greenfield, Reuben Lasker, and John Tucker. Data for each of the species will be published in detail elsewhere. The studies were supported by Grant GS 482 from the National Science Foundation and Grant RG 4578 from the Public Health Service, and funds from the Rockefeller Foundation. We are indebted to Drs. L. R. Blinks, D. P. Abbott, and R. L. Bolin for interest in the studies and for provision of facilities.

environmental factor or factors the cycle is correlated, and (4) ultimately to try to regulate the cycle by experimental variation of the factor or factors concerned. To date, only the first two objectives have been accomplished for a small number of species, and the third has been attempted. Experiments to vary the factors of the environment are being planned for several species, and one series is under way using the ochre star, *Pisaster ochraceus.*

The main difficulty in achieving the fourth objective is the inability to keep many of the marine animals alive for prolonged periods of time, even in aquaria with running sea water. Conditions are not natural, and the animals visibly sicken after several months and many die. An alternative is to attempt to modify conditions in the natural environment, but the magnitude of the ocean and the violence of winter storms makes tinkering even with inlets of the sea inadvisable. However, since the same species may occupy a wide range on the coast, one factor, namely temperature, is varied in nature and it may serve to give information on the relation between temperature and the gonadal cycle if specimens are collected from widely divergent habitats. At the present time the purple sea urchin, *Strongylocentrotus purpuratus,* is being sampled at Los Angeles, at Yankee Point near Monterey, and at Moss Beach near San Francisco.

The survey has had to be confined to relatively sessile or homing animals since an attempt to determine the gonadal cycle of the squid, *Loligo opalescens,* has emphasized to us the difficulty of studying such an active form. The gonads always seemed to be well developed in the specimens caught in Monterey Bay. It now appears that the animals come into the bay only to spawn.

MATERIALS AND METHODS

For the present, investigation has been confined to representatives of three phyla—the echinoderms, the mollusks, and the arthropods (crustaceans). A study of some of the worms is planned, and ultimately representatives of other phyla will be examined as well.

The species of echinoderms which have been investigated are *Pisaster ochraceous* (the ochre star), *Pisaster giganteus* (the giant starfish), *Pateria miniata* (the sea bat), *Strongylocentrotus purpuratus* (the purple sea urchin), *S. franciscanus* (the large red sea urchin), and *S. fragilis*[2] (the fragile sea urchin from deep water). The species of mollusks under investigation are the chitons, *Katherina tunicata* and *Mopalia hindsii;* the giant chiton, *Cryptochiton stelleri;* and red and black abalones, *Haliotis rufescens* and *H. crackerodii,* respectively. The crustaceans under study include the isopod, *Ligia occidentalis,* and the crabs, *Pachygrapsus crassipes* (the green shore crab), *Hemigrapsus nudus* (the purple shore crab), *Petrolistes cinctipes* (the porcelain crab), *Pugettia producta* (the kelp crab), and *Emerita analoga* (the sand crab). These specimens are usually collected at low tide once a month.

Many observations of the spawning of marine animals of the West Coast have been made, especially by the MacGinities (1949), both in the field and in the laboratory. While such information is interesting, it probably gives only the peak of the activity in the reproductive cycle. We have seen instances where the gonads of sea urchins were large and the animals ready to spawn, but they did not do so until something triggered them. Spawning in various animals may be triggered by any one of a number of factors—chemicals in the sea (including chemical secreted by one of the sexes on spawning), light or phases of the moon (Korringa, 1947), temperature change (Crisp, 1957), tidal rhythm and pressure (Korringa, 1947, etc., while the annual reproductive cycle probably depends upon some other factors. A method used in the past for determining an annual reproductive cycle is the size of the gonad at different times in the year (Bullough, 1951). This method is used here at least when the gonads are clearly separable from other tissues in the body, e.g., in the echinoderms. In that case the volume of the gonad, determined by adding the gonadal tissue to a graduate filled with sea water, divided by the weight of the animals was designated as the gonad index (Lasker and Giese, 1954). In later studies this value was multiplied by 100 to give a whole number. In recent work bits of gonads were examined microscopically, and tests for fertilizability of the eggs were made when possible. Eggs of starfishes and mollusks do not fertilize unless spawned naturally.

While in the chitons the gonad is clearly separable and can be

[2] This species perhaps should be called *Allocentrotes fragilis* according to Swann (1953). It occurs in water below 48 fathoms

measured as easily as in the echinoderms, in the abalones and lamellibranchs the gonad is interwoven with the digestive tissue. Therefore, in the abalones the digestive gland-gonad complex was frozen and sectioned, and tracings were made of the areas filled with gonadal tissues of representative sections throughout the gonad. Teased gonads were also examined for eggs and sperm. In the lamellibranchs the presence of mature eggs and sperm was used as a means of delineating the breeding season. Small immature eggs appear in a certain number of animals before the mature eggs show up. In this way the breeding condition can be quantized by counting the number of animals in which sex cells are indistinguishable and giving arbitrary ratings for appearance of immature cells, mature cells in some, mature cells in all, etc.

In crustaceans the gonadal tissue proved to be impossible to assay quantitatively because of difficulty in removing the delicate tissues intact from the animals. In the male, for example, the seminal vesicle becomes engorged with sperm and is easily torn. Therefore, the breeding condition was determined by counting the number of females carrying eggs as well as the state of development of the eggs. When the majority or all of the females carry eggs and the eggs are in an advanced state of development, the animals are considered to be in the height of the season.

Initially, twenty animals were sampled twice monthly, but the data were no more informative than data on a sample of ten animals gathered monthly; therefore, the latter sampling method was considered adequate for most purposes. Larger numbers are sampled when feasible.

Such other data as seemed pertinent were gathered in some cases, e.g., the hepatic index, determined in the same manner as the gonad index in the starfishes and the chitons. Chemical constituents of the gonads and the hepatic glands were determined and will be mentioned where pertinent in a discussion of the experimental results.

EXPERIMENTAL

Examination of Table I discloses that the breeding season is by no means the same for different species of marine animals taken from

TABLE I.   Breeding Seasons of Some West Coast Invertebrates

Phylum and Species[a]	Year	Maximum Gonad Index	Spawn Out
Echinodermata			
S. purpuratus	1952–53	Nov. (sec. Feb.?)	Dec. (Mar.)
S. purpuratus	1953–54	Jan. to May	May
S. purpuratus	1954–55	Feb.	Mar.–Apr.
S. purpuratus	1955–56	Nov.–Dec.	Jan.–Mar.
S. purpuratus	1956–57	Feb.–Apr.	May
S. franciscanus	1953–54	Feb.–Apr.	May
	1954–55	Jan.–Apr.	Apr.–May
	1955–56	May	May
S. fragilis[b]	1956–57	Feb.–Mar.	Apr.
P. ochraceus	1953–54	Apr.–May[c]	Apr.–May
	1954–55	Apr.–May[c]	May–June
	1955–56	Feb.–Apr.	Apr.
	1956–57	Jan.–Mar.	Apr.–May
P. giganteus	1956	Dec.–Jan.	Feb.
P. miniata[d]	1954–55	May–July	Aug.
Mollusca			
K. tunicata	1955–56	Mar.–May	May–June
	1956–57	Mar.–May	May–June
M. hindsii	1956–57	Nov.–Feb.	Mar.
H. rufescens[e]	1956–57	Apr.–June	July (?)
H. crackerodii[e]	1956–57	Apr.–June	July (?)
Arthropoda (Crustacea)			
H. nudus	1955–56	Jan.–Mar.	
	1956–57	Oct.–Dec.	Mar.
P. crassipes	1955–56	June–July	
	1956–57	May–July	July
P. cinctipes	1956–57	All year	
P. producta	1956–57	All year	
E. analoga	1956–57	June–Aug.	Sept.

[a] The full names are given under materials and methods.
[b] Records fragmentary and tentative owing to difficulties of regular dredging.
[c] Data of Feder (1956).
[d] *Patiria* has gametes all year round; the maximum is ill-defined.
[e] Dates are tentative, requiring more study.

approximately the same habitat (intertidal zone). A definite winter breeding season is evident for the sea urchins, for the starfish *P. giganteus*, for the chiton *M. hindsii*, and for the crab *H. nudus*. The ochre star (*P. ochraceus*) shows a spring breeding season, as do the abalones and the chiton *K. tunicata*, while the crabs *P. crassipes* and

E. analoga, and the seabat *P. miniata* show a spring to summer breeding season. Some, like the crabs *P. cinctipes* and *P. producta,* appear to breed all year round. Time does not permit examination of all the species cited, and therefore, only two are singled out to illustrate the approach, namely, the sea urchin *S. purpuratus* and the ochre star *P. ochraceus.*

The Purple Sea Urchin, *Strongylocentrotus purpuratus*

It is easiest to get eggs for experimental work from this species of sea urchin during the winter months; however, some usable eggs are obtainable during most of the year. To find one female with mature eggs in an unfavorable month, however, may require the sacrifice of a hundred or more animals, e.g., in July. This probably means that some animals may develop and mature eggs in almost any month of the year, but only during the winter season are all of the animals developing gametes. At the height of the gonad index all the females carry numerous eggs, and the eggs fertilize and develop. As the gonad index declines from its winter peak all the females usually have normal-sized eggs which fertilize and develop normally but the number of eggs per shrunken gonad is small. On the other hand, months later when the gonads have again grown in size and the average gonad index is large, the eggs are generally small and unfertilizable, many of them appearing as germinal vesicles. It is only as the gonad size becomes very large again with the approach of another breeding season that some of the females and later, all of the females, again have normal-sized fertilizable eggs.

The males are capable of producing motile sperm in any part of the year. When the gonads are large, spawning is easily induced by electric shock or by shaking. This does not occur when the gonad has shrunk, and only small quantities of sperm can be seen when a piece of the gonad is teased in sea water.

A number of pertinent facts have been discovered by statistical analysis of data gathered on the sea urchin. (1) The gonadal cycles of the males and females for any year are the same as shown by the data for the years 1952–53 and 1953–54 (Bennett and Giese, 1955). (2) The average size of gonads is similar in males and females at all times during the cycle. (3) During all months of the year gonad size is very variable, so that some individuals have smaller gonads during months of peak gonad index than some individuals during the months of low gonad index. This raises the question whether the same individual spawns several times during the year or whether only a single gonad cycle is found for each individual. The data do not permit an answer to this question. It has not been possible to induce spawning in the laboratory, although individuals have been kept in the aquaria during the spawning months of the year. It would also be difficult to determine to what extent the animal had spawned, although by determining the mass of the eggs this might be feasible. It is possible that spawning is related to lunar rhythms and is missed because of failure to make observations during the night (Korringa, 1947).

From the published data (Bennett and Giese, 1955; Lasker and Giese, 1954) it is quite clear that in two different years the breeding time is quite different, gonads reaching a peak size in November (with a questionable peak in February) in 1952–53, and a plateau for the months of December to May in 1953–54. Unpublished data for the succeeding years further emphasize the uniqueness of each year: February for 1954–55, November-December for 1955–56, and February-April in 1956–57.

The data for 1953–54 were taken from two points, one exposed to the open ocean (Yankee Point near Carmel), the other from a protected cove (Pescadero Point). Yet the two cycles parallel each other to a remarkable degree and indicate that local differences have very little to do with the onset of the growth in size and of the spawning of the animals; rather, some more general factor is operating. The data from the more distant stations now being tested are awaited with interest.

Pisaster ochraceus

Data on the ochre starfish are available for over four years, almost two from the work of Feder (1956) and two for succeeding years (Farmanfarmaian *et al.*, 1959, and work in progress). In all cases a single marked cycle is observable and, as seen in the data of Table I, the peak is reached in the spring at almost the same time each year. Extensive spawning was observed in May in 1953–54 and 1954–55 by Feder, both in the laboratory and in the field, although the gonad index did not decline at the same time. During 1955–56 and 1956–57 the spawning, as determined in our work by the fall in gonad size, occurred during April and April-May, respectively.

Again, statistical analysis shows that the cycle is the same for both males and females (Bennett and Giese, unpublished). It is also interesting that the gonads of the females always reach a relatively larger size than those of the males, by as much as a third, during the peak of the gonadal cycle.

It is not possible to test the fertilizability of the eggs, even at the peak of the gonadal cycle, unless they are shed naturally. In one case where eggs were spawned in the aquaria, sperm were also shed and the eggs were fertilized and developed. In the ochre starfish the males cannot be distinguished from the females during the months when the gonads are shrunken.

DISCUSSION

The ocean is such a highly constant environment that the small seasonal changes in temperature and chemical nature may not be sufficient to set off cyclic changes such as occur after the much more drastic temperature variations affecting terrestrial and fresh-water organisms. Photoperiod, however, may well play a role, at least for animals in the lighted zone of the ocean. It is of interest to determine whether the breeding cycles of the animals discussed in this report are correlated with any of the environmental variables, such as food, temperature, and light (for literature review, see Giese, 1959).

That food plays an important part in the reproductive cycles is suggested by the fact that a spectacular growth of some 20- to 25-fold in mass occurs during the period when the immature shrunken gonad grows to the size of the turgid gonad ready to spawn. Such expansion must require adequate food supply. Particular chemicals such as desoxyribonucleic acid in the male and ribonucleic acid in the female gonad may show an increase of about thirty-fold (Giese *et al.*, 1959). It is, of course, conceivable that the food for such increases in gonad size might come from the use of food in storage organs.

If the ochre star, *P. ochraceus*, is starved for a prolonged time, it fails to develop its gonads and sheds no eggs when its fellows, given adequate food, are spawning (Feder, 1956). It is therefore obvious that it requires food for maintenance of its gonads. This is interesting in view of the fact that the ochre star in the intertidal area near the Hopkins Marine Station lives a marginal existence and consumes only a relatively small mass of food in a year (Feder, 1956). Its food consists primarily of mussels, but it eats a variety of snails and limpets, as well as bivalves other than mussels.

In view of the small amount of food taken in and the paucity of organic compounds in the body fluid,[3] the rapid rise in size of the gonads is remarkable. However, it was noticed that the hepatic caecae shrink as the gonads increase in size. The relationship was almost quantitatively reciprocal, suggesting that the hepatic caecae continually store the food as it comes from the gut (Farmanfarmaian et al., 1959). Further, it was found that when glucose and amino acids are injected into the body fluid, they are rapidly removed (Giese, Huang, and Woo, unpublished). Presumably the hepatic caecae rapidly remove the nutrients and store them until needed by the gonad. The gonad is therefore not so dependent upon the immediate food supply. Something other than food must therefore trigger the development of the gonads.

The purple sea urchin also fails to develop sperm or eggs in the small number of animals that have been starved; in fact, the gonads shrink to a small fraction of their initial size. The major part of the food storage in this case seems to occur in the gonads. One might therefore suspect that the sea urchin would be more dependent upon the food supply and its variations than the starfish possessing hepatic caecae. However, whereas the ochre star is restricted to eating live animals, the purple sea urchin is quite omnivorous in the laboratory and apparently will take in quite a variety of live and dead food in the field, judging from the varied contents of its intestines, although its main food consists of algae. An omnivorous habit would tie an animal less firmly to the variations in the supply of any one type of food, e.g., the algae which have their own seasonal growth cycle. However, it is possible that the nutrient value of the food available varies. For example, young actively growing algae have a higher proportion of protein and would

[3] For example, monthly samples for a year showed an average of less than 2 mg % of nonprotein nitrogen, usually less than 1 mg % of reducing sugar and protein detectable only in traces (by paper electrophoresis).

therefore be more effective than old ones with a high proportion of rather difficultly digestible polysaccharides. Unfortunately, it is not possible at present to assess the full importance of this factor.

An attempt has been made to determine whether correlation exists between the temperature and the breeding cycle. The most extensive data, those upon the purple sea urchin and the ochre star, are given in Figs. 1 and 2. It will be noted that the temperature changes are slight but definite, and that in each case a decline in temperature is accompanied by growth of the gonads, while a rise in temperature is accompanied by spawning. Mere correlation does not constitute proof of

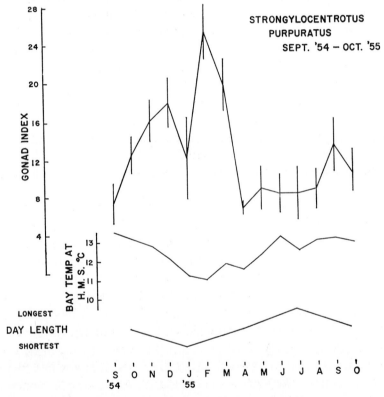

FIG. 1.   Gonad index of the purple sea urchin, *Strongylocentrotus purpuratus,* as correlated with temperature at the Hopkins Marine Station (H.M.S.) and with day length. The vertical lines on the gonad index graph indicate the spread of data for determinations at any one time (95% confidence limits).

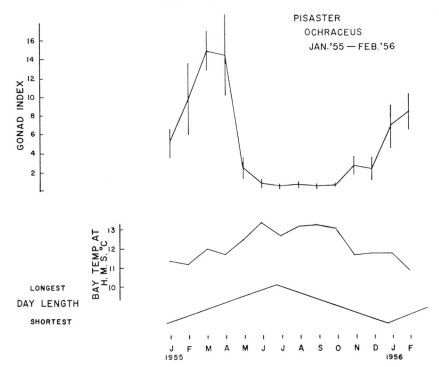

FIG. 2.   Gonad index for the ochre starfish, *Pisaster ochraceus,* as correlated with the temperature at the Hopkins Marine Station and with day length. The vertical lines on the gonad index graph indicate the spread in the data (95% confidence limits).

causative relationships. The temperature of laboratory animals should be controlled during this period, but sea urchins do not do well in the laboratory for prolonged periods of time. Experiments are under way to determine whether gonad development and spawning in the starfish can be controlled by temperature changes.

Crisp (1957) has briefly reviewed the literature pertaining to the effect of temperature on breeding. He notes that animals, which have a wide range but are characteristically in temperate waters, when living in northern waters show a marked restriction of the breeding season to the warmest months of the year. Loosanoff and Davis (1950) showed that *Venus arenaria* could be brought into breeding condition in winter by gradually raising the temperature of the water in which specimens are kept, provided they are supplied with adequate food.

Crisp (1957) tested effect of a rising and falling temperature on the breeding of the cold-water barnacles (*Balanus balanoides* and *Balanus balanus*) which normally breed once a year between November and February. When the animals were placed in tanks kept between 14° and 18°C, no copulatory activity or fertilization was observed. When taken to between 3° and 10°C, breeding commenced after one or two months, the interval depending upon the previous temperature and history. Both barnacles therefore require a period of cold for induction of breeding conditions. They may even be starved without altering the course of events (for a more detailed account see Giese, 1959).

The importance of temperature to breeding of some vertebrates that do not seem to be affected by photoperiod is reviewed by Bullough (1951). The data correlating temperature changes and induction of breeding are particularly good for the killifish, and indicative for the three-spined stickleback and the fresh-water perch, as well as for the edible frog and the American newt (*Triton viridescens*).

When the breeding of the sea urchin and the ochre starfish are compared with the photoperiod, distinct correlation is seen for the latter species, but no clear-cut relation in the former (Figs. 1 and 2). However, examination of the more extensive data in Table I shows that the breeding peak is different in successive years. Since photoperiod is invariant, even the slight differences in breeding cycles seen in these two species raise some doubt as to the correlation, and experiments are called for. It is quite likely that the spawning stimulus is different from the stimulus which leads to the development of the gonads. If so, then spawning might occur at almost any time during the period in which the gonads are enlarged, thus making the cycle appear quite different in two successive years. Early rains, for example, usually lead to spawning-out in the sea urchins; no data are available for the starfish. Experiments are clearly needed to establish whether the build-up of the gonads can be affected by lengthening the days when in nature they are decreasing in length, or suppressed by shortening the days when they are lengthening. Such experiments are in progress for the starfish.

That photoperiod governs the breeding cycle of many animals is too well known to require documentation. Photoperiodism in animals was discovered by Rowan (1925) for the Canadian junco, in which the breeding condition of the gonad can be induced in the dead of winter by lengthening the exposure of the birds to light. The literature for various invertebrates, along with that for vertebrates and plants, has been recently reviewed (Borthwick *et al.*, 1956). A search is desirable to learn the extent of photoperiodic regulation of annual gonadal cycles among marine animals which are otherwise subjected to a rather constant environment.

SUMMARY

1. The annual breeding cycles of a number of West Coast echinoderms, mollusks, and crustaceans have been determined, usually by measuring monthly the size of the gonad relative to the size of the animal.

2. Peaks of gonad size appear in winter, spring, or summer in different species, and some breed throughout the year.

3. Some correlation between fall in temperature and increase in gonad size of the purple sea urchin and the ochre star is observed, but no experiments studying the effects of varied temperature have yet been performed.

4. The increase in size of the gonad of the ochre star also correlates with the increase in day length; but no experiments on varied photoperiods have yet been performed.

5. The breeding peak for different years varies by several months for the purple sea urchin; the variability is less for the purple star.

6. The survey reveals several animals as promising material for experimental testing in the future.

REFERENCES

Bennett, J., and A. C. Giese. 1955. The annual reproductive and nutritional cycles in two western sea urchins. *Biol. Bull., 109,* 226–37.

Borthwick, H. A., S. B. Hendricks, and M. W. Parker. 1956. *Radiation Biology,* Vol. 3, Chap. 10. A. Hollaender, Editor. McGraw-Hill, New York.

Bullough, W. S. 1951. *Vertebrate Sexual Cycles.* Methuen, London.

Clark, L. B. 1941. Factors in the lunar cycle which may control reproduction in the Atlantic palolo. *Biol. Bull., 81,* 278 (abstr.).

Crisp, D. J. 1957. Effect of low temperatures on the breeding of marine animals. *Nature, 179,* 1138–39.

Farmanfarmaian, A., A. C. Giese, R. A. Boolootian, and J. Bennett, 1958.

Annual reproductive cycles in four species of west coast starfishes. *J. Exptl. Zool., 138* (2).

Feder, H. 1956. Natural history studies on the starfish *Pisaster ochraceus* (Brandt, 1835) in the Monterey Bay area. Ph.D. thesis, Stanford University, Stanford, Calif.

Giese, A. C. 1959. Annual reproductive cycles of marine invertebrates. *Ann. Rev. Physiol., 21,* 547–76.

Giese, A. C., L. Greenfield, H. Huang, A. Farmanfarmaian, R. A. Boolootian, and R. Lasker, 1959. Organic productivity in the reproductive cycle of the purple sea urchin. *Biol. Bull.* (in press).

Korringa, P. 1947. Relations between the moon and periodicity in the breeding of marine animals. *Ecol. Monographs, 17,* 347–81.

Lasker, R., and A. C. Giese. 1954. Nutrition of the sea urchin, *Strongylocentrotus purpuratus. Biol. Bull., 106,* 328–40.

Loosanoff, V. L., and H. C. Davis. 1950. Conditioning *V. mercenaria* for spawning in winter and breeding its larvae in the laboratory. *Biol. Bull., 98,* 60–65.

MacGinitie, G. E., and N. MacGinitie. 1949. *Natural History of Marine Animals.* McGraw-Hill, New York.

Rowan, W. 1925. Relation of light to bird migration and developmental changes. *Nature, 115,* 494–95.

Swann, E. F. 1953. The Strongylocentrotidae (Echinoidea) of the Northeast Pacific. *Evolution, 7,* 269–73.

Thompson, W. F., and J. Thompson. 1919. The spawning of the grunion (*Leuristhes tenuis*). California Fish and Game Comm., *Fish Bull., 3,* 1–29.

SECTION IX

Photoperiodism in the Vertebrates

VERTEBRATE PHOTOSTIMULATION

WILLIAM S. BULLOUGH
Birkbeck College, University of London, London, England

Within the space limitations it is not possible to give more than a brief introduction to what, during the past 30 years, has expanded into a vast field of research. As is well known, the original experiments were those of Rowan, who in 1925 reported the stimulation of the gonads of the Canadian junco to unseasonable sexual maturity by means of extra light in autumn. In the context of thought of those days, the design of Rowan's experiments showed great originality, and in 1957, the year of his death, it is particularly appropriate to pay him tribute for the fundamental part he has played in the subject of vertebrate photostimulation.

Today the study of the control of vertebrate breeding cycles by environmental variations has become fused with studies on the physiology of the ductless glands, of nutrition, of hair or feather moult, of the nervous system, of behavior, and of migration. Much of this field has been reviewed by Bullough (1951), and in this present additional review only those topics which appear to be of particular relevance to this conference are discussed.

LIGHT AND VERTEBRATE REPRODUCTION

First and foremost it is necessary to discuss the effects of light on vertebrate reproduction. In Rowan's original experiments the stimulus to gonad maturation was obtained by extra electric light given in the evenings at a time when the natural day length was shortening, although it should be noted that Rowan himself believed that the stimulus was due not to increasing periods of light but to increasing periods of muscular exercise (Rowan, 1928, 1929). Then arose a sharp difference of opinion between those who felt that the results must be held to imply that it is the increasing day length of late winter and early spring that normally induces the onset of the breeding season of the junco, and those who held that the stimulus obtained is in fact the result of an artificial laboratory technique which in no way can be taken as reflecting normal events in the wild. Nowadays there seems little reason to doubt that the gonad-stimulating effects of artificial light in autumn must be regarded as an exact parallel of those events which take place naturally every spring.

Recently, however, the importance of the day length as such has been questioned, and attention has been focused on the possible direct stimulatory effect of a reduced dark period (Jenner and Engels, 1952; Kirkpatrick and Leopold, 1952). It has been shown in the case of certain birds that a strong stimulus to gonad growth can be obtained in winter conditions if, without altering the number of hours of light per day, the long night is split into two shorter dark periods. It has therefore been concluded that the total number of hours of light received each day is unimportant, that the duration of the dark period is critical, and that our theories regarding vertebrate photostimulation must be amended. These conclusions have led to controversy, a number of authors including Farner *et al.* (1953), Hammond (1953), and Marshall (1955) having expressed scepticism that the dark period itself has any *active* role to play.

However, the results obtained do need some explanation, and it might be interesting to make the following speculation. It is possible that, except during any refractory period, daylight always exerts a stimulus to the production of gonadotropins in the birds in question, but that, if the night is too long, the glandular activity is depressed to such a degree that the succeeding short day is powerless to counteract it. A splitting of the night period might be all that is required to counteract the development of such an extreme depression and so permit the light stimulus to be felt.

This discussion has so far taken no account of species which do not breed in the spring or which are not diurnal, and to which consequently the same arguments cannot apply. Regarding nocturnal or subterranean animals there appears to be no reliable evidence at all, although of course spring-breeding nocturnal species may feel the effects of longer days in terms of shorter nights in the manner mentioned above. However, the evidence regarding autumn-breeding species is clear. From the early studies of Hoover and Hubbard (1937) on the brook trout, of Bissonnette (1941) on the goat, and of Yeates (1947) on the sheep, the conclusion emerges that in at least some autumn-breeding species a shortening day, or a lengthening night, is a critical factor in the stimulation of gametogenesis.

This conclusion is of great theoretical importance, showing as it does that a species may come to possess an annual breeding cycle which is attuned either to the increasing day length of spring or to the decreasing day length of autumn. It follows that the secretion of gonadotropins from the pituitary is not the necessary consequence of increasing day length as such, and that, because of some special need, a species may, through natural selection, be adjusted to receive the stimulus to gametogenesis from whatever kind of day length is typical of the most suitable time of the year.

OTHER EXTERNAL FACTORS AND VERTEBRATE REPRODUCTION

It is also evident that in many species, such as those which are subterranean, it cannot be anticipated that light will have any effect at all. Little or nothing is known of the methods of control of the reproductive cycles of such animals, but it has already been proved that some of the cold-blooded vertebrates, such as *Rana temporaria* (van Oordt and van Oordt, 1955), react not to changing light but to changing temperature.

Unfortunately, relatively little effort has been devoted to the study of vertebrates whose reproductive cycles are apparently controlled by factors other than light. There are many known examples of such vertebrates, and our ignorance of this matter is serious. There is the tropical bat described by Baker and Bird (1936), which is exposed to an almost unchanging length of night, which roosts in an almost thermostatic cave, but which has a sharply defined annual breeding season. There are many tropical birds which may breed in time to the onset of the rainy season (Marshall and Disney, 1957). There are frogs whose spawning period is controlled by temperature (van Oordt and van Oordt, 1955) or which live in deserts and breed in time to an erratic rainfall (Fletcher, 1889). There are fishes known to be influenced by temperature (Burger, 1939) or suspected of being controlled by the phase of the moon, perhaps as expressed through the tides.

In this connection it is also necessary to consider the effects of yet another group of external factors. While a relatively simple external variant such as increasing day length or increasing temperature may be all that is needed to stimulate gonad growth, it commonly happens that a whole complex of suitable external factors are necessary for final gonad maturation and for the production of fertile eggs. The whole environment of the animal must be felt to be suitable, often a mate must be present, and in some cases the social group must be properly constituted. Into the first of these categories may enter the effects of the weather and of the terrain, and into the second the effects of appropriate courtship display and sometimes, as in the case of animals like the rabbit, of copulation itself (Donovan and Harris, 1955). These influences from the outside world are felt through a variety of exteroceptive organs, and the resulting stimulus to the gonads is apparently due to a final spurt of activity on the part of the pituitary gland. Certainly the act of copulation is known to operate in this way in the female rabbit.

Evidently, therefore, a species may respond first to one or another of a variety of environmental factors of which changing day length is one example, and second to a complex of factors which may be appreciated through the skin (by contact with other individuals), through the nose (especially perhaps in shrews), through the ears (especially perhaps in song birds), and even through the taste buds. As each new facet of the necessary final "Gestalt" presents itself, so through nervous pathways the pituitary activity is stimulated to new levels and the gonads pass from potential to actual maturity. It may be surmised that a "good" experimental animal is one to which this final complex of factors is relatively unimportant, while a "poor" species is one to which it is all important.

THE NERVOUS SYSTEM AND VERTEBRATE REPRODUCTION

Whatever may be the dominant influences entering an animal from the external world, these influences must be translated into nervous energy, and it is probable that the center first affected is the brain. In the case of light entering the eyes to stimulate the growth of the gonads, the pathway of the stimulus via the optic nerves to the brain has been clearly demonstrated. Further it has been suspected that the hypothalamus must be a region of special importance in this respect, and that some stimulus must pass from the hypothalamus to the pituitary gland, which in turn stimulates gonad growth (Donovan and Harris, 1955).

It is appropriate to introduce at this point the problem of *internal* reproductive rhythms. Such internal rhythms have been known for a long time and they account, for instance, for the fact that the spring-breeding English minnow may show gonad growth even when the environment is maintained steadily in the winter condition (Bullough, 1951). The well-known refractory period may also be regarded as part of such a rhythm. It is probable that the reproductive cycles of many, if not most, vertebrates are under the dual control of an internal physiological rhythm and an external seasonal rhythm. Normally these two rhythms coincide and reinforce each other, but if they are made to clash experimentally, then it is the seasonal rhythm that ultimately gains the dominance.

It used to be suggested that the mechanism of the internal annual rhythm, like that of the shorter estrous rhythm, might prove to be based in the anterior pituitary gland. Today the tendency is to search inside the brain for the seat of both these rhythms, and particularly to examine the function of the hypothalamus, which is in such close connection with the pituitary stalk.

Thus it is possible to trace the pathway of the stimulus from the environment to the brain and perhaps to the hypothalamus, to postulate that the basis of the internal rhythm may be situated in the neighborhood of the hypothalamus, and to note that the hypothalamus is closely connected to the pituitary gland.

THE HYPOTHALAMUS

The nervous pathways of the brain, and in particular of the hypothalamus, thus stand out as regions of great potential interest to any study of vertebrate photostimulation. The hypothalamus is well developed in all vertebrates, and experiments by damage or by stimulation have shown, among other things, that this region of the brain powerfully influences temperature regulation, sugar and fat metabolism, the states of sleeping and waking, and the sexual activities.

An excellent review of the probable role of the hypothalamus in reproduction is that of Donovan and Harris (1955). They note evidence to show that experimental lesions of the anterior hypothalamus may result in gonad atrophy, while bilateral lesions posterior to the optic chiasma may result in constant oestrus. Electrical stimulation may also induce ovulation, and, in passing, it may be wondered whether the direct photostimulation demonstrated by Benoit (1955) is in fact a similar artificial technique.

Donovan and Harris discuss the route whereby the influence of the hypothalamus may pass to the pituitary, and they suggest that this influence must be hormonal in nature and must pass with the blood through the hypophyseal portal vessels which run alongside the pituitary stalk. On good evidence they discount Thomson and Zuckerman's (1954) theory that the reaction of the pituitary is not dependent on the integrity of the portal vessels. Of particular importance in this connection is the observation of Harris and Jacobsohn (1952) that sexual cycles are not reestablished in a hypophysectomized animal into which a new pituitary has been grafted unless this new pituitary is placed beneath the hypothalamus and revascularized by the portal vessels. The presence or absence of a nervous connection is evidently unimportant.

In summing up, Donovan and Harris suggest "that the external environment affects the reproductive process by means of nervous reflexes originating in a wide variety of sensory end-organs," that "such reflex activity would appear to be co-ordinated and integrated in the hypothalamus," and that the "hypothalamic nerve fibres liberate some humoral agent" which "is carried by the vessels into the sinusoids of the anterior pituitary gland."

While discussing this subject, it is also tempting to compare the wakefulness induced by the electrical stimulation of the hypothalamus with the *"Zugunruhe"* of the sexually stimulated bird preparing to migrate (Farner, 1955); to compare the obesity induced by lesions of the hypothalamus (Long, 1957) with the fat deposition that occurs also in birds about to migrate (Farner, 1955; Koch and de Bont, 1952); and to speculate whether in fact this region of the brain may not only be a highly important link in the chain connecting external light changes with internal gonad growth, but also the controlling influence behind the refractory period and the seat of the seasonal migratory urge.

Difficult as the hypothalamus is to manipulate, and crude as are our present techniques, it seems evident that a close study of this region of the brain will be an essential prerequisite to a full explanation of the mechanism of photostimulation in vertebrates.

CONCLUSIONS

1. Evidence has been reviewed to suggest that visible light *as such* does not induce any specific or essential photochemical transformation in any of those regions of the vertebrate system which are involved in the reproductive processes. In fact external stimuli other than light must be commonly involved in the control of vertebrate reproductive cycles. Any external stimuli, appreciated by the appropriate exteroceptors, must be translated into patterns of nervous energy which are in turn appreciated by the brain, or perhaps more specifically by the hypothalamus. In all cases it is evidently the increasing nervous activity which initiates and controls the reproductive rhythm.

2. It seems probable that most vertebrates are also normally subject to an inherent reproductive rhythm of greater or less strength. It does not appear possible that such a rhythm could be sufficiently accurately timed to control an annual cycle, as was pointed out long ago by Baker when he spoke of the necessity for periodically "putting the clock right." It is by reference to changes in the external world that the internal rhythm is adjusted every year. It is probable that this internal rhythm is also based in some such region as the hypothalamus so that it too may be considered as nervous in origin.

3. From these suggestions it appears that the onset of a new breeding season may be ascribed to a swing in the endocrinological balance induced by the long and steady "pressure" of appropriate nervous impulses arriving in the hypothalamus from the exteroceptors. The main

stimulus to gonad growth may be the result of an initial stimulus to only one exteroceptor, but for full gonad maturation adequate stimuli from a variety of exteroceptors may be essential.

4. In the absence of the appropriate initial external stimulus, some region of the brain, probably the hypothalamus, commonly seems to possess the power to exert the necessary "pressure" spontaneously at approximately the correct season. In the case of migrating birds that winter in the other hemisphere, it may well be that the earliest stirrings of gonad activity are normally induced by this internal rhythm, the external stimulus only beginning to exert its effect after the bird has returned across the equator into the new spring.

REFERENCES

Baker, J. R., and T. F. Bird. 1936. The seasons in a tropical rain forest (New Hebrides). IV. Insectivorous bats. *J. Linnean Soc. London, Zool., 40*, 143.

Benoit, J. 1955. See Discussion, *Mem. Soc. Endocrinol., 4*, 89.

Bissonnette, T. H. 1941. Experimental modification of breeding cycles in goats. *Physiol. Zoöl., 14*, 379.

Bullough, W. S. 1951. *Vertebrate Sexual Cycles.* Methuen, London.

Burger, J. W. 1939. Some experiments on the relation of the external environment to the spermatogenic cycle of *Fundulus heteroclitus* (L.). *Biol. Bull., 77*, 96.

Donovan, B. T., and G. W. Harris. 1955. Neurohumoral mechanisms in reproduction. *Brit. Med. Bull., 11*, 93.

Farner, D. S. 1955. The annual stimulus for migration: experimental and physiologic aspects. *Recent Studies in Avian Biology*, Chap. 7. Urbana.

Farner, D. S., L. R. Mewaldt, and S. D. Irving. 1953. The roles of darkness and light in the photoperiodic response of the testes of white crowned sparrows. *Biol. Bull., 105*, 434.

Fletcher, J. J. 1889. Observations on the oviposition and habits of certain Australian batrachians. *Proc. Linnean Soc. N. S. Wales, 4*, 357.

Hammond, J. 1953. Photoperiodicity in animals: The role of darkness. *Science, 117*, 389.

Harris, G. W., and D. Jacobsohn. 1952. Functional grafts of the anterior pituitary gland. *Proc. Roy. Soc. London, B139*, 263.

Hoover, E. E., and H. E. Hubbard. 1937. Modification of the sexual cycle in trout by control of light. *Copeia, 4*, 206.

Jenner, C. E., and W. L. Engels. 1952. The significance of the dark period in the photoperiodic response of male juncos and white-throated sparrows. *Biol. Bull., 103*, 345.

Kirkpatrick, C. M., and A. C. Leopold. 1952. The role of darkness in sexual activity of the quail. *Science, 116*, 280.

Koch, H. J., and A. F. de Bont. 1952. Standard metabolic rate, weight changes and food consumption of *Fringilla c. coelebs* L. during sexual maturation. *Ann. soc. roy. zool. Belg., 82,* 1.

Long, C. N. H. 1957. Studies on experimental obesity. *J. Endocrinol., 15,* vi.

Marshall, A. J. 1955. Reproduction in birds: the male. *Mem. Soc. Endocrinol., 4,* 75.

Marshall, A. J., and H. J. de S. Disney. 1957. Experimental induction of the breeding season in a xerophidous bird. *Nature, 180,* 647.

Rowan, W. 1925. Relation of light to bird migration and developmental changes. *Nature, 115,* 494.

———. 1928. Reproductive rhythm in birds. *Nature, 122,* 11.

———. 1929. Experiments in bird migration. I. Manipulation of the reproductive cycle: seasonal histological changes in the gonads. *Proc. Boston Soc. Nat. Hist., 39,* 151.

Thomson, A. P. D., and S. Zuckerman. 1954. The effect of pituitary-stalk section on light-induced oestrus in ferrets. *Proc. Roy. Soc. London, B142,* 437.

van Oordt, G. J., and P. G. W. J. van Oordt. 1955. The regulation of spermatogenesis in the frog. *Mem. Soc. Endocrinol., 4,* 25.

Yeates, N. T. M. 1947. Influence of variation in length of day upon the breeding season in sheep. *Nature, 160,* 429.

PHOTOPERIODISM IN FISHES IN RELATION TO THE ANNUAL SEXUAL CYCLE [1]

ROBERT WHITING HARRINGTON, JR.
Florida State Board of Health, Vero Beach, Florida

A brief, comprehensive review of experiments on photoperiodism in fishes is precluded by incoherent results requiring lengthy qualifications. In the present state of knowledge, meaningful comparisons between experiments, moreover, can be made only in the context of the annual reproductive cycle as a whole. A dearth of experiments long enough or of data sufficient to cover all periods of this cycle is noted by Atz (1957) in his inclusive review of the literature to the middle of 1956, with analyses of then unpublished material and tabular summaries of all experiments. Other pertinent reviews are those of Hoar (1951, 1955). Atz ascribes much of the difficulty in comparing experiments and some discrepant results with the same species to probable differences in response to day length by fishes at various periods of their cycles. With these cues, attention here will focus on crucial details of the few experiments in which the response mechanism has been related to the annual cycle. This narrows consideration mostly to the cyprinid cycle as studied chiefly in the bridled shiner, *Notropis bifrenatus,* in the European minnow, *Phoxinus phoxinus,* and to some extent in the specialized bitterling, *Rhodeus amarus,* and to the cycle of the three-spined stickleback, *Gasterosteus aculeatus,* concerning which additional information has appeared since the review of Atz.

THE CYPRINID SEXUAL CYCLE

Results of exposing fish to a long photoperiod at different seasons of the year (Harrington, 1947, 1950, 1956, 1957) are shown in Fig. 1. The time axis, with monthly intervals above and annual cycle of day

[1] Contribution No. 67, Entomological Research Center, Florida State Board of Health, Vero Beach, Florida.

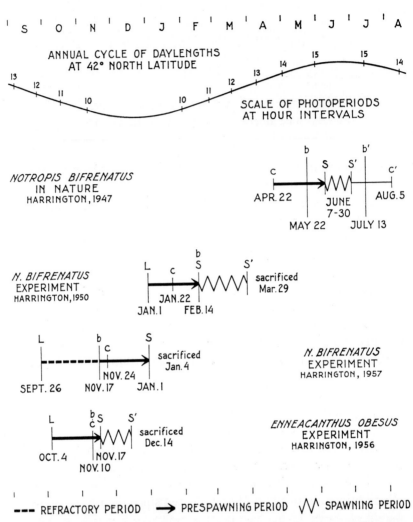

FIG. 1. Chronologies of natural and experimentally induced breeding periods of the bridled shiner, *Notropis bifrenatus,* and of an experimentally induced breeding period of the banded sunfish, *Enneacanthus obesus.* Dates of imposition of supraliminal photoperiod, L.; of earliest and latest recorded nuptial coloration, c and c′, sexual behavior, b and b′, and spawning, S and S′. (After Harrington, 1957.)

lengths below, records the fluctuations in the daily photoperiod at the latitude concerned, between about 9 hr at the winter, and 15 at the summer solstice. Diagrams below record events of a normal breeding cycle and of three cycles induced experimentally.

In bridled shiners in nature, the earliest sign of sexuality was nuptial color (c) first apparent April 22, when the daily photoperiod was 13½ hr, the earliest breeding behavior (b) was observed May 22, the earliest spawning (S) June 7, the last spawning (S') June 30, the last breeding behavior (b') July 13, and the last color (c') August 5. It is noteworthy that the breeding season ends long before the photoperiod has declined to the day length of April 22. The interval between the first outward sign of sexuality and the onset of spawning will be called the *prespawning period*. In nature, this numbered 46 days—spanned by the arrow—and in view of later experimental results was started by the advent of day lengths above a certain threshold.

In the preliminary experiment on the bridled shiner, the prespawning period began with the imposition of long days (L) January 1, ending 44 days later, at the first spawning (S), February 14. In an experiment on a centrarchid fish, the banded sunfish, *Enneacanthus obesus,* the prespawning period began with the imposition of long days (L) October 4, ending 45 days later, at the first spawning (S) November 17. In the final experiment on the bridled shiner, the long photoperiod (L) was begun September 26, but spawning did *not* occur 44 to 46 days later. On the contrary, the internal mechanism governing attainment of functional maturity was refractory to the stimulus of the long photoperiod for about the next 52 days—as symbolized by the broken line—first responding to this stimulus about November 17. The gonadal histology confirmed that the mechanism was refractory as late as October 26, the testes of a male killed November 16 showed only the start of spermiogenesis, the first outward sign of sexuality was breeding behavior (b) observed November 17, and the first spawning occurred 45 days after November 17—a time interval in conformity with the prespawning periods of the other experiments and with that surmised from field observations. Thus, a postspawning *refractory period,* from about mid-July to mid-November, appears to alternate with a *responsive period,* from about mid-November to mid-July. Several short-day fish and two males hatched from eggs spawned

January 1 were continued on normal days after the end of the experiment. All these fish reached maturity 5½ months later, within the normal spawning period.

The middle panel of Fig. 2 shows the effects in terms of maximal egg diameters of long versus short days on the maturity of the bridled shiners in the final experiment (Fig. 1). Egg numbers are shown on the vertical, egg diameters on the horizontal, with the larger diameters to the right. By December 23, contrasting effects of long versus short days are obvious. Egg measurements were made a week before and three days after January 1, when the first spawning occurred. Within this interval, the eggs of long-day fish advanced from penultimate to final maturity. Among short-day fish, there was a continuous slow increase in the minimum, mean, and modal diameters of the largest 50 eggs from each ovary, but after the first month maximum diameters were arrested at about 336 microns. In the absence of long days, egg maturation this time of year, as in the European minnow, *Phoxinus phoxinus* (Bullough, 1939 and Fig. 2), fails to go beyond an early stage of the secondary growth phase (period of yolk accumulation). The distributional spread of the largest 50 egg diameters decreases as more and more diameters approach the critical diameter (336 microns). No eggs of the long-day fish had exceeded this critical diameter by October 26, so that it cannot be inferred that the mechanism productive of later phases of the secondary growth period, i.e., of final maturation, had as yet been set in motion by the stimulus of long days so effective later. This egg-diameter distribution, however, is unique among all the others in being skewed. Its maximum is the same as in all short-day fish, but its mean is less than that of the same date in short-day fish, and its mode equals that reached only by January among short-day fish. Therefore, although the internal mechanism governing egg growth up to the critical diameter does not require long days for its operation, as shown by the ovaries of short-day fish, it can be speeded up by a long photoperiod.

Two different and successive internal mechanisms must therefore be recognized. The first, in operation at least since September and not requiring long days for its performance, governs egg diameter increase up to a critical maximum (336 microns). It responds, however, to a gratuitous long photoperiod with an accelerated increase in the num-

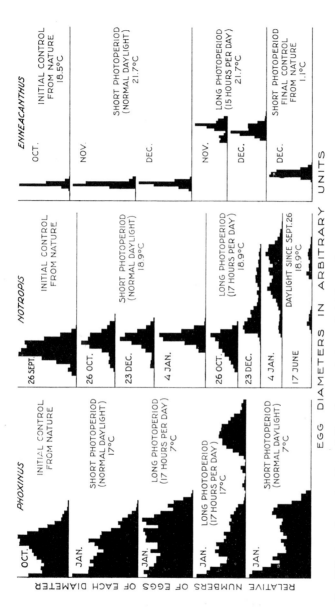

FIG. 2. Effects of contrasting daily photoperiods and high or low temperatures on fish maturity, in terms of maximal egg diameters in *Phoxinus phoxinus*, *Notropis bifrenatus*, and *Enneacanthus obesus*. (Adapted from Bullough, 1939; Harrington, 1956, 1957.)

655

bers of egg diameters reaching this maximum. The second mechanism, governing the final stages of maturation and essential for increase in egg diameters in excess of 336 microns, requires long days for its performance, at least out of season, but it is refractory to this stimulus before mid-November. The two sexes reached maturity simultaneously. The testes of short-day males remained quiescent, with stages up to primary spermatocytes. Those of the long-day males were the same until mid-November when spermiogenesis began.

In all experiments on *Notropis* the temperature was constant at a level near the average of the natural breeding season, so that for effects of various day length-temperature combinations on the cyprinid cycle one must turn to the experiments on *Phoxinus* (Fig. 2 and Bullough, 1939, 1940). As in *Notropis,* full maturity in either sex required long days combined with high temperature. Without this combination the early stages of the secondary growth phase were not surpassed in the ovaries, and primary spermatocytes were the most advanced stages reached in the testes. With short days, high temperature is inhibitory to *Phoxinus,* arresting egg development (Fig. 2), and although undoubtedly inhibitory to *Notropis* also, it permits a slow, steady increase in egg diameters (Fig. 2). Inhibition of egg development by high temperature in the absence of long days must be a widespread and important adjustment mechanism among fishes, for a similar effect is found in *Rhodeus* (Verhoeven and van Oordt, 1955), in *Enneacanthus* (Fig. 2 and Harrington, 1956), in *Apeltes* (Merriman and Schedl, 1941), and is consistent with the reaction of *Gasterosteus* to the same set of conditions (Baggerman, 1957). In all these forms, moreover, the inhibition by high temperature seems to be overridden by a long photoperiod. From the comparison of maximal egg diameters in *Phoxinus, Notropis,* and *Enneacanthus* under different conditions (Fig. 2), it appears likely that egg development in the absence of long days proceeds to a critical diameter at a rate inversely proportional to the temperature. At low temperature, judging from *Phoxinus* (Fig. 2), the rate of progress to the critical diameter is unaffected by day length, and gametogenesis does not proceed beyond the early stages in either sex (Bullough, 1939). Additional experiments on the interaction of day length and temperature on the cyprinid cycle at different seasons should prove rewarding. However, the failure of the same individuals of *Rhodeus* to react at a later season to the same set of stimuli that induced them to mature at an earlier season is no indication of the phase of responsiveness of individuals in the wild at the latter season. Therefore, the postulation of a different reaction to the same stimuli by *Rhodeus* at different seasons (Verhoeven and van Oordt, 1955) seems premature, and must be countered with the presumption that postspawning refractoriness had set in. This possibility is made the more likely by the fact that the ovipositor hardly reacts before the end of October (Duyvené de Wit, 1939), which taken in conjunction with the situation in *Notropis* suggests a postspawning refractory period in *Rhodeus* comparable to that in *Notropis*.

Figure 3 sums up the experimental results and defines a provisional terminology for the annual cyprinid sexual cycle. Superficially, an inactive or *vegetative period* alternates each year with an active or *reproductive period*. Underlying these is an intrinsic sexual rhythm in which a long *responsive period* (mid-November to mid-July) alternates with a shorter, *refractory period* (mid-July to mid-November). Long days imposed within the responsive period promptly start the *prespawning period,* with its *prespawning mechanism* governing occurrence of nuptial color, sexual behavior, and completion of gametogenesis. Its progress is measured by egg-diameter increments exceeding a critical diameter (an early stage of the secondary growth phase), and it ends with the first spawning. Thus begins the *spawning period,* which is consummatory and ends long before the environmental stimuli have declined to the threshold at which they initiated the prespawning period. A *refractory period* follows, for which the name *postspawning* period is appropriate. Long days imposed before the postspawning period ends, i.e., before mid-November, fail to activate the prespawning mechanism but accelerate egg-diameter increase up to, but not beyond, the critical diameter. The prespawning period appears to be the phase of the annual sexual cycle set right each year by the celestial clock. However, an internal reproductive rhythm capable of acting in the absence of the appropriate extrinsic stimuli, which normally synchronize it, has been inferred from the inability of four months of drastically reduced day length to prevent final maturity in *Phoxinus* although spermatogenesis was slightly, and oogenesis markedly, delayed (Bullough, 1940).

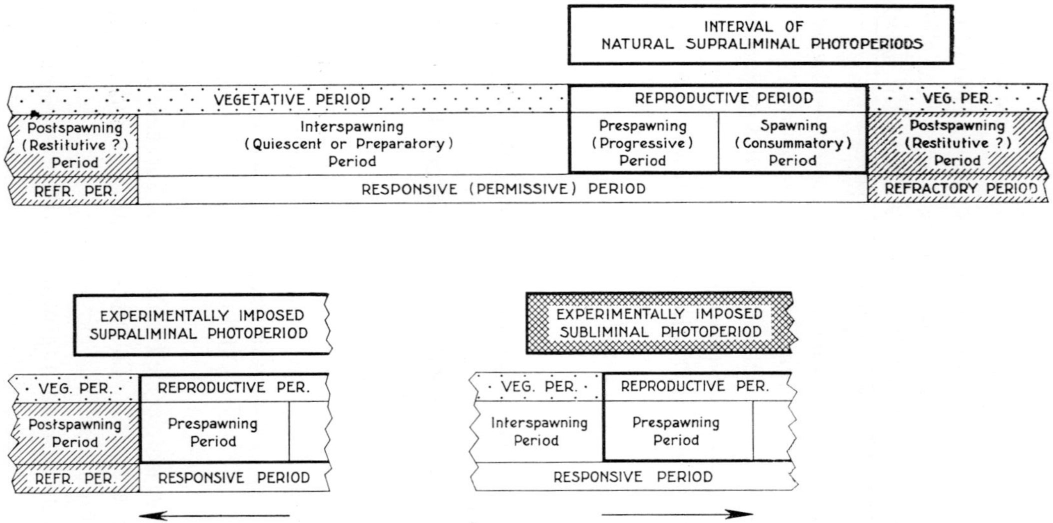

FIG. 3. Schemata of provisional terminology and relationships of the annual cyprinid sexual cycle based on data for *Notropis bifrenatus* and *Phoxinus phoxinus*. (After Harrington, 1957.)

THE GASTEROSTEID SEXUAL CYCLE

The gasterosteid (stickleback) cycle is the only fish sex cycle other than the cyprinid studied enough to afford comparisons as an annual entity. Although it has interested several workers (Craig-Bennett, 1931; Merriman and Schedl, 1941; vanden Eeckhoudt, 1946; Kazanskii, 1952; Baggerman, 1957), a fully coherent, integrated account of this cycle, with regard both to histophysiologic and behavioral responses to extrinsic factors at all seasons of the year cannot yet be given. Craig-Bennett (1931) described the normal seasonal changes in the testicular histology of *Gasterosteus aculeatus* and showed that spermatogenesis may be completed at variable intervals from as much as 2½ months to just in advance of functional maturity, and that breeding color is the concomitant of the latter, not the former. However, his conclusion (from experiments) that the sex cycle is unaffected by day length is contradicted by results obtained by others (vanden Eeckhoudt, 1946; Kazanskii, 1952; Baggerman, 1957). His experimental specimens (all males) developed nuptial color whether exposed to the ostensible short or long photoperiods (Craig-Bennett, 1931, pp. 238–248), which, if the results of the other experimenters are valid, implies an inadvertent covert source of effective supplementary illumination. Since the influence of temperature is meaningless without reference to day length and vice versa, uncertainty about lighting conditions makes uncertain the results ascribed to variant temperatures. It is clear, however, that in late summer the extinction of breeding color can be delayed by depressing, and hastened by elevating the temperature.

The experiments of vanden Eeckhoudt (1946) on *Gasterosteus* were begun between the middle and end of February, ending within two months; in all of them the temperature was the same (10°C). Males from the wild in both December and February had quiescent testes with lobules bulging with spermatozoa and walls bordered by resting spermatogonia, other cell types lacking, a condition strictly comparable to that of the autumn-winter testes of *Enneacanthus* (Harrington, 1956). Under increasing day length, however administered, this condition of the testes persisted, but a constant short day length (8 hr) caused the unexpected resumption of spermatogenetic activity, with spermatogonial mitoses, production of primary and secondary spermatocytes and even spermatids, and the formation of islets of proliferating cells within the previously formed sperm mass. These contrasting testicular states have their close if not identical counterparts in *Enneacanthus* but under almost opposite conditions. In *Enneacanthus,* spermatogenesis is completed early in autumn, and a quiescent testis persists thereafter under short day lengths whether at very low or at high temperature, whereas long days combined with high temperature cause a recrudescence of spermatogenesis coincident with the onset of precocious spawning. The interpretation of these results with *Gasterosteus* is complicated by the fact that the end of the experimental period virtually merged with the onset of the natural breeding period, whereas the results with *Enneacanthus* were obtained in mid-December far from the breeding period. Egg maturation in *Gasterosteus* was arrested by the constant short day length, but progressed with increasing day length, more rapidly when the same total amount of illumination was administered as multiple rather than as single daily exposures (see below). Only under continuous illumination did males mature completely and build nests, and females become very gravid.

Kazanskii (1951, 1952) in contrast to the findings of vanden Eeckhoudt, reports a lack of responsiveness in the same species (during December-January) at temperatures as low as 10°C. In experiments begun December 7 with fish fresh from the wild, when vitellogenesis is just commencing in the most advanced oocytes and yolk has not yet aggregated, continuous lighting at 20–22°C induced nest building in 16 days, complete egg maturation in 18, and spawning followed by parental care in 20. Maturation was slower at temperatures moderately below this. Even in natural daylight during winter, at 19–20°C maturation followed by spawning occurred within 37 to 45 days. The ovaries of females under continuous light at temperatures below 12–13°C remained unchanged from their condition at the onset of the experiment. In virtually day-long darkness at 17–19°C during two winter months there was ovarian status quo.

A fresh approach has recently been made in the study of the annual sex cycle of *Gasterosteus* (Baggerman, 1957). Starting at various times throughout the calendar year, different groups of fish were exposed simultaneously to contrasting combinations of day length and temperature ("experimental conditions"), often followed by simultaneous exposure of these variously treated groups to one and the same condition ("test condition"). In other experiments, fish were exposed to identical conditions but at different times of year, and subsequently half the fish of each group were exposed to one, and the other half, to the other of the same two contrasting test conditions. The evidentiary test (result capable of sensory verification) was always terminal: (1) maturation as manifest in nest building by males, oviposition by females, (2) its significantly prolonged suppression, (3) the time elapsing between onset of a pertinent stage in the experimental-test conditions and maturation. It was concluded that these fish may be in one of four physiological (possibly gonadal) phases, the first (Table I)

TABLE I. Physiological (Gonadal ?) Phases of the Three-spined Stickleback, *Gasterosteus aculeatus*. Operationally defined by their inferred responses (positive or negative) to each of the four combinations of high or low temperature and long or short days; a positive response means progression to the next or to any higher phase. (Adapted from Baggerman, 1957.)

Phase		High Temperature		Low Temperature	
		Long Days	Short Days	Long Days	Short Days
0		−	+	+	+ (?)
1	1a	+	−	−	+
	1b	+	−	+	−
2		+	+	+	+

confined to immature under-yearling fish, the other three successively traversed by adults reaching functional maturity. Each inferred physiological phase is operationally defined solely in terms of a characteristic pattern of positive or negative responses by fish presumed to be in that phase to each of four combinations of long or short and high or low temperature (Table I). By response is meant progression to the next or through to any higher phase. There is a difference between response and test, the former usually being subterminal. The two might be expected to converge only when a day length-temperature combination elicits a response in fish in the penultimate phase or causes a progression to full maturity through all phases above the one in question. Since the only evidentiary test is maturity as manifested by its stipulated attributes, intermediate phases cannot be tested for directly, but must be inferred from results of contrasting usually dual-stage experimental conditions. This methodology allows the perform-ance and evaluation in a given length of time of a much greater num-ber of experiments than that in which the terminal test is supplemented by initial and periodic histological diagnoses, but if the writer's under-standing of the argument is correct, it robs some of the conclusions of finality by its greater reliance on inductive inference, quite apart from that implicit in the nonparametric statistical analysis required by the small number of fish per experiment.

Nevertheless, a plausible pattern of four day length-temperature combinations differently conditioning four successive phases of the sexual cycle (Table I) is built by inferences from an impressive num-ber of ingenious experiments. For example, phase 0 was established by the fact that only very young under-yearling fish subjected to long days at high temperature (for over a year) failed to mature, whereas controls of the same age first exposed to one of the alternative condi-tions (Table I) and later to long days and high temperature did mature. On adults, the effects of long days and high temperature are consistent with their effects on *Phoxinus, Notropis, Enneacanthus et alia.* As none of the four combinations of day length-temperature (Table I) exerted influence on fish in phase 2 noticeably different from those of the other three combinations, phase 2 may represent merely a stage of maturity so advanced that further maturation is sub-stantially independent of such environmental influences. Under con-stant long days at high temperature (16 hr and 20°C), both sexes of *Gasterosteus* have about a 200-day cycle in which a reproductive and a nonreproductive period alternate. In females the nonreproductive period averaged about 168 days but in males was somewhat shorter. As Baggerman notes, the durations of the cycle in nature and in the laboratory would differ somewhat, because the extrinsic conditions are different, for in either case the inherent rhythm is doubtless modulated by the coaction of external and internal factors. In regard to the re-fractory periods in the cycles of *Gasterosteus* and *Notropis,* it is worth mentioning that in the annual cycles of some fishes, periods of refrac-toriness to hypophysis injection have been reported (Gerbilskii, 1950, 1951; Kazanskii, 1952; Vivien, 1941). The presumptive autumn spawning of *Esox vermiculatus* (Lagler and Hubbs, 1943), suggests a refractoriness ending in time for a stimulating day length-temperature combination afforded by the unseasonable extension of warm days, to take effect (see below).

Before the perplexing heterogeneity of experimental results obtained with *Gasterosteus* by the authors cited can be resolved into an intelligible pattern, the gonadal histology paralleling the onset and duration of Baggerman's phases needs to be determined. In *Gasterosteus,* as in *Enneacanthus* (Harrington, 1956), *Perca* (Turner, 1919), and apparently *Fundulus* (Matthews, 1938) and *Gambusia* (Geiser, 1924), spermatogenesis is completed far in advance of final maturation, so that the quantified progress of ovogenesis affords the more likely means of relating these phases to a measurable visible phenomenon. Day length is without influence on spermatogenesis in at least one of these forms (Burger, 1939, 1940; Matthews, 1939) contrary to the situation in *Phoxinus* (Bullough, 1939) and *Notropis* (Harrington, 1957), whereas there is no evidence so far of an ovarian cycle in this context unaffected by changes in day length (cf. Atz, 1957).

MODES OF DAY LENGTH MANIPULATION AND THEIR RELATIVE EFFECTIVENESS

The fish sex cycle has been influenced by several modes of day length manipulation, among them abrupt imposition of long days, as in most of the experiments so far cited, although in nature day length changes are gradual and continuous, so that it is pertinent to search for a common principle underlying the responses of fishes to the various modes of manipulation of proved effectiveness.

In the only autumn-spawning fish studied in this context, the brook trout, *Salvelinus fontinalis,* sexual maturity was hastened by reproducing a contracted version of the annual day length cycle such that day length diminished earlier than in nature (Hoover and Hubbard, 1937). Since day lengths were gradually increased and then decreased, the experiment failed to show whether the prior augmentation of day lengths was an indispensable precondition of this precocious maturity (Kleitman, 1949). Evidently it was not, for in subsequent experiments (Hazard and Eddy, 1951) maturity was hastened one month (insufficient for commercial uses) by a shortening of day lengths alone, and delayed by postponing the normal autumn shortening of day lengths. The earlier, alternative procedure advanced maturity four months, however, suggesting that the prior lengthening (or perhaps days over a certain length) may hasten completion of a preceding phase of maturation and pave the way for rapid final maturation when day lengths are shortened, and perhaps an inhibition is removed. The effectiveness of abrupt lengthening followed by abrupt shortening remains to be ascertained. Both gradual and abrupt lengthening have induced unseasonable maturation in fishes, but Baggerman (1957) demonstrated conclusively that abrupt increase is far more effective than gradual increase and induces a significantly earlier onset of maturity, at least in *Gasterosteus*. Two unusual instances of effective photoperiod alteration are worth mention. When transported from the Southern to the Northern Hemisphere, the South American fish *Jenynsia lineata* produced two clusters of broods within a single year, one during the Argentine spring-summer before it was transported and one during the Illinois spring-summer after it was transported (Turner, 1957), thus duplicating results of forced emigration in animals of other vertebrate classes (Bullough, 1951). That an anomalous second spawning period may sometimes occur in the wild out of season is indicated by the discovery (Lagler and Hubbs, 1943) of evidently fall-spawned young of the normally spring-spawning mud pickerel, *Esox vermiculatus,* in mid-November of an autumn so warm that spring-flowering plants such as *Forsythia* blossomed.

If it is stipulated that day length is here the paramount extrinsic factor governing secretion of gonadotropin by the pituitary, a supraliminal photoperiod is one that induces a daily sum of pituitary activity sufficient to maintain an effective blood level of gonadotropin. It follows that a daily light ration of adequate duration might be equally effective whether administered each day as a single long exposure or as a series of shorter ones. Rhythmic secretion-restitution fluctuations in the gonadotropic zone of the adenohypophysis of *Rhodeus* are reported to have a restitution phase of some duration (Bretschneider and Duyvené de Wit, 1947). This entails the possibility that a *subliminal* undisrupted photoperiod if administered in an evenly spaced series of shorter intervals of light adding up to the same number of hours of light per day might stimulate pituitary activity as effectively as a *supraliminal* (hence longer) undisrupted photoperiod. Thus the *daily duration of effective stimulation* might be increased without increasing the total hours of illumination per day. Some such effect, although differently construed, has been reported for birds. The critical experiment has not been performed with fishes, but in *Gasterosteus* a faster tempo of egg maturation was reported by vanden Eeckhoudt (1946) with a daily light ration of 20 min out of each hour gradually increased to 40 than with an undisrupted daily photoperiod of 8 hr gradually increased to 16, the total hours of illumination being the same. It remains to be demonstrated for fishes whether in this context "breaking the dark period (*scotoperiod*)" or "fractionating the photoperiod" is the more appropriate phrase. If thresholds of responsiveness to photic stimuli are concerned, daily duration of effective stimulation would seem to be the critical feature rather than total hours of daily light per se.

REFERENCES

Atz, James W. 1957. The relation of the pituitary to reproduction in fishes. In *The Physiology of the Pituitary Gland of Fishes,* by Grace E. Pickford and James W. Atz. New York Zoological Society, New York.

Baggerman, B. 1957. An experimental study of the timing of breeding and migration in the three-spined stickleback (*Gasterosteus aculeatus* L.). *Arch. neérl. Zool., 12,* 105–317.

Bretschneider, L. H., and J. J. Duyvené de Wit. 1947. Sexual endocrinology of non-mammalian vertebrates. *Monogr. Progr. Research in Holland* (11), 1–146.

Bullough, W. S. 1939. A study of the reproductive cycle of the minnow in relation to the environment. *Proc. Zool. Soc. London, A109,* 79–102.

————. 1940. The effect of the reduction of light in spring on the breeding season of the minnow (*Phoxinus laevis* L.). *Proc. Zool. Soc. London, A110,* 149–57.

————. 1951. *Vertebrate Sexual Cycles.* Methuen's Monographs on Biological Subjects. Methuen, London; Wiley, New York.

Burger, J. W. 1939. Some experiments on the relation of the external environment to the spermatogenetic cycle of *Fundulus heteroclitus* (L.). *Biol. Bull., 77,* 96–103.

————. 1940. Some further experiments on the relation of the external environment to the spermatogenetic cycle of *Fundulus heteroclitus. Bull. Mt. Desert Isl. Biol. Lab.,* 20–21.

Craig-Bennett, A. 1931. The reproductive cycle of the three-spined stickleback,

Gasterosteus aculeatus Linn. *Phil. Trans. Roy. Soc. London, B219,* 197–279.

Duyvené de Wit, J. J. 1939. Onderzoekingen over de sexueel-endocrine organisatie van *Rhodeus am.* Bl. en de betekenis van de legbuistest voor de endocrinologie in het algemeen. Thesis, Utrecht, Centen's Uitg. Mij. A'dam.

Eeckhoudt, J. P. vanden. 1946. Recherches sur l'influence de la lumière sur le cycle sexuel de l'épinoche (*Gasterosteus aculeatus*). *Ann. soc. roy. zool. Belg., 77,* 83–89.

Geiser, S. W. 1924. Sex ratios and spermatogenesis in the top minnow, *Gambusia holbrooki. Biol. Bull., 47,* 175–203.

Gerbilskii, N. L. 1950. Biological groups of the Kura osetr (*Acipenser güldenstädti persicus* Borodin) and measures for its reproduction in plants. *Doklady Akad. Nauk, S.S.S.R., 71,* 785–88 (in Russian).

———. 1951. Intraspecific biological groups of acipenserine fishes and their reproduction in the lower regions of rivers with regulated flow. *Rybnoe Khoziaistvo, 27,* 24–27 (in Russian). Translated by A. Petrunkevitch with foreword, references, and addendum by Grace E. Pickford. In *Systematic Zoology, 4,* 83–92 (1955).

Harrington, R. W., Jr. 1947. The breeding behavior of the bridled shiner, *Notropis bifrenatus* (Cope). *Copeia, 1947* (3), 186–92.

———. 1950. Preseasonal breeding by the bridled shiner, *Notropis bifrenatus,* induced under light-temperature control. *Copeia, 1950* (4), 304–11.

———. 1956. An experiment on the effects of contrasting daily photoperiods on gametogenesis and reproduction in the centrarchid fish, *Enneacanthus obesus* (Girard). *J. Exptl. Zool., 131,* 203–23.

———. 1957. Sexual photoperiodicity of the cyprinid fish, *Notropis bifrenatus* (Cope), in relation to the phases of its annual reproductive cycle. *J. Exptl. Zool., 135,* 1–47.

Hazard, T. P., and R. E. Eddy. 1951. Modification of the sexual cycle in brook trout (*Salvelinus fontinalis*) by control of light. *Trans. Am. Fisheries Soc., 1950,* 158–62.

Hoar, W. S. 1951. Hormones in fish. In *Some Aspects of the Physiology of Fish,* by W. S. Hoar, V. S. Black, and E. C. Black. *Publ. Ont. Fish. Research Lab., 71* (Univ. Toronto Biol. Ser. 59), 1–51.

———. 1955. Reproduction in teleost fish. *Mem. Soc. for Endocrinol., 4:* 5–24. Cambridge, at the University Press.

Hoover, E. E., and H. E. Hubbard. 1937. Modification of the sexual cycle in trout by control of light. *Copeia, 1937* (4), 206–10.

Kazanskii, B. N. 1951. Experimental analysis of the growth of the oocytes in fish. *Doklady Akad. Nauk, S.S.S.R., 80,* 277–80 (in Russian). (Quoted by Atz, 1957.)

———. 1952. Experimental analysis of intermittent spawning in fish. *Zool. Zh., 31,* 883–96 (in Russian).

Kleitman, Nathaniel. 1949. Biological rhythms and cycles. *Physiol. Revs., 29,* 1–30.

Lagler, K. F., and C. Hubbs. 1943. Fall spawning of the mud pickerel, *Esox vermiculatus* Lesueur. *Copeia, 1943* (2), 131.

Matthews, S. A. 1938. The seasonal cycle in the gonads of *Fundulus*. *Biol. Bull.*, *75*, 66–74.

———. 1939. The effects of light and temperature on the male sexual cycle in *Fundulus*. *Biol. Bull.*, *77*, 92–95.

Merriman, D., and H. P. Schedl. 1941. The effects of light and temperature on gametogenesis in the four-spined stickleback, *Apeltes quadracus* (Mitchill). *J. Exptl. Zool.*, *88*, 413–46.

Turner, C. L. 1919. The seasonal cycle in the spermary of the perch. *J. Morphol.*, *32*, 681–711.

———. 1957. The breeding cycle of the South American fish, *Jenynsia lineata*, in the Northern Hemisphere. *Copeia, 1957* (3), 195–203.

Verhoeven, B., and G. J. van Oordt. 1955. The influence of light and temperature on the sexual cycle of the bitterling, *Rhodeus amarus*. *Koninkl. Ned. Akad. Wetenschap. Amsterdam, Proc., C58*, 629–34.

Vivien, J. H. 1941. Contribution à l'étude de la physiologie hypophysaire dans ses relations avec l'appareil génital, la thyroïde et les corps suprarennaux chez les poissons sélaciens, et téléostéens, *Scyliorhinus canicula* et *Gobius paganellus*. *Bull. biol. France et Belg.*, *75*, 257–309.

PHOTOPERIODISM IN REPTILES

GEORGE A. BARTHOLOMEW
Department of Zoology, University of California, Los Angeles

Relatively little information is available on the reproductive physiology of reptiles, and much of the experimental work on reptilian endocrinology has been a repetition of classical work done originally on mammals. As a result, the data tend to be fragmentary and out of context biologically, and usually contribute little to the understanding of the factors controlling the timing of reproduction in this group. The literature on reptilian reproduction, though limited in comparison with that on birds and mammals, is still extensive enough to be confusing. At the present time, it is difficult to generalize beyond saying that the reproductive activities of a wide variety of reptiles are seasonal and that the major patterns of pituitary-gonad relations in reptiles are qualitatively similar to those that have been worked out for other terrestrial vertebrates.

A guide to the literature on the reproduction and natural occurring reproductive cycles of reptiles can be found in papers by Evans and Clapp (1940), Cieslak (1945), Miller (1948), Fox (1952), and Kehl and Combescot (1955). The present paper will review the scant literature on photoperiodism in reptiles, but its main purpose is the presentation of a point of view that may help to supply an appropriate ecological orientation to the problem of relating day length to breeding season in this group.

Although it is a familiar fact that many reptiles have markedly seasonal patterns of breeding, the role of environmental factors in the determination of this periodicity has been studied in only a few species and in no case has it been possible to make an adequate synthesis of physiological and ecological data. The paucity of information on photoperiodism in reptiles and its fragmentary nature is indicated by the brevity of the literature summary which follows. Mellish (1936) reported that exposure to continuous light and a temperature of 35°C for approximately two months during the winter caused only slightly greater testicular development in the horned lizard, *Phyrnosoma cornutum,* than that which occurred during hibernation in the same season. Since the mean hibernating temperature of this species is more than 15°C below the experimental temperature used, it is hard to tell whether or not the slight gonadal response was photoperiodically induced. Burger (1937) reported that in the turtle *Pseudemys elegans* an artificial increase of day length started in the middle of November inhibited the spermatogenic cycle already in progress and induced the initiation of a new cycle; this suggests that day length can contribute to the rhythm of the reproductive cycle. Clausen and Poris (1937) found that the daily addition of 6 hr of light starting in late November had a marked stimulatory effect on spermatogenesis in *Anolis carolinensis.* Using circumstantial natural history evidence, Baker (1947) suggested that lizards of the genus *Emoia* living in the New Hebrides are probably paced at least in part by day length in their reproductive periodicity. Miller (1948) reported that testicular development of *Xantusia vigilis* could be affected by light. Bartholomew (1950, 1953) found (1) that increased length of day was more important than increased temperature in accelerating gonadal growth in *Xantusia vigilis,* (2) that males were more responsive than females to photoperiodic changes, and (3) that rate of photoperiodic response of males increased directly with increasing temperature. Galgono (1951) examined the responses of *Lacerta sicula* to various combinations of temperature and photoperiod and suggested the interesting possibility that temperature might control spermatogenesis while photoperiod controlled testicular secretion.

If any one conclusion can be drawn from the welter of papers that have appeared during the 35-year history of research on animal photoperiodism, it is that the evaluation of the role of day length in the determination of breeding season cannot be made on the basis of laboratory data alone. A detailed familiarity with the natural history and behavior of an animal is as important as an analysis of its endocrine physiology and its responses to light. Although knowledge of reptile behavior and ecology lags behind that of birds and mammals, information is available which is pertinent to the understanding of the relation of day length to breeding season.

It is quite clear that, with the possible exception of forms living in the humid Tropics, the times of activity of terrestrial reptiles and hence the periods during which light can effect their endocrine system is dependent not only on day length but is profoundly affected by local conditions of temperature as well as by the fundamental behavioral dichotomy of nocturnality versus diurnality. Unlike fish and aquatic amphibians, which occupy an environment in which the rate and extent of temperature change are minimized by water, most reptiles live in an environment in which not only seasonal, but also daily and hourly changes in temperature can shape the pattern of their existence. To a person who has not himself studied reptiles, particularly lizards, in the field or who is not familiar with the literature on the ecology of reptiles, the dependence of these animals on temporary changes or local differences in temperature can hardly be anticipated. Certainly the performance of reptiles in the laboratory does not prepare one for it. In captivity at temperatures below their normal range of activity, nothing dramatic happens. The animals just slow down, and if the temperature is reduced sufficiently, they become torporous. At temperatures above their normal range, they merely seem unusually alert and restless. Field observations, however, have made it apparent that active reptiles maintain body temperature at a characteristic level (Cowles and Bogert, 1944). This level may be similar in species of the same genus occurring in markedly different climates, but differ by several degrees in sympatric species of different genera (Bogert, 1949). The extremes to which this adaptation to and maintenance of a characteristic range of body temperature may be pushed is shown with particular clarity by the desert iguana, *Dipsosaurus dorsalis,* which is frequently active at body temperatures in excess of 43°C (Cowles and Bogert, 1944), a level higher than that characteristic of most birds and mammals and above the lethal level for some species of *Sceloporus* (Cole, 1943).

Since reptiles are incapable of effective physiological thermoregulation, and the extent of their temperature acclimation (Dawson and Bartholomew, 1956) is quite restricted as compared with most poikilothermic animals (Bullock, 1955), the limited range of body temperatures characteristic of normal activity for any given species greatly restricts the daily periods of activity.

If there were no other complicating factors one could then claim that outside the humid Tropics day length could not be the primary factor timing reproduction in reptiles because the daily period of activity would be determined strictly by environmental temperature and the effective photoperiod would not be related to day length but to the diurnal temperature cycle of the environment. Lizards are, however, often active in environmental temperatures far below the range at which their performance is adequate for survival. They achieve this by raising their body temperature above ambient temperature by means of behavior patterns that allow the accumulation of heat from solar radiation or from the substratum which in turn has been heated by the sun. Pearson (1954) has shown with particular clarity the behavioral responses that allow a lizard, *Liolaemus multiformis,* which lives at an altitude of over 15,000 feet in Peru, to maintain a body temperature as much as 30°C above air temperature. At the other extreme some lizards may be active at ambient temperatures which exceed the range of body temperatures that they can tolerate. Norris (1953) gives a graphic picture of the manner in which the desert iguana by intermittent activity and frequent resorting to shade and burrows manages to occupy a habitat in which soil and temperatures are often above 50°C.

Although darkness or light will determine the period of potential activity depending on whether or not a reptile is nocturnal or diurnal, the actual daily period of activity will depend on temperature. Because environmental temperature in general increases with increasing day length, length of day can still be a primary factor, but the effective day length is determined by thermoregulatory behavior, not by sunrise or sunset. Consequently, in reptiles the relation between long days and short days may bear only a remote relationship to the concept as it was originally formulated for plants, and outside the Tropics, it may be meaningless.

These ecological relationships make the context of photoperiodism in reptiles (except aquatic forms) different from that of plants which cannot avoid or seek out the light except by tropisms, from that of fish and many amphibians for which water minimizes temperature changes, and from that of birds and mammals which are essentially independent of temperature in their activity. It may be suggested that terrestrial invertebrates face similar photoperiodic problems, but the length of most reptilian life cycles and the slowness with which they reach sexual maturity probably sets them apart.

The considerations presented above lead to the conclusion that even in the few instances in which a photoperiodic response in reptiles has been demonstrated in the laboratory, the interpretation of its reproductive importance requires that it be fitted into the pattern of daily activity under natural conditions; this in turn requires knowledge of the physiological and particularly the behavioral responses to temperature characteristic of the species being studied.

The complications imposed on the analysis of reptilian photoperiodism by behavioral temperature regulation are formidable, but recent work on the function of the pineal organ of lizards complicates the problem even further. It has been found (Stebbins, 1957; Stebbins and Eakin, 1958) that surgical removal of the parietal eye from lizards of several species (*Sceloporus occidentalis, Sceloporus undulatus, Uta stansburiana,* and *Uma inornata*) caused a significant extension of the duration of the daily periods which they spent exposed to sunlight but did not alter the range of body temperatures characteristic of normal activity. Thus in these lizards, and possibly in other iguanids, the effective photoperiod is determined in part by the response of the parietal eye as well as by the thermoregulatory behavior discussed in preceding paragraphs. In view of these findings it is of interest that about twenty years ago Clausen and Poris (1937) reported that pineal extirpation enhanced the photoperiodic response of male *Anolis*. It appears that an adequate analysis of the role of day length in the reproduction of lizards requires data on (1) activity temperatures, (2) the extent to which behavioral thermoregulation controls daily exposure to light, (3) the relations of the pineal body to activity patterns, and (4) the secretory responses of the pituitary to light.

In view of the restrictions placed on day length by behavioral factors related to thermoregulation, it would appear that photoperiodism in reptiles could best be investigated in an environment that allows normal activity at all seasons without elaborate thermoregulatory behavior. Such a condition is found in the humid Tropics. One of the Central American species of *Anolis, Ameiva,* or particularly *Sceloporus* would seem to be a likely form for experimental use.

They live in the humid Tropics, but are far enough from the equator to be exposed to considerable seasonal changes in day length.

It has recently been found that day length affects not only reproduction but also food consumption, appetite, and growth. Dessauer (1955a,b) suggested that the marked seasonal fluctuations in body fat, liver storage, and appetite found in *Anolis carolinensis* were influenced by day length. This suggestion was confirmed by Fox and Dessauer (1957), who found that 18 hours of light per day in fall and winter increased the appetite of both young and adult *Anolis carolinensis* and caused a conspicuous increase in growth of immature animals.

So far, little has been said about the physiological mechanisms of reptilian photoperiodism for the simple reason that little information is available. There can be no doubt, however, that the pituitary is an intermediary between light and the gonads. In lizards and snakes, as in birds (both the Squamata and birds are thought to be derived from some common diapsid ancestor), the skull is notably open and fenestrated. There is little doubt that in these reptiles light could reach the hypothalamus or pituitary directly through the orbit (as in some birds), or even through the otic region. Consequently, there is no a priori reason why the eye need be implicated as the initial receptor of the photoperiodic stimulus. It is, however, quite probable that in turtles the eye may be the receptor because turtles are anapsids and have an unfenestrated and relatively heavy skull through which light is not likely to penetrate to the pituitary region. It is, of course, safest merely to say that the mechanism of the reception of the light stimulus as well as its mode of endocrine mediation remains not only unknown, but almost unstudied. Here lies an intriguing field of research but one in which, judging by the history of research on photoperiodic mechanisms in other organisms, answers will prove elusive.

SUMMARY

Although photoperiodic responses have been demonstrated in the reproductive physiology of turtles and lizards, and in the feeding, and growth of at least one lizard, the biology of most terrestrial reptiles obscures the role of day length as a clearly delimited environmental stimulus. Under natural conditions the effects of day length on reptiles are inextricably intertwined with those of temperature; behavioral thermoregulation determines the effective day length to which most terrestrial reptiles are exposed and so can modify the effects of seasonal changes in photoperiod. Further complications are introduced by the fact that in several species of lizards the effective photoperiod is in part controlled by responses of the parietal eye which is involved in the regulation of the exposure to sunlight and the duration of the periods spent on the surface of the ground.

The physiological mechanisms through which the effects of day length are mediated in reptiles have not been studied in detail. It is possible that the pineal body is involved and possible that different receptor systems cause the pituitary response in anapsid and diapsid forms.

REFERENCES

Baker, J. R. 1947. The seasons in a tropical rain-forest. VI. Lizards (*Emoia*). *J. Linnean Soc. London, Zool., 41*, 243–47.
Bartholomew, G. A. 1950. The effects of artificially controlled temperature and day length on gonadal development in a lizard, *Xantusia vigilis. Anat. Record, 106*, 49–60.
————. 1953. The modification by temperature of the photoperiodic control of gonadal development in the lizard *Xantusia vigilis. Copeia, 1953*, 45–50.
Bogert, C. M. 1949. Thermoregulation in reptiles, a factor in evolution. *Evolution, 3*, 195–211.
Bullock, T. H. 1955. Compensation for temperature in the metabolism and activity of poikilotherms. *Biol. Revs., 30*, 311–42.
Burger, J. W. 1937. Experimental sexual photoperiodicity in the male turtle, *Pseudemys elegans* (Wied.). *Am. Naturalist, 71*, 481–87.
Cieslak, E. S. 1945. Relations between the reproductive cycle and the pituitary gland in the snake *Thamnophis radix. Physiol. Zoöl., 18*, 299–329.
Clausen, H. J., and E. G. Poris. 1937. The effect of light upon sexual activity in the lizard, *Anolis carolinensis*, with especial reference to the pineal body. *Anat. Record, 69*, 39–53.
Cole, L. C. 1943. Experiments on toleration of high temperature in lizards with reference to adaptive coloration. *Ecology, 24*, 94–108.
Cowles, R. B., and C. M. Bogert. 1944. A preliminary study of the thermal requirements of desert reptiles. *Bull. Am. Mus. Nat. Hist., 83*, 261–96.
Dawson, W. R., and G. A. Bartholomew. 1956. Relation of oxygen consumption to body weight, temperature, and temperature acclimation in lizards *Uta stansburiana* and *Sceloporus occidentalis. Physiol. Zoöl., 29*, 40–51.
Dessauer, H. C. 1955a. Effect of season on appetite and food consumption of the lizard, *Anolis carolinensis. Proc. Soc. Exptl. Biol. Med., 90*, 524–26.

————. 1955b. Seasonal changes in the gross organ composition of the lizard, *Anolis carolinensis*. *J. Exptl. Zool., 128,* 1–12.

Evans, L. T., and M. L. Clapp. 1940. The effects of ovarian hormones and seasons on *Anolis carolinensis*. *Anat. Record, 77,* 57–75.

Fox, W. 1952. Seasonal variation in the male reproductive system of Pacific Coast garter snakes. *J. Morphol., 90,* 481–554.

Fox, W., and H. C. Dessauer. 1957. Photoperiodic stimulation of appetite and growth in the male lizard, *Anolis carolinensis*. *J. Exptl. Zool., 134,* 557–76.

Galgano, M. 1951. Prime recerche intorno all'influenza della luce e della temperatura sul ciclo sesuale di *Lacerta sicula campestris* (Betta). *Boll. zool., 18,* 108–15.

Kehl, R., and C. Combescot. 1955. Reproduction in the reptilia. *Mem. Soc. Endocrinol., No. 4,* 57–74.

Mellish, C. H. 1936. The effects of anterior pituitary extract and certain environmental conditions on the genital system of the horned lizard (*Phyrnosoma cornutum,* Harlan). *Anat. Record, 67,* 23–33.

Miller, M. R. 1948. The seasonal histological changes occurring in the ovary, corpus luteum, and the testis of the viviparous lizard, *Xantusia vigilis*. *Univ. Calif. Publs. Zool., 47,* 197–224.

Norris, K. S. 1953. The ecology of the desert iguana *Dipsosaurus dorsalis*. *Ecology, 34,* 265–87.

Pearson, O. P. 1954. Habits of the lizard *Liolaemus multiformis multiformis* at high altitudes in southern Peru. *Copeia, 1954,* 111–16.

Stebbins, R. C. 1957. Studies of pineal function in lizards. *Anat. Record, 128,* 628–29.

Stebbins, R. C., and R. M. Eakin. 1958. The role of the "third eye" in reptilian behavior. *Am. Museum Novitates, No. 1870,* 1–40.

*Photoperiodic Control of Reproduction
and Migration in Birds*

THE ROLE OF LIGHT AND DARKNESS IN THE REGULATION OF SPRING MIGRATION AND REPRODUCTIVE CYCLES IN BIRDS [1]

ALBERT WOLFSON
Northwestern University, Evanston, Illinois

DAY LENGTH AND THE STIMULUS FOR SPRING MIGRATION

Experimental and physiological studies of the regulation of reproductive and migratory cycles in birds were initiated by Rowan (1925, 1929), who discovered that gonadal recrudescence could be induced out of season, in late fall and winter, by subjecting slate-colored juncos (*Junco hyemalis*) to artificial increases in day length. On the assumption that migratory behavior in the spring, when birds are flying north to their breeding grounds, was a phase of sexual behavior, Rowan tested the effect of experimentally induced gonadal recrudescence on migratory behavior by releasing juncos in winter, many months ahead of the normal time of their spring migration and with their gonads at various stages of development. From the results of these experiments, Rowan concluded that in the slate-colored junco, and other fringillids, the stimulus to migrate in the spring was regulated by external and internal factors. The external factor was the increasing day length after December 21. The internal factor was the production of sex hormones, which he correlated with the recrudescing gonads of spring and the regressing gonads of fall. The normal winter minimal gonad and the normal maximal gonad of the breeding period showed little or no hormone-producing interstitial tissue, and, hence, would not stimulate migratory behavior. From the results of later work with crows (*Corvus brachyrhynchos*) Rowan (1932) con-

[1] The investigations reported in this paper have been supported by the Graduate School of Northwestern University, the Society of Sigma Xi, and the National Science Foundation. I acknowledge with sincere gratitude the able assistance and valuable contributions of Hudson S. Winn, Max Shank, Tom Kemper, Ormsby Annan, Betty Annan, Bruce Belshaw, and Larry Greenburg to the research program in our laboratory.

cluded that the southward migration in fall appeared to be independent of the influence of the gonads.

Rowan's epochal work defined the basic problems and stimulated an experimental attack on the regulation of bird migration and gonadal cycles. Dr. Farmer (p. 717) has reviewed the progress which has been made on the photoperiodic control of annual gonadal cycles. He has also reviewed the physiological aspects of the stimulus for migration (1955). My studies and interest have centered around the problem of the stimulus for spring migration, and in this report I shall consider primarily the role of the external factor, day length. Since migratory behavior in the spring is closely linked with the recrudescence of the gonads, the role of light and darkness in the regulation of the annual gonadal cycle will also be considered. Complete reports of the unpublished studies from our laboratory which are cited in this paper will be published later elsewhere.

The first extensive series of experiments which were designed to test Rowan's hypothesis were performed by Wolfson (1940, 1942, 1945) in Berkeley, California, using the Oregon junco, a species closely related to the slate-colored junco. These experiments corroborated Rowan's observation that birds could be stimulated to migrate northward months ahead of time by subjecting them to artificial increases in day length in the late fall and winter. However, they also demonstrated that birds in breeding condition would migrate, which was contrary to Rowan's conclusion. Wolfson found that in addition to gonadal growth preceding migration, there was also a marked increase in body weight caused by large deposits of subcutaneous and intraperitoneal fat, which was a better criterion of a readiness to migrate than the condition of the gonad. Later studies demonstrated that the pituitary was also involved in this premigratory change in physiological state. Members of a nonmigratory race of the same species, which were exposed to the same environmental conditions in nature and in the laboratory, differed from migratory individuals in not showing marked deposition of fat or increase in body weight and in having a much faster rate of gonadal development which resulted in an earlier breeding season.

The relation between physiological changes induced by increasing day length and the actual release of migratory behavior are not known, and a discussion of this problem is beyond the scope of the present paper. It is important, however, to recognize that a marked change in physiological state precedes the onset of migration in the spring and that this state can be induced artificially in the laboratory by means of changes in day length. This state can easily be recognized in live birds by means of changes in body weight and observations of the fat depots. In all the experiments that will be described, the occurrence of this state is used as an indication of a readiness to migrate, but, with one exception, the birds were not released to determine their behavior. The reproductive organs were studied when birds were sacrificed. Thus, three manifestations of the premigratory state, increase in body weight, marked deposition of fat, and gonadal recrudescence, were studied. Data were obtained also on other phases of the annual gonadal cycle. That the premigratory physiological state is a good indicator of a readiness to migrate has been demonstrated by studies of migratory restlessness (Zugunruhe) in caged birds (Eyster, 1954; Farner, 1955, review; Weise, 1956).

DAY LENGTH AND TROPICAL AND TRANSEQUATORIAL MIGRANTS

The experiments of Rowan and Wolfson pointed clearly to the increasing day lengths of winter and spring as the environmental stimulus for spring migration, but there was a serious weakness in this aspect of Rowan's theory. Birds that wintered in the North Temperate Zone or northern sub-Tropical Zone would experience substantial increases in day length after December 21, but what about birds which wintered in the tropics, or on the equator, or in the Southern Hemisphere? In the northern Tropics the increases in day length would be slight; in the equatorial region there would be practically no change; in the Southern Hemisphere, the birds would arrive in November when the days were increasing in length, and after December 21 the days would decrease in length until spring migration was underway in March and April. Increasing day length, obviously, was not a feature of the environment on the wintering grounds of all migratory birds.

To overcome this weakness of Rowan's theory, Bissonnette (1937), on the basis of his studies of the gonadal cycle of the starling (*Sturnus vulgaris*), postulated that there was an inherent rhythm of activity of the pituitary gland; the gonads, therefore, were cyclical in their activity, since they were under the control of the pituitary. In the fall, birds migrated southward owing to regression of pituitary activity and did not breed on the wintering grounds because the pituitary and gonads were in a refractory phase. On the spontaneous recovery of the pituitary in late winter or spring, the birds were stimulated to migrate before or while the gonads recrudesced. Bissonnette's theory precluded any regulatory effect by day length in the Tropics and Southern Hemisphere.

Although there was ample experimental evidence for the existence of a "refractory period" in the fall when increasing day lengths would not stimulate gonadal growth—and Bissonnette made this very important contribution to the problem—it seemed that, if day length played a regulatory role in North Temperate species, it might play a similar role in species that winter in the Tropics and Southern Hemisphere. Since the days were not increasing in length in those areas, then perhaps some other aspect of day length was operating. It occurred to me that perhaps it was the total amount of light which the birds received in a given period of time that was important and not whether the day lengths were increasing, decreasing, or relatively constant. This idea was put forth as the "summation of day lengths" hypothesis (Wolfson, 1947). I shall discuss first at some length the experiments and data that pertain to this theory. Then I shall consider the refractory period.

DAY LENGTH AND INITIATION OF MIGRATORY AND REPRODUCTIVE RESPONSES

The first test of the summation hypothesis was the determination of the total amount of light that birds wintering at various latitudes received under natural conditions (Wolfson, 1952a). Experimental work notwithstanding, conditions in nature could well preclude the possibility that summation is a regulatory factor. These data showed only small differences in the summations from December 21 until the onset of migration in March or April. Hence, experimental studies were begun to test the hypothesis. Two species have been used extensively in our laboratory, the slate-colored junco and the white-throated sparrow (*Zonotrichia albicollis*). Both are Temperate Zone species and migrate through Evanston, Illinois, in spring and fall. Evanston is also within the wintering range of the junco.

If summation was a factor, wintering birds subjected to different daily doses of day length should show differences in time of response, with those receiving the most light in a given period of time, responding first. The cumulative action of daily photoperiods had been considered in relation to the testis cycle of nonmigratory starlings (Burger, 1939a,b, 1940) and house sparrows (*Passer domesticus*) (Bartholomew, 1949) and the molt cycle in the tropical weaver finches (*Euplectes, Vidua, Steganura*) (Brown and Rollo, 1940). The results of these investigations showed clearly the importance of the daily photoperiod and the existence of threshold values for stimulation and inhibition.

In the first series of experiments (Winn, 1950, Wolfson and Winn, 1948) birds were captured during the fall migration and were subjected to the following constant daily periods of light and darkness beginning December 4: 9L-15D; 12L-12D; 15.5L-8.5D; 20L-4D; 24L. One group of birds was also maintained under natural day lengths. Since this experiment, which, incidentally, was conducted twice, was designed to determine the response to different daily durations of photoperiod in 24-hr cycles, no attempt was made to differentiate between duration of light, duration of darkness, or proportion of light to darkness as the effective daily stimulus.

All groups developed the premigratory physiological state and in a definite sequence as follows: 24L, 20L, and 15.5L—40 days; 12L—80 days; natural (mean daily photoperiod 10 hr)—120 days; 9L—160 days. The response of the testis also occurred in a sequence. Marked testicular growth was observed in each group as follows: 24L, 20L—December; 15.5L—January; 12L—March; natural—April and May; 9L—November.

The results of these experiments showed clearly that the duration of the daily photoperiod (in a 24-hr cycle) determined the time when the premigratory physiological state occurred and when the testis reached complete spermatogenesis. In relation to Rowan's original theory, the significant results were (*a*) that constant day lengths, even when as short as 9 hr and without increase from the shortest winter days to which the birds are subjected in nature, induced the migratory state and (*b*) that there is a relation between length of the day and rate of response.

The interpretation of the results of these experiments and the earlier ones of Rowan and Wolfson was as follows (Wolfson, 1952a). The daily photoperiod, whether constant or increasing gradually, induces an increment of physiological change. The magnitude of the increment is proportional to the daily photoperiod, and it appears to be at maximum at 16 hr in a 24-hr cycle. The minimum is not known, but it is less than 9 hr. The *daily* increments of physiological change *summate* and eventually reach a threshold, at which time the responses are manifested. During the period of summation, or in induction period, no marked manifestations of the daily physiological increments were evident.

On the basis of the results obtained in the junco and the interpretation given above, day length could regulate the onset of migration in birds wintering in the Tropics and in the Southern Hemisphere. Even though the days are constant on the equator and are decreasing in the Southern Hemisphere after December 21, they could be well above the length of the daily effective photoperiod for the birds wintering there, judging from the studies of North Temperate species. This matter will be discussed later at greater length.

DAY LENGTH AND DURATION OF MIGRATORY AND REPRODUCTIVE RESPONSES

This first series of experiments demonstrated a relation between the duration of the photoperiod in a 24-hr cycle and the time of initiation of the fat and gonadal responses. Was there also a relation between the daily photoperiod and the maintenance or duration of these responses once they have begun? If so, then the daily photoperiod would be a highly significant factor in the regulation of the entire annual cycle and not just the initiation of spring migration and the breeding cycle. Some relevant data were available from the previous series of experiments, but a new series of experiments was designed specifically to answer this question. Birds were caught during the spring migration in April and May and subjected to constant day lengths of 9, 12, 20, and 24 hr (photoperiods in a 24-hr cycle), and to natural day lengths. The gonads were partly developed, and the birds showed also heavy fat deposits indicative of the migratory physiological state.

The results of these experiments were generally in accord with those of the previous series, but a number of remarkable differences were found. The longer photoperiods of 20 and 24 hr induced a more rapid and greater development of the gonads compared with the birds exposed to 12-hr photoperiods and to natural day lengths. This was especially true in some of the females. In the 9-hr group the gonads regressed almost immediately. In the previous experiment it was shown that a gonadal response could be induced with a constant 9-hr photoperiod, yet in this case regression occurred. In the present experiment the testes were in an advanced condition correlated with the natural day lengths of 14 hr or more at the start of the experiment. When the day length was reduced to 9 hr, perhaps the daily increment of gonadal stimulus was too small to meet the demands of the partly enlarged testis. This interpretation is suggested also by the fact that some of these birds initiated another gonadal cycle many months later, although held at the 9-hr photoperiod. However, whether complete spermatogenesis occurred was not determined. Was the reduction in day length as such responsible for the regression in the 9-hr group? Probably not, for in the 12-hr group, which experienced a reduction in day length (from natural conditions) of approximately 2 hr at the start of the experiment, gonadal growth continued, but at a slower rate apparently than in the natural group. The extent of development showed no marked differences, but one unexpected and highly significant difference did occur. In the natural, 20-, and 24-hr groups the gonads regressed (with one exception) after a few months of activity as occurs in nature. In the 12-hr group complete activity of the testes was maintained for about 9 months.

Fat deposition continued in all the groups, but the fat deposits disappeared first in the 9-hr group. The largest fat deposits were seen in the 12-hr group. The deposits disappeared (with one exception) in the natural, 20-, and 24-hr groups before they molted, but most of the birds in the 12-hr group retained their fat deposits for many months and failed to molt.

The results of the first series of experiments showed that the daily photoperiod determined the time at which the response begins. The results of the second series demonstrated that the daily photoperiod regulates also (*a*) the rate at which the response proceeds, (*b*) the degree of response, and (*c*) the duration of the active phase of the gonadal and fat cycles (or the time of gonadal regression). A few data suggest that the extent of gonadal regression is also influenced by the daily photoperiod.

ROLE OF LIGHT AND DARKNESS IN INITIATION OF MIGRATORY AND REPRODUCTIVE RESPONSES

At about the time the second series of experiments was concluded, Kirkpatrick and Leopold (1952, 1953) and Jenner and Engels (1952) demonstrated the importance of the dark period in the gonadal response to the daily cycle of light and darkness. In the studies in our laboratory described above, none of the experiments had been designed to distinguish between the roles of light and darkness. Hence, further experiments were undertaken to determine the role of the dark period in relation to the summation hypothesis.

If the effective stimulus is the amount of light that a bird receives in a day, or in a period of time, then birds receiving 20 hr of light per day in one dose or in four equal doses of 5 hr should respond equally well. In both cases the birds would receive the same total amount of light per 24-hr period. They would also receive the same ratio of light to darkness. The only basic difference would be the length of each cycle. Hence, in the first experiment the birds were subjected to 5-hr photoperiods followed by 1-hr dark periods (5L-1D) (Wolfson, 1953).

The results demonstrated clearly that a 6-hr cycle of 5L-1D was strongly stimulatory for the gonadal and fat responses. The extent and rapidity of response was similar to that in birds on a 20L-4D schedule, with a tendency toward a greater fat response and a greater reproductive response in the females. The changes in body weight

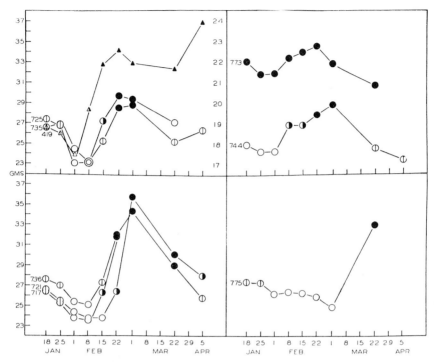

FIG. 1.   Changes in body weight and fat deposition for the birds that responded to treatment with a schedule of 5L-1D. Circles are used for white-throated sparrows, triangles for the junco; scale for body weight of the junco on right side of upper left graph. Fat deposition at each point indicated as follows: open symbol = no fat; line through symbol = little fat; half of symbol filled in = medium fat; symbol filled in completely = heavy fat. Experiment began on January 25. Each number and curve represents an individual bird. Note differences in time and extent of response.

and fat deposition are shown in Fig. 1. The individual curves show the variations in the amount and time of response.

These results were interpreted as supporting the summation thesis that the daily amount of light regulates the rate of response. However, since the proportion of light to darkness per 24 hr and per cycle were the same, there was the possibility that this proportion was the effective stimulus and not the daily dose of light. The work of Kirkpatrick and Leopold (1952) and Jenner and Engels (1952) pointed to the duration of the dark period in a 24-hr cycle as the regulatory factor in the daily schedule, but their experiments, which involved interrupting the dark period with a brief period of light, did not rule out the proportion of light to darkness as the effective daily stimulus. For example, in the schedules used, 8.25L-7D-1.75L-7D (Jenner and Engels, 1952) and 9L-7D-1L-7D (Kirkpatrick and Leopold, 1952) the first cycle of light and darkness in the 24-hr period was close to a 1:1 ratio and the light period was longer. This could have been the effective cycle of the 24-hr period. The second cycle, with its much greater proportion of darkness might not have been stimulatory. The next experiments in our laboratory involved the use of an interrupted-night schedule and a related one to examine the role of the ratio of light to darkness. The schedules were as follows: 8L-7.25D-1.5L-7.25D and 8L-8D. In the first schedule, the 16-hr dark period was interrupted with 1.5 hr of light. In the second, the 8L-8D simulated the 8L-7.25D part of the interrupted night schedule.

The birds responded similarly under both treatments. A preliminary analysis of the data indicates that the rate of response was close to that in birds exposed to 15.5L-8.5D. Hence, both of these schedules acted like the long days (15.5L, 20L) of the earlier series of experiments. Yet, the amount of light in a 24-hr period was only 9.5 hr in the interrupted night schedule. In the 8L-8D schedule, the amount of light alternated from 8 to 16 hr per 24-hr period. With a schedule of 8 hr or 9.5 hr of light per day in one dose in a 24-hr cycle, birds do not respond in eight or ten weeks.

The results of these experiments confirmed the work of Kirkpatrick and Leopold (1952) and Jenner and Engels (1952) and pointed to the length of the night or dark period in a 24-hr cycle as the regulatory part of light-darkness schedules which induce photoperiodic responses. An alternative explanation was put forth by Farner *et al.* (1953a,b). They suggested that the daily dark period per se has no positive function; rather, there is a persistent carry-over period which follows the end of the photoperiod, and the effective part of a photoperiodic schedule is the photoperiod plus the carry-over period. They envisioned the carry-over period as having a duration of a fraction of an hour to several hours and as a probable function of the duration and nature of the preceding photoperiod. Rate of testicular response was interpreted as a direct function of the summated daily gonadotropic effects of the photoperiods and the carry-over periods. The interpretation of Farner *et al.* is in agreement with the hypothesis of summation of daily physiological increments, but they suggested the carry-over period as an additional effective part of the photoperiodic cycle.

Digressing for a moment, I should like to point out in relation to this problem of the role of light and darkness that although the work in our laboratory showed clearly a relation between rate of response and the daily photoperiod, the experiments were not designed to distinguish between the roles of the photoperiod, the dark period, or a relation between them. The summation hypothesis was stated initially in terms of the response to day lengths, or photoperiods, but it was pointed out later that these terms were used only relatively. The role of the dark period in the daily schedule will be discussed shortly, but I wish to distinguish here between the theory of summation of daily increments of physiological change in response to an effective photoperiodic schedule, over which there is no disagreement, and the role of light and darkness in the daily photoperiodic cycle, over which there is disagreement. The theory of summation, it must also be pointed out, is only an interpretation at present; there is no objective evidence for it.

The results of the two experiments just reported were interpreted as demonstrating an inhibitory effect of a long dark period. But they also showed that the ratio of the durations of the light and dark periods might also be a factor. The next experiment was designed to test the role of the ratio of light to darkness and to obtain data bearing on the existence of a carry-over period. The schedule chosen was 1L-2D. In each cycle there was the same proportion of light to darkness and the same total amounts as in a schedule of 8L-16D, which is *not* stimulatory. If the birds failed to respond, then it would seem unlikely that there was an effective carry-over period. The birds showed an excellent and rapid gonadal response. The results demonstrated again that only a small total amount of light per day, in this case 8 hr, is highly effective when there is no long inhibitory period of darkness. Since the proportion of light to darkness in each cycle was inhibitory (1L-2D), and since the total amounts of light and darkness per day (8L and 16D) were also inhibitory, the positive results ruled out both of these as effective aspects of the daily photoperiodic cycle. They pointed instead to the effectiveness of small amounts of light per day when there was no long period of darkness or to the existence of carry-over periods, depending on one's interpretation.

To examine further the possible role of a long period of darkness as an inhibitory factor, the pertinent experiments in the literature were examined and another experiment was performed in our laboratory. The experiments in the literature (Burger *et al.*, 1942; Farner *et al.*, 1953a,b; Jenner and Engels, 1952; Kirkpatrick, 1955; Kirkpatrick and Leopold, 1952, 1953) showed that in most cases birds responded to "light periods" given either as flashes of light or when broken up with dark periods, as long as there was no single long dark period of about 14 hr duration in a 24-hr period. There were some exceptions. In some cases, the flashing "schedules" were not effective, for example, 5 sec L-15 sec D and 0.1 sec L-5 sec D (Burger *et al.*, 1952). In the experiments of Farner *et al.* (1953-a,b), the response was poor in some cases, but only with a schedule of 12.2L-11.8D was there a clear-cut failure to respond (9 out of 12 birds) when the duration of a continuous dark period was less than 14 hr. The other experiments that they reported and interpreted in terms of carry-over also had no continuous dark periods long enough to inhibit the light periods. The experiments in the literature seemed to me to favor the interpretation of a long period of darkness as inhibitory, but there was also a basis for a carry-over effect of the photoperiod.

To test the effect of an inhibitory period of darkness after an effective series of light periods, the following schedule was used in the next experiment in our laboratory: (1L-0.25D)[7]-1L-14.25D. This schedule provided eight 1-hr periods of light as in the 1L-2D schedule and a similar total of 8 hr of light in 24 hr. It differed in having only 15-min dark periods interspersed among the 1-hr light periods and in having one long continuous period of darkness that was known to be inhibitory. The birds failed to respond, and this schedule not only failed to initiate a response, but also failed to maintain the reproductive condition of some birds which were already active at the beginning of the experiment. These results can be interpreted as supporting the inhibitory role of long periods of darkness, and it is tempting to do so. It can also be argued that a 15-min period of darkness did not allow enough time for the complete use of the carry-over periods of the 1-hr photoperiods and, hence, the effective photoperiods and carry-over periods could not exceed a total of about 10 to 12 hr. The data did not permit a clear-cut choice between these alternative explanations.

If a long dark period was inhibitory, what would happen if such a period was used after a 1L-2D schedule? This was done with the following schedule: $(1L-2D)^7$-1L-16D. The birds showed an excellent response. Since an effective period of light treatment was not inhibited by a known inhibitory dark period, these results demonstrated the importance of the light period as the effective stimulus. But this interpretation is also open to question. In this experiment the cycle was 38 hr long. The effective light period, despite interruptions with dark periods, was 22 hr long, whereas the dark period was only 16 hr long. In a 38-hr cycle perhaps a dark period of 16 hr is not inhibitory.

Another experiment employing a cycle longer than 24 hr also appears to support the importance of the light period. The schedule used was 12L-16D, and it was designed to test the simultaneous effect of a daily period of light which was known to be stimulatory (12L) and a daily period of darkness which was known to be inhibitory (16D). The experiment began in December and continued to May. The gonadal and fat responses were excellent and showed some similarity to these responses under a schedule of 12L-12D. These results, in my opinion, point to the light period as the effective period, but again the experimental design does not permit a clear-cut choice. Further studies employing longer dark periods are needed before a final conclusion can be reached. If such studies show that the daily response to an effective daily photoperiod cannot be negated by a strongly inhibitory dark period, as this experiment suggests, then it is obviously the light period that is the effective part of the photoperiodic cycle. The inhibitory role of the dark period would then be merely a matter of semantics. A long night would be inhibitory only because it did not permit a longer or effective period of light.

It is impossible at this time to distinguish precisely between the roles of light and darkness in the regulation of the gonadal and fat responses. However, some things seem clear: (1) The total amount of darkness in a 24-hr cycle is not the equivalent of the same amount of darkness given in a single dose. (2) Short cycles within a 24-hr period are equivalent to 24-hr cycles with regard to stimulation (5L-1D and 20L-4D), but they are not equivalent with regard to failure to stimulate, or "inhibition" (1L-2D and 8L-16D) as indicated in (1). (3) With different effective schedules of light and darkness within a 24-hr cycle, there is a difference in rate, extent, and duration of response. (4) Whatever the roles of light and darkness, the *daily* photoperiodic schedule is the critical external factor that results in physiological "increments of response" which summate and are eventually manifested, or are readily observable and measurable as gonadal growth, spermatogenesis, fat deposition, and increase in body weight.

DAY LENGTH AND THE REFRACTORY PERIOD

After a period of activity, the gonads regress spontaneously. In nature, this occurs after the breeding season, some time in July and August for most North Temperate species. During this period, long days or increasing days cannot induce gonadal activity and, hence, it has been called the refractory period. The natural termination of this period varies with the species, but it occurs usually in October or November. The refractory state can also be produced in the laboratory. Burger reviewed the status of the problem of regulation of reproductive cycles in 1949 and aptly stated that "attention has been focused too narrowly on the progressive phase of the reproductive cycle."

Since both the migratory and breeding cycles are closely in phase with environmental conditions, it seems unlikely that the refractory period, or the entire annual gonadal cycle, is regulated by fixed inherent rhythms of the gonads or the pituitary which operate spontaneously as some investigators have suggested (Bissonnette, 1937; Blanchard, 1941; Blanchard and Erickson, 1949; Marshall, 1951; Wagner and Stresemann, 1950).

Juncos in nature experience a reduction in day length during the summer and fall, and it was plausible that decreasing day lengths, or short days, or long nights, could regulate the duration of the refractory period. Burger (1947) and Bissonnette (unpublished data, cited by Burger, 1947) showed that treatment with long days in the starling eventually induced a refractory period which could only be dissipated by treatment with short days. Miller (1948, 1951) found that treatment with long days begun in the fall in the migratory golden-crowned sparrow (*Zonotrichia atricapilla*) prevented the occurrence of gonadal growth at the normal time in the spring.

To determine the effect of day length on the refractory period in the junco and white-throated sparrow, birds whose cycles had been accelerated by exposure to 20 hr of light per day and which were in a refractory period were treated with short days beginning July 14. One group was exposed to 9 hr of light per day, the other to 12 hr per day. In addition, there was a group retained under natural day lengths. After six weeks of this treatment they were exposed to long days (20L-4D) beginning August 27. The experiment terminated on October 22. The juncos that were pretreated with 9-hr and 12-hr photoperiods showed an excellent response, whereas the birds pretreated with natural day lengths did not (Wolfson, 1952b). The response in the white-throated sparrows was similar, but fewer individuals responded in the 12-hr group (Wolfson, unpublished data). This experiment was repeated again in the fall during the natural refractory period, and the results were generally similar (Wolfson and Shank, unpublished data). In a related group of experiments, birds were exposed to 20-hr photoperiods for a maximum of 6 months beginning in the refractory period (October and early November) to test the effect of a strong stimulatory photoperiod. With few exceptions, the birds failed to respond, even at the normal time of the gonadal response in the spring (Wolfson, 1952b).

The results of these experiments showed that the duration of the refractory period was regulated by day length. Short days hastened the termination of the refractory period, whereas long days prolonged it. Whether the effective part of the photoperiodic cycle was the period of light or the period of darkness, or a relation between them,

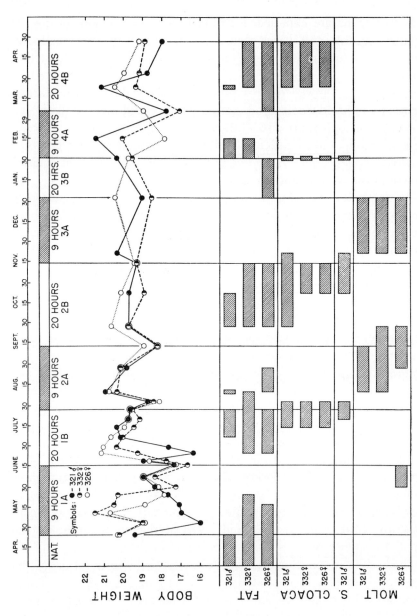

Fig. 2. Responses in juncos for duration of experiment. Body weight is given in grams. See text for explanation.

694

remained to be determined. However, before experiments were undertaken to determine this, another experiment was performed to test the results of the above experiments.

If there is a physiological preparation on short days for a subsequent response to long days, then it should be possible to induce a response several times within one year, even though juncos normally show only one period of gonadal activity and two periods of fat deposition annually. Production of repeated cycles was attempted by exposing birds to alternating periods of short days (9L-15D) and long days (20L-4D) (Wolfson, 1954). The lengths of the periods varied, but in a total of 369 days, juncos were exposed to four periods of short days and five periods of long days, including the initial natural long days of April. Five periods of gonadal activity (including the initial active state when the experiment began), five periods of fat deposition, and two molts occurred within the 369 days. These are indicated in Fig. 2. Gonadal growth, fat deposition, and increase in body weight were correlated with long days. Gonadal regression, loss of fat deposits and decrease in body weight were correlated with short days. These correlations became less distinct as the experiment progressed. Figure 3 shows the marked changes in body weight and fat deposition during the first periods of short and long days. Prior to this study, Rowan (1929), Miyazaki (1934), Damsté (1947), and Burger (1947) had induced more than one period of gonadal activity in a year in different species of birds. In Fig. 2, duration of response is indicated by horizontal bars except in a few cases where they indicate only occurrence on the date of observation. Fat response indicates presence of medium or heavy fat deposits. Molt response is comparable to the annual molt. S. refers to occurrence of sperm, which were obtained by applying pressure to the seminal vesicles (Wolfson, 1952c).

The results of this experiment confirmed the conclusion of the previous series on the refractory period that short days in the fall regulate a reaction that enables the bird to respond to subsequent photoperiodic treatment. Without this "preparatory period" the bird does not respond. Although the bird is "refractory" to long days in the fall, it is undergoing a response which is regulated by day length (short days) and which is necessary for a subsequent response. Hence,

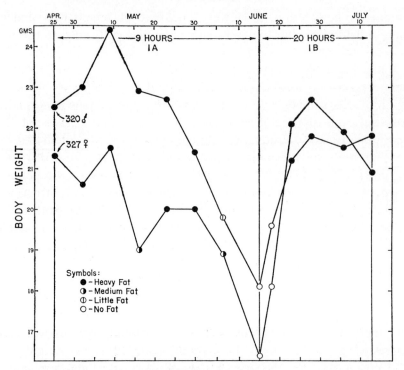

FIG. 3. Changes in body weight and fat deposition in two juncos for the first cycle of short and long days.

it seems more appropriate to call it the preparatory period or phase. This period is then followed by the progressive phase.

ROLE OF LIGHT AND DARKNESS IN REGULATION OF REFRACTORY PERIOD

Having established the requirement for short days during the preparatory period, the next problem was the determination of the effective part of the short days. Was it the short photoperiods or the long dark periods? A variety of schedules was used during the natural refractory period which was followed by subsequent treatment with long days (20L-4D) beginning in December. The schedules used and their effectiveness in inducing the preparatory phase are summarized.

Effective Schedules

8L-16D   12L-12D

Ineffective Schedules

4L-8D-4L-8D   5L-1D-5L-1D-5L-1D-5L-1D
6L-6D-6L-6D   8L-7.25D-1.5L-7.25D

These results demonstrated that it was not a short period of light
per se, nor the total amount of light and darkness in a given day, nor
the proportion of light to darkness in a short cycle that was effective.
Rather, it was a single period of darkness, 12 hr long, or longer, in a
24-hr cycle that was the effective part of a short day. A 16-hr dark
period was generally more effective than a 12-hr period, which seems
to be near the threshold for the minimum effective duration of the
dark period.

The next question was whether a 16-hr dark period per se was the
effective stimulus, or whether a long single dose of light was inhibitory. To answer this, birds were exposed to schedules of 16L-16D
and $(1L-2D)^7 + 1L + 16D$ during the preparatory period and then
treated with long days (20L-4D). Both schedules were ineffective
and corresponded to long days. That they were actually long days was
established by the response of birds to those same schedules during
the winter. The results suggest that a 16-hr dark period per se is not
the effective stimulus. There apparently is some relation between the
duration of the light period and the duration of the dark period, or
there is a single dose of light which is inhibitory irrespective of the
length of the dark period. Further studies are needed to explore these
alternatives.

Another question of interest was whether a bird can "store" each
daily increment of response. If it could, what would the response be
to alternating short and long days? The schedule used was 8L-16D,
16L-8D. It turned out to be a long day during the preparatory period
and during the subsequent progressive period. This may have been
due to the fact that the bird was reacting to the schedule not on a daily
basis, but rather as 8D-8L and 16D-16L, both of which are known to
act like long days. To answer the question of whether the bird can
store a daily stimulus until a threshold is reached, or whether continu-

ous daily effective photoperiodic schedules are required, further experimentation is needed.

DISCUSSION AND SUMMARY

When the results of all the experiments that have been described so far are considered in relation to migratory behavior and reproductive rhythmicity, it is evident that day length in nature plays an important regulatory role in a number of ways. I shall consider migration and reproduction separately, since the data and the interpretations, although similar, are not identical for both. Also, in view of our ignorance of the precise roles of light and darkness, I shall summarize the regulation of migration and reproduction first in terms of day length, with particular reference to what goes on in nature, and then consider the roles of light and darkness. Finally, the question of an inherent rhythm of the endocrine glands involved and the problem of day length in relation to the timing of spring migration in equatorial and transequatorial migrants and to breeding cycles in the tropics will be discussed.

Day Length and Migration

The data available demonstrate that two phases or periods are involved in the timing of spring migration. The first occurs in the late summer and fall and is the preparatory phase; the second begins in late fall and continues through the winter until the time of migration in the spring and is the progressive phase. The preparatory phase is prerequisite to the progressive phase.

The preparatory phase in nature is apparently regulated by the shorter day lengths of the fall. In the laboratory, this phase was induced at different seasons of the year by subjecting birds to short days (9L-15D). Twelve hours of light per day appears to be near the threshold for the maximum day length which can act like a short day.

Long days (16L-8D) inhibit the occurrence of the preparatory phase and the appearance of the subsequent progressive phase. Therefore, the short days of fall are actually regulating the occurrence of the migratory behavior which appears six to seven months later. The time required for the completion of the preparatory phase is six weeks or less. Whether the duration of the preparatory phase is related to the length of the short day has not been determined, but a few relevant data suggest that there may be some relation between the length of the dark period and the rate at which the preparatory phase proceeds.

After the preparatory phase has been completed, the progressive phase begins. In nature, it probably begins automatically, but *the rate at which it proceeds* is governed by day length. The occurrence of the spring premigratory physiological state was induced in juncos by means of long days in about 40 days. This was about 80 days ahead of its natural occurrence. With a short day (9L-15D) the same state appeared in about 160 days, which was 40 days later than its occurrence in nature. The maximum rate of response occurred with a day length as short as 15.5 hr; the minimum rate occurred with a day length of 9 hr, but shorter day lengths were not tried. Nine hours was used as the minimum, because this is about the shortest day to which juncos are exposed in nature.

It is important to emphasize here that the progressive phase proceeded *when there was no increase in day length.* When the birds were exposed to 9-hr photoperiods beginning December 4, they had already undergone the preparatory phase under natural day lengths. On December 4 their day length was reduced from approximately 10 hr under natural conditions (including civil twilight) to 9 hr, and it remained constant at 9 hr thereafter. Yet, these birds achieved the spring premigratory physiological state, on the basis of their fat deposition and body weight. Their reproductive organs were, however, somewhat below the normal. Would such birds actually migrate? During 1957 over 200 birds were held on 9-hr days from December to June and then released. A preliminary analysis of the data shows that about 60% undertook a migration.

In view of our earlier knowledge which showed the stimulatory effect of increasing day lengths during the winter, it must be emphasized that gradually increasing day lengths (or an increase in day length) are not necessary to induce spring migration. The role of day length, once the birds are ready to respond, is the *regulation of the rate* at which the response proceeds. The progressive phase proceeds spontaneously *without increases in day length* and when the days are as short as the shortest days in December and remain short. This is a major change from the conclusions of the earlier experiments in which migration was induced out of season by subjecting birds to artificial increases in day length (Rowan, 1929; Wolfson, 1942, 1945).

After the birds are in the premigratory physiological state, the length of time they remain in this state is a function of day length. Long days dissipate the state more quickly than short days, and under short days (12L-12D and 9L-15D) the birds may not lose their fat. A change from long days to short days will also dissipate the state rapidly (Fig. 3).

In nature, the spring premigratory physiological state ends when the birds arrive on their breeding grounds, or shortly afterward. After the breeding season, the gonads regress, the birds molt, and subsequently, there is a physiological change, which precedes the onset of fall migration. Nothing is known about the factors which regulate this state. When the fall migration gets underway in September and October the day lengths have reached a value which is effective for the beginning of the preparatory phase of the next spring migration. And thus a new cycle begins.

Role of Light and Darkness in the Migratory Cycle

The available data suggest that in the preparatory phase, the effective part of the short days is the dark period. It seems likely that there is a dark-dependent response which requires a daily uninterrupted dark period of at least 12 hr duration. This response cannot occur when a greater total amount of darkness is given per 24 hr in smaller doses, for example 4L-8D-4L-8D. Or, if the dark-dependent reaction goes on during short dark periods, it cannot summate to give an effective daily response, or a response after the lapse of many days. The absence of an inhibitory reaction produced by long days is apparently not a factor, since with short periods of light, the same small total amount of light per day, and the same ratio of light to darkness the preparatory phase did not occur (for example, 4L-8D-4L-8D was negative, whereas 8L-16D was positive; 6L-6D-6L-6D was negative, whereas 12L-12D was positive). However, more studies are needed to establish this point, because of the possibility of carry-over effects of the light periods. The responses induced by each daily effective period of darkness summate. Eventually, the bird completes the preparatory phase and is prepared to begin the progressive phase.

Although the present data favor the interpretation that the uninterrupted period of darkness is the effective stimulus of the short day, the result of 16L-16D experiment indicates that this interpretation must be accepted tentatively. If a 16-hr dark period in a 24-hr cycle is the effective stimulus of a short day, why does not the preparatory phase occur under a schedule of 16L-16D? Obviously, a 16-hr dark period per se is not the only factor governing the reaction in the preparatory phase. A long light period can negate the positive effect of a long dark period. The ratio does not seem to be an important factor, since 12L-12D gives a positive effect. Here again, the problem of carry-over effects of the photoperiods may be involved; nevertheless it is clear that the data show some effect of the photoperiod. Thus, although the evidence points to the dark period as the critical factor in a short day, there also seems to be some relation between the photoperiod and the dark period, the net effect of which may be positive or negative, depending on the length of the photoperiod.

One final and significant observation must be noted, which bears on the previous statement that the progressive phase proceeds spontaneously once the preparatory phase has been completed. A schedule of 12L-12D is uniformly effective in the preparatory phase in late July and August. Yet, when birds were treated with this schedule beginning in October and were *retained under the same conditions* until May, well past the natural occurrence of the premigratory physiological state, or were treated with 20-hr photoperiods beginning in December, many failed to respond. Birds held under natural day lengths during fall and then treated with a schedule of 12L-12D beginning in December responded well. If 12L-12D is an effective schedule for preparation in late summer and is also an effective schedule for the progressive phase, why did not the birds treated with 12L-12D beginning in October respond uniformly? To determine whether the birds held until May had undergone the preparatory phase, a few remaining birds were treated with 20-hr photoperiods beginning in late May. They responded well, and hence, had completed the preparatory phase. The failure in these birds was apparently in the progressive phase. There was also failure in the preparatory phase, since some birds which were exposed to 20-hr photoperiods beginning in late December, also failed to respond. The differences in "preparation" and "responsiveness" between the birds treated in summer and fall may stem from the differences in the history of the birds before the experiments. Whatever the explanation, what is significant is the observation that in some birds exposure to a schedule of 12L-12D in the fall modified the day length requirements of the progressive phase, or changed the requirements for the spontaneous initiation of the progressive phase.

In the progressive phase, both the light and dark periods have been suggested as the controlling part of the photoperiodic cycle. Jenner and Engels (1952), and Kirkpatrick and Leopold (1952, 1953) and Kirkpatrick (1955) state that the dark period is the critical factor. Farner *et al.* (1953a,b) state that the effective stimulus is the light period and the carry-over effects of the light periods. In these studies only the reproductive response was used, but the ideas are applicable to the migratory response and hence are discussed here.

The results of our studies of the migratory response can be interpreted to support either hypothesis. The available data do not permit a clear-cut choice. Perhaps they do not because *both light and darkness* play important roles in the daily photoperiodic schedule. The results of the experiments using the schedules 16L-16D and 12L-16D seem to me to favor the light period (and any carry-over periods) as the effective daily stimulus. It should be noted here also that birds exposed to continuous light responded well and as rapidly as birds exposed to schedules of 20L-4D and 15.5L-8.5D. Whatever the effective stimulus is, the *daily* responses to it summate and ultimately induce the migratory response.

An interesting difference between the "light and dark" reactions of the preparatory and the progressive phases is that in the preparatory phase, where the dark period seems to be the critical factor, the effects of shorter dark periods in a 24-hr cycle do not summate to give an effective daily stimulus. In the progressive phase, where the light appears to be the critical factor, the effects of short light periods do summate to give an effective daily stimulus when there is no inhibitory duration of darkness in a 24-hr cycle. In the preparatory phase a long light period *per day* appears to be inhibitory, whereas in the progressive phase, a long dark period *per day* appears to be inhibitory. In both phases, the data show clearly that the 24-hr cycle is highly significant. It is possible that an inherent 24-hr rhythm or other innate rhythms in the bird are related to the migratory and reproductive responses to photoperiodic schedules, and this must be explored in future studies.

Day Length and Reproduction

The regulation of the reproductive cycle in the male also occurs in two phases, the preparatory and the progressive. The preparatory phase occurs in late summer and fall, the progressive phase in late fall, winter, and spring. As with migration, the preparatory phase is prerequisite to the progressive phase.

The regulation of the preparatory phase by day length is the same as that for migration. There are some differences, however, in the responsive phase. A 9-hr photoperiod per day induced migration at a slow rate. However, only one junco showed a good testicular response (complete spermatogenesis, but not maximum size) under a 9L-15D schedule and that was almost twelve months after the experiment began (December 4 to November 23). The other birds which were sacrificed during the course of the experiment, showed only a slight development. Hence, a short photoperiod is much more retarding in the progressive phase of the reproductive cycle.

The minimum photoperiod that will induce a reproductive response varies with the species, the duration of the experiment, and what is defined as a response. House sparrows showed maximum testicular development on constant 10-hr photoperiods per day (Bartholomew, 1949). In the starling, 9.5-hr photoperiods per day were effective for complete development (Burger, 1953). In a more carefully controlled experiment, Miller (1955) showed that a 10-hr photoperiod was not sufficient for complete development of the testes in the golden-crowned sparrow, a migratory form, but it was sufficient for complete development in a nonmigratory form (*nuttalli*) of the white-crowned sparrow (*Zonotrichia leucophrys*). Miller's experiment terminated on September 20, which was about two months sooner than the time it took the junco to show a good (but not complete) response with a constant 9-hr photoperiod per day (Winn, 1950, Wolfson, 1952a). The minimum effective day length for some testicular response seems to be 8.5 hr for the starling (Burger, 1949), about 8 or 9 hr for the house sparrow (Bartholomew, 1949; Farner and Wilson, 1957), 9 hr for the slate-colored junco (Winn, 1950) and 10 hr for the golden-crowned sparrow. In most of these studies, however, the effectiveness of shorter day lengths was not explored.

Once the preparatory phase has been completed, the progressive phase is probably initiated spontaneously and proceeds at a rate which is determined by the day length. Complete spermatogenesis was first achieved in about 35 days under the longest days, 24L; 20L-4D; in about 75 days with a schedule of 15.5L-8.5D; in about 150 days with a 12L-12D schedule; and in about 166 days under natural day lengths.

In the experiment in which a schedule of 12L-12D was used beginning in the fall, some of the birds did not initiate a migratory responsive phase spontaneously, even though they had completed the preparatory phase. With regard to the reproductive response, most of the birds did not initiate the progressive phase spontaneously, even though most had completed the preparatory phase.

The duration of maximal reproductive activity is also regulated by day length. The shortest durations were produced by long days, the longest by days with 12-hr photoperiods. With a schedule of 12L-12D begun in April, a few birds maintained reproductive activity three to six times as long as the normal duration of about two months.

Regression of reproductive activity occurs spontaneously, and the time that it occurs is obviously under the control of day length. It can also be induced by short days. After regression the birds enter the preparatory phase, and a new cycle is ready to begin.

Role of Light and Darkness in the Reproductive Cycle

The conclusions and discussion given above in relation to the migratory cycle are applicable here and need not be repeated.

Inherent Rhythm and Migratory and Reproductive Periodicity

Ever since the discovery that day length influences the reproductive and migratory cycles, there have been suggestions that these cycles, in whole or in part, are regulated by internal rhythms which are independent of external factors such as day length. Among current investigators, Blanchard (1941) and Marshall (1951, 1955) emphasize the role of an internal rhythm. The studies reported here and the recent work of Burger (1953), Farner and Wilson (1957), and Miller (1954a,b, 1955) demonstrate the regulation of the entire annual cycle by day length. Moreover, day length does not act like a trigger that sets off an inherent cycle with an innate periodicity and amplitude. Every phase of the reproductive and migratory cycles has been shown to be influenced by day length—the time of occurrence, the rate of development, the extent of development, and the duration of the preparatory and progressive phases. Only one process appears to be inherent, and that is the initiation and occurrence of regression of the testes after a period of reproductive activity. However, the time of regression and the extent of regression can be manipulated by day length. More studies are needed to determine whether the process of regression and the reorganization of the testis are independent of environmental factors (Marshall, 1951). After regression and reorganization of the testes have occurred, the cycle enters the preparatory phase, which is clearly regulated by day length.

Another possible inherent aspect of the cycle is the initiation of the progressive phase. After birds have completed the preparatory phase, the migratory response and spermatogenesis usually begin spontaneously. But they do not occur until after the completion of the preparatory phase.

If the initiation and occurrence of regression and the initiation of the progressive phase are inherent processes and independent of external factors, their periodic occurrence may be called an inherent rhythm. The term rhythm, however, would apply only to the *alternation of these processes* and could not be construed as implying the time of occurrence, rate of development, amplitude, or duration of the various phases in the cycle, all of which have been clearly shown to be influenced by day length. Further studies are needed that will permit precise definition of the physiological responses during the photoperiods and the dark periods before we will be able to distinguish between inherent and independent reactions and reactions induced and regulated by environmental factors. Admittedly, the present interpretations which are based only on the manifest responses are not satisfactory.

In this connection, we have data from our laboratory which show that a few birds, held under constant long days during the spring, summer, and fall, initiated another gonadal cycle spontaneously in the fall (Winn, 1950; Wolfson, 1955). In these instances, the preparatory phase was completed under long days. In another instance, one bird exposed to 20-hr photoperiods beginning April 6 did not undergo regression and remained in continuous reproductive activity for a little more than a year. Although these few birds are exceptions, they indicate the tentative nature of our present interpretations.

Day Length and the Timing of Spring Migration in Equatorial and Transequatorial Migrants

On the basis of the experimental results and the interpretations presented here, the timing of spring migratory behavior in migrants wintering on the equator, in the Tropics, or in the Southern Hemisphere can be explained. Experimental work must be done with equatorial and transequatorial migrants to test the hypothesis presented, but the data available so far for North Temperate species support it. The relatively constant day lengths of the equatorial region can no longer be regarded a priori as nonregulatory. Constant photoperiods of 12 hr have been shown to be effective, and the duration of the photoperiod, moreover, regulates the rate of response. Hence, birds wintering in the equatorial region could be responding to the relatively constant day lengths of 12 hr. The birds that cross the equator and winter in the sub-Tropics or temperate regions of the Southern Hemisphere are exposed to gradually increasing day lengths after they arrive in late October or November and to gradually decreasing day lengths after December 21, which reach a value of about 12 hr on March 21. Therefore, the birds are exposed during their entire stay on the wintering grounds to long days which, although they increase gradually to a maximum and then decrease gradually to 12 hr, would remain at an effective photoperiodic level, judging from our experimental work with juncos.

The main problem in equatorial and transequatorial migrants, as I see it, is not the effect of the day lengths on the wintering grounds, but the relation between day length and the preparatory phase and the initiation of the progressive phase. At the outset, it seems highly probable that there is a preparatory phase in these birds that is regulated by day length rather than being a self-regulated spontaneously expressed rhythm. Unlike the junco, these migrants would not experience days shorter than about 12 to 13 hr, or nights longer than about 11 to 12 hr. Is this a short enough day or a long enough night to complete a preparatory phase? Since some juncos could "prepare" on a constant 12L-12D schedule, it is probable that these migrants could also prepare under the photoperiodic conditions they would experience while migrating from their North Temperate breeding grounds to their wintering grounds from September to November. Since only six weeks of treatment with 12L-12D in July and August was enough to complete the preparatory phase in the junco, it is highly probable that equatorial and transequatorial migrants would be exposed to a sufficient number of 12- to 13-hr days during the period of fall migration to complete their preparatory phase. An alternative explanation is that the effective day lengths during the preparatory phase are longer than those in the junco. Species differences in the relation between day length and the preparatory and progressive phases are to be expected. It is interesting to note that in nature juncos winter where they will experience dark periods longer than 12 hr; hence, spontaneous initiation of the progressive phase is assured. The regulation of the preparatory phase and of the initiation of the progressive phase is the critical problem in the regulation of spring migration in equatorial and transequatorial migrants.

Once the preparatory phase is over, it is highly probable that the long days of the equatorial region and the Southern Hemisphere, whether they were relatively constant, increasing, or decreasing, would regulate the rate at which the progressive phase proceeded.

Engels (p. 759) has presented a few data on the growth of the testes in relation to photoperiod in an excellent transequatorial migrant, the bobolink (*Dolichonyx oryzivorus*), but the data are probably applicable to the premigratory physiological state. His data, although not conclusive, suggest the existence of a preparatory phase which requires short days for its completion and which is prevented by long days. As in the junco, day lengths of 12 hr were short enough for the occurrence of the preparatory phase, but 10-hr days were more effective during treatment for eight weeks. Photoperiods of 14 hr per day inhibited the preparatory phase. Data from our laboratory (unpublished) on body weight and fat deposition for two captive bobolinks demonstrate an excellent premigratory physiological state, with much more extensive fat deposition and greater increase in body weight than has ever been observed in the North Temperate species we have studied. Experimental studies with equatorial and transequatorial migrants are currently underway in our laboratory and will test further the hypothesis of summation as applied to the preparatory and progressive phases.

Day Length and Breeding Cycles in the Tropics

Breeding seasons cannot be explained simply by any one factor in the environment. Moreover, it is not possible to extrapolate directly from experimental studies of the gonadal cycle to breeding cycles in the Tropics, particularly when North Temperate species were used in the experimental studies. Nevertheless, in view of our understanding of the regulation of gonadal cycles in North Temperate species it seems desirable to examine briefly the summation hypothesis and the related interpretations in relation to breeding cycles in the Tropics. The basic premise in the discussion which follows is that breeding is preceded by gametogenesis; therefore, what controls gametogenesis plays a fundamental role in the regulation of breeding seasons. After gametogenesis occurs, or is initiated, other factors certainly come into play to regulate the time and duration of breeding. (See Wolfson, 1952a, for a more detailed discussion of day length and breeding cycles in the Tropics.)

Studies of breeding cycles at all latitudes led Baker (1938) to the conclusion that "the main proximate causes of the breeding seasons of birds in nature are thought to be temperature and the length of day in the boreal and temperate zones, and rain and/or intensity of insolation near the equator." Recently, a reexamination of the problem led to the same general conclusion that day length and temperature in the higher latitudes and humidity and rainfall in the Tropics are correlated with the breeding seasons (Lack, 1950a,b; Moreau, 1950; Skutch, 1950; Thomson, 1950; Voous, 1950). The significance of these climatic factors is believed to lie in their effect on food supply. Breeding seasons are regarded as an adaptation and occur apparently when the young can be reared at the time of maximum food supply. If the breeding season is adapted to environmental conditions operating toward its close other factors must be postulated for the initiation of the cycle. Although day length and temperature are acceptable for higher latitudes, in the Tropics both "are too nearly constant to offer a possible explanation" (Thomson, 1950, p. 182).

There is little doubt that the early experimental studies which employed increasing and decreasing day length to alter the gonadal cycle and the fact that day length and temperature vary periodically in higher latitudes have played a large part in the derivation of the above conclusions. Our experimental findings, however, suggest that day length should not be ruled out as a regulatory factor in the Tropics simply because it is relatively constant.

A pertinent question is whether tropical species respond to day length. More experimental studies with tropical species are urgently needed to answer this question, but the data from two series of experiments (Brown and Rollo, 1940; Rollo and Domm, 1943) and other observations suggest that the gonadal and molt cycles of some tropical and equatorial birds can be altered by changes in day length. Experiments were performed in the Chicago area with whydahs and weavers (*Steganura, Euplectes,* and *Vidua*) which were imported from Africa. The results demonstrated clearly that the daily photoperiod was a fundamental factor in determining the time of molt, the type of plumage, and probably the activity of the gonads.

Observations on the breeding season of birds transported from the Tropics or Southern Hemisphere to northern latitudes (Baker and Ranson, 1938) show that some tropical species change the time of their breeding season to correspond with the seasons in the Northern Hemisphere. For the tropical species that do not change it has been suggested that they have an internal rhythm which is not readily altered by environmental conditions. Another possible explanation is that the day length requirements of these species is such that the time of the breeding season in relation to the calendar year is not altered. The most detailed observations on the effect of transport on a tropical species are those of Orr (1945). These are especially significant because the species used, Galápagos finches (*Geospiza* sp.) are restricted to the Galápagos Islands. The individuals transported were taken within 60 miles of the equator and shipped to the San Francisco area, where they arrived in April. The normal breeding period in the Galápagos Islands extends from mid-December to April and is correlated with the rainy season, but breeding, to a limited extent, may occur in almost every month of the year. The captive birds in San Francisco bred from March to November inclusive, but the nesting period for most of the captive birds was confined to spring and summer. In this case, as in others cited by Baker, it is probable that day length is the factor responsible for the change in breeding season. Observations on the molt cycle also suggest that it was influenced by day length. When some of the finches were slightly over a year old, they were in a plumage which in the Tropics takes about three years to attain.

A number of other correlations point to a relationship between day length and reproduction in the Tropics. (1) In many tropical species which occur on both sides of the equator the breeding periods in the northern and southern populations are correlated with the seasons and, hence, occur at opposite times of the year (Baker, 1938; Chapin, 1932). Frequently this is associated with the wet or dry season, but often it is not. (2) In many groups of birds, and even in a species with wide distribution, clutch size tends to be smaller in the Tropics than in the temperate latitudes (see Lack, 1947, for review). In the domestic fowl, egg laying (which is not homologous with clutch size) is greatly influenced by latitude (Whetham, 1933; Romanoff and Romanoff, 1949). (3) The maximum size of active testes in tropical species is only 8 to 67 times the size of minimum inactive testes, whereas in temperate species it ranges from 267 to 2096 times the minimum size (Moreau *et al.*, 1947).

The gonadal response in experimental juncos and white-throated sparrows simulated some of the correlations between latitude and reproductive activity. Birds subjected to 20-hr photoperiods achieved breeding condition rapidly, showed a tendency toward larger and more active gonads, and exhibited maximal activity for only a short period. Juncos held at 12-hr photoperiods achieved breeding condition at a slower rate, showed a tendency toward smaller and less active gonads, remained sexually active for long periods of time, and demonstrated a tendency toward larger testes in the regressed condition.

During the last few years additional studies have been made of breeding cycles in the Tropics, a few experiments have been performed, and the effect of external factors, particularly drought and rainfall, on reproduction has been studied (Keast and Marshall, 1954; Marshall and Disney, 1956, 1957; Miller, 1954a,b; Serventy and Marshall, 1957).

Miller has shown that in the uniform environment of the Magdalena Basin in Colombia (3°12′ N. Lat.) 8 out of 10 species studied showed acyclic and uncoordinated breeding; two species showed coordinated and cyclic breeding. All the species showed "evidence of possessing the same innate mechanism basic to cyclic breeding as north temperate species. This consists of need for rest, or assumption of a refractory state, and a basic tendency to progressive recrudescence." Miller regards these physiological attributes, and the fact that young passerines are able to breed at ages of 4 to 9 months, as the only known elements to be thought of as an inherent rhythm. He regards day length, or light stimuli, as sufficient to surpass threshold needs in the innate mechanism, and as a regulator of the duration of refractoriness, rate of recrudescence, and duration of breeding condition.

In the cyclic species, he suggests that other stimuli also come into play to retard or advance the phases of the innate rhythmic tendencies. (It is also possible that these species differ from the acyclic species in their response to photoperiods and dark periods.) Miller's data and interpretations are in general agreement with the hypothesis and interpretations put forth earlier (Wolfson, 1952a) and elaborated in this paper.

Marshall and Disney (1956) have tested the response of an equatorial bird, *Quelea quelea,* to increased photoperiods. One experimental group received 5 min of light daily at dusk; the other received an additional 5 hr of light. Treatment was given for eight weeks. The birds which received only 5 min additional per day failed to respond, whereas the birds receiving an additional 5 hr per day responded. On the basis of the data presented in this preliminary paper, the response appears to be slight. The authors state that the results give no support to Wolfson's summation hypothesis, but they have misunderstood the hypothesis. Many more experimental data are needed to test the hypothesis for this species. For example, no data are given on the existence or duration of the preparatory phase. From their results, it seems possible that the birds had not yet completed the preparatory phase. Other information is also needed: What is the effective *daily* photoperiod or dark period during the preparatory and progressive phases? Is there any relation between the daily photoperiod or the daily dark period and *the rate of response* in these same phases?

Keast and Marshall (1954) have made extensive studies of reproduction and breeding seasons in relation to drought and rainfall and found that the gonads may remain inactive for a succession of seasons during a prolonged drought. Desert species can respond quickly to rainfall, or its effects, and nesting may begin within a few days of heavy precipitation, irrespective of day length and light increment. Marshall and Disney (1957) on the basis of an experimental study of the induction of the breeding season in a xerophilous species concluded that an internal rhythm of reproduction exists which is modifiable by external conditions, including possibly rainfall and social stimulation. They state that it is unlikely that the breeding seasons of truly equatorial vertebrates are controlled by photoperiodicity, and that many equatorial and other species have evolved a reproductive response to rainfall or its effects. Too few data are presented in this preliminary report to evaluate their conclusions with respect to the effect of rainfall on reproduction. In a field study Serventy and Marshall (1957) demonstrated a widespread reproductive response to precipitation, or its effects, in wild birds in western Australia during abnormally wet autumn periods.

In summary, the relation between day length and the gonadal cycle in tropical species is not known, but the point that must be emphasized is that day length cannot be ruled out a priori as a fundamental regulator of migration and breeding cycles in the Tropics simply because it is relatively constant. In a similar vein, day length cannot be ruled out at other latitudes, because not all birds are breeding when the days are increasing, or because the gonads begin their growth phase when the day lengths are decreasing or relatively constant.

When day length is suggested as a regulatory factor at all latitudes, it is not meant to imply that all birds will react to it in precisely the same manner.

On the basis of the more recent findings presented in this paper, it is clear that the day length conditions in the Tropics could regulate the gonadal cycles in a variety of ways, and it is not reasonable to think of light only in relation to the progressive phase. Our experiments indicate that day length not only regulates the time of initiation of the progressive phase of the testis, but also the rate and amplitude of the progressive phase, the duration of maximum activity, the time of initiation, rate, and extent of regression, and the duration of the preparatory phase. There is no reason to believe that all these aspects will be regulated by day length in precisely the same manner in all species. Nor must all these aspects be regulated by day length. Regulation of a few is all that is needed for day length to be a primary factor in the timing of breeding seasons. It should be recalled that races of the same North Temperate species responded differently to identical experimental conditions of day length. When tropical species have been studied experimentally as intensively as North Temperate species, they will surely show differences in their response to light and dark periods. Moreover, other environmental factors, such as rainfall, diet, and psychic factors, may prove to be important, with different degrees of effectiveness, in modification of the preparatory, progressive, and regressive phases. Only day length has been shown so far to be a primary regulatory factor, and its relation to gametogenesis and reproductive rhythmicity in tropical species remains to be determined by extensive experimental studies.

REFERENCES

Baker, J. R. 1938. The relation between latitude and breeding seasons in birds. *Proc. Zool. Soc. London, A108,* 557–82.

Baker, J. R., and R. M. Ranson. 1938. The breeding seasons of southern hemisphere birds in the northern hemisphere. *Proc. Zool. Soc. London, A108,* 101–41.

Bartholomew, G. A. 1949. The effect of light intensity and day length on reproduction in the English sparrow. *Bull. Museum Comp. Zool. Harvard Univ., 101,* 433–76.

Bissonnette, T. H. 1937. Photoperiodicity in birds. *Wilson Bull., 49,* 241–70.

Blanchard, B. D. 1941. The white-crowned sparrows (*Zonotrichia leucophrys*) of the Pacific seaboard: environment and annual cycle. *Univ. Calif. Publs. Zool., 46,* 1–178.

Blanchard, B. D., and M. M. Erickson. 1949. The cycle in the Gambel sparrow. *Univ. Calif. Publs. Zool., 47,* 255–318.

Brown, F. A., Jr., and M. Rollo. 1940. Light and molt in weaver finches. *Auk, 57,* 485–98.

Burger, J. W. 1939a. On the relative roles of increased and constant periods of illumination in the sexual photoperiodic activation of the male starling. *J. Exptl. Zool., 80,* 249–57.

———. 1939b. Some aspects of the roles of light intensity and the daily length of exposure to light in the sexual photoperiodic activation of the male starling. *J. Exptl. Zool., 81,* 333–41.

———. 1940. Further studies on the relation of the daily exposure to light to the sexual activation of the male starling (*Sturnus vulgaris*). *J. Exptl. Zool., 84,* 350–61.

———. 1947. On the relation of day-length to the phases of testicular involution and inactivity of the spermatogenetic cycle of the starling. *J. Exptl. Zool., 105,* 259–67.

———. 1949. A review of experimental investigations on seasonal reproduction in birds. *Wilson Bull., 61,* 211–30.

———. 1953. The effect of photic and psychic stimuli on the reproductive cycle of the male starling, *Sturnus vulgaris. J. Exptl., Zool., 124,* 227–39.

Burger, J. W., T. H. Bissonnette, and H. D. Doolittle. 1942. Some effects of flashing light on testicular activation in the male starling (*Sturnus vulgaris*). *J. Exptl. Zool., 90,* 73–82.

Chapin, J. P. 1932. The birds of the Belgian Congo, Pt. I. *Bull. Am. Museum Nat. Hist., 65.*

Damsté, P. H. 1947. Experimental modification of the sexual cycle of the greenfinch. *J. Exptl. Biol., 24,* 20–35.

Eyster, M. B. 1954. Quantitative measurement of the influence of photoperiod, temperature and season on the activity of captive song birds. *Ecol. Monographs, 24,* 1–28.

Farner, D. S. 1955. The annual stimulus for migration: experimental and physiologic aspects. *Recent Studies in Avian Biology,* A. Wolfson, Editor, University of Illinois Press, Urbana, Ill., pp. 198–237.

Farner, D. S., L. R. Mewaldt, and S. D. Irving. 1953a. The roles of darkness and light in the activation of avian gonads with increased daily photoperiods. *Science, 118,* 351–52.

———. 1953b. The roles of darkness and light in the photoperiodic response of the testes of white-crowned sparrows. *Biol. Bull., 105,* 434–41.

Farner, D. S., and A. C. Wilson. 1957. A quantitative examination of testicular growth in the white-crowned sparrow. *Biol. Bull., 113,* 254–67.

Jenner, C. E., and W. L. Engels. 1952. The significance of the dark period in the photoperiodic response of male juncos and white-throated sparrows. *Biol. Bull., 103,* 345–55.

Keast, J. A., and A. J. Marshall. 1954. The influence of drought and rainfall on reproduction in Australian desert birds. *Proc. Zool. Soc. London, 124,* 493–99.

Kirkpatrick, C. M. 1955. Factors in photoperiodism of bobwhite quail. *Physiol. Zoöl., 28,* 255–64.

Kirkpatrick, C. M., and A. C. Leopold. 1952. The role of darkness in sexual activity of the quail. *Science, 116,* 280–81.

———. 1953. Photoperiodicity in animals: the role of darkness. *Science, 117,* 389–91.

Lack, D. 1947. The significance of clutch-size. *Ibis, 89,* 302–52; *90:* 25–45.

———. 1950a. Breeding seasons in the Galápagos. *Ibis, 92,* 268–78.

———. 1950b. The breeding seasons of European birds. *Ibis, 92,* 288–316.

Marshall, A. J. 1951. The refractory period of testis rhythm in birds and its possible bearing on breeding and migration. *Wilson Bull., 63,* 238–61.

———. 1955. Reproduction in birds: the male. *Mem. Soc. Endocrinol., 4,* 75–93.

Marshall, A. J., and H. J. deS. Disney. 1956. Photostimulation of an equatorial bird (*Quelea quelea*, Linnaeus). *Nature, 177,* 143–44.

———. 1957. Experimental induction of the breeding season in a xerophilous bird. *Nature, 180,* 647–49.

Miller, A. H. 1948. The refractory period in light-induced reproductive development of golden-crowned sparrows. *J. Exptl. Zool., 109,* 1–11.

———. 1951. Further evidence on the refractory period in the reproductive cycle of the golden-crowned sparrow. *Auk, 68,* 381–83.

———. 1954a. Breeding cycles in a constant equatorial environment in Colombia, South America. *Acta XI Congr. Intern. Ornithologici, Basel,* 495–503.

———. 1954b. The occurrence and maintenance of the refractory period in crowned sparrows. *Condor, 56,* 13–20.

———. 1955. The expression of innate reproductive rhythm under conditions of winter lighting. *Auk, 72,* 260–64.

Miyazaki, H. 1934. On the relation of the daily period to the sexual maturity and to the moulting of *Zosterops palpebrosa japonica. Sci. Repts. Tohoku Imp. Univ., 4th Ser., Biol., 9,* 183–203.

Moreau, R. E. 1950. The breeding seasons of African birds. 1. Land birds. 2. Sea birds. *Ibis, 92,* 223–67; 419–33.

Moreau, R. E., A. L. Wilk, and W. Rowan. 1947. The moult and gonad cycles of three species of birds at five degrees south of the equator. *Proc. Zool. Soc. London, 117,* 345–64.

Orr, R. T. 1945. A study of captive Galápagos finches of the genus *Geospiza. Condor, 47,* 177–201.

Rollo, M., and L. V. Domm. 1943. Light requirements of the weaver finch. 1. Light period and intensity. *Auk, 60,* 357–67.

Romanoff, A. L., and A. J. Romanoff. 1949. *The Avian Egg.* Wiley, New York.

Rowan, W. 1925. Relation of light to bird migration and developmental changes. *Nature, 115,* 494–95.

———. 1929. Experiments in bird migration. I. Manipulation of the reproduc- *Hist. Soc., 39,* 151–208.

tive cycle: seasonal histological changes in the gonads. *Proc. Boston Nat*

————. 1932. Experiments in bird migration. III. The effects of artificial light, castration and certain extracts on the autumn movement of the American crow (*Corvus brachyrhynchos*). *Proc. Natl. Acad. Sci. U. S., 18,* 639–54.

Serventy, D. L., and A. J. Marshall. 1957. Breeding periodicity in Western Australian birds: with an account of unseasonal nestings in 1953 and 1955. *Emu, 57,* 99–126.

Skutch, A. F. 1950. The nesting seasons of Central American birds in relation to climate and food supply. *Ibis, 92,* 185–222.

Thomson, A. L. 1950. Factors determining the breeding seasons of birds: an introductory review. *Ibis, 92,* 173–84.

Voous, K. H. 1950. The breeding seasons of birds in Indonesia. *Ibis, 92,* 279–87.

Wagner, H. O., and E. Stresemann. 1950. Über die Beziehungen zwischen Brutzeit und Ökologie mexikanischer Vögel. *Zool. Jahrb., 79,* 273–308.

Weise, C. M. 1956. Nightly unrest in caged migratory sparrows under outdoor conditions. *Ecology, 37,* 275–87.

Whetham, E. O. 1933. Factors modifying egg production with special reference to seasonal changes. *J. Agr. Sci., 23,* 383–418.

Winn, H. S. 1950. Effects of different photoperiods on body weight, fat deposition, molt, and male gonadal growth in the slate-colored junco. Doctoral dissertation, Northwestern University, Evanston, Ill.

Wolfson, A. 1940. A preliminary report on some experiments on bird migration. *Condor, 42,* 93–99.

————. 1942. Regulation of spring migration in juncos. *Condor, 44,* 237–63.

————. 1945. The role of the pituitary, fat deposition, and body weight in bird migration. *Condor, 47,* 95–127.

————. 1947. Summation of day lengths versus increasing day lengths as the external stimulus for gonadal recrudescence and fat deposition in migratory birds. *Anat. Record, 99,* 89.

————. 1952a. Day length, migration, and breeding cycles in birds. *Sci. Monthly, 74,* 191–200.

————. 1952b. The occurrence and regulation of the refractory period in the gonadal and fat cycles of the junco. *J. Exptl. Zool., 121,* 311–26.

————. 1952c. The cloacal protuberance—a means for determining breeding condition in live male passerines. *Bird-Banding, 23,* 159–65.

————. 1953. Gonadal and fat response to a 5:1 ratio of light to darkness in the white-throated sparrow. *Condor, 55,* 187–92.

————. 1954. Production of repeated gonadal, fat, and molt cycles within one year in the junco and white-crowned sparrow by manipulation of day length. *J. Exptl. Zool., 125,* 353–76.

————. 1955. Absence of a refractory period in the gonadal cycle of juncos exposed to 20-hour photoperiods. *Anat. Record, 122,* 454–55.

Wolfson, A., and H. S. Winn. 1948. Summation of day lengths as the external stimulus for photoperiodic responses in birds. *Anat. Record, 101,* 70–71.

PHOTOPERIODIC CONTROL OF ANNUAL GONADAL CYCLES IN BIRDS

DONALD S. FARNER
State College of Washington, Pullman

This discussion is concerned primarily with photoperiodic controls of the annual gonadal cycles of certain Temperate Zone species of birds. Because of the investigations in our laboratories, special attention will be directed at times toward the cycle of a migratory race of white-crowned sparrow, *Zonotrichia leuchophrys gambelii.** This emphasis gives the advantages of direct knowledge and availability of illustrative material. Nevertheless, very extensive use will be made of the results of other investigations on different species, for the advantages of both comparison and completeness. This will have the effect of creating a composite picture of many aspects of the phenomenon. It must be borne in mind that the creation of such composite pictures is somewhat hazardous since it is probable that photoperiodic control mechanisms among birds may be polyphyletic in origin and that there may be basic differences among the control mechanisms of various species. This discussion, except for a few comparisons which appear appropriate, will not consider the mechanism of the photoperiodically induced increase in egg production in the domestic fowl. This decision is made not only because photoperiodism in the female domestic fowl is the subject of another paper in this symposium, but also because this mechanism in a domestic species of essentially tropical origin may be only superficially similar to that of Temperate Zone wild species.

It must be borne in mind constantly that, for the species under consideration, the gonadal cycle obviously is only one of a complex of

* These investigations have been supported by the Office of Naval Research, Contract Nonr 1520(00), and by funds made available for biological and medical research by the State of Washington Initiative Measure No. 171. I wish to acknowledge with sincere gratitude the invaluable contributions of L. R. Mewaldt, Andreas Oksche, J. R. King, A. C. Wilson, Donald Laws, R. D. McGreal, S. D. Irving, and Conrad A. Donovan.

717

interrelated annual cycles all of which are probably photoperiodically timed in one way or another. Among these cycles are an annual metabolic cycle, which is expressed patently in premigratory fat deposition, and the migratory cycle itself. Our knowledge of the control of these two cycles has been summarized by Wallgren (1954), Farner (1955), Weise (1956), Wagner (1956), Rautenberg (1957), and King (1957). Unquestionably also the molting cycle is photoperiodically controlled although perhaps quite indirectly. At present it appears not possible to construct a satisfactory rational hypothesis for a control system.

Of the photoperiodically controlled annual cycles, the gonadal cycles, and, more particularly, the testicular cycles have received the greatest attention and are consequently best understood. The seasonal cycle in avian testicular size was apparently known to Aristotle (Etzold, 1891; Disselhorst, 1908). More than a half century ago Etzold (1891) and Schäfer (1907) suggested a possible functional relation between day length and the vernal testicular development. In a practical way, however, photoperiodic control of testicular cycles was actually practiced artificially in very early times in the Netherlands (Damsté, 1947) and in Japan (Miyazaki, 1934) in order to obtain unseasonal singing in males. The pioneer investigations, however, were those of Rowan (1925, 1926, 1938b) with *Junco hyemalis* and those of Bissonnette (1930, 1931a) with *Sturnus vulgaris*. Since these early studies sufficient information has been accumulated to indicate that photoperiodic controls of gonadal cycles must be operative in at least 27 species among 12 families of birds (Table I). Among the more recent reviews of this phenomenon are those of Burger (1949), Galgano and Mazzi (1951), Hammond (1954), and Aschoff (1955).

NATURE OF TESTICULAR GROWTH

It has been possible to develop a more satisfactory quantitative approach in our investigations with *Zonotrichia leucophrys gambelii* by recognizing the form of the growth curve of the testes (Farner and Wilson, 1957a,b). When males are subjected to constant daily photoperiods of stimulatory duration, the testes increase in weight approxi-

TABLE I.   Some Species in Which Photoperiodic Stimulation of Gonadal Development Has Been Demonstrated Experimentally

Species	Sex	Reference
Anatidae		
Anas platyrhynchos	♂	Walton (1937)
Domestic ducks—Rouen, Pekin	♂, ♀	Benoit (1934, 1935g, 1936a, 1950a,b); Benoit and Assenmacher (1953a,b); etc.
Tetraonidae		
Bonasa umbellus	♂, ♀	Clark *et al.* (1936, 1937)
Phasianidae		
Colinus virginianus virginianus	♂, ♀	Clark *et al.* (1936); Bissonnette and Csech (1936, 1937); Glass and Potter (1944); Kirkpatrick and Leopold (1952); Baldini *et al.* (1954); Kirkpatrick (1955)
Phasianus colchicus	♂, ♀	Clark *et al.* (1936, 1937); Bissonnette and Csech (1936, 1937)
Columbidae		
Zenaidura macroura carolinensis	♂, ♀	Cole (1933)
Corvidae		
Cyanocitta cristata	♂, ♀	Bissonnette (1939)
Corvus brachyrhynchos	♂	Rowan (1932)
Turdidae		
Phoenicurus phoenicurus	♂	Schildmacher (1938a,b)
Erithacus rubecula	♂	Schildmacher (1937, 1938a,b); Putzig (1937, 1938)
Sylviidae		
Sylvia atricapilla	♂	Schildmacher (1939)
Prunellidae		
Prunella modularis		Vaugien (1948)
Sturnidae		
Sturnus vulgaris	♂, ♀	Bissonnette (1930, 1932, 1933, etc.); Bissonnette and Wadlund (1931)
Zosteropidae		
Zosterops japonica	♂, ♀	Miyazaki (1934); Kobayashi (1954c)
Ploceidae		
Passer domesticus	♂, ♀	Kirschbaum (1933); Riley (1936); Ringoen and Kirschbaum (1937); Riley and Witschi (1938); Polikarpova (1940); Vaugien (1948); Bartholomew (1949)
Passer montanus		Vaugien (1948)

TABLE I (Continued)

Species	Sex	Reference
Fringillidae		
Fringilla coelebs		Vaugien (1948)
Pyrrhula rubicilla		Vaugien (1948)
Serinus canaria	♂, ♀	Takewaki and Mori (1944); Vaugien (1948); Kobayashi (1954c)
Carduelis elegans	♂, ♀	Vaugien (1948, 1956a,b)
Chloris chloris	♂	Damsté (1947); Schildmacher (1956)
Loxia curvirostra		Schildmacher and Rautenberg (1953)
Junco hyemalis	♂, ♀	Rowan (1925, 1926, 1938); Wolfson (1952a, 1953); Jenner and Engels (1952); Engels and Jenner (1956)
Junco oreganus oreganus		Wolfson (1942)
Junco oreganus shufeldti	♂	Wolfson (1942)
Junco oreganus thurberi	♂	Wolfson (1942)
Junco oreganus pinosus	♂	Wolfson (1942)
Zonotrichia leucophrys leucophrys	♂	Wolfson (1954)
Zonotrichia leucophrys gambelii	♂, ♀	Farner and Mewaldt (1952, 1953); Wolfson (1945)
Zonotrichia leucophrys pugetensis	♂	Wolfson (1945); Bailey (1950)
Zonotrichia leucophrys nuttalli		Wolfson (1942, 1945)
Zonotrichia atricapilla	♂	Miller (1948, 1949, 1951, 1954); Wolfson (1945)
Passerella iliaca		Wolfson (1945)
Melospiza melodia		Wolfson (1945)

mately as a logarithmic growth curve from resting weight (2 mg or less) to about 200 mg (maximum weight is about 600 mg). Thus,

$$\log_{10} W_t + \log_{10} W_0 + kt \qquad (1)$$

where W_0 is the initial testicular weight in milligrams and W_t is the weight after t days (Fig. 1). For photoperiods of the same duration, k for first-year birds is about 1.16 times as great as for adults. W_0 for first-year birds is about 0.7 mg whereas it is about 2 mg for adults.

Since equation (1) represents a fairly close approximation of testicular growth as a function of time, the rate constant k is useful in comparing birds subjected to various photoperiodic treatments. For example, it is of importance (Farner and Wilson, 1957b) to examine k as a function of the length of the daily photoperiod (p) (Fig. 2). It is to be noted that for values of p from about 9.5 to 18 hr, k

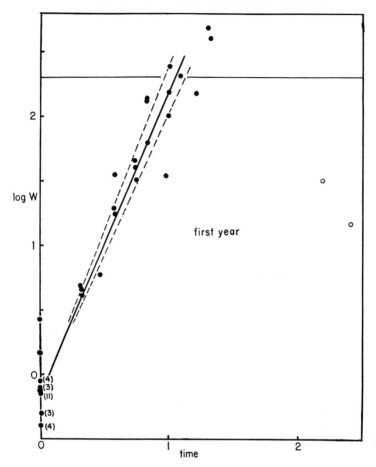

FIG. 1. Combined testicular weights (W) of first-year *Zonotrichia leucophrys gambelii* as a function of time with constant daily photoperiods of stimulatory duration. Time is in arbitrary units. Closed circles represent developing testes; open circles represent regressing testes. (From Farner and Wilson, 1957b.)

approximates a linear function of p. The nature of the relationship between k and p for values of p less than about 9.5 hr is uncertain. When $p = 8$, k must be very close to zero; however, the normal variation in resting testicular weights makes an exact evaluation impossible. It must be remembered, however, that k is a logarithmic rate constant and consequently that daily testicular growth increments for values of

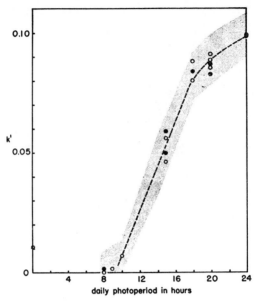

F IG. 2. The rate of testicular development as a function of the daily photoperiod in *Zonotrichia leucophrys gambelii*. See equation (1) for definition of rate constant, *k*. Open circles represent samples of first-year birds; closed circles represent adjusted means for samples of adults. Light intensity is supramaximal. (From Farner and Wilson, 1957b.)

k approaching zero are almost negligible. However, the nature of the lower tail of the curve in Fig. 2 does have obvious theoretical interest and should be subjected to further investigation. The linear portion of the curve in Fig. 2 may be approximated by

$$k_{\text{1st yr.}} = 0.009(p - 9.1) \tag{2}$$

It would be of substantial interest to examine other species with respect to the functional relationships between W_t and t as well as between p and k. The data of Winn (1950) for *Junco hyemalis*, although somewhat more variable than those for *Zonotrichia leucophrys gambelii*, suggest a conformance with equation (1). The same is possibly true for those of Burger (1948) for *Sturnus vulgaris*. Our own analysis of the data for *Passer domesticus* from Bartholomew (1949), Vaugien (1952a,b), and Farner and Wilson (unpublished) indicates a conformance with equation (1) and further that k as a function of p is similar to that illustrated in Fig. 2 except that the slope may be slightly steeper and is displaced somewhat to the left.

PHOTOPERIODICALLY INDUCED TESTICULAR DEVELOPMENT AS A FUNCTION OF LIGHT INTENSITY

In his early investigation of photoperiodism in *Sturnus vulgaris,* Bissonnette (1931b) found that the rate of testicular development was a positive function of light intensity (white light from incandescent lamps) for intensities up to about 180 lux (16.5 ft-c). For the same species Burger (1939) demonstrated nicely that increasing intensity from about 50 to about 2000 lux (5 to 190 ft-c) is non-stimulatory if the length of the photoperiod is too short. In other words, the requirement of a day length above a certain minimum cannot be replaced simply by increasing intensity of periods of subliminal duration. Bartholomew (1949) has studied carefully with *Passer domesticus* the role of intensity (white light from fluorescent lamps) in the rate of testicular development. In winter an intensity of 0.4 lux (0.04 ft-c) was very slightly effective. A greater rate of response was obtained at 110 lux (10.3 ft-c) than at 7.5 lux (0.7 ft-c) whereas the rate was not increased further by increasing intensity to 2600 lux (244 ft-c). Kirkpatrick (1955) found that the rate of photoperiodic testicular response in *Colinus virginianus* (17-hr daily photoperiods with incandescent lamps) was probably maximum at intensities as low as 1 lux (0.1 ft-c). However, the time required by females to produce the first egg appears to be an inverse function of intensity up to at least 3200 lux (300 ft-c). In our laboratory the rate of testicular development in *Zonotrichia leucophrys gambelii* has been studied as a function of light intensity (white light from incandescent lamps). In winter it was found that the rate constant k of equation (1) was greater at 31 lux (3.0 ft-c) than at 11 lux (1.0 ft-c) but that there was no appreciable increase in k for intensities up to 375 lux (35 ft-c). Intensities lower than 11 lux could not be used since the birds could not be trained to feed in such dim light. The functional relationship between k and intensity for low intensities must therefore be explored by means of another approach.

By way of comparison, it is of interest to note that our rate-intensity curve for *Zonotrichia leucophrys gambelii* is somewhat similar to that for egg production in the domestic fowl in which no appreciable increase was obtained by increasing intensity from 10 lux (1 ft-c) to 330 lux (30 ft-c) (Roberts and Carver, 1941).

As Burger (1949) has aptly observed, it is essential that studies of the role of light intensity be refined by use of monochromatic or narrow-band light. This is particularly important in view of the differences in response to different parts of the visible spectrum.

PHOTOPERIODICALLY INDUCED TESTICULAR DEVELOPMENT AS A FUNCTION OF WAVELENGTH

The early investigations of Bissonnette (1932b,c,d, 1933a,b, 1936, 1937; Bissonnette and Wadlund, 1931) demonstrated clearly for *Sturnus vulgaris* that red light stimulates testicular development whereas green light is ineffective. Burger's (1943) investigations with the same species demonstrated a good response in the range of 0.58 to 0.68 micron and that far red and near infrared are nonstimulatory. Similarly, red has been found to be effective and green ineffective in gonadal stimulation in *Passer domesticus* (Ringoen, 1942) and in the domestic turkey (Scott and Payne, 1937).

In the domestic fowl, at supramaximal intensities, red light is as effective as white light in maintaining high egg production (Roberts and Carver, 1941). In domestic ducks also it is red light that is most effective in stimulating testicular development (Benoit 1936b, 1938a) with the range of maximum effectiveness being about 0.60 to 0.74 micron (Benoit and Ott, 1938, 1944; Benoit, 1950b; Benoit, Walter, and Assenmacher, 1950a, b). It is very important to note that when testicular development is stimulated by conducting light directly to the hypothalamus, yellow, green, and blue are effective; the implications of this will be discussed subsequently. Suffice it to note here that these investigations suggest that photostimulation of gonadal development does not involve entirely the same receptors as are involved in vision; possibly the receptors may be entirely distinct and quite possibly they are, at least in part, nonocular (Benoit, 1950b).

EFFECT OF INTERRUPTED LIGHT IN PHOTOPERIODICALLY
INDUCED TESTICULAR DEVELOPMENT

It has been demonstrated in domestic ducks (Benoit, 1936a), *Sturnus vulgaris* (Burger, Bissonnette, and Doolittle, 1942), *Colinus virginianus* (Kirkpatrick and Leopold, 1952; Kirkpatrick, 1955), *Junco hyemalis* (Jenner and Engels, 1952), and *Zonotrichia leucophrys gambelii* (Farner, Mewaldt, and Irving, 1953a,b) that a given total duration of light becomes more effective in stimulating testicular development if it is broken into shorter periods. In general the effectiveness appears to increase as the duration of the intervening dark periods is reduced. In all these experiments, although comparisons of rates cannot always be made accurately, it appears that the rate of response rarely, if ever, exceeds that of a continuous light period equal in duration to the experimental light periods plus the intervening dark period(s), a relationship of fundamental importance in the interpretation of the effects of interrupted light.

The recognition of the logarithmic nature of testicular growth in *Zonotrichia leucophrys gambelii* has permitted a more precise examination of the interrupted-light phenomenon by comparisons of the values for k of equation (2) for a wide variety of photoperiodic treatments (Farner and Wilson, 1957a, and unpublished data). In Fig. 3 it is readily apparent that 6 hr of light (incandescent lamps, supramaximal intensity) in equally spaced 50-min photoperiods causes the same rate of testicular development as a single daily photoperiod of about 12 hr. These investigations also show clearly that the effectiveness of very short photoperiods is a function of the intervening dark period. Thus 2-sec flashes with 15-min intervening dark periods are ineffective, whereas 2-sec flashes with either 58-sec or 8-sec dark intervals give near maximum values for k. Similarly, with intervening dark periods of 15 min, 2-sec light flashes, as noted above, are ineffective, whereas 20-sec light periods give near maximum values of k.

These and other data (Farner and Wilson, unpublished) lead us to the hypothesis that somewhere in the response mechanism there is a rate-limiting reaction which, during the light period, produces very rapidly a substance which is essential for the photoperiodic response and that during the dark period this essential substance decays at a rate much slower than its rate of formation so that the stimulation of testicular development persists temporarily after the end of the photoperiod. We (Farner, Mewaldt, and Irving, 1953a,b) have referred to this period of continued effect during the dark as the "carry-over period." Our data require the assumption that k is effectively a positive function of the concentration of the hypothetical

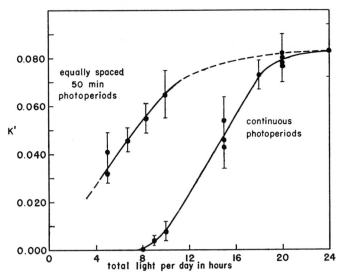

FIG. 3.   A comparison of the rates of testicular development for single daily photoperiods and equally spaced 50-min photoperiods in first-year *Zonotrichia leucophrys gambelii*. See equation (1) for definition of rate constant, k. Light intensity is supramaximal.

substance only up to a concentration somewhat lower than equilibrium concentration during the photoperiod. The data suggest that a period of the order of a minute is required for the process to go from dark concentration to equilibrium concentration of the photoperiod, and that the time required for the substance to decay back to minimum dark concentration is of the order of a few hours (Farner and Wilson, 1957a). This hypothesis, which has value in considering the nature of the response mechanism and in the design of experiments, is consistent with all the data from a wide variety of photoperiodic treatments of *Zonotrichia leucophrys gambelii*. It appears to be consistent with the data from the above-cited experiments of other investigators with interrupted light as well as with the results of similar investigations with egg production in the domestic fowl (Dobie, Carver, and Roberts, 1946; Staffe, 1950, 1951; Weber, 1951; Wilson and Abplanalp, 1956).

It is to be emphasized that our hypothesis assigns no positive role to the dark periods either in experimental patterns involving interrupted light or to night under natural conditions. To us it appears at this time unnecessary to assume that there is a critically important dark-dependent phase (Jenner and Engels, 1952), particularly in view of the fact that no pattern of interrupted light gives a greater response than continuous light over the same period. Likewise, although some semantic difficulties may be involved, it appears unnecessary to assign an inhibitory role to darkness (Kirkpatrick and Leopold, 1952) despite the attractiveness of the analogy with long-day plants. Rather it would seem more in keeping with the Law of Parsimony simply to regard the dark period as one in which there is no active light effect and that the photoperiodic effect is a function only of the light periods.

MECHANISM OF THE PHOTOPERIODIC TESTICULAR RESPONSE

Rowan (1928, 1929) reached the conclusion, from experiments with *Junco hyemalis,* that testicular development is caused by exercise resulting from the increased light rather than by light per se. However, experiments with several other species, including *Sturnus vulgaris* (Bissonnette, 1932a; Burger, Bissonnette, and Doolittle, 1942; Burger, 1943, 1949), *Passer domesticus* (Riley, 1940; Kendeigh, 1941), *Zonotrichia leucophrys gambelii* (Farner and Mewaldt, 1953, 1955a), and domestic ducks (Benoit, 1935a; Benoit and Ott, 1944) fail to sustain this hypothesis. The suggestions of wakefulness caused by light (Rowan, 1937, 1938a,b; Wolfson, 1941), rather than light per se, as the cause of testicular development present rather formidable semantic difficulties so that further discussion of them appears fruitless at present.

Although there can be little doubt that it is light per se, or rather orange-red light per se, which causes the photoperiodically induced testicular development, there is far less certainty concerning the identity and nature of the receptors involved. As indicated above, the band of effective wavelengths indicates that the receptors probably can be no more than part of those involved in vision and that some nonocular receptors may be involved. It is of interest to note here that in the domestic duck the pupillary reflex has a maximum response in the yellow, whereas the photoperiodic testicular response has a maximum sensitivity to red-orange (Benoit, Assenmacher, and Walter, 1952). It is evident from the experiments of Ringoen and Kirschbaum (1937, 1939) with *Passer domesticus* and those of Benoit (1934) with domestic ducks that the receptors must be in the ocular region. Benoit and his colleagues subsequently attacked the problem of photoreception in an extensive series of experiments which show quite unequivocally that both ocular and extra-ocular reception are involved. That ocular receptors are involved is clearly evident from comparison of responses of birds with sectioned optic nerves and intact birds to a weak source of light (Benoit and Assenmacher, 1953b; Benoit, Assenmacher, and Walter, 1953). Beginning in 1935 (Benoit, 1935e,f,h), by means of extraordinarily ingenious and interesting experiments with domestic ducks, Benoit and his colleagues have demonstrated photoreception in the hypothalamus and rhinencephalon. (See Benoit 1936a, 1937, 1950b; Benoit and Ott, 1944; and Benoit and Assenmacher, 1953a, for general reviews and descriptions of these experiments.) The encephalic sites of photoreception have been detected by conducting light with fine quartz rods and glass tubes (Benoit, Walter, and Assenmacher, 1950a,b). Evidence to support the natural feasibility of encephalic reception was obtained by demonstrating that appreciable quantities of light penetrate to the brain via the orbit of the intact bird (Benoit, Assenmacher, and Manuel, 1952, 1953; Benoit, Tauc, and Assenmacher, 1954a,b). Of particular significance in these experiments is the much greater penetration of red light as compared with green and blue, although the latter are stimulatory if they actually reach the surface of the hypothalamus (Benoit, Walter, and Assenmacher, 1950a). These data have fundamental significance in view of the functional relationship between wavelength and testicular response as noted previously.

It is obvious then, at least in domestic ducks, that both ocular and encephalic receptors are involved in photostimulated testicular development. It appears obvious also (Benoit and Assenmacher, 1953b, 1954a, 1955) that for equal intensities of light, the encephalic receptors may be more sensitive. In view of the fact that in the intact animal they would be subjected to lower intensities, it is not possible at present to designate quantitatively the possible relative roles of the two groups of receptors.

Although a detailed knowledge of the tracts involved is lacking, it is obvious that impulses from the ocular receptors, and presumably also from the hypothalamic receptors, exert an effect on neurosecretory cells of the hypothalamus. A series of experiments with domestic ducks (Assenmacher and Benoit, 1953a,b, 1956; Benoit and Assenmacher, 1954b; 1955) have led to the conclusion that a regulatory material (identical with, or similar in behavior to, the Gomori-positive neurosecretory material) formed by the cells of hypothalamic nuclei passes down the axons of these cells into the median eminence, where at least some of the material passes into the capillaries of the hypothalamo-adenohypophysial portal system, which then transports it to the adenohypophysis. In these experiments it was found that either sectioning the hypothalamo-hypophysial tract above the "special zone" (the zone of contact between the portal capillaries and the loops of the neurosecretory axons), of the median eminence, or sectioning the hypothalamo-adenohypophysial portal system (including insertion of a hard disc to prevent reestablishment of circulation) eliminated the testicular response to photostimulation and caused atrophic changes in the cephalic lobe of the adenohypophysis. On the other hand, in birds with the stalk sectioned below the "special zone," leaving the portal circulation intact, both the photoperiodic testicular response and the cephalic lobe were normal. Shirley and Nalbandov (1956) found marked ovarian atrophy in the domestic fowl after section of the stalk including complete severance of the portal circulation.

Although it is obvious that the photoperiodic testicular response involves neurosecretory cells of the hypothalamus, their axons, and the hypothalamo-adenohypophysial portal system, it must not be assumed that this simply involves an elevated production and trans-

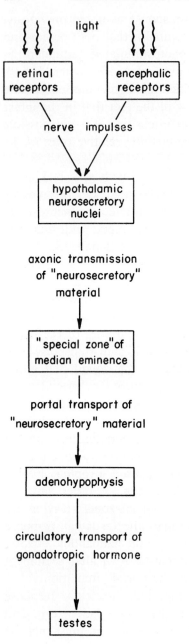

FIG. 4. A schematic representation of the mechanism of photoperiodic stimulation of testicular growth. (Based largely on the investigations of Benoit and colleagues.)

port of Gomori-positive neurosecretory material. Studies of the hypo-thalami of *Zonotrichia leucophrys gambelii* in our laboratory (Oksche, Farner, and Laws, unpublished) with a variety of photoperiodic patterns indicate that the situation must be considerably more com-plex. This is emphasized also by the annual cycle of hypothalamic neurosecretory activity in the domestic fowl (Legait, 1955; Legait and Legait, 1955). If one bears in mind the numerous other regula-tory functions of the hypothalamo-hypophysial system and the as yet incompletely understood relationship between the Gomori-positive neurosecretory material and the active regulatory principle, it is obvious that we are contending with a complex situation which requires much additional investigation.

In the discussion above, it has been indicated, both explicitly and implicitly, that the adenohypophysis is an essential element in the response system. The dependence of gonadal function on the adeno-hypophysis is, of course, general among vertebrates. In birds this has been demonstrated by the marked gonadal atrophy which follows hypophysectomy (see, for example, Hill and Parkes, 1934; Nalbandov and Card, 1943; Nalbandov, Meyer, and McShan, 1946; Frantz, 1954); by failure of hypophysectomized birds to show a photo-periodic testicular response (Benoit, 1936c, 1937); by the demonstra-tion of gonadotropic hormones in avian adenohypophyses (see, Greeley and Meyer, 1953; Breneman, 1955; and many others); and by demonstration of gonadal development following injection of gonadotropins in hypophysectomized or intact birds (see, for example, Schildmacher, 1938a; Miller, 1949; Riley and Witschi, 1938; Udintsev, 1948; and Vaugien, 1955, 1956a,b for examples among passerine species; see Breneman, 1955, for a recent résumé).

Figure 4 summarizes schematically, largely on the basis of the investigations of Benoit and colleagues, the mechanism of the photo-periodic response as we envision it at present.

REFRACTORY STATE OF TESTICULAR PHOTOPERIODIC RESPONSE MECHANISM

It is a common experience among investigators that there is a period following a complete gonadal cycle, either naturally or artificially induced, during which no photoperiodic response can be induced regardless of the length of the daily photoperiod. This phenomenon was noted by Riley (1936) in *Passer domesticus,* and by Schildmacher (1938a) in *Phoenicurus phoenicurus.* The approximate times of the termination of the refractory period for some passerine species under natural conditions are recorded in Table II. Figure 5 gives a more detailed illustration for a single species, *Zonotrichia leucophrys gambelii.* There appears to be little or no information on the natural duration of the refractory period in nonpasserine species. It appears

TABLE II.   Natural Termination of Refractory Period of Passerine Species of Northern Hemisphere (Modified from Farner, 1954)

Species	Area	Termination of the Natural Refractory Period	Reference
Sturnus vulgaris	Connecticut	Before mid-Nov.	Burger, 1949
Passer domesticus	Illinois, Iowa	Between 30 Sept. and mid-Nov.	Riley, 1936, Kendeigh, 1941
Phoenicurus phoenicurus	Germany	Early Nov.	Schildmacher, 1938a, 1939
Serinus canaria	Japan	Early Oct.	Kobayashi, 1954b
Junco hyemalis	Alberta	Late Oct.	Rowan, 1929
Junco hyemalis	Illinois	Mid-Nov.	Wolfson, 1952b
Junco oreganus	California	After mid-Oct.	Wolfson, 1945
Zonotrichia atricapilla	California	Early Nov.	Miller, 1948, 1954
Zonotrichia leucophrys nuttalli	California	Mid-Oct.	Wolfson, 1945; Miller, 1954
Zonotrichia leucophrys pugetensis	California	Mid-Oct.	Wolfson, 1945; Miller, 1954
Zonotrichia leucophrys gambelii	California, Washington	Late Oct.	Miller, 1954; Farner and Mewaldt, 1955

that the multiple cycles obtained in a single year by Miyazaki (1934) with *Zosterops japonica,* by Wolfson (1954) with *Zonotrichia leucophrys* and *Junco hyemalis,* by Damsté (1947) with *Chloris chloris,* and by Burger (1947) with *Sturnus vulgaris* are, in part, attributable to regression resulting from reduction of the daily photoperiod before the development of refractoriness. Interpretations of this sort must be developed with caution, since, at least in some species, the duration of the refractory period is inversely related to the duration of the daily photoperiod (Burger, 1949; Wolfson, 1952b, 1954; Vaugien, 1954b). Apparently also in some species refractoriness will continue indefinitely with long daily photoperiods (Burger, 1947; Miller, 1951, 1954; Wolfson 1952b; Vaugien, 1952a,b). Caution must be exercised in generalizing, however, since Benoit, Assenmacher, and Brard (1956) have shown that drakes kept in continuous light will pass through several testicular cycles with gradually decreasing amplitude but with greater and more irregular frequency.

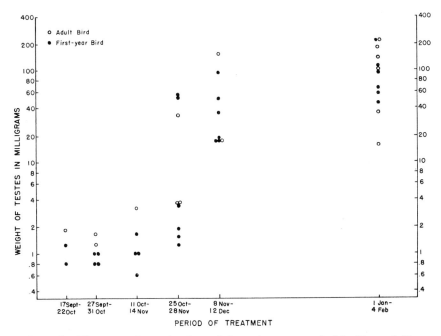

FIG. 5.   The natural termination of the refractory period in *Zonotrichia leucophrys gambelii*. Open circles represent first-year birds. Closed circles represent adults. Birds were tested for refractoriness by subjecting them to 15-hr daily photoperiods of supramaximal light for the periods indicated. (From Farner and Mewaldt, 1955.)

The actual site of refractoriness is still incompletely known. Since the gonads of refractory birds, of at least several species, can be caused to develop by the injection of gonadotropic hormones (Riley and Witschi, 1938; Schildmacher, 1939; Miller, 1949; Vaugien, 1954b, 1955, 1956a; Benoit *et al.*, 1950), it seems evident that the site is not gonadal. In domestic drakes the gonadotropin content of the adenohypophysis is relatively high during the refractory period

(Benoit, Assenmacher, and Walter, 1950b); furthermore (1950a) castration during the refractory period fails to cause hypertrophy of the adenohypophysis and unilateral castration fails to cause the usual hypertrophy of the intact testis. These observations suggest that the site of refractoriness must be at, or above, the level of the hypophysis; possibly it is hypothalamic.

It is of interest to note that in many species the first-year birds are also refractory in late summer and that the refractoriness terminates at about the same time as in the adults. The only well-known exception appears to be that of *Passer domesticus* in which the young become susceptible to photoperiodic gonadal activation earlier in fall (Riley, 1936; Davis, 1953). The question as to whether refractoriness in first-year birds is the same as that of the adults which have completed a gonadal cycle is still unanswered.

The basic cause of refractoriness is likewise still uncertain. Hypotheses involving gonadal feedback mechanisms have been considered, but attempts to obtain experimental support for them have thus far been relatively unsuccessful. In our laboratory we were able to obtain only a partial reduction of the photoperiodic response by testosterone treatment of *Zonotrichia leucophrys gambelii* (Farner and Wilson, unpublished data) and no apparent suppression with progesterone (Laws and Farner, unpublished data). Burger (1949) was similarly unsuccessful in treatment of *Sturnus vulgaris* with testosterone. On the other hand, Kobayashi (1954b) has been able to reduce markedly the photoperiodic responses in *Zosterops japonica* with simultaneous treatment with either testosterone or estradiole. Of very substantial interest is the demonstration by Bailey (1950) of an inhibition of light-induced gonadal development by prolactin in *Zonotrichia leucophrys pugetensis*. Possibly the normal sequence of events in the adenohypophysis following photostimulation is an increased production first of the gonadotropin(s) which stimulate testicular development after which, possibly because of a gonadal feedback mechanism or possibly because of a feedback mechanism operating at the level of the hypothalamus and adenohypophysis, comes an increased production of prolactin which could be responsible, directly or indirectly, not only for the development of incubating and brooding behavior but also for the development of refractoriness. In this conjunction it is also important to note that Lofts and Marshall (1956) have shown that prolactin causes a testicular involution similar to postnuptial metamorphosis in *Passer domesticus, Chloris chloris,* and *Fringilla coelebs.* Hypothetically then, it is possible to see how the sequence in the production of pituitary gonadotropins might cause gonadal development (and thence the reproductive behavior associated with sex hormones), incubating and brooding behavior, development of refractoriness, and regression of the gonads.

In closing the discussion of the refractory period it is necessary to direct attention briefly to the behavior of the testes during the refractory period. During this period (Marshall, 1949a, 1950, 1951, 1952, 1955) there is a fatty degeneration of the tubules and a loss of lipoid materials from the cells of Leydig. The collapsed metamorphosed testis soon forms a new interstitium and tunic and thereafter slowly clears the tubules of debris from necrotic spermatozoa. Marshall has referred to this period as a *refractory period* on the basis of his conclusion, from histologic studies, that at this time the testes cannot be caused to develop. Obviously this *testicular refractory period* of Marshall, although it may occur at the same time as the refractoriness of the photoperiodic response mechanism, must be clearly distinguished from the period of refractoriness of the response mechanism as discussed above. There is a real need for a careful investigation to ascertain experimentally if there is a time in the period of testicular metamorphosis when the testis cannot respond to the gonadotropins from the anterior pituitary.

PHOTOPERIODIC CONTROL OF OVARIAN CYCLES

In general it appears that in those species in which photoperiodic control can be demonstrated for the testicular cycle there is also a photoperiodic control of the ovarian cycle. However, it is certainly the experience of all investigators of passerine species that, although males may be brought into full reproductive state (production of spermatozoa) by simply increasing the daily photoperiod adequately, such treatment alone causes only partial ovarian development. Thus it appears that whereas the daily photoperiod may be the primary timer, other factors are relatively more important and essential than in the male. The investigations of Polikarpova (1940) with *Passer domesticus* and Vaugien (1948) on *Serinus canaria* show that complete sexual development of the females of these species apparently requires photoactivation of the female, the presence of a photoactivated male, nesting material, and nesting site. Burger (1953) has also emphasized the relative importance of psychic factors in the development of female *Sturnus vulgaris*.

EVALUATION OF PHOTOPERIODISM IN CONTROL OF ANNUAL GONADAL CYCLES OF TEMPERATE ZONE SPECIES OF BIRDS

Because of the limitations established earlier for this discussion and also because of the species which have been investigated experimentally, this evaluation will be effected entirely with respect to species which occur at relatively high latitudes. For such species I am definitely of the conviction that the annual vernal increase in day length, together with, in many species, at least, the shorter days of autumn which cause the elimination of refractoriness, constitute the primary timing scheme for the annual gonadal cycles of both sexes. Furthermore, it now appears possible that all the annual cycles in these species are timed, in one way or another, in this way.

I hasten to emphasize that the photoperiodic timer is the *primary* timer and that there are many modifying mechanisms, the relative importances of which may vary greatly among different species. Benoit and Assenmacher (1955) have discussed extensively the various factors and mechanisms which may modify the function of the hypothalamo-hypophysial axis. The role of psychic factors in the sexual development of females (Polikarpova, 1940; Vaugien, 1948; Burger, 1949, 1953) has been noted above. Burger (1953), Vaugien (1954a), and Benoit, Assenmacher, and Brard (1956) have found experimentally a variety of psychic effects on testicular development.

Environmental temperature has often been considered as a possible modifying factor in photoperiodically stimulated gonadal development. That it is often, at least, relatively unimportant is evident from the responses obtained in zero and subzero temperatures (Rowan, 1925, 1926; Bissonnette, 1937; Schlidmacher, 1938a,b; Polikarpova, 1940). However, more detailed quantitative investigations of the effect of environmental temperature on *Sturnus vulgaris* (Burger, 1948), *Zonotrichia leucophrys gambelii* (Farner and Mewaldt, 1952; Farner and Wilson, 1957b), and *Junco hyemalis* (Engels and Jenner, 1956) show that environmental temperature may have a small but significant modifying role.

Possibly we can then envision a scheme in which the basic timer is the genetically fixed photoperiodic response mechanism, with the temporal and spatial differences in the time of attainment of full sexual development being attributable to "psychic" factors, differences in environmental temperature, and possibly other modifying influences such as nutritional factors (Bissonnette, 1932c, 1933a). Presumably the potential magnitude of the modifying effects varies among different species. Such a scheme could account adequately for the well-known irregular annual differences in rates of gonadal development such as noted by Marshall (1949b).

In the vast literature on reproductive cycles in birds the suggestion of innate cycles has appeared frequently (see, for example, Marshall, 1951). If "innate cycle" is intended to mean a cyclic phenomenon with a precision and frequency characteristic of most avian reproductive activity, I am of the definite opinion that there exists at present no unequivocal evidence that it occurs in any species. On the other hand, there is evidence that in some species there may be an innate tendency for gonadal development in a constant environment. The most striking example of this comes from the series of testicular developments and regressions observed by Benoit, Assenmacher, and Brard (1955, 1956) in drakes placed in either constant darkness or in constant light. In both instances the "cycles" were irregular both in amplitude and frequency. Miller (1955) has shown that *Zonotrichia leucophrys nuttalli* held on midwinter daily photoperiods of 10 hr underwent a considerable testicular development by early May, several months later than the normal time for the attainment of the corresponding degree of development under natural conditions. Similar treatment of *Zonotrichia atricapilla* caused a slight testicular development by early July when maximum development is attained with natural daily photoperiods. In our laboratory (Laws and Farner, unpublished data) we found no testicular development in *Zonotrichia leucophrys gambelii* held in 8-hr daily photoperiods from midwinter to October. On the other hand, Schildmacher (1956) found that *Chloris chloris* showed a considerable degree of testicular development on 8-hr photoperiods, although several months behind the attainment of corresponding degrees of development under normal daily photoperiods. *Zonotrichia leucophrys nuttalli* and *Chloris chloris* are both early breeders. In our laboratory (Farner, unpublished) we have noted similar responses with a small number of *Passer domesticus,* another early breeder, held on short daily photoperiods. Miller (1955) has interpreted his data as indication of an "innate" reproductive rhythm. It is possible that this interpretation is correct, although I think that it would be wiser to defer such a designation until the rate of testicular development (k of equation 1) as a function of the photoperiod (p) is established experimentally, for it is possible that each of the above cited cases may still represent a photoperiodic response. If, for these species, the curves representing k as a function of p are similar to that in Fig. 2 but with lower tails such that k is a continuous positive function of p until p is equal to, or approaches, zero, then these testicular developments could be interpreted properly as photoperiodic.

Although the photoperiodic testicular response has been demonstrated extensively in birds (Table I), it is only recently (Farner and Wilson, 1957b) that a quantitative demonstration has been made of its dominant importance in the timing of the testicular cycle. Knowing k empirically as a function of p (equation 2), and knowing the natural duration of the daily photoperiods, we were able to "predict" testicular weight for a particular date by,

$$\log_{10} W_n = \log_{10} W_0 + \sum_{i=1}^{n} k_i \qquad (3)$$

where n is the number of days beyond the date of beginning of testicular development. Fluctuations in light intensity because of cloudiness and other factors were ignored because of the low maximal light intensity of the response. It was also necessary to ignore possible differences in wavelength composition between the artificial light, which was used in establishing the experimental rates, and natural light; differences in response resulting from such differences are probably small, again because of the low maximal threshold of the response. Data on

body weight appeared to rule out any appreciable nutritional differences. Appropriate modifications were made for the small effect of environmental temperature. The date of attainment of testicular weight
of 100 mg was selected for prediction since, at this stage of development, the increase in testicular weight still conforms closely to equation (1). The date predicted for 100-mg testes on the basis of
experimentally established rates using equation (3) was about 10 days
earlier than the date at which this is attained in nature. The "predicted" date is within the statistical error of the basic measurements.
Therefore, it can be concluded that for this species the photoperiodic
mechanism is of predominant importance in timing the testicular cycle.
Since the responses obtained with many other Temperate Zone species
(Table I) are of a similar order of magnitude, a generalizing extension of this conclusion appears to be in order.

It appears appropriate to conclude this evaluation of the photoperiodic control of gonadal cycles with a brief consideration of a
phenomenon which has caused some misgivings concerning the general validity of the theories of photoperiodic control. I have in mind
here the phenomenon of autumnal sexual activity which has been
extensively noted, particularly in resident species. (See, for example,
Benoit, 1950b; Bullough, 1942, 1943; Marshall, 1952.) Although
the necessary experimental evidence is lacking, it appears to me that
existing data in no way argue against a fundamentally important
photoperiodic timer if one makes the following very plausible assumptions: (1) that the curve representing k as a function of p (Fig. 2)
is displaced somewhat to the left or that it has a definite lower tail
with k being a more substantial positive function of p for values of
p down to about 9 hr; (2) that the refractoriness of the photoperiodic
response mechanism is ended relatively early (August or early
September) while day lengths are still sufficiently long to cause
appreciable stimulation of the photoperiodic mechanism, (3) and, as
is quite obviously the case from field studies, that these species must
be somewhat more temperature sensitive and possibly more sensitive
to "psychic" factors. These characteristics would then permit an
autumnal gonadal development which varies from year to year depending on weather conditions. Thus also the differences in vernal
gonadal development, which can be correlated well with weather

conditions, can be explained readily. These differences are usually more striking in early-breeding resident species than in migratory species. Although this scheme has a plausible basis in our existing knowledge, it is, of course, essentially hypothetical and must be tested experimentally. Any examination of this hypothetical scheme must consider a possible difference between spring and fall in the ratio and sequence of production of the tubule-stimulating gonadotropin (follicle-stimulating hormone) and the gonadotropin(s) (Nalbandov, Meyer, and McShan, 1951) which cause the formation of the cells of Leydig and stimulate them to secrete. It is to be hoped that the necessary experiments will be forthcoming in the near future.

REFERENCES

Aschoff, J. 1955. Jahresperiodik der Fortpflanzung beim Warmblütern. *Studium Generale, 8,* 742–76.
Assenmacher, I., and J. Benoit. 1953a. Contribution à l'étude des relations de la substance Gomori-positive avec le complexe hypophysaire et la gonadostimulation chez le canard domestique. *Compt. rend., 236,* 133–35.
———. 1953b. Répercussions de la section du tractus porto-tubéral hypophysaire sur la gonadostimulation par la lumière chez le canard domestique. *Compt. rend., 236,* 2002–2004.
———. 1956. Nouvelles recherches sur les relations entre la neurosécrétion hypothalamique, le system porte hypophysaire et l'activité gonadotrope de la préhypophyse. *Compt. rend., 242,* 2986–88.
Bailey, R. E. 1950. Inhibition with prolactin of light-induced gonad increase in white-crowned sparrows. *Condor, 52,* 247–51.
Baldini, J. T., R. E. Roberts, and C. M. Kirkpatrick. 1954. The reproductive capacity of bobwhite quail under light stimulation. *Poultry Sci., 33,* 1282–83.
Bartholomew, G. A. 1949. The effect of light intensity and day length on reproduction in the English sparrow. *Bull. Museum Comp. Zool. Harvard College, 101,* 433–76.
Benoit, J. 1934. Activation sexuelle obtenue chez le canard par l'éclairement artificiel pendent la période de repose génital. *Compt. rend., 199,* 1671–73.
———. 1935a. Stimulation du développement testiculaire par l'éclairement artificiel. *Compt. rend. soc. biol., 118,* 664–68.
———. 1935b. Rôle des yeux dans l'action stimulante de la lumière sur le développement testiculaire chez le canard. *Compt. rend. soc. biol., 118,* 669–71.
———. 1935c. Rôle de l'hypophyse dans l'action stimulante de la lumière sur le développement testiculaire chez le canard. *Compt. rend. soc. biol., 118,* 672–74.
———. 1935d. Influence de la lumière naturelle sur la croissance testiculaire

chez le canard au cours de la reprise sexuelle saisonniére. *Compt. rend. soc. biol., 120,* 131–33.

————. 1935f. Stimulation par la lumière artificielle du développement testiculaire chez des canards aveuglés par énucléation des globes oculaires. *Compt. rend. soc. biol., 120,* 136–39.

————. 1935f. Stimulation par la lumière artificielle du développement testiculaire chez des canards aveuglés par section du nerf optique. *Compt. rend. soc. biol., 120,* 133–36.

————. 1935g. Maturité sexuelle et ponte obtenues chez la cane domestique par l'éclairement artificiel. *Compt. rend. soc. biol., 120,* 905–908.

————. 1935h. Nouvelles expériences relatives à la stimulation par la lumière du développement testiculaire chez le canard. *Compt. rend., 201,* 359–62.

————. 1936a. Facteurs externes et internes de l'activité sexuelle. I. Stimulation par la lumière de l'activité sexuelle chez le canard et la cane domestiques. *Bull. biol. France et Belg., 70,* 487–533.

————. 1936b. Activation du fonctionnement hypophysaire par des radiations lumineuses chez le canard domestique. *Rev. Physiotherapie, 2,* 86–94.

————. 1936c. Hypophysectomie et éclairement artificiel chez le canard mâle. *Compt. rend. soc. biol., 120,* 1326–28.

————. 1937. Facteurs externes et internes de l'activité sexuelle. II. Etude du mécanisme de la stimulation par la lumière de l'activité testiculaire chez le canard domestique. Rôle de l'hypophyse. *Bull. biol. France et Belg., 71,* 393–437.

————. 1938a. Action de divers éclairements localisés dans la region orbitaire sur la gonadostimulation chez le canard mâle impubère. Croissance testiculaire provoquée par l'éclairement direct de la région hypophysaire. *Compt. rend. soc. biol., 127,* 909–14.

————. 1938b. Rôle des yeux et de la voie nerveuse oculo-hypophysaire dans la gonadostimulation par la lumière artificielle chez le canard domestique. *Compt. rend. soc. biol., 129,* 231–34.

————. 1950a. Reproduction, caractères sexuels et hormones. Déterminisme du cycle sexuel saisonnier. In *Traité de Zoologie,* Vol. 15, pp. 384–478. Pierre-P. Grasse, Editor. Masson et Cie., Paris.

————. 1950b. Les glandes endocrines. In *Traité de Zoologie,* Vol. 15, pp. 290–334. Pierre-P. Grasse, Editor, Masson et Cie., Paris.

Benoit, J., and I. Assenmacher. 1953a. Rapport entre la stimulation sexuelle préhypophysaire et la neurosécrétion chez l'oiseau. *Arch. anat. microscop. et morphol. exptl., 42,* 334–86.

————. 1953b. Rôle des photo-récepteurs superficiel et profond dans la gonadostimulation par la lumière chez les oiseaux. *J. physiol. Paris, 45,* 34–37.

————. 1954a. Sensibilité comparée des récepteurs superficiels et profonds dans le réflexe photosexuel chez le canard. *Compt. rend., 239,* 105–107.

————. 1954b. Rapport entre la stimulation sexuelle préhypophysaire et la neurosécrétion chez l'oiseau. *Pubbl. staz. zool. Napoli, 24* (Suppl.), 27–31.

————. 1955. Le controle hypothalamique de l'activité préhypophysaire gonadotrope. *J. physiol. Paris, 47,* 427–567.

Benoit, J., I. Assenmacher, and E. Brard. 1955. Évolution testiculaire du canard domestique maintenu à l'obscurité totale pendant une longue durée. *Compt. rend., 241,* 251–53.

———. 1956. Étude de l'évolution testiculaire du canard domestique soumis très jeune à un éclairement artificiel permanent pendant deux ans. *Compt. rend., 242,* 3113–15.

Benoit, J., I. Assenmacher, and S. Manuel. 1952. Pénétration, variable selon la longueur d'onde, des radiations visible jusqu'à l'hypothalamus et au rhinencéphale, à traverse la région orbitaire, chez le canard. *Compt. rend., 235,* 1695–97.

———. 1953. Pénétration des radiations visibles jusqu'à l'encephale à travers le région orbitaire, chez le canard. Sa mesure par un procédé photographique. *Compt. rend. soc. biol., 147,* 40–45.

Benoit, J., I. Assenmacher, and F. X. Walter. 1950a. Réponses du mécanisme gonado-stimulant à l'éclairement artificiel et de la préhypophyse aux castrations bilatérale et unilatérale, chez, le canard domestique mâle, au cours de al période de regression testiculaire saisonnière. *Compt. rend. soc. biol., 144,* 573–77.

———. 1950b. Activité gonadotrope de l'hypophyse du canard domestique, au cours de la régression testiculaire saisonnière et de la prépuberté. *Compt. rend. soc. biol., 144,* 1403–1407.

———. 1952. Différences de sensibilité de la rétine du canard aux radiations colorées dans le réflexe pupillaire et dans le réflexe opto-sexuel. *Compt. rend. soc. biol., 146,* 1027–30.

———. 1953. Dissociation expérimentale des rôles des récepteurs superficiel et profond dans la gonadostimulation hypophysaire la lumière chez le canard. *Compt. rend. soc. biol., 147,* 186–191.

Benoit, J., and R. Kehl. 1939. Nouvelles recherches sur les voies nerveuses photoréceptrices et hypophysostimulantes chez le canard domestique. *Compt. rend. soc. biol., 131,* 89–96.

Benoit, J., P. Mandel, F. X. Walter, and I. Assenmacher. 1950. Sensibilité testiculaire aux hormones gonadotropes hypophysaires chez le canard domestique, au cours de la période de régression testiculaire saisonniere. *Compt. rend. soc. biol., 144,* 1400–1403.

Benoit, J., and L. Ott. 1938. Action de lumières de différentes longeurs d'ondes sur la gonado-stimulation chez le canard mâle impubère. *Compt. rend. soc. biol., 127,* 906–909.

———. 1944. External and internal factors in sexual activity. Effect of irradiation with different wave-lengths on the mechanisms of photostimulation of the hypophysis and on testicular growth in the immature duck. *Yale J. Biol. Med., 17,* 27–46.

Benoit, J., L. Tauc, and I. Assenmacher. 1954a. Mesure photoélectrique de la pénétration transorbitaire des radiations visibles jusqu'au cerveau, chez le canard domestique. *Compt. rend., 239,* 451–53.

———. 1954b. Nouveaux résultats de mesure photoélectrique de la pénétration de radiations lumineuses visibles jusqu'au cerveau, par le côté et la sommet de la tête, chez des canards blancs et pigmentés. *Compt. rend. 239,* 508–10.

Benoit, J., F. X. Walter, and I. Assenmacher. 1950a. Nouvelles recherches relatives à l'action de lumières de différentes longuers d'onde sur la gonadostimulation du canard mâle impubère. *Compt. rend. soc. biol., 144,* 1206–11.

————. 1950b. Contribution à l'étude du réflexe opto-hypophysaire gonado-stimulant chez le canard soumis à des radiations lumineuses de diverses longueurs d'ondes. *J. Physiol., 42,* 537–41.

Bissonnette, T. H. 1930. Studies on the sexual cycle in birds. I. Sexual maturity, its modification and possible control in the European starling (*Sturnus vulgaris*). *Am. J. Anat., 45,* 289–305.

————. 1931a. Studies on the sexual cycle in birds. IV. Experimental modification of the sexual cycle in males of the European starling (*Sturnus vulgaris*) by changes in the daily period of illumination and of muscular work. *J. Exptl. Zool., 58,* 281–320.

————. 1931b. Studies on the sexual cycle in birds. V. Effects of light of different intensities on the testis activity of the European starling (*Sturnus vulgaris*). *Physiol. Zoöl., 4,* 542–74.

————. 1932a. Light or exercise as factors in sexual periodicity in birds. *Science, 76,* 253–55.

————. 1932b. Studies on the sexual cycle in birds. VI. Effects of white, green, and red lights of equal luminous intensity on the testis activity of the European starling (*Sturnus vulgaris*). *Physiol. Zoöl., 5,* 92–123.

————. 1932c. Possible relation of age at sexual maturity in birds to daily period, intensity, and wave length of light. *Science, 75,* 18–19.

————. 1932d. Light and diet as factors in relation to sexual periodicity. *Nature, 129,* 612.

————. 1933a. Light and sexual cycles in starlings and ferrets. *Quart. Rev. Biol., 8,* 201–208.

————. 1933b. Inhibition of the stimulating effect of red light on testis activity in *Sturnus vulgaris* (starling) by a restricted diet. *Biol. Bull., 65,* 452–68.

————. 1936. Sexual photoperiodicity. Influence of varying quantities and qualities of light on sexual activity in plants and animals, an example of the interaction of genetic and environmental factors in conditioning the expression of characters. *J. Heredity, 27,* 171–80.

————. 1937. Photoperiodicity in birds. *Wilson Bull., 49,* 241–70.

————. 1939. Sexual photoperiodicity in the blue jay (*Cyanocitta crista*). *Wilson Bull., 51,* 227–32.

Bissonnette, T. H., and A. G. Csech. 1936. Eggs by pheasants and quail induced by night lighting. *Science, 83,* 392.

————. 1937. Hatching pheasant chicks on Christmas day. *Am. Naturalist, 71,* 525–28.

Bissonnette, T. H., and A. P. R. Wadlund. 1931. Spermatogenesis in *Sturnus vulgaris:* refractory period and acceleration in relation to wave length and rate of increase of light ration. *J. Morphol., 52,* 403–27.

————. 1932. Duration of testis activity of *Sturnus vulgaris* in relation to type of illumination. *J. Exptl. Biol., 9,* 339–50.

Breneman, W. R. 1955. Reproduction in birds: the female. *Mem. Soc. Endocrinol., 4,* 94–113.

Bullough, W. S. 1942. The reproductive cycles of the British and Continental races of the starling (*Sturnus vulgaris* L.). *Phil. Trans. Roy. Soc., B231,* 181–246.

——. 1943. Autumn behavior and the resident habit of many British birds. *Nature, 151,* 531.

Burger, J. W. 1939. Some aspects of the roles of light intensity and daily length of exposure to light in the sexual photoperiodic activation of the male starling. *J. Exptl. Zool., 81,* 333–40.

——. 1940. Further studies on the relation of the daily exposure to light to the sexual activation of the male starling (*Sturnus vulgaris*). *J. Exptl. Zool., 84,* 350–61.

——. 1943. Some effects of colored illumination on the sexual activation of the male starling. *J. Exptl. Zool., 94,* 161–68.

——. 1944. Testicular response to androgen in the light-stimulated starling. *Endocrinology, 35,* 182–86.

——. 1947. On the relation of day-length to the phases of testicular involution and inactivity of the spermatogenetic cycle of the starling. *J. Exptl. Zool., 105,* 259–67.

——. 1948. The relation of external temperature to spermatogenesis in the male starling. *J. Exptl. Zool., 109,* 259–66.

——. 1949. A review of investigations on seasonal reproduction in birds. *Wilson Bull., 61,* 211–30.

——. 1953. The effect of photic and psychic stimuli on the reproductive cycle of the male starling, *Sturnus vulgaris. J. Exptl. Zool., 124,* 227–39.

Burger, J. W., T. H. Bissonnette, and H. D. Doolittle. 1942. Some effects of flashing light on testicular activation in the male starling (*Sturnus vulgaris*). *J. Exptl. Zool., 90,* 73–82.

Clark, L. B., S. L. Leonard, and G. Bump. 1936. Light and reproduction in game birds. *Science, 83,* 268.

——. 1937. Light and sexual cycle of game birds. *Science, 85,* 339–40.

Cole, L. J. 1933. The relation of light periodicity to the reproductive cycle, migration and distribution of the mourning dove (*Zenaidura macroura carolinensis*). *Auk, 50,* 284–96.

Damsté, P. H. 1947. Experimental modification of the sexual cycle of the greenfinch. *J. Exptl. Biol., 24,* 20–35.

Davis, J. 1953. Precocious sexual development in the juvenal English sparrow. *Condor, 55,* 117–20.

Disney, H. J. De S., and A. J. Marshall. 1956. A contribution to the breeding biology of the weaver finch *Quelea quelea* (Linnaeus) in East Africa. *Proc. Zool. Soc. London, 127,* 379–87.

Disselhorst, R. 1908. Gewichts- und Volumszunahme der männlichen Keimdrüsen bei Vögeln und Säugern in der Paarungszeit; Unabhängigkeit des Wachstums. *Anat. Anz., 32,* 113–17.

Dobie, J. B., J. S. Carver, and J. Roberts. 1946. Poultry lighting for egg production. *Wash. State Coll. Agr. Expt. Stas., Bull. 471.*

Engels, W. L., and C. E. Jenner. 1956. The effect of temperature on testicular recrudescence in juncos at different photoperiods. *Biol. Bull.*, *110*, 129–37.

Etzold, F. 1891. Die Entwicklung der Testikel von Fringilla domestica von der Winterruhe bis zum Eintritt der Brunst. *Z. Wiss. Zool.*, *52*, 46–84.

——. 1954. Northward transequatorial migration of birds. *Sci. Rev.* (*New Zealand*), *12*, 29–30.

Farner, D. S. 1955. The annual stimulus for migration: Experimental and physiologic aspects. In *Recent Studies in Avian Biology*, pp. 198–237. University of Illinois Press, Urbana, Ill.

Farner, D. S., and L. R. Mewaldt. 1952. The relative roles of photoperiod and temperature in gonadal recrudescence in male *Zonotrichia leucophrys gambelii*. *Anat. Record*, *113*, 612.

——. 1953. The relative roles of diurnal periods of activity and diurnal photoperiod in gonadal activation in male *Zonotrichia leucophrys gambelii* (Nuttall). *Experientia*, *9*, 219–21.

——. 1955a. Is increased activity or wakefulness an essential element in the mechanism of the photoperiodic response of avian gonads? *Northwest Sci.*, *29*, 53–65.

——. 1955b. The natural termination of the refractory period in the white-crowned sparrow. *Condor*, *57*, 112–16.

Farner, D. S., L. R. Mewaldt, and S. D. Irving. 1953a. The roles of darkness and light in the activation of avian gonads with increased daily photoperiods. *Science*, *118*, 351–52.

——. 1953b. The roles of darkness and light in the photoperiodic response of the testes of white-crowned sparrows. *Biol. Bull.*, *105*, 434–41.

Farner, D. S., and A. C. Wilson. 1957a. The relation of single daily photoperiods to numerous short repeated photoperiods in testicular development in the white-crowned sparrow, *Zonotrichia leucophrys gambelii*. *Minerva Fisioterapica*, *2*, 78.

——. 1957b. A quantitative examination of testicular growth in the white-crowned sparrow. *Biol. Bull.*, *113*, 254–67.

Frantz, W. L. 1954. Some effects of hypophysectomy on the domestic hen (*Gallus domesticus*). *Ohio J. Sci.*, *54*, 335–41.

Galgano, M., and V. Mazzi. 1951. Modalità di regolazione dei cicli sessuali foto- e termoperiodici nei vertebrati. *Riv. biol.*, *Perugia*, *43*, 21–69.

Glass, B. P., and G. E. Potter. 1944. Effects of photoperiodicity on egg production of female quail. *Proc. Trans. Texas Acad. Sci.*, *27*, 79–81.

Greeley, F., and R. K. Meyer. 1953. Seasonal variations in testes-stimulating activity of male pheasant pituitary glands. *Auk*, *70*, 350–58.

Hammond, J. Jr. 1954. Light regulation of hormone secretion. *Vitamins and Hormones*, *12*, 157–206.

Hill, R. T., and A. S. Parkes. 1934. Hypophysectomy of birds. III. Effects on gonads, accessory organs, and head furnishings. *Proc. Roy. Soc.* (*London*), *B116*, 221–36.

Jenner, C. E., and W. L. Engels. 1952. The significance of the dark period in the photoperiodic response of male juncos and white-throated sparrows. *Biol. Bull.*, *103*, 345–55.

Kendeigh, S. C., 1941. Length of day and energy requirements for gonadal development and egg-laying in birds. *Ecology*, *22*, 237–48.

King, J. R. 1957. Premigratory adiposity in the white-crowned sparrow (*Zonotrichia leucophrys gambelii*). Doctoral thesis, State College of Washington, Pullman, Wash.

Kirkpatrick, C. M. 1955. Factors in photoperiodism of bobwhite quail. *Physiol. Zoöl., 28*, 255–64.

Kirkpatrick, C. M., and A. C. Leopold. 1952. The role of darkness in sexual activity of the quail. *Science, 116*, 280–81.

Kirschbaum, A. 1933. Experimental modification of the seasonal sexual cycle of the English sparrow, *Passer domesticus. Anat. Record, 57* (Suppl.), 62.

Kobayashi, H. 1954a. Effects of lengthening daily light period on molting, thyroid and thyrotropin contents of the pituitary body of the canary. *Annotationes Zool. Japon., 27*, 19–21.

———. 1954b. Loss of responsiveness of the sex gland to the stimulus of light and its relation to molting in the canary. *Annotationes Zool. Japon., 27*, 128–37.

———. 1954c. Inhibition by sex steroids and thyroid substance of light-induced gonadal development in the passerine bird, *Zosterops palpebrosa japonica. Endocrinologia Japonica, 1*, 51–55.

Legait, E., and H. Legait. 1955. Manifestations de neurohémocrinie au cours du cycle annuel et de la couvaison chez la poule Rhode-Island. *Compt. rend., soc. biol., 149*, 559.

Legait, H. 1955. Variations indépendantes d'activité des noyaux paraventriculaires et supraoptiques au cours du cycle annuel et de la couvaison chez la poule Rhode-Island. *Compt. rend. soc. biol., 149*, 175.

Lofts, B., and A. J. Marshall. 1956. The effects of prolactin administration on the internal rhythm of reproduction in male birds. *J. Endocrinol., 13*, 101–06.

Marshall, A. J. 1949a. On the function of the interstitium of the testis. The sexual cycle of a wild bird, *Fulmaris glacialis* (L.). *Quart. J. Microscop. Sci., 90*, 265–80.

———. 1949b. Weather factors and spermatogenesis in birds. *Proc. Zool. Soc. London, 119*, 711–16.

———. 1950. Mechanism and significance of the "refractory period" in the avian testis cycle. *Nature, 166*, 1034.

———. 1951. The refractory period of testis rhythm in birds and its possible bearing on breeding and migration. *Wilson Bull., 63*, 238–61.

———. 1952. The interstitial cycle in relation to autumn and winter sexual behavior in birds. *Proc. Zool. Soc. London, 121*, 727–40.

———. 1955. Reproduction in birds: the male. *Mem. Soc. Endocrinol., 4*, 75–93.

Marshall, A. J., and H. J. de S. Disney. 1956. Photostimulation of an equatorial bird (*Quelea quelea* Linnaeus). *Nature, 177*, 143–44.

Miller, A. H. 1948. The refractory period in light-induced reproductive development of golden-crowned sparrows. *J. Exptl. Zool., 109*, 1–11.

———. 1949. Potentiality for testicular recrudescence during the annual refractory period of the golden-crowned sparrow. *Science, 109*, 546.

———. 1951. Further evidence on the refractory period in the reproductive cycle of the golden-crowned sparrow. *Auk, 68*, 380–83.

————. 1954. The occurrence and maintenance of the refractory period in crowned sparrows. *Condor, 56,* 13–20.

————. 1955. The expression of innate reproductive rhythm under conditions of winter lighting. *Auk, 72,* 260–64.

Miyazaki, H. 1934. On the relation of the daily period to the sexual maturity and to the moulting of *Zosterops palpebrosa japonica. Sci. Repts. Tôhoku Imp. Univ., 9,* 183–203.

Nalbandov, A. V., and L. E. Card. 1943. The effects of hypophysectomy on growing chicks. *J. Exptl. Zool., 94,* 387–411.

Nalbandov, A. V., R. K. Meyer, and W. H. McShan. 1951. The role of a third gonadotrophic hormone in the mechanism of androgen secretion in chicken testes. *Anat. Record, 110,* 475–94.

————. 1946. Effect of purified gonadotropes on the androgen secreting ability of testes of hypophysectomized cocks. *Endocrinology, 39,* 91–104.

Polikarpova, E. 1940. Influence of external factors upon the development of the sexual gland of the sparrow. *Compt. rend. acad. sci. U.R.S.S., 26,* 91–95.

Putzig, P. 1937. Von der Beziehung des Zugablaufs zum Inkretdrüsensystem. *Vogelzug, 8,* 116–30.

————. 1938. Weitere Versuche über die Beziehungen der Keimdrüsen zum Zugverhalten. *Vogelzug, 9,* 189–99.

Rautenberg, W. 1957. Vergleichende Untersuchungen über den Energiehaushalt des Bergfinken (*Fringilla montifringilla* L.) und des Haussperlings (*Passer domesticus* L.). *J. Ornithol., 98,* 36–64.

Riley, G. M. 1936. Light regulation of sexual activity in the male sparrow (*Passer domesticus*). *Proc. Soc. Exptl. Biol. Med., 34,* 331–32.

————. 1940. Light versus activity as a regulator of the sexual cycle in the house sparrow. *Wilson Bull., 52,* 73–86.

————. 1942. Relationship of gonad-stimulating activity of female domestic fowl anterior pituitaries to reproductive condition. *Endocrinology, 30,* 537–41.

Riley, G. M., and E. Witschi. 1938. Comparative effects of light stimulation and administration of gonadotropic hormones in female sparrows. *Endocrinology, 23,* 618–24.

Ringoen, A. R. 1942. Effects of continuous green and red light illumination on gonadal response in the English sparrow, *Passer domesticus* (Linnaeus). *Am. J. Anat., 71,* 99–116.

Ringoen, A. R., and A. Kirschbaum. 1937. Correlation between occular stimulation and spermatogenesis in the English sparrow (*Passer domesticus*). *Proc. Soc. Exptl. Biol. Med., 36,* 111–13.

————. 1939. Factors responsible for the sexual cycle in the English sparrow, *Passer domesticus* (Linnaeus). Ocular stimulation and spermatogenesis; effect of increased light ration on spermatogenesis. *J. Exptl. Zool., 80,* 173–86.

Roberts, J., and J. S. Carver. 1941. Electric light for egg production. *Agr. Eng., 22,* 357–60.

Rowan, W. 1925. Relation of light to bird migration and developmental changes. *Nature, 115,* 494–95.

————. 1926. On photoperiodism, reproductive periodicity and the annual

748 REPRODUCTION AND MIGRATION IN BIRDS

migrations of birds and certain fishes. *Proc. Boston Soc. Nat. Hist., 38,* 147–89.

———. 1928. Reproductive rhythm in birds. *Nature, 122,* 11–12.

———. 1929. Experiments in bird migration. I. Manipulation of the reproductive cycle: seasonal histological changes in the gonads. *Proc. Boston Soc. Nat. Hist., 39,* 151–208.

———. 1932. Experiments in bird migration. III. The effects of artificial light, castration and certain extracts on the autumn movement of the American crow (*Corvus brachyrhynchos*). *Proc. Natl. Acad. Sci. U. S., 18,* 639–54.

———. 1937. Effects of traffic disturbance and night illumination on London starlings. *Nature, 139,* 668–69.

———. 1938a. London starlings and seasonal reproduction in birds. *Proc. Zool. Soc. London, 108,* 51–77.

———. 1938b. Light and seasonal reproduction in animals. *Biol. Revs., 13,* 374–402.

Schäfer, E. A. 1907. On the incidence of daylight as a determining factor in bird migration. *Nature, 77,* 159–63.

Schildmacher, H. 1937. Zur Physiologie des Zugtriebes. III. Versuche mit künstlich verlängerter Tagesdauer. *Vogelzug, 8,* 107–14.

———. 1938a. Hoden und Schilddrüse des Gartenrotschwanzes *Phoenicurus ph. phoenicurus* (L.) unter dem Einfluss zusätzlicher Belichtung im Herbst und Winter. *Biol. Zentr., 58,* 464–72.

———. 1938b. Zur Auslösung der Frühlings-Zugunruhe durch Wärme bei gekäfigten Rotkehlchen, *Erithacus r. rubecula* (L.). *Vogelzug, 9,* 7–14.

———. 1938c. Zur Physiologie des Zugtriebes. IV. Weitere Versuche mit künstlich verlängerter Tagesdauer. *Vogelzug, 9,* 146–52.

———. 1939. Über die künstliche Aktivierung der Hoden einiger Vogelarten im Herbst durch Belichtung und Vorderlappenhormone. *Biol. Zentr., 59,* 653–57.

———. 1955. Photoperiodizität des Stoffwechsels beim Vogel. *Acta XI Congr. Intern. Ornithologici, 1954,* 655–57.

———. 1956. Physiologische Untersuchungen am Grünfinken, *Chloris chloris,* im künstlichen Kurztag und nach "hormonaler Sterilisierung." *Biol. Zentr., 75,* 327–55.

Schildmacher, H., and W. Rautenberg. 1953. Zur Fortpflanzungsphysiologie und Haematologie der Hausgans. *Wiss. Z. Univ. Greifswald, math.-nat. Reihe, Reihe Nr. 5,* 345–51.

Scott, H. M., and L. F. Payne. 1937. Light in relation to the experimental modification of the breeding season of turkeys. *Poultry Sci., 16,* 90–96.

Shirley, H. V., and A. V. Nalbandov. 1956. Effects of transecting hypophyseal stalks in laying hens. *Endocrinology, 58,* 694–700.

Staffe, A. 1950. Weitere Untersuchungen über die Wirkung des Lichtschocks auf die Legeleistung. *Geflügelhof, 13,* 446–49, 510–14.

———. 1951. Belichtung und Legeleistung beim Huhn. *Experientia, 7,* 399–400.

Takewaki, K., and H. Mori. 1944. Mechanism of molting in the canary. *J. Fac. Sci., Imp. Univ. Tokyo, IV, 6,* 547–75.

Udintsev, S. D. 1948. Vliianie gonadotropnovo preparata na polovuiu sistemu

Passer domesticus L. i *Passer montanus* L. v zimnii sezon. *Doklady Akad. Nauk, S.S.S.R.*, *60*, 941–45.

Vaugien, L. 1948. Recherches biologiques et expérimentales sur le cycle reproducteur et la mue des oiseaux Passeriformes. *Bull. biol. France et Belg.*, *82*, 166–213.

———. 1951. Régression testiculaire et avènement de la mue chez le moineau domestique, en été. *Compt. rend.*, *232*, 2486–88.

———. 1952a. Sur le conditionnement des cycles sexuels du moineau domestique, par la lumière naturelle et la lumière artificielle. Nécessité de l'obscurité temporaire. *Compt. rend.*, *234*, 364–66.

———. 1952b. Sur l'activité testiculaire, la teinte du bec et la mue du moineau domestique soumis, en hiver, à l'éclairement artificiel continu. *Bull. soc. zool. France*, *77*, 395–407.

———. 1952c. Sur le conditionnement par la lumière et la chaleur du cycle testiculaire du moineau domestique. *Bull. soc. zool. France*, *76*, 335–39.

———. 1954a. Effet de la section des rémiges sur la réponse sexuelle du moineau domestique soumis à l'éclairement artificiel. *Bull. biol. France et Belg.*, *88*, 52–67.

———. 1954b. Influence de l'obscuration temporaire sur la durée de la phase réfractaire du cycle sexuel du moineau domestique. *Bull. biol. France et Belg.*, *88*, 294–309.

———. 1955. Sur les réactions ovariennes du moineau domestique soumis, durant le repos sexuel, à des injections de gonadotrophine sérique de jument gravide. *Bull. biol. France et Belg.*, *89*, 1–15.

———. 1956a. Influence de la durée du jour sur l'activité sexuelle du chardonneret mâle. *Compt. rend. soc. biol.*, *242*, 2253–54.

———. 1956b. Ponte du chardonneret induite, en toutes saisons par l'injection de gonadotrophine équine. *Compt. rend.*, *245*, 444–46.

Wagner, H. O. 1956. Die Bedeutung von Umweltfaktoren und Geschlechtshormonen für den Jahresrhythmus der Zugvögel. *Z. vergleich. Physiol.*, *38*, 355–69.

Wallgren, H. 1954. Energy metabolism of two species of the genus *Emberiza* as correlated with distribution and migration. *Acta Zool. Fennica*, *84*, 1–110.

Walton, A. 1937. On eclipse plumage of the Mallard (*Anas platyrhyncha platyrhyncha*). *J. Exptl. Biol.*, *14*, 440–47.

Weber, W. A. 1951. Influence of the light shock on the laying potential. *Proc. Ninth World's Poultry Congr., Paris*, *2*, 99–101.

Weise, C. M. 1956. Nightly unrest in caged migratory sparrows under outdoor conditions. *Ecology*, *37*, 275–87.

Wilson, W. O., and H. Abplanalp. 1956. Intermittent light stimuli in egg production of chickens. *Poultry Sci.*, *35*, 532–38.

Winn, H. S. 1950. Effects of different photoperiods on body weight, fat deposition, molt, and male gonadal growth in the slate-colored junco. Doctoral dissertation, Northwestern University, Evanston, Ill.

Witschi, E., A. J. Stanley, and G. M. Riley. 1937. Gonadotropic hormones of the hypophysis of the turkey. *Proc. Soc. Exptl. Biol. Med.*, *36*, 647–51.

Wolfson, A. 1941. Light versus activity in the regulation of sexual cycles of birds: The role of the hypothalamus. *Condor*, *43*, 125–36.

————. 1942. Regulation of spring migration in juncos. *Condor, 44,* 237–63.

————. 1945. The role of the pituitary, fat deposition, and body weight in bird migration. *Condor, 47,* 95–127.

————. 1952a. Day length, migration, and breeding cycles in birds. *Sci. Monthly, 74,* 191–200.

————. 1952b. The occurrence and regulation of the refractory period in the gonadal and fat cycles of the junco. *J. Exptl. Zool., 121,* 311–26.

————. 1953. Gonadal and fat response to a 5:1 ratio of light to darkness in the white-throated sparrow. *Condor, 55,* 187–92.

————. 1954. Production of repeated gonadal, fat, and molt cycles within one year in the junco and white-crowned sparrow by manipulation of day length. *J. Exptl. Zool., 125,* 353–76.

INTERRUPTED DARK PERIOD: TESTS FOR REFRACTORINESS IN BOBWHITE QUAIL HENS *

CHARLES M. KIRKPATRICK
Purdue University Agricultural Experiment Station, Lafayette, Indiana

The bobwhite quail (*Colinus virginianus*) lends itself well to laboratory studies where a wild, native gallinaceous species is required. The species reproduces in confinement, can be held in a minimum of space for indefinite periods, and needs no special feed beyond a balanced poultry ration. Disease is no problem if premises are uncontaminated, if the birds are kept on wire, and if diseased stock is not introduced. In general, the management of bobwhites for experiments is so similar to the management of chickens that some might question whether confined quail are "wild" or whether they are, in fact, semidomesticated. However, quail have never been selected, their breeding period remains strictly seasonal unless changed experimentally, and such quail when released go wild and do not domesticate.

Various gallinaceous birds have been induced to lay off-season eggs by extending the day length with artificial lights (pheasants, Martin, 1935; pheasants and quail, Bissonnette and Csech, 1936; ruffed grouse, Clark *et al.*, 1937; chukar partridge, Funk *et al.*, 1941; willow ptarmigan, Höst, 1942). If these early experiments suffered for want of fancy equipment or goodly number of experimental birds, they were impressive for winter induction of eggs, sometimes at quite low temperatures.

More recently (Kirkpatrick and Leopold, 1952) it has been shown that a long night of 14 hr inhibits the reproductive responses in bobwhites, and that interruption of this dark period with 1 hr of light causes quail to produce fertile eggs. When the 1-hr interruption is applied at the midpoint of the dark period, the intensity threshold for oviposition is between 1.0 and 10.0 ft-c after treatments for about

* Journal Paper No. 1202 from Purdue University Agricultural Experiment Station in cooperation with the Indiana Department of Conservation.

30 days (Kirkpatrick, 1955). Sperm are produced at a threshold between 0.1 and 1.0 ft-c. The principle of the dark-period interruption has been demonstrated by others (Farner *et al.,* 1953; Jenner and Engels, 1952). Farner's group took exception to the idea that the dark period plays an active role in inhibiting a reproductive response, and hypothesized that a light interruption merely augments a carry-over period of gonadotropic activity following the photoperiod. However this controversy may be resolved, it is clear that full sexual activity or no sexual activity results from the same number of light hours by varying the length of the dark period.

In various experiments the interrupted dark period technique has been used for stimulating the growth of gonadal tissue in quail in which age, environmental temperature, and breeding history have been the variables. The experiments considered here were undertaken to determine whether a refractory period is characteristic of female quail. Data were obtained from groups of females of different ages, and from similarly aged birds having different breeding histories or postlaying rest periods.

The refractory period has been variously defined, but the aspects of it as stated by Miller (1954) for perching birds will suffice for our purposes. Refractoriness is characterized by the regression of the gonads from the breeding state even under prolonged treatment with long daily light periods; and resting birds in regression may fail to respond to light stimulation if they have not been inactive long enough. Thus the refractory period seems to fulfill a requirement for rest and inactivity, following natural or induced reproductive activity, before breeding is possible again. The length of the refractory interval has been determined for juncos (Wolfson, 1952) and white-crowned sparrows (Farner and Mewaldt, 1955). Although refractoriness is usually measured by the gonad response to stimulation, the gonadotropic role of the pituitary is an essential part of the response mechanism (Farner and Mewaldt, 1955), and the swelling gonad may indirectly manifest the pituitary response. If the gonad fails to enlarge, however, there might be some question as to whether the gonadotropic action of the pituitary alone was inhibited, the gonad response, or both.

Nearly all experiments with refractoriness have been devoted to the testicular cycle (Burger, 1949; Marshall, 1951). Wolfson (1952) studied the refractory period in female juncos, but the existence of refractoriness in female Galliformes remained uninvestigated. The only source of information may be analogies from domesticated species, but there is always the hazard of reasoning from domesticated to wild species. An interesting clue is found in a minor experiment with bobwhites in which three hens and one cock were under continuous light for more than a year. Fertile eggs were laid by all hens for 223 days and by one hen for 344 days (Baldini *et al.*, 1954). This evidence, admittedly from small numbers, is not in agreement with one of the aspects of the refractory period as defined for passerines, namely, that in quail the breeding condition was maintained indefinitely by light treatment. It appeared that quail likewise may not conform to the other aspect of the refractory condition. If quail hens gave a positive response to light stimulation, applied at different intervals after a period of natural reproduction, the case for no refractoriness in quail hens would be strengthened. Experiments were undertaken to investigate this question.

MATERIALS AND METHODS

Six groups of female bobwhites differing in respect to breeding condition were compared following similar light treatments. The physical facilities were similar to those detailed for earlier experiments (Kirkpatrick, 1955). Each group was exposed 42 or 43 days to an intensity of 30 to 35 ft-c on a 24-hr cycle divided as follows: 9 hr of light, 7 hr of darkness, 1 hr of light, 7 hr of darkness. The birds were held two or three to a cage with individuals from groups A, B, and C (Table I) mixed in each cage to insure the same average environmental conditions for those groups. At the end of the exposure periods the birds were sacrificed and the excised organ weights determined to the nearest milligram. The values shown in Table I are averages for the individual ratios comprising each group.

The groups for comparison were selected especially for their differences in breeding history. All birds in the A groups were of the same age. Groups A1 and A2 had experienced a season of normal reproduction in outdoor cages. Groups A3 and A4 had been pre-

TABLE I. Effect of Dark-Period Interruption on Reproductive Tissue Weights of Postlaying and Juvenile Bobwhite Hens

Group, Condition and Number Used	Average Rest	Period of Lighting	Ovary Weight / Body Weight × 1000 mg %	Oviduct Weight / Body Weight × 1000 mg %
A1 Postlaying (5)	8 weeks	Unlighted—posted Sept. 21	0.3	1.0
A2 Postlaying (16)	8 weeks	Sept. 30–Nov. 13	1.4	4.5
A3 Nonlaying (5)	[a]	Unlighted—posted Sept. 20	0.4	0.1
A4 Nonlaying (11)	[a]	Sept. 30–Nov. 12	1.1	2.3
B 154-day-old juveniles (12)	[a]	Sept. 30–Nov. 13	4.9	13.7[b]
C 92-day-old juveniles (10)	[a]	Sept. 30–Nov. 13	0.7	3.7[c]
D1 Postlaying (5)	13 weeks	Unlighted—posted Nov. 8	0.4	0.8
D2 Postlaying (17)	13 weeks	Nov. 5–Dec. 17	1.3	2.4
E Postlaying (8)	2 weeks brooding	Aug.–Oct. 42 days	1.6	4.3

[a] No previous reproductive development.
[b] 4 hens laid by 42d day.
[c] 1 hen laid by 42d day.

754

vented from reproducing by exposure to short days of artificial light for 10 months prior to this experiment. Groups B and C had not previously reproduced. Group D birds differed from group A birds by a longer rest period after egg laying. Group E birds with the shortest rest period were put on light treatments directly as they were taken from the nest after a two-week period of intensive brooding. For the purpose of determining whether gonadal stimulation is possible after a period of production with no intervening rest period, it seemed that these groups representing various intervals of rest might give useful information from tissue weight responses to identical stimulating treatments.

RESULTS AND DISCUSSION

Before treatments started, three of the groups were checked by sacrifice to establish the basic, unstimulated condition of the reproductive tissues. Group A3 was a sample of birds maintained previously for nearly a year on a short day. The values for this group may be regarded as basic. In check groups A1 and D1, the values for the ovary are well within those for the basic condition, while the magnified values for the oviduct in these groups may be accounted for by the lag in oviduct regression after periods of production not experienced by group A3. For the purpose of comparison with values from treated birds, whether or not we assume that a refractory group had been sampled, the basic ovary to body weight ratio appears to be 0.3 to 0.4 and the oviduct relationship 0.8 to 1.0 mg % (Table I).

The indices for the treated birds of all groups show significant increases over the basic condition. The magnitude of increase is 3 or 4 times in the ovary relationship and 3 to 5 times in the oviduct relationship. From a consideration of postlaying groups only, nothing in their responses suggests a refractory condition. Even the incubating hens, presumably under the influence of prolactin (Riddle *et al.*, 1935), developed to a slightly greater extent than most of the other postlaying group with long rest periods. Without the positive response of group E, the responses of A2 and D2 might be interpreted as being dependent upon a conditioning for stimulation by 8 or 13 weeks of rest; but the significant and similar response of group E shows that no rest was necessary beyond the amount preceding lighting, which was a two-week term of incubation. Group E was not deemed large enough to divide for a pretreatment check, so the indices for this group before treatment are unknown, opening to question the absolute amount of increase after treatment. Otherwise the evidence indicates that the length of the rest period is not an important factor in the possible refractoriness of bobwhite hens.

The response of group A4, the nonlaying adults, is of interest because of its smaller increase than any of the other adult groups. Assuming some tissue exhaustion or systemic depletion in the post ovulatory groups, we might have expected group A4 to have responded with a superior development of latent resources. There is no apparent explanation for the mediocre performance. One can only hypothesize that the receptivity of aging reproductive tissues to stimulation is conditioned by previous functional periods.

Although the evidence indicates that postbreeding bobwhite hens, regardless of the length of the postovulatory period, are not absolutely refractory to light, a relative refractoriness of the adult hens is suggested by comparisons with the performance of juveniles. The 5-month juveniles of group B gave a much greater response than either the adults or the younger juveniles of group C. The experiment with juveniles was repeated with similar results, 6-month juveniles giving a greater response than adults or 3½-month juveniles. Considering the superior juvenile response, one is reminded that fall courtship display among wild galliform birds is well known. Good presumptive evidence that such displays are based upon sexual precocity is found in the reports of fall spermatogenesis in juvenile pheasants (Hiatt and Fisher, 1947; Kirkpatrick and Andrews, 1944). Since off-season gonadal activity of pheasants is characteristic of juveniles, it might be reasoned that hitherto undeveloped tissues of juvenile quail hens are more light-sensitive than regressed tissues of older hens. Although old bobwhite hens are not completely refractory, their slower hypertrophy of reproductive tissues perhaps indicates ovarian fatigue rather than a relative pituitary refractoriness. The positive ovarian and oviduct responses of the postlaying adult is good indirect evidence that light-induced release of gonadotropins from the pituitary was not materially blocked by a refractory condition.

SUMMARY

When groups of bobwhite quail hens of different ages and breeding histories were given the same interrupted dark period treatment, positive ovarian and oviduct responses, regardless of the length of the postlaying rest, showed that such rest is not required before another period of production can be induced. The accumulated evidence is strong that postlaying bobwhite hens are not refractory in the usual sense as applied to passerine birds.

REFERENCES

Baldini, J. T., R. E. Roberts, and C. M. Kirkpatrick. 1954. The reproductive capacity of bobwhite quail under light stimulation. *Poultry Sci., 33,* 1282–83.

Bissonnette, T. H., and A. G. Csech. 1936. Eggs by pheasants and quail induced by night lighting. *Science, 83,* 392.

Burger, J. W. 1949. A review of experimental investigations on seasonal reproduction in birds. *Wilson Bull., 61,* 211–30.

Clark, L. B., S. L. Leonard, and G. Bump. 1937. Light and the sexual cycle of game birds. *Science, 85,* 339–40.

Farner, D. S., L. R. Mewaldt, and S. D. Irving. 1953. The roles of darkness and light in the photoperiodic response of the testes of white-crowned sparrows. *Biol. Bull., 105,* 434–41.

Farner, D. S., and L. R. Mewaldt. 1955. The natural termination of the refractory period in the white-crowned sparrow. *Condor, 57,* 112–16.

Funk, E. M., J. C. Hamilton, and H. L. Kempster. 1941. Game bird investigations, *Univ. Missouri Agr. Expt. Sta. Bull. 453.*

Hiatt, R. W., and H. I. Fisher. 1947. The reproductive cycle of ring-necked pheasants in Montana. *Auk, 64,* 528–48.

Höst, P. 1942. Effect of light on the moults and sequences of plumage in the willow-ptarmigan. *Auk, 59,* 388–403.

Jenner, C. E., and W. L. Engels. 1952. The significance of the dark period in the photoperiodic response of male juncos and white-throated sparrows. *Biol. Bull., 103,* 345–55.

Kirkpatrick, C. M. 1955. Factors in photoperiodism of bobwhite quail. *Physiol. Zoöl., 28,* 255–64.

Kirkpatrick, C. M., and F. N. Andrews. 1944. Development of the testis in the ring-necked pheasant. *Anat. Record, 89,* 317–24.

Kirkpatrick, C. M., and A. C. Leopold. 1952. The role of darkness in sexual activity of the quail. *Science, 116,* 280–81.

Marshall, A. J. 1951. The refractory period of testis rhythm in birds and its possible bearing on breeding and migration. *Wilson Bull., 63,* 238–61.

Martin, L. E. 1935. Pheasant eggs in winter. *Game Breeder and Sportsman, 39,* 95.

Miller, A. H. 1954. The occurrence and maintenance of the refractory period in crowned sparrows. *Condor, 56,* 13–20.

Riddle, O., R. W. Bates, and E. L. Lahr. 1935. Prolactin induces broodiness in fowl. *Am. J. Physiol., 111,* 352–60.

Wolfson, A. 1952. The occurrence and regulation of the refractory period in the gonadal and fat cycles of the junco. *J. Exptl. Zool., 121,* 311–26.

THE INFLUENCE OF DIFFERENT DAY LENGTHS ON THE TESTES OF A TRANSEQUATORIAL MIGRANT, THE BOBOLINK
(*Dolichonyx oryzivorus*)*

WILLIAM L. ENGELS

Department of Zoology, University of North Carolina, Chapel Hill

Birds that breed in one hemisphere and spend the nonbreeding season in the other experience two periods of increasing day lengths every year instead of one. Since they are exposed to two light cycles while undergoing only one reproductive cycle, the question has often been raised as to the possibility (or impossibility) of photoperiodism playing a role in the cycle of their annual reproduction. Of the speculations put forth, none as yet has been based on results of experiments with transequatorial migrants, because, as far as I know, no such experiments have been made. It is the complete lack of published data in this important area that prompts me to report the following experimental results, even though they are so obviously meager.

THE LIGHT SCHEDULE IN NATURE

The breeding grounds of the bobolink lie in eastern and central North America, mainly between 40° and 50° N. Lat.; breeding occurs chiefly in June and terminates in July. Before mid-August an exodus occurs, and the breeding grounds are essentially emptied before September. The vast majority of the population has passed beyond the southern shores of the United States by mid-October. Day lengths meanwhile have decreased from more than 15 hr (sunrise—sunset) to less than 12 hr (Fig. 1). The duration of the period of these short days depends on the time taken by the birds to reach the equator. I have been unable to find precise data on this point.

* These studies were supported in part by a research grant (E-356) from the National Institutes of Health, Public Health Service, which was administered by Charles E. Jenner.

759

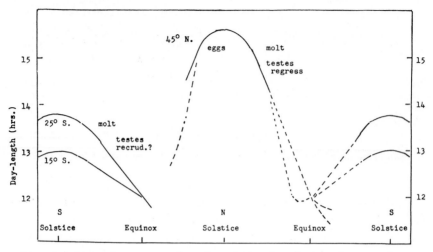

FIG. 1. Approximate annual cycles of day length (sunrise-sunset) to which bobolinks (*Dolichonyx oryzivorus*) are exposed. Broken lines indicate northward and southward migrations. Precise data are lacking for onset of northward migration and also for arrival in the Southern Hemisphere. The duration of the southward migration appears to be rather variable, especially in the southern United States; the probable extremes are indicated.

The "wintering" grounds lie in South America, mainly between 15° and 25° S. Lat. Once across the equator, the bobolinks are exposed to days more than 12 hr long, increasing up to about 14 hr at the time of the southern solstice; after the solstice, days again decrease to about 12 hr at the March equinox. I do not know when the northward migration begins; presumably this occurs sometime during March. Once again north of the equator, the birds are exposed to very rapidly lengthening days, not only because day length now is increasing everywhere in the Northern Hemisphere, but also because the *rate* of this increase increases rapidly in the higher latitudes toward which the birds are moving.

SECONDARY SEX CHARACTERISTICS

Bobolinks are seasonally sexually dimorphic. The male nuptial plumage develops after a molt in the Southern Hemisphere and presumably is complete before the onset of the northward migration. Another molt follows the breeding season, the new plumage being essentially like that worn by the female the year around. Our observations with caged birds suggest that the control of the male nuptial plumage is independent of the testis, developing regularly in alternation with "henny" plumage, as in the African weaver finches studied by Witschi (1955).

In addition to the cock plumage, the sexually active male has a deeply pigmented, jet black beak (in contrast to the light brown or horn-colored beak of the female and the sexually inactive male designated as *neutral* in Tables I and II). This beak pigmentation is

TABLE I. Summary of Experiments with Male Bobolinks Captured during Northward Migration in Early May, 1955 (35° 47′ N. Lat.) and Exposed to 16-hr Photoperiods until September 15 (Two males in each group)

Group	Photoperiods	Beak Color	Left Testes June 1
A	14 hr Sept. 15—June 1	Remained neutral	1.6 mm³, inactive
B	10 hr Sept. 15—Dec. 21 14 hr Dec. 21—June 1	1 black, March 23 (fading June 1); both black March 30	180 mm³, sperm bundles
C	12 hr Sept. 15—June 1	Pigment began mid- May; black June 1	8.0 mm³, 1st meiotic division

controlled apparently by the male sex hormone (as in the domestic sparrow and some other birds). Daily intramuscular injection of 20 μg of testosterone propionate resulted in diffuse pigmentation of the beak in about 5 days, both in females and sexually inactive males, and in deep pigmentation in about 14 days. Daily drops of 5 to 10 μg of testosterone propionate applied directly to the beak produced blackening of the fleshy rim of the nostril and angle of the mouth in females in 3 to 5 days and a narrow black line on the adjacent horny beak in 8 to 11 days. These results are completely in agreement with those reported for the domestic sparrow (Pfeiffer *et al.*, 1944) and justify the use of beak pigmentation as a criterion for testicular activity.

TABLE II. Summary of Experiments with Male Bobolinks Captured during Northward Migration in Early May, 1956 (35° 47′ N. Lat.) and Exposed to 16-hr Photoperiods until October 1 (Two males in each group)

Group	Photoperiods	Beak Color	Left Testes
D	10 hr Oct. 1—June 13 24 hr June 13—Aug. 1	Remained neutral at least to June 13. Black before July 31	7.4 mm³ June 7, 1st meiotic division 172 mm³ Aug. 1
E	10 hr Oct. 1—Nov. 26 14 hr Nov. 26—June 13 24 hr June 13—Sept. 10	Pigment beginning by Feb. 13. (?) Black, Feb. 27 Fading (?) July 31	No data.
F	12 hr Oct. 1—Nov. 26 14 hr Nov. 26—June 13 24 hr June 13—Aug. 4	Both became blackish between Apr. 1– Apr. 15 Fading, Aug. 14	ca. 120 mm³ June 2 38 mm³ Aug. 14, re- gressing
G	16 hr Oct. 1—June 13 24 hr June 13—Sept. 10	Remained neutral[a] (at least to May 20)	1.4 mm³ Aug. 1

[a] Pigmentation experimentally produced through daily injections of 20 µg testosterone
propionate May 16 to 28 and May 30 to June 4; still quite black June 13, but returned to
neutral sometime before July 31.

EXPERIMENTS AND RESULTS

The experiments and results are summarized in Tables I and II.
All the bobolinks used were captured in fowling nets at the same
locality, near Raleigh, North Carolina, during early May from north-
wardly migrating flocks. They were held through the summer on 16-hr
photoperiods. During August all the birds molted, more or less completely, developing essentially "henny" plumage, and the black pigment disappeared from the beak. They then were exposed to various
photoperiods beginning September 15 (Table I) or October 1 (Table
II) in ventilated, light-tight compartments. In each compartment two
100-watt white fluorescent tubes delivered about 150 ft-c of light to
the floor of the cage.

The results of the first experiments (Table I), indicate a photo-refractory phase which is maintained for at least 8½ months by 14-hr photoperiods (group A). Termination of this photorefractory phase evidently was brought about by a prolonged exposure to 10-hr photo-periods, followed by full recrudescence of the testes on 14-hr photo-periods (group B). Constant 12-hr photoperiods not only permitted passage from the photorefractory to the photoreceptive phase, but also permitted (stimulated?) a slow recrudescence of the testes (group C) at least to the beginning of production of secondary spermatocytes and also to the production of sufficient sex hormone to cause pigmen-tation of the beak.

In later experiments (Table II), attempts were made to define further the conditions under which the photorefractory phase might be terminated and testicular recrudescence permitted or stimulated. Constant 10-hr photoperiods apparently retarded production of sex hormone at least until June 13 (group D) but obviously released the birds from the photorefractory phase and permitted some regrowth of the testes. Eight weeks exposure to 10-hr photoperiods beginning October 1, followed by 14-hr photoperiods (group E), brought about beak pigmentation before the end of February and maintained this pigmentation for some months. Similarly, the combination of 8 weeks exposure to 12-hr photoperiods beginning October 1 and then 14-hr photoperiods (group F) evidently released photorefractoriness and permitted eventually full recrudescence of the testes, with sufficient production of sex hormone by mid-April to produce blackening of the beak. In a final experiment photorefractoriness was apparently again demonstrated, no beak pigmentation developing after 8 months ex-posure to 16-hr photoperiods (group G).

CONCLUSIONS

These experiments demonstrate that a photoperiodic response does occur in this transequatorial migrant. Just as in North Temperate Zone species (cf. Burger, 1949), the postbreeding season is character-ized by a photorefractoriness which is maintained by continuously long photoperiods (groups A, G), but which is broken by a period of short photoperiods (groups B, E, F). On continued 10-hr photoperiods (group D) there occurs eventually at least a slight recrudescence of the testes, just as, for example, in crowned sparrows (Miller, 1955) and juncos (Engels and Jenner, 1956). Recovery from photorefractoriness while exposed to 12-hr photoperiods (group C) has been reported also for juncos (Wolfson, 1952).

The deviations of the response (groups E, F) from previously established patterns are those which would be made necessary by the "winter" sojourn in the Southern Hemisphere spring and summer. After exposure to only 10 hr of light per day for as long a time as 8 weeks, a minimum of at least 11 weeks on 14-hr days was required to reach a level of sex hormone production manifested by beginning of beak pigmentation (group E). This level almost certainly coincides with that stage of spermatogenesis when most primary spermatocytes are in the process of division. It would be expected, I am confident, that, under lighting schedules such as given to the bobolinks in group E, testes of juncos, crowned sparrows, and similar North Temperate Zone migrants would in 11 weeks not only have attained this stage, but actually would also have reached maximum development, with mature sperm, at a much earlier time.

The results with group F, compared to those with group E, seem to be especially significant in interpreting this peculiarity of the bobolink response. If full recovery from photorefractoriness actually had occurred during 8 weeks both on 10-hr and on 12-hr photoperiods, then one would expect that, on the 14-hr photoperiods that followed, beak pigmentation would develop at about the same time in both groups. Instead, the group F birds were 6 to 8 weeks behind the group E birds in showing this response. It appears to me that the most reasonable explanation of this difference is that complete release from photorefractoriness had not in fact occurred during the period of short days, that transition from the photorefractory phase to a photoreceptive phase took place during the 14-hr photoperiods and occurred earlier in the case of those birds that previously had been exposed to the shorter photoperiod. Consideration of Fig. 1 indicates that recovery from photorefractoriness necessarily must occur in nature during or after exposure to long days following an earlier period of shorter days. The results with our groups E and F show that the photoperiodic mechanism of bobolinks is indeed adapted to this requirement.

All in all, the results of these experiments are quite compatible with the hypothesis advanced by Farner (1954) concerning photoperiodism and transequatorial migrants. The essential points in this hypothesis include (1) "a characteristically longer refractory period"; (2) the escape from short autumn days and the retarding effect on refractory-period release of the lengthening days of the Southern Hemisphere spring; and (3) the eventual release from photorefractoriness, sometime after the southern solstice, and subsequent photostimulation on the still long, even though shortening, days of the Southern Hemisphere summer.

SUMMARY

Experiments with the bobolink, a transequatorial migrant, demonstrate the existence of a postbreeding photorefractoriness which is maintained by continuously long days but which is broken by a period of short days. Birds exposed to 14-hr photoperiods after 8 weeks on 10-hr photoperiods show testicular response several weeks earlier than do birds on the same 14-hr day after 8 weeks on 12-hr photoperiods. This is interpreted to mean that full recovery from photorefractoriness occurred on the long day, the time of its occurrence depending on the nature of the previous exposure to short days. The data and their interpretation are in accord with the day length cycles experienced by bobolinks in nature.

REFERENCES

Burger, J. W. 1949. A review of experimental investigations on seasonal reproduction in birds. *Wilson Bull., 61,* 211–30.

Engels, W. L., and C. E. Jenner. 1956. The effect of temperature on testicular recrudescence in juncos at different photoperiods. *Biol. Bull., 110,* 129–37.

Farner, D. S. 1954. Northward transequatorial migration of birds. *Sci. Rev. (New Zealand), 12,* 29–30.

Miller, A. H. 1955. The expression of innate reproductive rhythm under conditions of winter lighting. *Auk, 72,* 260–64.

Pfeiffer, C. A., C. W. Hooker, and A. Kirschbaum. 1944. Deposition of pigment in the sparrow's bill in response to direct applications as a specific and quantitative test for androgen. *Endocrinology, 34,* 388–99.

Witschi, E. 1955. Vertebrate gonadotrophins. *The Comparative Endocrinology of Vertebrates,* Pt. I. *Mem. Soc. Endocrinol., No. 4,* pp. 149–165.

Wolfson, A. 1952. The occurrence and regulation of the refractory period in the gonadal and fat cycles of the junco. *J. Exptl. Zool., 121,* 311–25.

PHOTOPERIODISM IN THE FEMALE DOMESTIC FOWL

R. M. FRAPS

Agricultural Research Service, United States Department of Agriculture,
Beltsville, Maryland

The scope of this paper is perhaps narrower than its title may suggest, being limited to a discussion of relationships between photoperiodicity and certain aspects of reproductive behavior in the hen. Photoperiodic effects on ovarian function, as reflected in rate of production and timing of oviposition are first reviewed. An examination of the role of photoperiodicity in the hen's ovulation cycle follows.

There is little or no reason to doubt that photoperiodic effects on ovarian function are mediated, in the hen as in other vertebrates, through the central nervous system to the pituitary gland, thence via the gonadotropic hormones to the ovary. The basic relationships are described elsewhere in these proceedings by Professor Bullough (p. 641). The mechanism by which the central nervous system, and particularly the hypothalamus, may control and integrate pituitary activity has recently been thoroughly reviewed by Harris (1955) and cogently discussed by Greer (1957). Except for matters of detail, this important subject will not be referred to further.

PHOTOPERIODICITY AND LAY BEHAVIOR

Two differing expressions of lay behavior are associated with photoperiodicity in the hen. One has to do mainly with the onset and rate of egg production, the other with the time of day at which eggs are laid.

Rate of Production

Pease (in Marshall, 1956) writes that *Gallus bankiva,* when kept in captivity in England, generally lays and incubates a clutch of about a dozen eggs in late spring or early summer. He notes further that most fancy breeds in which there has been little or no selection for egg production behave similarly. The effect of light in these domesticated birds is thus to time the appearance of a strictly limited breeding season, as in wild birds generally (Marshall, 1936, 1942, 1956; Rowan, 1938).

It is common knowledge that in breeds and strains of domestic fowl developed for egg production, the restricted breeding season (in its rigorous sense) has been eliminated. Hammond (1954) summarizes the changed role of season succinctly. ". . . the fowl has been so modified by selection that a season can now be defined in only a statistical sense: the effect of light is observed not on extent of season but on relative rates of production." Rate of production is measured as the number of eggs laid over a given number of days, expressed in percent. An egg a day over any number of days thus signifies a rate of 100%.

Natural Photoperiods.   The effects of seasonal photoperiodicities are well defined in most fowl. In a now classical paper, Whetham (1933) described the correlation between day length and rate of egg production over a wide range of latitudes. Onset of seasonally increasing production generally preceded onset of longer days; this "incomplete correlation" was thought to arise out of low relative rates of change in light ration preceding onset of longer days. Whetham noted also that the effect of increasing day length was greater in low- than in high-producing hens.

In early maturing, high-producing breeds or strains, pullets hatched in March or April may begin to lay during September or October, i.e., during the season of decreasing—even rapidly decreasing—day length. Such birds are not "short-day" animals; day length, though decreasing, is adequate to assure sexual maturity. If the birds are maintained under natural light, production declines or ceases after a time and subsequently exhibits the usual seasonal increase associated with lengthening days.

Artificial Photoperiods.   The value of supplemental light in altering egg production has long been known. Baker and Ranson (1932) mention the application of light by the Spaniards over a century before 1932 for this purpose. Speaking presumably of this country,

Dobie *et al.* (1946) state that the first reported use of artificial lighting for poultry houses appeared in 1889.

In practice, artificial photoperiodicities are commonly used to stimulate egg production during fall and winter months, when production is normally low. Under prolonged photostimulation, production declines, much as it does after the period of high production during the spring months. The usual effect of lights is therefore to advance the "curve" or peak of production, just as "the breeding season" may be advanced in wild birds. Total annual production is not greatly increased in high-producing strains by the use of lights.

(*a*) *Length of light day.* A long-standing and still common practice in stimulating winter egg production is to use lights from 4:00 A.M. into daylight. Kennard and Chamberlain (1931) and Penquite and Thomson (1933) reported equally good production under 24-hr lights.

A critical and extensive investigation of the effect of length of light day on production was carried out by Roberts and Carver (1941).* Artificial light was used (daylight excluded) on White Leghorn pullets selected as high-producing birds. At light intensities of 7.5 ft-c, 13 hr of light daily resulted in practically maximal production. Daily light periods of less than 13 hr led to decreased production. Light periods greater than 13 hr (to 19 hr) failed to increase production appreciably, and production under continuous light was somewhat less than under 13- to 19-hr photoperiods.

Dobie *et al.* (1946) tested the effectiveness of supplementing winter daylight (ca. 9 hr) with 15 hr light (1 ft-c) or 4 hr light (3 ft-c) before, following, or as 2 hr before, 2 hr following, the hours of daylight. Their results indicated no significant differences in egg production. Dobie *et al.* concluded that the only condition for maximal photostimulation is that a total of 13 hr light be supplied.

Platt (1953), supplementing daylight with "dim red light," reported the effect on production to be equivalent to that from white light, 3:00 A.M. to daybreak. As used by Platt, some of the stimulating effect of red light may have been due to the "carry-over" effect noted below.

* The results of Roberts and Carver (1941) were apparently republished, with results of other studies, by Dobie, Carver, and Roberts in 1946.

Moore and Mehrhof (1946) compared the egg production of hens subjected to periodic increments in light ration with that of hens under continuous light. The periodic increases consisted of 2-hr additions, at 14-day intervals, to the initial natural day (October in Florida). Periodic increments effected a greater initial response in egg production than did all night lighting, but this differential was not maintained and the overall performance of hens under continuous light was slightly though not significantly superior. It would be interesting to know if smaller increments than those used by Moore and Mehrhof would prove stimulatory over a longer time.

Byerly and Moore (1941) compared the effect of 14 hr light, 12 hr darkness (26-hr day) with that of 14 hr light, 10 hr darkness (24-hr day). Rate of production was considerably greater for hens on the 26-hr day. The authors believed their results to "show conclusively that it was possible to lengthen the clutch* by synchronizing dark and light periods with the hen's natural ovulation cycle," thus suggesting something akin to an endogenous rhythm. As far as is known, this interesting suggestion has not been investigated further.

(b) *Intermittent lighting.* Roberts and Carver (1941) reported that 3 hr of intermittent light daily (1 light, 5 dark—1 light, 4 dark —1 light, 12 dark) yielded production above that of 10 hr continuous light. Dobie *et al.* (1946) compared the effect of 10 hr continuous light with a base day of 8 hr to which a supplemental period of 2 hr was interposed at differing times within the 14 hr (total) darkness. The effect of the interposed 2 hr light was increasingly effective as the maximal period of darkness was decreased. In a similar experiment based on a total day length of 13 hr, no significant differences were observed. Dobie *et al.* concluded that "if thirteen hours of light are furnished, a period of eleven hours of darkness is not too long for best production."

Wilson and Abplanalp (1956) compared the effects of intermittent light and unbroken light at total durations believed to be suboptimal for egg production. Intermittent light was given at 4-hr intervals, 90, 60, 45, 15, 5, and 1 min during each interval. Generally, intermittent

---

* The term "clutch" refers here to the number of eggs laid on consecutive days.

lighting resulted in higher egg production than did the same daily ration given continuously.

In the experiments of Platt (1953) noted previously, red light was used to divide the dark period. No direct comparison can be made, however, between Platt's results and effects of red light used to lengthen the natural day.

High-intensity light for one or a few short periods (5 to 20 sec) during the night has been shown to stimulate or maintain high egg production in the hen (Staffe, 1950, 1951; Weber, 1951), an effect comparable with those of more conventional forms of intermittent lighting, though intensity possibly plays a role here not usually encountered.

Within limits, a given total daily light ration is apparently more effective in stimulating or maintaining egg production in the hen when applied intermittently than it is as a single photoperiod. As far as ovarian response is concerned, the effect appears to be similar to that observed in wild birds. As Farner et al. (1953a,b) suggest, the greater effectiveness of intermittent lighting in the hen may be explained by the "carry-over period" of gonadotropic activity after the cessation of a photoperiod.

(c) Intensity and wavelength. According to Roberts and Carver (1941; also Dobie et al. 1946), no significant differences were observed in production under light intensities of 1.0 to 31.3 ft-c at feed troughs, "provided the hens receive 13 hr of Mazda light per day." Nicholas et al. (1944) reported no effect on production of intensities ranging from 0.5 to 38.0 ft-c. The minimal intensity for the maintenance of even high production is obviously quite low.

Curiously, no study of the effects of wavelength comparable to that of Benoit and Ott (1944) in the immature male duck has been made in the hen. Scott and Payne (1937) found that early morning use of unfiltered white light, or red light only, stimulated early egg production in the turkey, but blue or blue-green light failed to do so. The greater effectiveness of red (i.e., long) wavelengths is in accord with results in the duck (Benoit and Ott, 1944). It seems generally assumed that the response of the fowl is similar; certainly red lights of low (?) intensity stimulate or maintain high production (cf. Platt,

1953). In view, however, of the low intensity of white light required to maintain production, an analysis of the effects of wavelengths at equal energy levels might prove of interest.

With supplementary ultraviolet (bactericidal) sources of peak intensity at 2537 angstrom units in rooms artificially lighted and from which daylight was excluded, Barott *et al.* (1951) reported 10 to 19% increases in annual production over a period of five years. The effect could not be attributed to bactericidal properties of the lamps nor to elaboration of vitamin D. Carson and Beall (1955), however, using similar sources of ultraviolet to supplement a basic schedule of 14 hr incandescent light daily, found no effect on egg production; these authors suggest that the differing outcome of their experiments may have been due to temperature differences which were conducive, in the tests of Barott *et al.,* to more efficient operation of the ultraviolet lamps.

(*d*) *Photoperiod and activity.* For a long time after the effectiveness of supplemental light on egg production had become well known, the additional light was widely believed to afford merely increased opportunity for a special form of activity—feeding. It is of some interest that Goodale (1923) questioned this view in the early twenties. Whetham (1933) suggested stimulation through the anterior pituitary body. About the same time Bissonnette (1933) came to a similar conclusion, reasoning from his experiments on the European starling.

The stimulatory effects of light were shown by Rider (1938) to be independent of the availability of feed during hours of artificial lighting. Rider's results were confirmed by Callenbach *et al.* (1943), who stated that a daily feeding period of 10 hr was adequate for maximal egg production. Roberts and Carver (1941) made the interesting observation that hens under 3 hr intermittent illumination daily consumed more feed—and produced at a higher rate—than did birds receiving 10-hr continuous light daily. As was noted by Hammond (1954), the stimulatory effects of "shock" lighting, of ultraviolet, and of Platt's "dim red lights" do not "prolong the period of feeding or of obvious activity."

Time of Lay

As a rule, the domestic fowl in regular production lays an egg a day on two or more successive days, does not lay on one day, and then again lays on two or more successive days. The eggs laid on consecutive days have long been and continue to be known as a clutch (Jull, 1952). It has been pointed out that the clutch in this sense is something quite different from the clutch of the ornithologist, a nest complement or brood (Romanoff and Romanoff, 1949; Hutt, 1949). More recently, the eggs laid on successive days have been referred to as a sequence (Fraps, 1954), a term equally applicable to the daily succession of ovipositions and other events.

Normal Photoperiods.   Under natural lighting the hen lays only during daylight hours. The eggs constituting a sequence are not laid, however, at the same time of day on consecutive days. In a typical sequence of moderate length (e.g., 3 to 6 or 7 eggs) the first egg is laid during early morning hours and successive eggs are laid later on consecutive days until, with lay of an egg in mid- or late afternoon, the sequence is completed. The eggs of a sequence are thus laid not only during daylight, but within restricted hours of daylight.

The timing of lay under controlled photoperiods is similar in all respects to timing of lay under equivalent natural photoperiods. By reversing a 12-hr photoperiod, Warren and Scott (1936) demonstrated the dependence of time of lay on the prevailing alternation of light and darkness. Some 50 to 70 hr were required for restoration of characteristic sequence relationships with the reversed day. Eggs were laid in darkness as well as under lights during the period of adjustment. Warren and Scott concluded that the influence of photoperiodicity in regulation of oviposition occurred sometime before ovulation.

Exceptional Photoperiods.   There have been few investigations directly of the effects of unusual photoperiods on the timing of oviposition, and many reports make no mention of the subject.

(*a*) *Twenty-six-hour days.*   In experiments referred to earlier, Byerly and Moore (1941) found that sequence lengths were much greater for hens under 14 hr light–12 hr dark (26-hr day) than for hens under 14 hr light–10 hr dark (24-hr day). Hens under the 26-

hr day laid many of their eggs in the dark, usually within the two hours before onset of light. Such ovipositions were regularly followed by ovulation. Apparently the timing of oviposition bore the same relation to *onset* of darkness whether the dark period was 12 or 10 hr.

(*b*) *Continuous uniform lighting.* Under continuous and uniform illumination (daylight excluded), Warren and Scott (1936) found that hens laid at any hour of the twenty-four. Records of individual hens indicated that the usual intervals between successive eggs were somewhat greater than for the same hens under normal photoperiods. Intervals of greater length, presumably corresponding to the interval between sequences under natural photoperiods, occurred with some regularity, but with lesser frequency than under usual lighting conditions. According to Warren and Scott, neither exercise nor restricted feeding (6:00 A.M. to 6:00 P.M.) prevented lay of eggs over the 24-hr period.

McNally (1946) confirmed the findings of Warren and Scott (1936) in battery-caged hens when feed was available at all times. When feed was available for only 12 hr of the twenty-four, however, the continuously lighted hens observed by McNally laid a considerably larger proportion of their eggs during the 12 hr of feeding with light than during the equal period of light without available feed.

Fraps *et al.* (1947) subjected battery-caged hens previously maintained for several months under a 14-hr photoperiod (daylight excluded) to continuous illumination, with water and ample feed always available. Over a period of 4 weeks, the hens continued to lay out their sequences almost exactly as they had under the 14-hr photoperiod. When the continuously lighted hens were allowed feed only from 8:00 A.M. through 4:00 P.M., practically all eggs came to be laid between 6:00 A.M. and 6:00 P.M. When allowed feed between 8:00 P.M. and 4:00 A.M. the periodicity of lay was reversed.

Wilson and Abplanalp (1956) reported that hens under continuous illumination (daylight excluded) laid a larger proportion of eggs during afternoon and evening hours; however, a good number of eggs were laid during every hour of the twenty-four. The pattern of lay was attributed to feeding and management practices.

(*c*) *Continuous nonuniform lighting.* Warren and Scott (1936) stated that there were no reports of laying at night by hens maintained under daylight plus continuous night lights, indicating that the lay behavior of hens so lighted differed from that of hens under continuous, uniform lighting. This was found to be true, hens "under continuous artificial light supplemented by daylight" laying only during the normal daylight period. These and related observations led Warren and Scott to suggest that the influence of light on lay behavior was psychological.

In comparing the effects of continuous lighting (plus daylight) and periodic increments to daylight, Moore and Mehrhof (1946) reported oviposition to be confined to the period of natural daylight.

(d) *Intermittent lights.* In the experiments of Wilson and Abplanalp (1956) referred to earlier, lay of eggs was recorded at hourly intervals. Taking totals of eggs laid by all groups under intermittent lighting, the distribution was found to be fairly comparable amongst the six 4-hr periods of illumination. There was, however, a tendency toward concentration of lay at or around the hour at which the hens were subjected to the limited photoperiods. Records for individual hens were not published.

Light and Other Factors.   The restriction of oviposition to relatively limited hours of the 24 in hens under continuous and uniform light was attributed by McNally (1946) to activity associated with feeding, by Fraps *et al.* (1947) to activity associated with "maintenance" operations. In the hens observed by Fraps *et al.,* the time of maximal activity was plainly associated with replenishment of feed, an operation performed daily between 8:00 and 9:00 A.M. Although ample feed always remained in the troughs, the arrival of the daily bounty was regularly accompanied by great activity and much noisy anticipation. Toward evening overt activity was much reduced, and little was observed after about 6:00 to 8:00 P.M.

Bastian and Zarrow (1955) have shown that activity in hens on a 13-hr photoperiod is largely limited to the photoperiod. But as Hammond (1954) observes, it is also true that "activity can vary the pattern and exposure to light." Activity undoubtedly determined the pattern of *relative* exposure to light in the hens observed by Fraps *et al.;* the same was probably true in the experiments described by McNally (1946) and, to a limited extent, in those of Wilson and Abplanalp

(1956). It will be recalled, however, that Warren and Scott (1936) did not alter the random distribution of eggs laid over the 24 hr by limiting the availability of feed to a daily 12-hr period. Possibly other stimuli were more effective than feeding, or activity associated with feeding, in maintaining the individual hen's pattern of exposure to light, but the nature of such stimuli is not clear. The restriction of lay to the period of daylight under continuous artificial light plus daylight, or under supplementary all-night lighting, clearly involves a definite pattern of diurnal activity, set largely by daylight. Presumably the period of diurnal activity is associated with a greater exposure to light than can occur during the period of inactivity, even though the hens were under light continuously.

Bastian and Zarrow (1955) have reported that enforced "wakefulness" plus light, but neither alone, on the night preceding ovulation of the first follicle of the hen's sequence delays its ovulation by approximately the extent of the added period of wakefulness plus light. The authors suggested "that the normal restriction of ovulation to a given period each day . . . is the result of physiological inhibition of the follicle release mechanism by the daily period of light and activity." Since hens may lay in complete darkness (Rider, 1938; Wilson and Woodward, p. 787), it would be of interest to know the relationship between patterns of lay and activity under such conditions.

THE ROLE OF PHOTOPERIOD IN TIMING OF OVULATION

The lay of an egg is of course the terminal event in a series of processes and antecedent events which include growth and maturation of the ovarian follicle, nervous activation of the anterior pituitary gland to effect release of ovulation-inducing hormone (OIH), and ovulation. Basically, the processes culminating in ovulation appear to be much the same in birds and mammals. Ovulation in the hen, however, like oviposition, occurs at progressively later hours until the sequence is completed. We must account therefore not merely for ovulation as such, but also for the retardation in time of day at which successive ovulations take place and finally, for the conditions under which ovulation fails to occur on the single day separating sequences. These relationships have been described elsewhere in some detail (Fraps, 1954, 1955a,b).

Cycles

In Fig. 1, successive ovipositions in a 3-member sequence appear as L_1, L_2, and L_3. No egg is laid on the following day, and a new sequence is initiated on the day thereafter with the oviposition L_1'. The sequence of ovipositions together with events between the terminal oviposition of one sequence and the first oviposition of the next

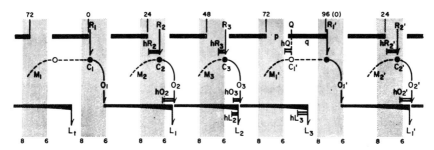

FIG. 1. Time relationships in a 4-day cycle ($n = 3$). Lighted hours 6:00 A.M.–8:00 P.M.; hours of darkness, 8:00 P.M.–6:00 A.M., are set off by the vertical stippled bands.

constitutes the oviposition cycle. This is a cycle in a limited and rigorous sense, i.e., the course of events returns to its proximate starting point. The cycle as defined here includes only a single day on which oviposition fails to occur. Cycle length is thus equal, in days, to sequence length plus 1, or to $n + 1$.

The ovulation cycle consists similarly of the sequence of ovulations, O_1, O_2, and O_3 of Fig. 1 and events between O_3 and O_1'. Preceding the ovulation cycle is the OIH release cycle; onset of each release is indicated by R_1, R_2, and R_3 in Fig. 1, and R_1' marks the beginning of another cycle. A cycle at the nervous level precedes the cycle of OIH releases; the effects of photoperiod are expressed in this neural component of the mechanism of OIH release.

Sequences and Lag. The difference in times of day at which successive ovipositions take place has been defined as lag (Fraps, 1954). The interval between successive ovipositions in any sequence is thus $24 + h$ hours, where h represents lag. In the 3-member sequence of of Fig. 1, hL_2 and hL_3 represent lag in time of ovipositions L_2 and L_3 respectively. The "asynchronous rhythm in the time of egg laying" of

Bastian and Zarrow (1952) is "asynchronous" from day to day by the extent of lag.

Times of successive ovulations in the sequence may be estimated from times of oviposition (Rothchild and Fraps, 1949), or lag values in the ovulation sequence may be estimated directly from lag values in the oviposition sequence (Fraps, 1955b). Lag of the second ovulation of the sequence shown in Fig. 1 is indicated by hO_2, lag of the third ovulation by hO_3. Lag values for ovulation sequences, calculated from the extensive data of Heywang (1938) on length of interval between successive eggs, are shown in Fig. 2 for sequences of 2 to 13 ovulations. The solid part of each column in each histogram represents lag with respect to the preceding ovulation (daily lag). The height of solid plus lined columns represents cumulative lag at successive places beyond the second of each sequence, total lag in each sequence being so measured at the last position.

There are obviously some well-defined regularities in the lag patterns of Fig. 2. Lag in the first place (there is only one place where n

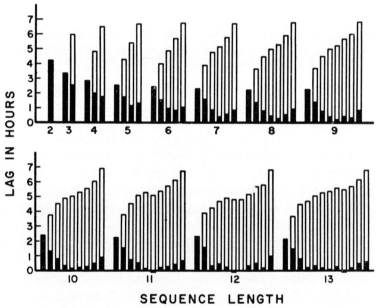

FIG. 2. Lag in ovulation sequences numbering 2 to 13 members.

$= 2$) is greater than at any other place in the sequence, decreasing gradually with increasing sequence length until $n = 7$ or 8 and remaining thereafter fairly constant. In sequences of five or more members, lag in the terminal place or two is somewhat greater than at the immediately preceding place or places. Minimal values of lag gradually decrease with increasing sequence length, and approach or equal zero in the longer sequences ($n = 10$ to 14). The number of ovulations in a sequence may therefore be increased indefinitely with no increase in total lag or other characteristics as long as daily lag fluctuates around zero. For the sequences of Fig. 2, total lag is in fact practically constant (ca. 7 hr) for $n = 7$ or greater.

The Period of Lapse.   As we have seen, total lag measures those hours of the twenty-four over which ovulation may occur. Since the onset of OIH release is assumed to occur for all members of a sequence at a constant interval (ca. 7 to 8 hr) before ovulation, lag relationships are the same with respect to these events and are so represented in Fig. 1. The open periods between the heavy bars near the top of Fig. 1 represent the hours of the twenty-four during which onset of OIH release may occur, the bars the hours during which onset of release never occurs. On the last day of the cycle (hr 72 to 96) onset of OIH release fails to occur either during the period of usual release, p, or during the following hours, q, the period of lapse.

The courses by which follicles become mature are indicated schematically by the curves M_1, M_2, M_3, and M_1' of Fig. 1. The essential point is that each follicle in continuing cycles attains maturity (or becomes ovulable) in a constant relationship to the preceding ovulation. The first or C_1' follicle of any sequence therefore matures (curve M_1') long before it is actually ovulated. This is demonstrated by the fact that the injection of luteinizing preparations at about the time Q of Fig. 1 readily induces ovulation (Neher and Fraps, 1950). Moreover, progesterone, which apparently acts through the nervous component of the OIH release mechanism (Fraps, 1955a) also induces ovulation after injection at about the time Q. These and other observations (Fraps, 1955a,b) lead to the conclusion that not only does the ovary carry an ovulable follicle at about the time Q, but also that the pituitary is capable of full response at or about this time. It follows that nervous activation of the pituitary fails to take place at about the time Q or, indeed, at any time during the hours delimited as q.

Mechanisms

An hypothesis proposed earlier (Fraps, 1954, 1955a,b) is based on the following assumptions: (i) The nervous component of the OIH release mechanism exhibits a 24-hr periodicity in thresholds of response to ovarian hormones; thresholds of response vary quantitatively during those hours of the twenty-four over which response may occur; during the hours of lapse, thresholds are beyond the level of response. (ii) Blood concentrations of ovarian hormones "exciting" the neural component of the OIH release apparatus increase by substantially the same course after each release of OIH (or LH) in cycles of given length. It follows that each "curve" of increasing excitation hormone concentration beyond that associated with the first excitation of a sequence is retarded, in time of day, by the extent of lag at the preceding OIH release.

Relationships between diurnally recurrent rhythmicity in the nervous component of the OIH release mechanism and excitation hormone concentrations are shown schematically in Fig. 3 for a 7-day cycle (n

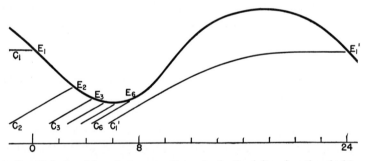

Fɪɢ. 3. Relationships between diurnal rhythmicity in thresholds of response by the nervous component of the OIH release mechanism and excitation hormone concentrations for a 7-day cycle ($n = 6$). Zero hour, about 10 ᴘ.ᴍ.; hour 8, about 6:00 ᴀ.ᴍ.

$= 6$). The curve passing through E_1, E_2, $E_3 \cdot \cdot \cdot E_6$; E_1' represents the course of diurnal variation in thresholds of response to excitation hormone (ordinates). This rhythmicity in thresholds of response is assumed to recur daily. Curves C_1, C_2, $C_3 \cdot \cdot \cdot C_6$ and C_1' represent terminal excitation hormone concentrations associated with maturation of follicles likewise designated *at ovulation*. The levels at which successive concentration curves intercept the curve describing diurnal rhythmicity in thresholds of response determine times of successive excitations E_1, E_2, E_3 · · · E_6. The timing of successive excitations thus depends not merely on the displacement of excitation hormone curves, but also on the *time of day* at which threshold values are attained.

The C_1' curve is displaced by the extent of lag at E_6. It fails to reach threshold levels at or around hour 8 of day 7 because of this displacement *in relation to* increasing threshold requirements for excitation. With the recurrence of decreasing threshold requirements, excitation E_1' occurs at hour 24, which is hour 0 of the first day of a new cycle. Excitation E_1 of Fig. 3 is understood to have been similarly determined.

The possibility that the excitation hormone may be progesterone or a progestin has been discussed elsewhere (Fraps, 1955a,b). But estrogen has been shown to delay ovulation under circumstances which suggest that it acts by increasing excitation threshold requirements (Fraps, 1954; Fraps and Fevold, 1955). If estrogen levels vary with successive releases of OIH (or LH), such variations might well be important in the normal cycle. Answers to these and other questions will be required for a clearer formulation of the excitation cycle.

Huston and Nalbandov (1953) discovered that irritation of the magnum of the hen's oviduct by a contained object or a surgical thread prevented ovulation as long as 20 to 30 days without, however, interrupting the secretion of hormones required for maintenance of the ovary, oviduct, and comb. These findings led to two generalizations (Nalbandov, 1953): (i) Luteinizing hormone (LH), like follicle-stimulating hormone, is secreted at a continuous base level, over and above which the pituitary periodically releases greater quantities to induce ovulation. (ii) The presence of an object, or of an egg, in the magnum suppresses, over neurogenic pathways, the periodic release of LH for ovulation. When the egg clears the magnum, neurogenic suppression ceases and LH is released for ovulation. Nalbandov (1953) notes that this theory does not account for timing of the first LH release of the sequence. This first release, as well as termination of the sequence of releases, might possibly be associated with certain phases of photoperiodicity.

Bastian and Zarrow (1955) have proposed a somewhat different hypothesis to account for "the asynchronous ovulatory cycle of the domestic hen." They recognize "two separate and independent cycles" which interact to produce the ovulatory cycle: (i) The release of LH (OIH) is assumed to be continuous over a relatively long period (e.g., 8 hr) during the same hours every night, "even when a follicle is not ovulated the next day." (ii) The maturation of ovarian follicles is assumed to be gradually completed at more or less regular intervals. Ovulation occurs if a sufficiently mature follicle is subject to LH. Ovulation does not occur if a follicle of insufficient sensitivity for response to LH passes through the hours of LH release. During the same hours of the following night this follicle is highly sensitive to LH and is therefore ovulated as the first of a new cycle.

However much the views of Bastian and Zarrow (1955) and this author may differ in some respects, we are in agreement in assigning to photoperiodicity the role of timing the appearance of a period of high sensitivity in the neural component of the OIH (or LH) release mechanism. We are clearly not yet able to formulate time relationships between photoperiod and neural behavior in the hen within anything like the close limits demonstrated by Everett and Sawyer (1950) and Everett (1956) to exist in the rat. This, however, should not prove to be an impossible task.

SUMMARY AND CONCLUSIONS

The response to seasonal photoperiods by the common domestic fowl differs from that of most wild birds in the absence of a strictly limited "breeding season," exhibiting instead variation in rates of egg production. Under natural photoperiods, maximum production may be advanced to late fall or winter months by artificial light regimens similar to those which so advance the breeding season in many wild species. Activity or time available for feeding plays no part in the stimulatory effects of photoperiod on production; the stimulatory effects are transmitted by the central nervous system to the pituitary body, thence by gonadotropins to the ovary.

Oviposition occurs only during lighted hours under natural or equivalent artificial photoperiods; reversal of photoperiod reverses the restricted hours of lay after 50 to 70 hr. Under uniform continuous light oviposition may occur at any hour of the 24, or only within restricted hours of the twenty-four in association with feeding or maintenance practices. Patterns of activity may impose patterns of varying exposure under uniform illumination and thus restrict the period of lay. The restriction of oviposition to daylight hours when daylight is supplemented with either continuous or all-night lighting suggests response to intensity differentials, possibly with the intervention of "psychological" factors.

One role of photoperiodicity in the hen's ovulation cycle is to time the appearance of a period of low thresholds to ovarian hormones in the neural component of the mechanism controlling the release of ovulation-inducing hormone (OIH) from the pituitary. The period of low thresholds (or high sensitivity) has a duration of not over 8 or 9 hr, and its onset is thought to follow rather closely (1 to 3 hr) upon the onset of darkness. With appropriate assumptions regarding relationships between concentrations of ovarian hormones and neural thresholds, most of the characteristics of the ovulation cycle (and thus of the oviposition cycle) can be accounted for, however formally. At the least, the restriction of oviposition within lighted hours is seen to have a basis in the association between photoperiod and a similarly restricted phase of neural control over pituitary activity.

REFERENCES

Baker, J. R., and R. M. Ranson. 1932. Factors affecting the breeding of the field mouse (*Microtus agrestis*). *Proc. Roy. Soc. London, B110*, 313–22.

Barott, H. G., L. G. Schoenleber, and L. E. Campbell. 1951. The effect of ultraviolet radiation on egg production in hens. *Poultry Sci., 30,* 409–16.

Bastian, J. W., and M. X. Zarrow. 1952. Failure of nembutal to block ovulation in the hen. *Proc. Soc. Exptl. Biol. Med., 79,* 249–52.

————. 1955. A new hypothesis for the asynchronous ovulatory cycle of the domestic hen (*Gallus domesticus*). *Poultry Sci., 34,* 776–88.

Benoit, J., and L. Ott. 1944. External and internal factors in sexual activity. Effect of irradiation with different wave-lengths on the mechanisms of photostimulation of the hypophysis and on testicular growth in the immature duck. *Yale J. Biol. Med., 17,* 27–46.

Bissonnette, T. H. 1933. Does increased light absorption cause increased egg production in the fowl? *Poultry Sci., 12,* 396–99.

Byerly, T. C., and O. K. Moore. 1941. Clutch length in relation to period of illumination in the domestic fowl. *Poultry Sci., 20,* 387–90.

Callenbach, E. W., J. E. Nicholas, and R. R. Murphy. 1943. Effect of light and availability of feed on egg production. *Penn. Agr. Expt. Sta. Bull. 455.*

Carson, J. R., and G. Beall. 1955. Absence of response by breeder hens to ultraviolet energy. *Poultry Sci., 34,* 256–62.

Dobie, J. B., J. S. Carver, and June Roberts. 1946. Poultry lighting for egg production. *Wash. Agr. Expt. Sta. Bull. 471.*

Everett, J. W. 1956. The time of release of ovulating hormone from the rat hypophysis. *Endocrinology, 59,* 580–85.

Everett, J. W., and C. H. Sawyer. 1950. A 24-hour periodicity in the "LH-release apparatus" of female rats, disclosed by barbiturate sedation. *Endocrinology, 47,* 198–218.

Farner, D. S., L. R. Mewaldt, and S. D. Irving. 1953a. The roles of darkness and light in the activation of avian gonads. *Science, 118,* 351–52.

———. 1953b. The roles of darkness and light in the photoperiodic response of the testes of white-crowned sparrows. *Biol. Bull., 105,* 434–41.

Fraps, R. M. 1954. Neural basis of diurnal periodicity in release of ovulation-inducing hormone in fowl. *Proc. Natl. Acad. Sci. U. S., 40,* 348–56.

———. 1955a. The varying effects of sex hormones in birds. *Mem. Soc. Endocrinol., 4,* 205–19.

———. 1955b. Egg production and fertility in poultry. *Progress in the Physiology of Farm Animals, 2,* 661–740. Butterworths Scientific Publications, London.

Fraps, R. M., and H. L. Fevold. 1955. Delaying action of gonadotrophins on ovulation in the hen. *Proc. Soc. Exptl. Biol. Med., 90,* 440–46.

Fraps, R. M., B. H. Neher, and I. Rothchild. 1947. The imposition of diurnal ovulatory and temperature rhythms by periodic feeding of hens maintained under continuous light. *Endocrinology, 40,* 241–50.

Goodale, H. D. 1923. The influence of certain methods of management on egg production. I. Their influence on winter egg production. *Poultry Sci., 3,* 173–79.

Greer, M. A. 1957. Studies on the influence of the central nervous system on anterior pituitary function. *Recent Progr. Hormone Research, 13,* 67–104.

Hammond, J., Jr. 1954. Light regulations of hormone secretion. *Vitamins and Hormones, 12,* 157–206.

Harris, G. W. 1955. *Neural Control of the Pituitary Gland.* Monographs Physiological Society, No. 3. Edward Arnold Ltd., London.

Heywang, B. W. 1938. The time factor in egg production. *Poultry Sci., 17,* 240–47.

Huston, T. M. and A. V. Nalbandov. 1953. Neurohumoral control of the pituitary in the fowl. *Endocrinology, 52,* 149–56.

Hutt, F. C. 1949. *Genetics of the Fowl.* McGraw-Hill, New York.

Jull, M. A. 1952. *Poultry Breeding.* Wiley, New York.

Kennard, D. C., and V. D. Chamberlin. 1931. All-night light for layers. *Ohio Agr. Expt. Sta. Bull. 476.*

McNally, E. H. 1946. Time of lay in relation to time of feeding of hens maintained under continuous and periodic lighting. *Anat. Record, 96,* 588.

Marshall, F. H. A. 1936. The Croonian lecture: sexual periodicity and the causes which determine it. *Phil. Trans. Roy. Soc. London, 226,* 423–56.

———. 1942. Exteroceptive factors in sexual periodicity. *Biol. Revs., 17,* 68–90.

———. 1956. *The Breeding Season. Marshall's Physiology of Reproduction,* Vol. 1, Pt. 1, pp. 1–42. A. S. Parkes, Editor. Longmans, Green, New York.

Moore, O. K., and N. R. Mehrhof. 1946. Periodic increase in lighting versus continuous lighting for layers. *Florida Agr. Expt. Sta. Bull. 420.*

Nalbandov, A. V. 1953. Endocrine control of physiological functions. *Poultry Sci., 32,* 88–103.

Neher, B. H., and R. M. Fraps. 1950. The addition of eggs to the hen's clutch by repeated injections of ovulation-inducing hormone. *Endocrinology, 46,* 482–88.

Nicholas, J. E., E. W. Callenbach, and R. R. Murphy. 1944. Light intensity as a factor in the artificial illumination of pullets. *Penn. Agr. Expt. Sta. Bull. 462.*

Penquite, R., and R. B. Thomson. 1933. Influence of continuous light on leghorns. *Poultry Sci., 12,* 201–05.

Platt, C. S. 1953. Maintaining winter egg production by the use of dim red light. *Poultry Sci., 32,* 143–45.

Rider, P. L. 1938. The influence of light on growth and reproduction of the domestic fowl. Unpublished Master's thesis, Ohio State University, Columbus.

Roberts, June, and J. S. Carver. 1941. Electric light for egg production. *Agr. Eng., 22,* 357–62, 364.

Romanoff, A. L., and A. J. Romanoff. 1949. *The Avian Egg.* Wiley, New York.

Rothchild, I., and R. M. Fraps. 1949. The interval between normal release of ovulating hormone and ovulation in the domestic hen. *Endocrinology, 44,* 134–40.

Rowan, W. 1938. Light and seasonal reproduction in animals. *Biol. Revs., 13,* 374–402.

Scott, H. M., and L. F. Payne. 1937. Light in relation to the experimental modification of the breeding season in turkeys. *Poultry Sci., 16,* 90–96.

Staffe, A. 1950. Weitere Untersuchungen über die Wirkung des Lichtschocks auf die Legeleistung. *Der Geflügelhof, 13,* 446–49, 510–14.

———. 1951. Belichtung und Legeleistung beim Huhn. *Experientia, 7,* 399–400.

Warren, D. C., and H. M. Scott. 1936. Influence of light on ovulation in the fowl. *J. Exptl. Zool., 74,* 137–56.

Weber, W. A. 1951. Influence of light shock on the laying potential. *Proc. 9th World's Poultry Congr., Paris, 2,* 99–101.

Whetham, Elizabeth O. 1933. Factors modifying egg production with special reference to seasonal changes. *J. Agr. Sci., 23,* 383–418.

Wilson, W. O., and H. Abplanalp. 1956. Intermittent light stimuli in egg production of chickens. *Poultry Sci., 35,* 532–38.

EGG PRODUCTION OF CHICKENS IN DARKNESS

W. O. WILSON and A. E. WOODARD
Poultry Husbandry Department, University of California, Davis

In the course of selection for high egg production, poultry breeders have apparently favored hens with low light requirements. Experiments were designed to determine the amount of light per 24 hr necessary for an all-or-none response for egg laying in White Leghorns. Since we had obtained 70% egg production with 6 min of light per 24 hr (Wilson and Abplanalp, 1956), it seemed desirable to try complete darkness. The results of these tests are reported herein.

The SCW Leghorn hens used in the tests were kept in individual cages. They were trained to eat and drink in darkness by exposing them to intermittent light for several days before the start of the test. The room in which the hens were kept was darkened with black polyethylene film and ventilated by fans equipped with suitable light traps. Feed and water were constantly available. The eggs were collected daily, the attendant using a miniature flashlight to record eggs. The amount of light inside was approximately 0.0002 ft-c during the midday hour.

The first test was with 60 laying hens kept in three separate pens of 20 hens each. The hens in the second test were a select group of 40 hens that laid at a high rate.

The results of egg production for the five-week test period are shown in Fig. 1. In the first test, egg production dropped from 66 to 23% in the fourth week and increased very slightly the last week. At the end of the dark period the hens were moved outside, and egg production increased rapidly. In the second test egg production decreased less rapidly. It was still 43% in the fourth week of darkness. A respiratory disease caused considerable mortality and a decline in egg production in the fifth week. Thirty-six percent of all hens were laying at the end of the test. The lowered egg-production rate was due to cessation of egg production by individual hens. Production of hens

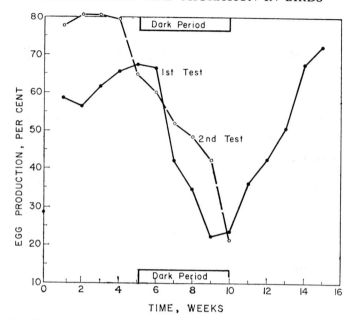

Fɪɢ. 1.   Egg production of hen in tests 1 and 2 during five weeks of darkness. Test 2 was terminated at the end of the dark period.

that continued to lay was 60.2 and 77.1 % for the first and second tests, respectively.

The loss in body weight was associated with pausing. The hens that paused lost approximately 20% of their initial weight, whereas those that laid throughout the test lost only 2.8 and 10.7% of their initial weight in tests 1 and 2, respectively.

One might assume that a hen that does not stop laying immediately because of darkness would continue to mature and lay only those ova that were in the process of maturation before the bird was deprived of light. If so, most hens would stop laying after about 10 to 14 days. We observed that 43 and 5% of the hens stopped laying in the second week in the first and second test, respectively.

It is apparent from these tests that some hens in our strain of White Leghorns did not require light for either ovulation or oviposition, and that factors other than light had a regulatory influence on these functions.

REFERENCE

Wilson, W. O., and H. Abplanalp. 1956. Intermittent light stimuli in egg production of chickens. *Poultry Sci.,* 35, 532–38.

SECTION XI

*Control of Periodic Functions
in Mammals by Light*

EXPERIMENTAL MODIFICATION OF MAMMALIAN ENDOGENOUS ACTIVITY RHYTHMS *

KENNETH S. RAWSON
Zoology Department, University of Wisconsin, Madison

Endogenous rhythms of approximately 24 hr have been demonstrated in both vertebrate and invertebrate animals. Review papers of Welsh (1938), Kleitman (1949), and Aschoff (1954) provide extensive summaries. The stimuli which govern the expression of an endogenous rhythm arise within the animal rather than from any cyclic aspect of the environment. Daily cycles of light and dark or high and low temperatures regulate the rhythms of animals so that they coincide with the 24-hr cycle of the natural environment.

I shall describe a method used to measure the rhythms of small mammals, discuss the responses of mice (*Peromyscus*) to various treatments with light, and present results obtained by varying the body temperature.

The motor activity of an animal has been used by many investigators to measure the endogenous 24-hr rhythm. Aschoff (1952) has recorded total activity in spring-mounted cages and has found that the time of maximum activity fluctuates about a constant mean value. These fluctuations may, however, amount to as much as ±2 hr per day (Aschoff, 1955).

I find that, for rodents, restricting the recorded activity to running in a wheel provides an accurate measure of the endogenous 24-hr rhythm, although some of the total activity, for instance that associated with feeding or movement in the nest, is not recorded. The recording cage provides food, water, and a nest in a stationary part with free access to a running wheel 10 inches in diameter. Standard experimental conditions are: constant darkness, continuously available food

* A part of this material is from the author's doctoral dissertation, Harvard University (see Rawson, 1956). Work was supported in part by a predoctoral fellowship from the National Science Foundation and in part by a grant from the Wisconsin Alumni Research Fund.

and water, and an ambient temperature constant within $\pm 2°C$ and without daily fluctuations. The running wheel operates an electric switch which, through a counting circuit, moves a penpoint on the recording paper. The pen is reset to the base line every minute; so the envelope of the solid graph represents the rate of turning of the wheel in revolutions per minute.

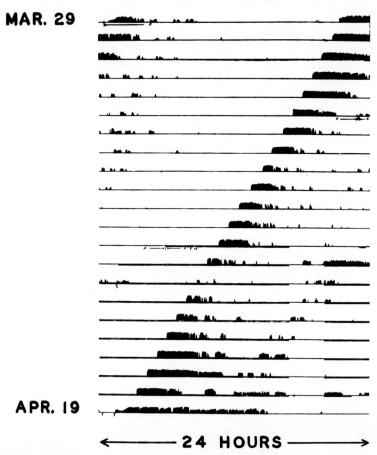

MAR. 29

APR. 19

← —— **24 HOURS** ——→

Fig. 1.   Twenty-two-day records of running activity of a female adult *Peromyscus* in constant darkness. Abscissa, 24-hr time span running from left to right. Ordinate, successive days from top to bottom. Ordinate of each daily record, number of revolutions of running wheel per minute. Maximum rate shown about 125 rev/min. Period of rhythm, 23 hr 10 min.

Figure 1 shows a record of a white-footed mouse, *Peromyscus leucopus noveboracensis,* recorded in constant darkness. The maximum rate shown here is about 125 revolutions per minute. Each horizontal line represents a single 24-hr span. Twenty-two days' records are shown from the top to the bottom of the figure. The records can be read accurately to within about 2 min. It is evident from the graph that the onset of activity forms a very accurate measure of the period of the rhythm, while the total amount and the duration of the activity may vary from day to day. In constant darkness,

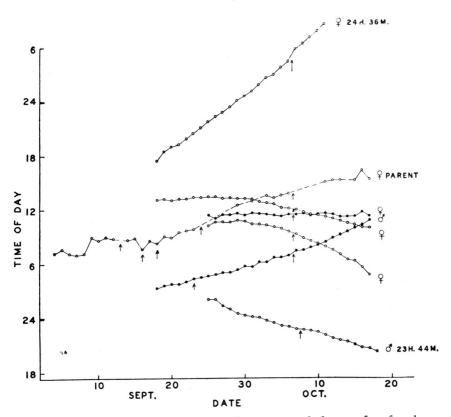

FIG. 2. Times of onset of activity in constant darkness of a female *Peromyscus* and her litter of six young. Animals recorded in separate cages. Disturbance with a light in adding food indicated by arrows. Ordinate is extended beyond midnight in both directions to aid in following records of two mice. Young born August 20.

this particular animal became active 50 min earlier each day or, in other words, the period of its rhythm was 23 hr 10 min.

The fact that the periods recorded simultaneously for a number of *Peromyscus* range from values slightly less than 23 hr to slightly in excess of 24 hr shows that no external cyclic clue is involved. Figure 2 illustrates this point, showing the times of onset of activity of a female *Peromyscus* and her litter of six young born and raised in constant darkness. Each young mouse was removed to a separate cage on the day of the beginning of its appearance on this graph. The divergence of the period lengths of the rhythms of the young mice and their mother differs from the results of similar experiments obtained by Aschoff (1955) for *Mus,* in which the young had approximately the same period length as the mother.

Although the 24-hr rhythm is basically endogenous, it is sensitive to, and may be synchronized by, some environmental factors. Of these factors light has the strongest effect.

LIGHT EFFECTS

The effect of constant light on nocturnal rodents is to cause a daily delay in the time of onset of activity as long as the light persists. A quantitative exponential relationship between the light intensity and the magnitude of the daily delay of the midpoint of activity was first shown by Johnson (1939) for *Peromyscus.* My own results confirm this relation (Rawson, 1956).

Presenting 12 hr of light during the period when the mouse is active produces a delay equal to that produced by constant light. If the light of the same intensity is presented only during the inactive period, there is no delaying effect on the rhythm.

This differential response to light allows an animal with a rhythm shorter than 24 hr to bring its endogenous activity rhythm into synchrony with the 24-hr cycle of light and dark. Figure 3 shows the synchronization of a rhythm of period shorter than 24 hr (actually 22 hr 50 min) to a 24-hr light cycle with 12 hr light per day. The double horizontal line in the figure indicates the occurrence of the light. The basic rhythm returned when the animal was again subjected to constant darkness.

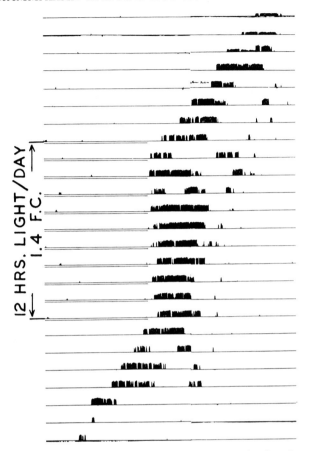

FIG. 3.   Twenty-five-day record of running activity of a female *Peromyscus*. Initial rhythm in constant darkness 22 hr 50 min. Twelve-hour light period indicated by horizontal line under daily record. Coordinates as in Fig. 1.

A mouse with an endogenous rhythm longer than 24 hr is also able to synchronize its activity to a 24-hr light cycle. In Fig. 4 the record of such a mouse is given. Spans of 2 hr of light per day were presented for nine consecutive days and are represented by the short horizontal lines under the daily activity records. In this case the light fails to cause a delay in the time of onset of the active period, but rather stops the progressive shift of the rhythm, synchronizing it to 24 hr. Another *Peromyscus* which had a period in constant darkness of 24 hr 10 min

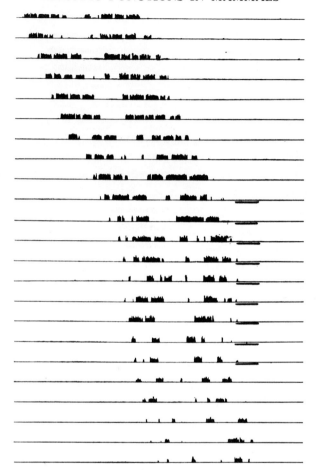

FIG. 4.   Twenty-three-day record of running activity of a young female *Peromyscus* with a period length in constant darkness of 24 hr 40 min. Light cycle of 2 hr light per day presented for 9 days (short horizontal lines under daily record). Coordinates as in Fig. 1.

synchronized to a 24-hr cycle of 12 hr light per day. This animal was then subjected to constant light and showed a daily delay in the onset of activity of about 30 min. In constant darkness it again showed a period of about 24 hr 10 min. Similar observations with *Peromyscus* have been made (Pittendrigh, personal communication). Apparently light presented at the end of the period of activity has a different effect from light presented either continuously or near the beginning of the active period.

Diurnal birds (Wagner, 1930; Aschoff, 1953) and lizards (Hoffmann, 1955) have rhythms typically shorter than 24 hr in constant light and longer than 24 hr in constant darkness. I have attempted to confirm this relation for a diurnal mammal, using the chipmunk *Tamias striatus lysteri* as the experimental animal. The recorded rhythms of these animals were less consistent than those of *Peromyscus,* showing major shifts in the phase of the rhythm as a result of small disturbances. Of the eight animals studied only three showed clear responses to constant light and constant darkness. One of these records is shown in Fig. 5. An initial rhythm of 24 hr 15 min in dim constant light is followed by a rhythm of approximately 26 hr 15 min in constant darkness. The period length then returned to about 24 hr 30 min in constant light. Another chipmunk had a 23-hr rhythm in constant light (0.5 ft-c) and a 24-hr 40-min rhythm in constant darkness. The third chipmunk showed a 23-hr rhythm in constant light (0.34 ft-c) and a 25-hr rhythm in constant darkness. The responses of the three chipmunks are consistent with the responses of other diurnal vertebrates.

TEMPERATURE EFFECTS

Investigations of endogenous rhythms in invertebrates have shown these rhythms to be nearly independent of tissue temperature within the normal ecological temperature range of these poikilothermic organisms (see Bruce and Pittendrigh, 1956). With the method described for accurately measuring the periods of mammalian activity rhythms, it was possible to investigate the effects of changes in body temperature on the 24-hr rhythms of normally homoiothermic mammals.

Lowering the body temperature of *Peromyscus* under sodium pentobarbital anesthesia for periods of from 5 to 8 hr lengthened the period during which the cooling occurred. This resulted in a measurable delay in the time of onset of the following active period. The average body temperature during the period of cooling was deter-

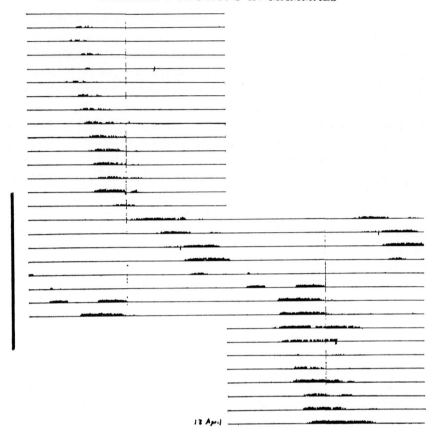

13 April

FIG. 5.   Thirty-two-day record of running activity of a female chipmunk. First and last periods in constant dim light (0.5 ft-c). Duration of period of constant darkness in middle of record shown by vertical heavy line. The record has been repeated (double width) to show the activity pattern passing the limit of the initial 24-hr span. Otherwise coordinates as in Fig. 1.

mined, and from these values a temperature coefficient (Q_{10}) for the rhythm was calculated. For seven cases in which the body temperature was depressed 6° to 17°C, the Q_{10} values ranged from about 1.1 to 1.4. In three cases the body temperature was maintained at 37°C under anesthesia. In two of the cases there was no delay in the onset of activity, while the delay shown by the third case was probably due to disturbing the animal with light during its active period (repair of an apparatus failure) (Rawson, 1956).

Two hamsters (*Mesocricetus auratus*) were cooled by the method of Andjus and Smith (1954) to body temperatures averaging 14°C and 17°C for periods of about 3 hr. Both experiments gave Q_{10} values of 1.1. All these values are low compared with the temperature coefficients of 2 to 3 frequently encountered in biological systems.

I approached this problem in another way, studying the effects of ambient temperatures on the activity rhythms of two species of bats, *Myotis lucifugus* and *Eptesicus fuscus*. Recordings of these animals were made, using spring-mounted cages with the time of onset of the major burst of total activity used as the measure of the rhythm. Since these bats are essentially poikilothermic when inactive, it was possible to vary tissue temperature simply by changing the environmental temperature. The average period length could be determined over a span of several days at each temperature. Q_{10} values were calculated from the differences between the mean values of the period length of the rhythm at different temperatures ranging from 10°C to 22°C. Ten determinations made with two animals resulted in Q_{10} values uniformly low, ranging from 1.04 to 1.07 (Rawson, 1956).

The results presented show that these mammalian endogenous activity rhythms are nearly, but not completely, temperature-independent. The low temperature coefficients found suggest that the rhythm is not directly dependent for its timing on the *rate* of metabolism of some part of the organism. In accord with this view I have been unable to alter the rhythm of *Peromyscus* by increasing the metabolic rate of animals in a cold environment or by the administration of drugs having metabolic effects.

SUMMARY

These 24-hr rhythms are endogenous, can exhibit a remarkable degree of accuracy, and are stable relative to many environmental and experimental variables. I have so far succeeded only in the experimental alteration of the period of the rhythm by varying light conditions and body temperature. The modification of the endogenous rhythm by light is of importance to the animal in synchronizing it to the 24-hr cycle of the environment. The effect of tissue temperature on the rhythm is minor; however, it may prove to be of particular value in determining the exact physiological mechanisms involved in the endogenous rhythm.

REFERENCES

Andjus, R. K., and A. Smith. 1954. Revival of hypothermic rats after arrest of circulation and respiration. *J. Physiol.*, *123*, 66P–67P.

Aschoff, J. 1952. Aktivitätsperiodik von Mäusen im Dauerdunkel. *Pflügers Arch. ges. Physiol.*, *255*, 189–96.

———. 1953. Aktivitätsperiodik bei Gimpeln unter natürlichen und kunstlichen Belichtungsverhaltnissen. *Z. vergl. Physiol.*, *35*, 159–66.

———. 1954. Zeitgeber der tierischen Tagesperiodik. *Naturwiss.*, *41*, 49–56.

———. 1955. Tagesperiodik bei Mäusestämmen unter konstanten Umgebungsbedingungen. *Pflügers Arch. ges. Physiol.*, *262*, 51–59.

Bruce, V., and C. S. Pittendrigh. 1956. Temperature independence in a unicellular "clock." *Proc. Natl. Acad. Sci. U. S.*, *42*, 676–82.

Hoffmann, K. 1955. Aktivitätsregistrierungen bei frisch geschlüpften Eidechsen. *Z. vergl. Physiol.*, *37*, 253–62.

Johnson, M. S. 1939. Effect of continuous light on periodic spontaneous activity of white-footed mice (*Peromyscus*). *J. Exptl. Zool.*, *82*, 315–28.

Kleitman, N. 1949. Biological rhythms and cycles. *Physiol. Revs.*, *29*, 1–30.

Rawson, K. S. 1956. Homing behavior and endogenous activity rhythms. Ph.D. Thesis, Harvard University, Cambridge, Mass.

Wagner, H. O. 1930. Über Jahres und Tagesrhythmus bei zugvögeln. *Z. vergl. Physiol.*, *12*, 703–24.

Welsh, J. H. 1938. Diurnal rhythms. *Quart. Rev. Biol.*, *13*, 123–39.

EXPERIMENTS ON LIGHT AND TEMPERATURE IN A WILD MAMMAL WITH AN ANNUAL BREEDING SEASON

LEMEN J. WELLS

Department of Anatomy, University of Minnesota, Minneapolis

The breeding season of the ground squirrel (*Citellus tridecemlineatus*) occurs in the spring, soon after the animals emerge from hibernation. During the summer, in males and females, the reproductive tract retrogresses to a juvenile-like condition, and the hypophysis cerebri is no longer rich in gonadotropin.

Using incandescent bulbs and a time switch, we began experiments on the daily ration of light in the autumn. The light was increased gradually, within a period of 2 months, from 12 hr per day to 22 hr per day. Thereafter, such animals were given 22 hr of light per day for 3 months. These treatments failed to hasten the functional development of certain endocrine glands: gonads, hypophysis, adrenals, and thyroid (Moore *et al.*, 1934; Simmons, 1934; Wells, 1935; Zalesky, 1934, 1935).

Subjection of animals to a constant temperature of 4°C, beginning in the spring, produced definite effects (Wells, 1938; Wells and Zalesky, 1940; Zalesky and Wells, 1940). The gonads failed to undergo retrogression, the hypophysis continued to show a high level of gonadotropin, and the adrenal cortex resembled that found during the breeding season.

Experimental combinations of light and temperature were tried: ultraviolet and 4°C; 12 hr of light per day (incandescent bulbs) and 18°C; darkness and summer room temperature. The effects upon the endocrine glands were like those in experiments in which temperature alone was modified (Wells, 1938; Wells and Zalesky, 1940; Zalesky and Wells, 1940).

The several observations suggest that in this species low environmental temperature stimulates the functioning of the hypophysis cerebri (the master gland) and that the amount of light per day does not influence this gland.

REFERENCES

Moore, C. R., G. F. Simmons, L. J. Wells, M. Zalesky, and W. O. Nelson. 1934. On the control of reproductive activity in an annual-breeding mammal (*Citellus tridecemlineatus*). *Anat. Record, 60,* 279–89.

Simmons, G. F. 1934. A study of sexual periodicity and its control in the female rodent *Citellus.* Dissertation, The University of Chicago Library, Chicago.

Wells, L. J. 1935. Seasonal sexual rhythm and its experimental modification in the male of the thirteen-lined ground squirrel (*Citellus tridecemlineatus*). *Anat. Record, 62,* 409–47.

———. 1938. Gonadotropic potency of the hypophysis in a wild male rodent with annual rut. *Endocrinology, 22,* 588–94.

Wells, L. J., and M. Zalesky. 1940. Effects of low environmental temperature on the reproductive organs of male mammals with annual aspermia. *Am. J. Anat., 66,* 429–47.

Zalesky, M. 1934. A study of the seasonal changes in the adrenal gland of the thirteen-lined ground squirrel (*Citellus tridecemlineatus*), with particular reference to its sexual cycle. *Anat. Record, 60,* 291–321.

———. 1935. A study of the seasonal changes in the thyroid gland of the thirteen-lined ground squirrel (*Citellus tridecemlineatus*), with particular reference to its sexual cycle. *Anat. Record, 62,* 109–37.

Zalesky, M., and L. J. Wells. 1940. Effects of low environmental temperature on the thyroid and adrenal glands of the ground squirrel, *Citellus tridecemlineatus. Physiol. Zoöl., 13,* 268–76.

PHYSIOLOGIC 24-HOUR PERIODICITY IN HUMAN BEINGS AND MICE, THE LIGHTING REGIMEN AND DAILY ROUTINE [1]

FRANZ HALBERG, ERNA HALBERG, CYRUS P. BARNUM and JOHN J. BITTNER

The Division of Cancer Biology, Department of Pathology and the Department of Physiologic Chemistry, University of Minnesota, Minneapolis, and the Cambridge State School and Hospital, Cambridge, Minnesota

Among the various characteristics of a given periodic function, we want to measure, of course, its period, amplitude, and phase. The omission of such measurements is hardly a matter of choice; it is a problem of practicability, which often can be overcome. It may be appropriate, therefore, to allude first to the uses (and limitations) of the periodogram technique, as it can be applied to biologic wave analysis. Some illustrative results may stimulate endeavors for improving the measurement of cyclic characteristics in physiologic work beyond the application of periodograms, which serve herein merely as first approximations. Periodograms will then be applied to the study of daily periodicity, as it occurs in blinded animals, apparently in the absence of photic effects. Thereafter, we shall turn to basic mechanisms, which maintain certain rhythms in an "aperiodic" environment: *inter alia,* the adrenal cycle and a periodic sequence of events in the cell. Thus we shall set the stage for exploring a broad field of photic effects, exerted at different levels of mammalian organization. It will become apparent that certain *phase* relations of 24-hr periodic functions are critically controlled by the environment, while the *period* of the same phenomena is relatively independent of light and temperature. Most of the data will describe mice, but the studies were carried out with man in mind, and findings on human beings will be included. For several

[1] Supported by the Elsa U. Pardee Foundation, the Department of Public Welfare, State of Minnesota, the American Cancer Society, the U. S. Public Health Service, the Graduate School at the University of Minnesota, and the United States Testing Company, Hoboken, New Jersey.

functions, a comparison of the environmental "lock-in" of rhythm in human beings and mice will reveal important differences in phase. This interesting species difference notwithstanding, certain basic mechanisms such as the adrenal cycle are shared by several mammals. Some type of a periodic cellular sequence of events in turn most likely characterizes many forms of life, including those devoid of conventional hormones and/or nerves.

The term "periodicity analysis" will be used with reference to various methodological and other considerations arising from the study of physiologic 24-hr periodicity (Halberg, in press). The choice of this term, not qualified as to length of period, is made for the sake of brevity. The term circadian [(L) *circa,* about + (L) *dies,* day] will be used to denote daily periods which may differ from 24 hr by not more than a few hours. Circadian periods thus may be slightly shorter or longer than 24 hr. Other definitions have been given elsewhere (Halberg, 1953, 1955a, and in press).

METHOD

In mammals, the lighting regimen of the environment affects, of course, many body functions, the approach to its effect on a given function, in turn, being largely determined by the available techniques. But over and above the choice of a given biochemical or biophysical procedure, the analysis of lighting effects upon body rhythms, or the study of the rhythms themselves, poses additional methodological problems. The choice of experimental animal, the uncertainties of measurement and sampling procedure (Halberg, 1946; Koehler *et al.,* 1956), the conditions of study, the variability of time series, and the analytical statistics that become thus indispensable—all of these are general problems of periodicity analysis. Our particular approach to them has repeatedly been discussed (Halberg, 1953, 1955a, and in press). Only one point may deserve emphasis herein, in view of its broader potential usefulness in biologic research. It is the desirability of obtaining numerical estimates of the period and the amplitude in our work on a given biologic periodicity, just as we do in dealing with a physical periodicity. But to get these two estimates reliably is much more difficult in the case of physiologic rhythms than in that of physical periodicities, since the former phenomena do not exhibit the strict regularity of the latter. The "regularity" of data on physiologic periodicity is usually only an approximation. Thus arises the knotty problem of how to acquire a quantitative description of bodily periodicity in terms of sample estimates of period and amplitude. The short-range data, which are quite adequate in order to establish the occurrence of a given physiologic rhythm, no longer are satisfactory —more extensive time series are usually required. To long-range data in turn, mathematical methods may be applied, such as the periodogram or correlogram analysis—yet such methods have their limitations. The dangers associated with the use of various formulas for periodicity analysis must also be recognized, if we are to apply such mathematical methods fruitfully. Let us therefore note, first, what periodograms are not likely to do reliably for periodicity analysis, before we illustrate their uses.

In the past, periodograms, among other computational procedures, have repeatedly been employed for the detection of periodicity in a given geophysical or other time series. Similar searches for physiologic periodicity, carried out merely by the application of a mathematical method to an arbitrary biologic time series, are not recommended herein as the procedure of choice, since spurious as well as real periods may thus be described, while real ones occasionally may be concealed (Gumbel *et al.,* 1953). Indeed, different "periodicities" may be obtained from the same time series by the use of different formulas. Along these lines of thought, justified criticisms of the periodogram have been made (Cole, 1957). But by references to such examples, the entire field of periodicity analysis must not be discredited. We can use periodograms for the study of physiologic periodicity without searching for some imaginary period (Koehler *et al.,* 1956). The method can be applied to phenomena for which, under appropriate circumstances of observation, the reality of a given period has empirically been noted and for which, in addition, the statistical significance of the periodicity has independently been ascertained. If, then, the periodogram will yield periods other than those anticipated, the reality of such periods, in turn, can again be checked empirically, in additional studies. By proceeding along such lines, we minimize the dangers of dealing with spurious periodicities, i.e., with artifacts of the periodogram. Just as we use other averages in medical research, we may then compute periodograms in order to describe the average period or amplitude of a given bodily rhythm.

Thus, the important use of the periodogram consists of the quantitative description of periodicities in terms of the sample estimates of both period and amplitude. These summary constants are obtained by establishing certain relationships between the data on the one hand, and the sines and cosines of certain trial periods chosen by ourselves on the other hand. The method of obtaining Schuster periodogram estimates of the period (τ) and the amplitude (C) for physiologic time series consisting of discrete data has been outlined elsewhere (Koehler *et al.,* 1956). Tables also are available which should facilitate the computation of certain periodograms by reducing the labor involved (Koehler *et al.,* 1956). Moreover, if periodograms become desirable on a larger scale, it is expedient to obtain them with the help of electronic computers (Fig. 1).

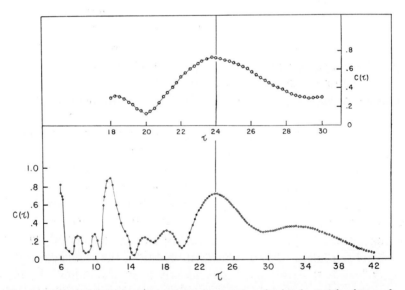

FIG. 1.   Periodogram on rectal temperatures obtained at 4-hr intervals for several days, from an individual mouse. Peak at ⌐24 hr is well defined, describing an empirically verified period. Shorter periods described by higher peaks also come to the fore. Such a detailed analysis by electronic computer would require an undue amount of conventional computing.

Important features of the periodogram are: (1) its maximum occurs for the trial period which corresponds to the period of our function studied, and (2) the value of its maximum is the amplitude C of our function. For an arbitrary function, the periodogram may exhibit any shape whatsoever. But if the periodogram has a well-defined maximum point, the abscissa of this point may be taken as the estimate of the period and the ordinate as the estimate of the amplitude (Koehler *et al.*, 1956).

In dealing with such estimates, we must realize, of course, that they represent descriptive rather than analytical statistics. The adequacy of the description (i.e., the precision and sampling variability of the estimates τ and C) depends heavily upon the precision and fundamental variability of the original measurements. The usefulness of periodograms in exploring questions concerning both the reality of a periodicity and the sampling behavior of the estimates of its period and amplitude thus also depends upon the precision and basic variability of the original measurements. Moreover, as has been emphasized earlier, the uncertainties of repeated physiologic measurements also must be considered in this connection.

Let us now illustrate the application of the periodogram technique to the study of the rhythm in body temperature of intact mice. Rectal

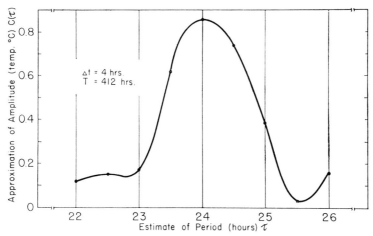

FIG. 2.   Periodogram computed from the mean rectal temperature data of a group of male CBC mice ($\Delta t = 4$ hr, $T = 412$ hr).

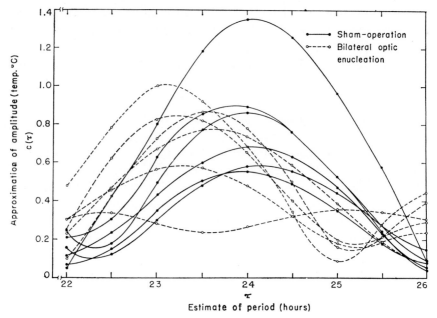

FIG. 3.   Slight but clear shortening of period (τ) of temperature rhythm during the first month after blinding revealed by periodograms on data from individual mice. Note that such circadian periods vary from animal to animal.

temperatures, measured at 4-hr intervals ($\Delta t = 4$ hr), over a period T of several days, served for the computation of the curves in Figs. 2–5. The maximum at about 24 hr (but not always at exactly 24 hr) stands out clearly, unmasked from the interference of shorter-term variations in rectal temperature such as are associated with the spurts of activity and feeding of rodents (cf. Fig. 1).

Next, we shall examine the periodogram as applied to the study of temperature rhythm in human beings. Rectal temperatures were measured at $\Delta t = 1.5$ hr for $T = 97.5$ hr, on several human subjects. Periodograms computed for the group mean of rectal temperature are shown in Fig. 6. All the data obtained on the group of subjects served for computing the curve drawn as a continuous line; only one-half of the data was used for the computation of the curve shown as a dotted line, every second group mean of the time series being omitted. It is readily apparent from Fig. 6 that the periodogram technique yielded

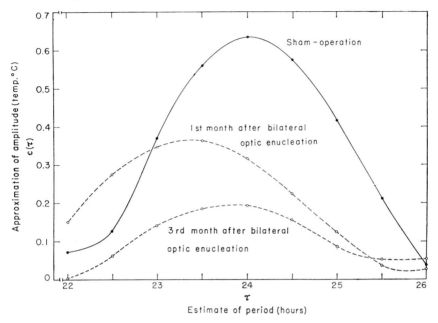

F<small>IG</small>. 4.   During the third month after operation, differences in the circadian temperature periods of individual blinded mice bring about a decrease in amplitude of the mean for the blinded group.

results which describe the daily periodicity studied in terms of both its period and its amplitude. Moreover, the periodogram based upon Δt = 3 hr is roughly comparable to that based upon $\Delta t = 1.5$ hr. Consequently, in subsequent studies on the subjects, measurements were made at 3-hr intervals, rather than at intervals of 1.5 hr. This reduction by one-half of the number of measurements certainly eased the workload of the investigators. But, possibly, a more important consequence of the choice of $\Delta t = 3.0$ over $\Delta t = 1.5$ is the probable reduction of interference (by measurement) with the phenomenon studied (Halberg, in press; Koehler *et al.*, 1956).

Other illustrative periodograms are shown in Fig. 7. We check such results invariably by the empirical interpretation of plots of the measurements, which served for their computation, but this is not always easy, when T is short and τ is close to 24 hr, and we also need a measure of variability of the estimates of τ and C, a measure not yielded in the Schuster periodogram. By using the extended Cramer-Rao in-

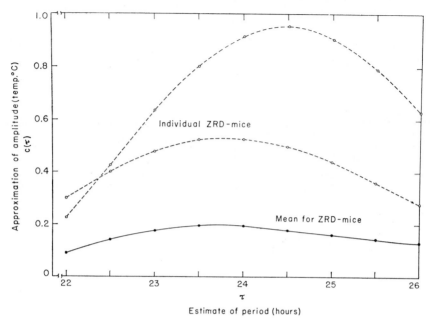

F<small>IG</small>. 5. Circadian periods in rectal temperature of ZRD mice, born blind for several generations. The decrease in amplitude of mean again indicates desynchronization among animals constituting the group (cf. Fig. 4).

equality, dealing with the case when nuisance parameters are present (Lehman, 1950), M. Rao, in our department, has worked out a lower bound for the variance of the estimated period, thereby enhancing the value of periodograms for analyses of time series to which a periodic model does not strictly apply. For these cases, the use of correlograms (Kendall, 1948) and of other computational procedures (cf. Parzen, 1957a,b) also is pertinent. Probably existing models will have to be "dressed up" with a few stochastic processes, an endeavor started at the University of Minnesota by M. Rao, under the guidance of Professor I. R. Savage. Such mathematical operations, in themselves not a biologist's goal, are tools which can contribute substantially to the reliability and reproducibility of studies on rhythms, particularly in clinical research, for which the degree of standardization achieved in work on experimental animals is not easily attainable. We shall allude again to periodograms of physiologic data, while, at this point, we

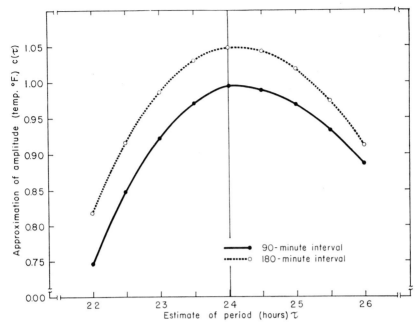

FIG. 6.   Two periodograms computed from the same data on mean rectal temperature of a group of male institutionalized patients. All the data were used in one case ($\Delta t = 90'$), while every second group mean of the time series was omitted in the other case ($\Delta t = 180'$) ($T = 97.5$ hr).

divert our attention away from the mathematical description of a periodicity to some experimental findings which concern the underlying mechanisms.

ANALYSIS OF MECHANISMS

Circadian Periods in the Mammal at Several Levels of Physiologic Organization

As a first approximation to analyses of the mechanisms involved in certain mammalian physiologic 24-hr periodicities, we shall herein distinguish those factors which *maintain* a rhythm from those that synchronize it with its environment. We are attempting this distinction, since as we shall see, a physiologic rhythm can run independently of the 24-hr clock and thus can exhibit phase differences with respect to

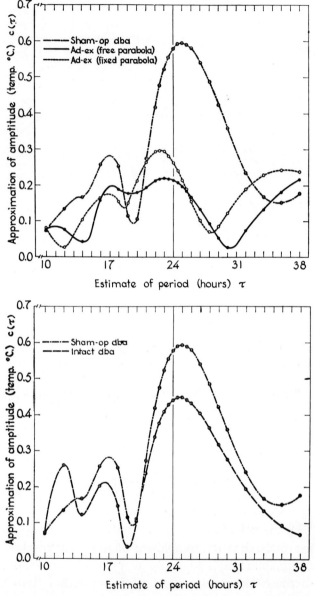

Fig. 7.   Periodograms of temperature variation after adrenalectomy or sham operation in mouse. Note decrease in amplitude and shortening of period of mean temperatures after adrenalectomy and the opposite effect of sham operation.

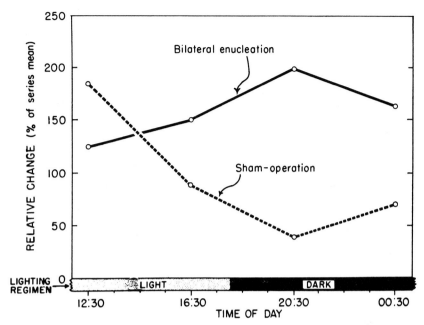

FIG. 8. Corroboration of impression with respect to possible phase differences in eosinophil rhythm of blinded and sham operated animals. Temporary antiphase brought about by operation of circadian periods.

the environmental day. Circadian periods that may be slightly yet significantly different from 24 hr can thus come to the fore. The significance of such periods, e.g., of 23 hr and 20 min duration, for our interpretation of rhythms lies in the fact that we know of no environmental periods of corresponding lengths and consequently we can assume that they are self-determined from within the organism, rather than forced upon it from without. Those circadian periods that are significantly different from 24 hr also constitute the major methodologic pitfalls for those who want to "control" daily rhythms by sampling always at the *same* time of day in an endeavor to obtain comparable data; actually, by such a procedure one makes certain to sample at *different* physiologic times, as soon as free-running periods prevail.

Among mammalian functions other than motor activity, we have studied more extensively the dissociation of rectal temperature rhythm from the environmental time scale, e.g., after blinding of

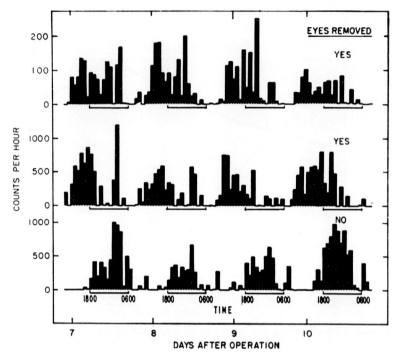

Fɪɢ. 9.   Circadian activity periods of two blinded mice compared with activity of a sham-operated mouse.

mice (Halberg, 1954b, Halberg and Visscher, 1953b, 1954a,b) (Fig. 3).

For the mouse, Fig. 8 reveals data on the eosinophil rhythm, and Figs. 9 and 10 on the rhythm in gross motor body activity, measured according to Bruss *et al.* (1958). It may be suggested that a variety of mammalian functions can "free-run," and that their circadian periods may underlie the dissociation of activity rhythm from the environment, revealed already by some of the earlier work of Johnson (1939), Calhoun (1945), Aschoff (1951), Nothdurft (1951), and Browman (1952) (for review see Aschoff, 1958). With respect to the activity rhythm in the mouse, it is interesting (1) that blinding and the maintenance in continuous darkness have similar effects, (2) that mice born anophthalmic also may exhibit circadian periods (Fig. 5), and (3) that the free-running period of activity rhythm of mice kept in

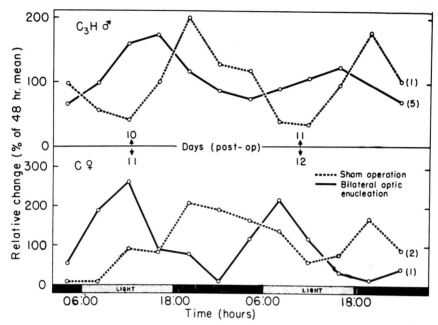

FIG. 10.   Circadian activity periods after blinding in two stocks of mice.

constant darkness is relatively independent of environmental temperature (Fig. 11) (cf. Pittendrigh, 1954). If, then, under several conditions we see different bodily rhythms dissociating themselves from the local time scale, we may remember that thereby (1) the rhythm itself is not lost, (2) "physiologic time" is still being kept by periodic functions, and (3) it is simply a new (average) period which has come to the fore. This has been ascertained after blinding for the rhythms in temperature, blood eosinophils, and body activity of mice, and can also be suggested on the basis of spot checks for the rhythm in pinnal mitoses. In our rectal temperature data, the free-running circadian period is slightly but clearly shorter than 24 hr, a circumstance that accounts for the differences in phase of rhythm between blinded mice and sham-operated mice and this period can be measured as may be seen in Fig. 4, which exhibits periodograms describing the behavior of mean temperatures after blinding. It is apparent that, on the average, during the first month after operation we deal with a shortening of

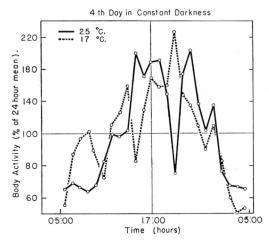

Fig. 11. Circadian periods of body activity in mice kept at different temperatures. Data suggest operation of some mechanisms of temperature compensation for maintenance of circadian periods in gross motor activity.

period. Figure 3 shows, in turn, periodograms computed for data on individual mice. It may be seen, first, that five of the six periodograms exhibit periods shorter than 24 hr. Second, this shortening in period (after blinding) is not the same in all the animals constituting the group. Third, it is pertinent that, at later time points after blinding, there is a tendency toward a resynchronization of the rhythms in blinded and in sham-operated mice. During the third month after blinding, this tendency comes clearly to the fore in the periodogram (Fig. 4); a visual inspection of the plot of mean temperatures, in turn, reveals the tendency toward resynchronization quite clearly at 5 months after blinding but less clearly at 3 months after blinding. In this case, the periodogram detected what the inspection of the data may have missed, and, what is more important, the inference made from the periodogram on data obtained at 3 months after blinding was confirmed by the data obtained another 2 months later.

The above data suggest that stimuli received by the eye can synchronize the 24-hr rhythm in rectal temperature with the environmental time scale, since upon removal of the eyes a dissociation of the rhythm from the environment is seen (Halberg, Visscher, and Bittner, 1954). These data also suggest that stimuli other than those received by the eyes may eventually gain control of the timing of rhythm, and this effect in turn may account for the tendency toward resynchronization seen at the later time points after blinding. For the purpose of analysis, these data thus are of twofold interest.

First, they reveal that the time scale of physiologic 24-hr periodicity need not always be synchronized with the environmental clock hour. Of necessity we go by the local time in our work and, accordingly, we exhibit the clock hour on the abscissas of our graphs. But in doing so, we endeavor to study physiologic time relations rather than occurrences at a given clock hour. We can achieve the former goal reliably only if we ascertain the degree to which the two time scales, the physiologic and the environmental clock hour, are synchronized.

Second, the data analyzed in Fig. 3 reveal the role played by sensory inflow in the synchronization of the two time scales, that of the body and that of the environment. It is from this point of view that we may refer to the synchronizing effect as a result primarily of factors from without.

The terms "Zeitgeber," "clue," and "cue" correspond more or less to "synchronizer" (Halberg, Visscher, and Bittner, 1954), the last term being used herein partly following a line of thought expressed earlier by Kleitman (1949) (see also Kalmus, 1953). With reference to "clues" it has been stated, however, that ". . . their importance lies in the maintenance of rhythm and in keeping it in phase with the environment" (Cloudsley-Thompson, 1956).

The term "Zeitgeber," or "time-giver," in turn, has been qualified so that its meaning is restricted to the synchronizing effect, and "maintenance" is not included among the effects of a "time-giver" (Aschoff, 1954, 1958). The definition of "Zeitgeber" thus is identical to that of synchronizer.

It is important that in the absence of a given dominant synchronizer, such as photic stimuli received by the eye, a given rhythm continues to occur, even though it may do so with a different timing. Therefore, we may postulate the existence of intrinsic mechanisms, which account for the maintenance of rhythm and which normally interact with the extrinsic synchronizer of rhythm. To use a crude and inadequate analogy, we segregate those factors which "set the clock" along the environmental time scale (synchronization, primarily, but not exclu-

sively, from without) from the chain of gear wheels as it is actuated
by springs and weights (maintenance, critically, but not exclusively,
from within).

We have much to learn about those factors concerned with the
maintenance of rhythms, and it seems likely that nervous, endocrine,
and metabolic interactions are involved. At the time of this writing,
however, the role of the adrenals, at least, seems established as a
critical factor in the maintenance of several 24-hr periodicities in the
mammal, even though many of the pertinent data represent merely
spot checks; the nature of the variables involved often limits the frequency of sampling. Thus, for the following considerations, time series
of sufficient length for the numerical estimation of the period or the
amplitude, e.g., by periodograms, are not available. In viewing Fig.
12, we are dealing only with the day-night differences in certain 24-hr

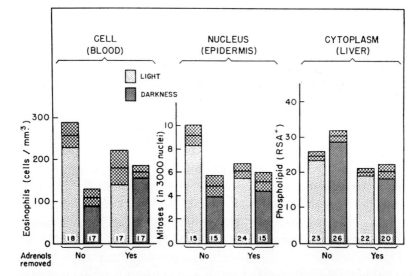

Fig. 12. Effects of adrenalectomy upon blood eosinophils, epidermal
mitoses, and hepatic phospholipid metabolism in the mouse.

periodic variables, selected from several levels of physiologic organization. This figure reveals, however, that such differences are significant
in the presence of the adrenals, but are not statistically significant after
removal of the adrenals (Halberg, Barnum, and Vermund, 1953;

Halberg, Visscher, and Bittner, 1953; Halberg *et al.*, 1956; Vermund *et al.*, 1956). This also applies for human beings, as far as the eosinophil rhythm is concerned (Halberg *et al.*, 1951; Hobbs *et al.*, 1954; Kaine *et al.*, 1955). Moreover, it seems likely that the three variables shown in Fig. 12 are not the only 24-hr periodic variables controlled by the adrenals, since the effect of adrenal hormones has justly been referred to as being almost "ubiquitous" (Sayers, 1950). On the other hand, we know of at least one rhythm (studied with sufficiently frequent sampling in verified cortical adrenal insufficiency) which is not abolished by adrenalectomy, i.e., that in the iron content of human serum (Hamilton *et al.*, 1950; Howard, 1952). At any rate, it may be emphasized that those variables illustrated in Fig. 12 have four characteristics in common. First, they exhibit 24-hr periodicity, and second, they respond in a typical fashion to corticoid administration, as do many other body functions, including the corticoids of blood and urine and the urinary 17-ketosteroids (Appel and Hansen, 1952; Doe *et al.*, 1954, 1956; Forsham *et al.*, 1944; Laidlaw *et al.*, 1954; Migeon *et al.*, 1956; Pincus, 1943; Pincus *et al.*, 1948; Tyler *et al.*, 1954). Thirdly, and decisively for the experimenter interested in relations of the adrenal to periodicity, these indices can be quantitatively studied in a verified state of cortical adrenal insufficiency. Fourthly, the same indices undergo critical changes in their 24-hr periodic behavior under conditions of documented cortical adrenal insufficiency. It has therefore been suggested that the adrenals may be essential for the maintenance of 24-hr periodicity in these body functions (Halberg and Visscher, 1952; Halberg *et al.*, 1951, 1956; Vermund *et al.*, 1956). Additional lines of evidence, while not meeting all the four criteria listed above, nonetheless support as well as extend the conclusion that the adrenals play an important role in the maintenance of 24-hr periodicity. Thus, numerous reports on physiologic 24-hr periodicity describe variables affected by (or dependent upon) adrenal regulation, cortical as well as medullary (references in Halberg, Visscher, and Bittner, 1953). Furthermore, adrenal periodicity, while it is responsive to changes in the external and internal milieus, persists in the absence of those periodic environmental changes which usually determine its temporal placement within the 24-hr period.

It has been suggested, therefore, that a 24-hr adrenal cycle (Halberg, 1953, 1955a; Halberg and Visscher, 1952), may deserve consideration as a critical mechanism underlying our adaptation to daily activities; what seems at least equally important, this cycle integrates the periodic functioning of metabolism in different parts of the body, and thus it serves our preparation for activity. Just as the sexual cycle describes endogenously regulated changes preparatory to copulation and subsequent fertilization, the 24-hr adrenal cycle may describe the process of preparation for each activity in the life of animals and man, necessary for day-to-day survival. The many similarities between the eosinophil and the activity rhythm in mice and in man have served to postulate this hypothesis, which is supported by data obtained in documented states of adrenal insufficiency (Fig. 12) (Brown and Dougherty, 1955; Halberg, Visscher, and Bittner, 1953; Halberg *et al.*, 1951; Kaine *et al.*, 1955). Just as the preparation of smears from the fluid content of the vagina enables the observer to follow the cyclic and other changes of the vaginal and cervical epithelium, the determination of endogenous changes in number of circulating blood eosinophils has proved a simple method for the evaluation of a 24-hr adrenal cortical cycle in mice and in man. *If* judiciously used, this method is dependable. Its use reveals that the 24-hr cycle resembles the sex cycle in being controlled by steroidal hormones. The adrenal cycle differs, however, from the sex cycle, in its persistence under circumstances known to suppress the sex cycle (i.e., a 50% reduction in dietary carbohydrate and fat) (Halberg and Visscher, 1952). Furthermore, the adrenal cycle is already developed, many years before the menstrual cycle starts (Halberg and Ulstrom, 1952). It might be concluded that the 24-hr adrenal cycle is the biologically more essential mechanism.

The Adrenal Cycle

In recognizing the adrenal cycle as a physiologic entity concerned with the maintenance of mammalian periodicity, we adopt a view which is at variance with the unqualified assumption that the 24-hr changes of adrenocortical secretion constitute "responses to the stresses of daily life." The latter interpretation does not distinguish adrenal periodicity from other phenomena that are more directly and more immediately dependent upon environmental control. This same interpretation has further presupposed a "basal" level of adrenocortical activity during sleep and/or rest; thus it seems to ignore the intrinsic aspects of 24-hr periodic cortical adrenal secretion and its time relations to other functions which normally also are periodic.

Figure 13 reveals a rhythm of the gland itself, as evaluated by a morphologic index, the number of mitoses in the cortex. In keeping with earlier data obtained in spot checks at only two times of day on mice (Halberg, Frantz, and Bittner, 1957) and rats (Mühlemann *et*

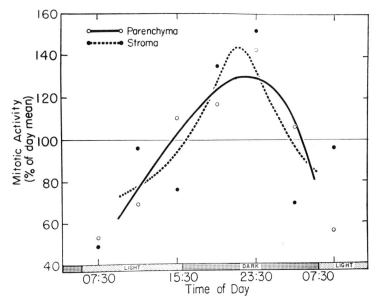

FIG. 13.   Mitotic rhythm in adrenal cortical parenchyma and stroma.

al., 1955), mitotic activity has reached a peak by the middle of the daily dark period. The relation of mitosis to secretion in the gland has been discussed elsewhere (Halberg, Frantz, and Bittner, 1957) on the basis of the time relations of the daily rhythms in eosinophils and in parenchymal adrenal mitoses: eosinophil counts revealed trends that were roughly opposite to those of cortical mitoses. It was suggested as a "probabilistic" relationship (Rashevsky, 1955) that mitotic activity in the cortex increases daily when the hormone is released from the gland and decreases when hormone secretion is resumed (Fig. 14).

By contrast to cortical adrenal mitoses, skin mitoses are roughly in phase with the eosinophil rhythm.

In the course of the experiment partly summarized in Fig. 13, pools of serum from the same mice were obtained for corticosterone determination carried out in different laboratories (Halberg, Peterson, and Silber, in press), as well as more recently in Minnesota (Fig. 14).

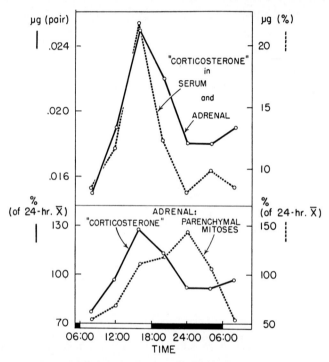

Fig. 14.   Twenty-four-hour rhythms of corticosterone in mouse blood and adrenal in relation to mitoses in glandular parenchyma.

Blood levels of corticosterone in mice were found to exhibit 24-hr periodicity, and the peak blood levels were reliably reproduced at about 16:00, with light daily from 06:00 to 18:00. What seems more important, Fig. 14 further reveals periodic changes in the hormone content of the adrenal cortex itself, and the timing of the adrenal corticosterone rhythm supports the suggestion that mitotic activity in the adrenal cortex proceeds when the hormone is released from the gland.

Also of great physiologic interest is the study of other rhythms, with their time relations to the adrenal cycle, e.g., the onset of blood corticosterone rise and the initiation of motor activity. With this in mind, we may discuss the time relations of body activity and serum corticosterone in data from two experiments in which the serum pools were obtained for corticosterone determination, while motor activity was evaluated during the same period in an electronic actometer on comparable mice. It would appear that the corticoid curve rises prior to the major daily bursts in motor activity, and almost certainly the corticoid curve does not lag behind that of activity. The data thus agree with the suggestion (Halberg, 1953) that the adrenal cycle describes processes occurring, at least in part, in preparation for our daily activities, rather than solely as immediate reactions to them.

Cellular Mechanisms

The mere fact that periodicity exists in lower forms of life, devoid of conventional nerves and hormones, suggests that periodicity may characterize cellular functions even in the absence of a superimposed control such as the adrenal cycle. It is therefore hardly surprising to find in the mammal as well, that 24-hr periodicity is a characteristic of the intracellular level of organization. As in the case of unicellular forms, one of the most obvious periodicities of the cell is that in its mitotic activity. Moreover, in the mammal, with its cells grouped to form tissues or organs, the rhythms of mitoses from one organ to the next, or, in a given tissue, from one region to the next, pose problems of timing that are of physiologic interest. In the mouse, for instance, there is a remarkable degree of synchrony of the epidermal mitotic rhythms in ear pinna and in the interscapular area of back skin (Chaudhry, 1956). In the same species, the timing of mitotic rhythms in liver parenchyma (Halberg, 1957) and in skin epidermis shows a surprising degree of synchronization, as far as data obtained at 4-hr intervals over 24-hr periods are concerned, i.e., at a "magnification" $(\Delta t) = 4$ hr (Halberg, Barnum, Silber, and Bittner, 1958). At a much lower "magnification" it was found in the rat that the mitotic rhythms of pinnal epidermis, of oral mucosa, and of connective tissue in the periodontal membrane also are roughly synchronized (Halberg, Zander, Houglum, and Mühlemann, 1954). The same applies to mitoses in pouch and pinnal epithelium of the hamster (Chaudhry *et al.*, 1958). Thus, on one hand, we may postulate for mitotic rhythms in several tissues and in different species, the operation of systemic controlling mechanisms (which are of obvious interest to the student of cancer). On the other hand, in the mouse, the mitotic rhythm of adrenal parenchyma exhibits important phase differences as compared to the rhythms in liver parenchyma or skin epidermis. This finding, in turn, may be used to suggest that the "night-watchman," the adrenal, assumes a schedule which is quite different from that of tissues, the activity of which it guards. Moreover, in speaking thus of activity we may not have to restrict ourselves to mitotic behavior in the adrenal and elsewhere but, perhaps, we may also draw inferences from the mitotic behavior of a given tissue to its "functional" activity along the 24-hr scale. In this connection, it is pertinent that Peter (1940), among others, has suggested that the factors which regulate mitosis vary inversely with the function of an organ. In the thorough and extensive studies of Blumenfeld (1942), mitotic activity in the renal cortex was minimal at the time of maximal urinary excretion and maximal at the time of minimal urinary excretion. In the submaxillary gland, the same author has found an inverse relationship between the rates of mitotic activity and of functional activity in association with food intake. In view of the foregoing evidence, the basic processes of a cell were divided by Blumenfeld into functional and vegetative activities. One state ceases when the other begins; cells undergo division during the vegetative state, upon cessation of the functional state. With this background of thought, it seemed desirable, of course, to deal more specifically with those cellular processes which characterize in biochemical terms the alternating states of "functional" and "vegetative" activity. We set out in Minnesota to undertake this task of "resolving" cellular events in metabolism along the 24-hr scale. For our first studies we chose mouse liver and a "whole-animal" approach. The simple assumption underlying our work was as follows: if cellular functions normally exhibit 24-hr changes in rate, periodicity analysis ought to reveal important differences in phase of rhythms, for those functions that are dissociated in time (e.g., "functional" versus "vegetative"). The results obtained for a few variables were studied by the combination of several techniques, namely of periodicity analysis

(Halberg, 1953, and in press) and the use of a radiotracer and of differential centrifugation. Moreover, concomitantly, the proportion of cells in mitosis also was determined on slices from the livers used for metabolic work. A two- to threefold decrease in the relative specific activity of DNA (counts/min/μg of DNA P as percentage of counts/min/μg of acid soluble P) was noted from 08:00 to 24:00 and was followed by a sharp peak at 04:00. The interval between the peak in the RSA of DNA and that of mitosis was ~8 hr. This may be considered to be an estimate of the lag period between DNA synthesis and mitosis in intact immature mouse liver (Jardetzky et al., 1956) and is in accord with the 6- to 12-hr lag period noted at a "lower magnification" for regenerating liver (Barnum et al., 1957). In contrast to DNA, however, RSA of both microsomal and nuclear RNA increased rapidly from 16:00 to 20:00 and then gradually dropped to the lower morning values. These results indicate, first, that the metabolism of nucleic acids as well as mitosis, are 24-hr periodic metabolic functions. Second, that certain aspects of cytoplasmic and nuclear RNA metabolism are roughly in phase with each other, and third, that they are dissociated in phase from peak DNA metabolism by a lag of ~8 hr. Finally, another lag period of ~8 hr normally exists between DNA synthesis and mitosis in the immature growing liver.

The relation of peak DNA metabolism to mitosis seems to be of particular interest; the results alluded to above suggest at least certain similarities in the timing of cellular processes, in the mouse (Barnum et al., 1957; Hornsey and Howard, 1956; Jardetzky et al., 1956), on the one hand, and in two plant species, bean and lily (Howard and Pelc, 1953; Taylor and McMaster, 1954) on the other. While at the present state of our knowledge such similarities represent only parallelisms, they seem to deserve further work, particularly since they are of radiobiologic interest (Howard, 1956). It is pertinent in this connection, that the plant studies, as well as work on mouse ascites tumors (Hornsey and Howard, 1956), were done without periodicity analysis. The Minnesota work carried out along the 24-hr scale, however, has already yielded data which may be used for suggesting and sketching —in admittedly crude terms—some chemical stages of a "metabolic clock," at least in one mammalian organ. Rather than speaking of "functional" and "vegetative" states (or of catabolic and anabolic or

of "dissimilatory" and "assimilatory" phases—useful first approximations), in the case of mouse liver, we may now refer to at least three
metabolic stages, each of ~8 hr duration. A first period, A, is marked
off by the peaks of mitosis and phospholipid; during the latter part of
A, daily motor activity of mice is being initiated. The second period,
B, between the peaks of phospholipid (or RNA) and DNA, represents
an "active" motor period of the mouse as a whole. The third period,
C, between the peaks of DNA and mitosis, may be regarded as preparatory for growth and repair; C can be subdivided, in turn, into two
subperiods, one preceding the glycogen peak (C_1) and the other following it (C_2). Is C_2 the "vegetative" state par excellence? The question poses itself, whether an undisturbed C_2 may not constitute an important condition for truly "recuperative" rest. By allowing for the
species differences in the phase of various mammalian rhythms (which
we shall bring to the fore later), we may further raise the question
whether the advantages of an undisturbed C_2 may provide a metabolic
basis for the claim that *homo sapiens,* adapted to a diurnal schedule,
rests more "beneficially" during the early hours of the night than thereafter. At the present state of our knowledge on human metabolic
periodicity such considerations remain hypothetical. In the mouse,
however, it can be shown that our choice of the "right timing" may be
just as important for obtaining a given cellular effect as are our choices
of the "right hormone" and the "right dose" (Fig. 15) (Litman *et al.,*
1958).

The first period, A, between the peaks of mitosis and phospholipid
describes, perhaps, the metabolic preparation for daily motor (and
other?) activity. It is probably during A, that the adrenal cortex interacts periodically with cellular metabolism in immature mouse liver and
perhaps in some other tissues as well. Information is available at least
with respect to the chemical nature of the adrenal hormone involved,
even though the pertinent data were obtained with an oxycorticoid
which is not the principal such corticoid of the species studied. With
this qualifying restriction, i.e., that cortisone (instead of corticosterone) was studied, it seems interesting that this 11-oxycorticoid raises
the RSA of phospholipid phosphorus in liver cytoplasm of adrenalectomized mice from levels, which are clearly below the physiologic
range, to values that appear to be within that range. More important,

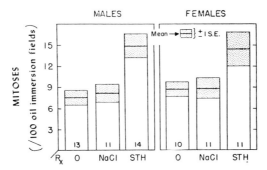

FIG. 15. A single STH injection is reproducibly associated with increased hepatic mitotic counts in mice if times of injection as well as of killing are appropriate (Injection at 16:30; killing at about 12:30; light from 06:00 to 18:00, for instance). The same dose of STH did not elevate mitotic count when given with the same interval between injection and killing at certain other times.

cortisone does so in doses of 5 $\mu g/20$ g of body weight, while epinephrine in the same doses does not bring about the effect (Halberg *et al.*, 1956). Furthermore, desoxycorticosterone, in doses 100-fold larger, barely reproduced the effect of 5 μg of cortisone. These findings are in keeping with the assumptions that (1) the 24-hr periodicity in the RSA of phospholipid phosphorus from mouse liver cytoplasm, which is obliterated by adrenalectomy, is largely dependent upon the periodic secretion of adrenal hormones, that (2) the cortex plays a more critical role in this connection than the medulla, and that (3) among the corticoids, 11-oxysteroids are more critical than 11-desoxysteroids. Furthermore, in the intact animal, the daily phospholipid peak was found to occur at the time of periodic eosinopenia (Halberg *et al.*, 1956; Vermund *et al.*, 1956) following with a lag of about 4 hr, the time of high blood levels of "corticosterone." For the time being, the period A, during which periodic adrenal interaction with cellular mechanisms occurs under physiologic conditions, may be divided into two subperiods: A_1 between the mitotic peak (of liver) and the blood corticoid peak, and A_2 between the blood corticoid peak and the hepatic phospholipid peak.

Further work in endocrinology and metabolism may be facilitated by information regarding the "right" time of hormone action (cf. Kalmus' (1957) terminology)—and work on direct cellular effects of corticoid in period A may be a case in point, since information is lacking as to how such an oxycorticoid effect is exerted. Oxycorticoids have also been called "sugar hormones"—is their effect upon periodicity related to that upon carbohydrate metabolism? Is it exerted upon some phosphorylating step, which need not involve an immediate precursor of phospholipid and which may be relatively independent of phospholipid formation as a whole? Is glycogen deposition in the liver a *sine qua non* for its rhythmicity? Can we account for the dissociation, along the 24-hr scale, of the peaks in hepatic glycogen and blood oxycorticoid simply by feeding time and by suggesting that, for a while after the initiation of feeding, sugar is being used up at a rate comparable to that at which it is being made available? To our knowledge there is no critical evidence supporting such views. What are the time relations of blood oxycorticoid and liver glycogen during starvation, while these rhythms persist? A partial answer to these questions may, perhaps, be obtained from studies of (1) the sequence in which the various peaks of periodic cellular events are altered by adrenalectomy, and of (2) the time relation of such alterations to changes in periodic glucose resorption from the gut and gluconeogenesis from protein.

In 1940 Hamar concluded that the daily variations in glucose resorption from the small intestine of rats may result either from the periodic hormone secretion of the adrenal cortex or from periodicity in the sensitivity of the intestinal epithelium to cortical hormones. Today, his inferences remain timely, even though the data upon which they were based describe "adrenalectomized" rats probably possessing ectopic cortical tissue, a circumstance stated by Hamar. It is further pertinent that by 1935, Ågren had reported that the rhythm in liver glycogen was not demonstrable in adrenalectomized rats. This author, in turn, suggests that he dealt with true cortical adrenal insufficiency; the extremely low or zero values which he recorded for liver glycogen in most of his rats may be used to support his conclusion for this majority of his animals. Ågren's data have recently been recomputed, however, as relative curves, by Sollberger (1955a,b) who comments on the surprising similarity of the rhythms in liver glycogen of starved and adrenalectomized rats. In relative curves, changes are expressed as percent of series mean, e.g., for the purpose of eliminating undue effects brought about by differences in operating level. With respect to Ågren's data, however, the changes shown by relative curves may depend upon a few animals, which possibly constitute a subgroup to be ignored, rather than emphasized, i.e., rats with incomplete cortical insufficiency. If, in turn, we should contemplate eliminating those animals with the higher values of liver glycogen from Ågren's data— and we would have to do so arbitrarily—the remainder of the values is too low (and the analytical error at such levels is perhaps too high?) for any conclusion other than that, for all practical purposes, glycogen disappears from adrenalectomized rat liver throughout the 24-hr period. Sollberger (1954, 1955a,b), who has substantially contributed to the problem of glycogen rhythm in liver as well as to the statistical aspects of rhythms in general, has recognized this knotty problem (personal communication) which persists despite a vast amount of work on other aspects of hepatic rhythms (Beringer, 1950; Boutwell et al., 1948; Dean, 1944a,b; Ekman and Holmgren, 1947, 1949; Forsgren, 1928; Gerritzen, 1940; Higgins et al., 1932, 1933; Holmgren, 1931, 1941; Holmquist, 1931; Jores, 1940; Möllerström, 1940; Petren, 1939; Sjoegren et al., 1938). Whether a 24-hr periodic carbohydrate metabolism is essential for cellular rhythmicity, or whether it is merely an adequate carbohydrate supply that (1) is required for such rhythms, and (2) is driven by the adrenal, as are other periodicities—this is one of the pertinent questions (cf. Bullough, 1955). In this connection, on one hand, the persistence of glycogen rhythm in the liver of starved animals suggests that feeding per se is not critical with respect to 24-hr periodicity (Ågren et al., 1931). On the other hand, in the starved animal, gluconeogenesis from protein seems to depend on a periodic corticoid secretion, as do certain other functions that are periodic. Thus, in the light of available knowledge, we cannot go beyond suggesting that an adequate carbohydrate supply is an essential condition for metabolic rhythms in mammalian cells. But at the same time, in the absence of the adrenal cortex, the carbohydrate supply per se need not be a sufficient condition for such cellular rhythms to occur.

Whatever the intimate mode of adrenal interaction with metabolism may be, our assumption that the adrenal is a pacemaker of a *periodic* sequence of cellular events may have heuristic value, if the varied actions of corticoid are thus amenable to a simple interpretation. The "ubiquitous" role played by corticoid (Sayers, 1950) may then be attributed to an effect upon one or a few specific links of a normally periodic chain(s) of metabolic events, and it need not be derived from a more direct cortical adrenal participation in a large number of biochemical processes. This same adrenal "driving" of cellular metabolism, at a rate and in a mode blended with superimposed and juxtaposed controls (pituitary, hypothalamic, and other), could substantially account for the efficiency of overall body adaptation to demands from the outside.

Other Integrative Functions

It is on the basis of data from experiments involving gland removal, with and without hormone replacement, that we have come to regard the adrenal cortex as a pacemaker of 24-hr periodic mammalian metabolism. Comparable data are not available, however, on the problem of the extent to which the adrenal medulla participates in the same phenomenon. It is well known that epinephrine in the adrenal (Euler and Holmquist, 1934) as well as *inter alia* in the blood (Lehmann and Michaelis, 1943) exhibits 24-hr periodicity, and what is more important, it is one neurohumor, among other agents, that affects many functions which also are regulated by corticoids (Halberg, 1954a; Ramey and Goldstein, 1957). But the observation of 24-hr periodicity (a phenomenon which is common) cannot be used, in itself, to suggest that the variable for which it is observed is responsible for 24-hr rhythms in other functions. Moreover, "neurohumoral" regulations serve primarily the more immediate adaptations of the body in "emergency reactions" (Cannon, 1929). It is probably via the integration of their shorter-term effects that they exert an important control upon 24-hr rhythms. The same considerations may apply for rhythms noted in Minnesota for 5-hydroxytryptamine in mouse brain (Albrecht *et al.*, 1956) and for the best known breakdown product of 5-hydroxytryptamine, namely 5-hydroxyindoleacetic acid, in human urine (Figs. 16, 17) (Wadsworth, *et al.*, 1957) (cf. Page, 1958).

In Minnesota, we also have explored the role played by the pituitary with respect to rhythms in epithelial mitoses (Zander *et al.*, 1954) and

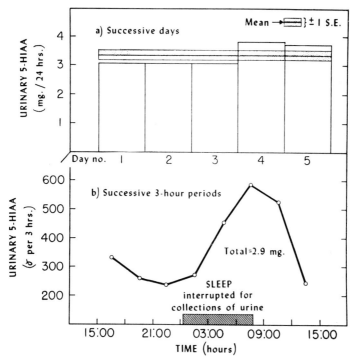

FIG. 16. Variation in urinary 5-hydroxyindoleacetic acid excretion in a medically normal human male. In this case, variability along the 24-hr scale seems to be larger than that from day to day.

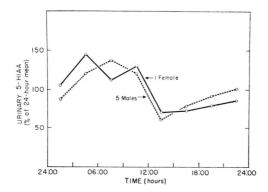

FIG. 17. Periodicity of 5-hydroxyindoleacetic acid excretion in medically normal students.

rectal temperature (Ferguson *et al.,* 1957) of mice. These rhythms were altered by hypophysectomy, but were not obliterated thereby. The most prominent effect of hypophysectomy was a decrease in amplitude of rhythm (Fig. 18; cf. also Müller and Giersberg, 1957). Moreover, periodograms revealed circadian periods, the dispersion of which among individual animals was significantly greater in the hypophysectomized group than in a group of intact mice studied concomitantly ($P < 0.05$; analyzed by Professor E. Johnson). A reduction in degree of synchronization of rhythms among individual mice thus came to the fore at one month after hypophysectomy. Moreover,

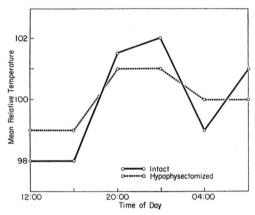

FIG. 18. Decrease in amplitude of temperature rhythm, about one month after hypophysectomy ($T = 4$ days; $\Delta t = 4$ hr). Mouse.

evidence for desynchronization between the rectal temperature rhythm and the lighting regimen was obtained at 5 months after hypophysectomy (Ferguson *et al.,* 1957). It seems interesting that at 5 months after blinding, stimuli other than those received by the eye had gained some control of the timing of rhythms that were desynchronized (free-running) at earlier time points after removal of the eyes. At a comparable interval after hypophysectomy and in the presence of the eyes, desynchronization of temperature rhythm and lighting regimen apparently occurs. Some role of the pituitary in synchronization may thus be unmasked, but this pituitary effect is probably indirect, since it must be based upon observations made late after the operation when secondary endocrine and metabolic changes are prominent (Ferguson *et al.*, 1957).

Earlier in this symposium, Doctor Bullough clearly sketched the links involved in the mediation of effects of light upon the sex cycle. His thoughts come to mind, while we face the task of examining the role of those structures that mediate and modulate effects exerted by lighting schedules upon the phase of 24-hr rhythms. We start out, as Doctor Bullough did, with synchronizing environmental stimuli, such as light or sound, that are received by "transducers" such as the eye or the ear, respectively. Potentials thus evoked are transmitted corticipitally, by conductors to centers in the brain, but, for the moment, we need not travel all the way to the striate area or to other special sensory areas of the cerebral cortex. For the conduction of photic effects, it is of interest that some fibers of the optic nerve go to the hypothalamus and to the reticular formation. For the conduction of visual, as well as of auditory, visceral, and somatic input, it also seems pertinent that impulses evoked by these various peripheral afferent stimuli can be conducted corticipitally through the central brain stem (Allen, 1923; Bremer, 1935; French *et al.*, 1952, 1953a,b; Ingram *et al.*, 1951; Magoun, 1952; O'Leary and Coben, 1958; Russell, 1957; Starzl *et al.*, 1951), as well as over classic (lateral) sensory pathways. Moreover, potentials recorded medially show a lack of modality segregation, interaction and attenuation of succeeding responses on multiple stimulation, and diffuse cortical distribution, among other characteristics which make them particularly attractive to the student of 24-hr periodicity. Is it at the site of these potentials, perhaps in the reticular formation of the brain that, after the removal of biologic "noise," the multitude of synchronizing impulses reaching nervous centers is mixed, weighted, and combined? These are important functions, since we are exposed, often at the same time, to a variety of stimuli, yet ordinarily only one stimulus will be dominant, a few will be modulating, while other sensory input remains silent with respect to phase of rhythms. Such biologic noise removal, as well as mixing, weighting, and combining, must go on continuously, since the dominance of a given stimulus is never "dictatorial." To cite an example from the Minnesota work, ordinarily the lighting regimen is the dominant synchronizer of the eosinophil rhythm in mice (Halberg,

Visscher, and Bittner, 1953), but the feeding time can also govern the phase of rhythm under certain conditions (idem.), and under other conditions either noise or smell may do the same (Halberg, Visscher, and Bittner, 1954).

Thus a centrally situated area in the brain stem, functioning as a unit, is subject to excitation by peripheral sensory input. Effects of such excitation in turn lead to electrical activation of the cerebral cortex and behavioral arousal of the animal (French *et al.,* 1952). The status of our knowledge on the role played by the cerebral cortex with respect to 24-hr periodicity has been discussed by Bykow, on the basis of I. P. Pavlov's thesis ". . . that all (or we may say cautiously almost all) reactions in animals, which can change as a function of ex- perimental conditions, are brought about by temporary connections established in the highest, phylogenetically youngest, and most per- fected parts of the central nervous system" (Bykow, 1953). It is via such connections that the cerebral cortex probably participates in the control of phase of rhythms, but the added question arises whether the cerebral cortex is essential for the occurrence of 24-hr periodicity. The latter question, however, has tentatively been answered in the negative, at least with respect to sleep and wakefulness (Kleitman, 1952). Minnesota work on the same problem may be of interest, even though it does not decide the question just raised. Thus, in hemiparetics with epilepsy, the rhythms in rectal temperature and blood eosinophils per- sist after the removal of one hemisphere, with or without certain of the subcortical ganglia on one side, left or right (Halberg, French, and Gully, 1958). In this case, however, we do not deal with the complete removal of the cerebral cortex. In the same connection, let us allude to the behavior of rhythms (Fleeson *et al.,* 1957) during regression induced by intensive electroshock therapy (R.E.S.T.) (Glueck *et al.,* 1957). "Regression" represents a degree of dissociation from the en- vironment seldom seen in humans. The patients are mute, disoriented owing to complete memory loss, are doubly incontinent, and show neurological changes associated with extrapyramidal tract activity. Data on two paranoid and one catatonic schizophrenic female patients, obtained in Minnesota (Fleeson *et al.,* 1957) (before, during, and after R.E.S.T.), reveal that the rhythms in eosinophils and tempera- ture persist during the "regressed" state (induced by the daily administration of two shocks at 8 A.M. and two at 8 P.M., for 10, 11, and 12 days, respectively). The results indicate a high degree of independence of these rhythms, from the cerebral functions which are gravely altered, if not obliterated, by R.E.S.T. In the periodogram, the value for the trial period of about 12 hr was consistently lower than the peak found at about 24 hr, despite the continuance of the 12 hourly shock schedule for almost two weeks. As compared to other more physiologic studies on the possible adaptation of human beings (Kleitman and Kleitman, 1953; Lewis and Lobban, 1954, 1957a,b; Mills, 1951) or experimental animals (Tribukait, 1954, 1956) to unusual schedules, the R.E.S.T. results differ in the circumstance that R.E.S.T. may, perhaps, be regarded as a drastic "stressor" (Selye, 1953, 1954, 1956). This stressor, applied at intervals of 12 hr, failed to imprint a dominating 12-hr schedule upon certain 24-hr rhythms. That R.E.S.T. should do so at all can be expected only by those who choose to regard 24-hr rhythms as direct reactions to the 24-hr schedule of the "stresses" of daily life. This seems hardly a useful approach, since in doing so one inadvertently ignores the organism's own integrated sequence of 24-hr periodic events. It seems pertinent that Selye, by contrast to others, to our knowledge has refrained from using the not uncommon "interpretation" of physiologic rhythms as "stress reactions" (i.e., as exogenous effects unqualified as to endogenous circadian organization).

If during the first week of 12 hourly R.E.S.T., there was a transient shortening of τ ($=$ average period for temperature or eosinophil variation in a given patient), this almost certainly did not exceed 1 hr or so. It would appear that (1) physiologic periodicity represents a mechanism that adapts to changes in schedule, as long as such changes are, so to speak, within reason; (2) but that under the conditions of 12 hourly shocks, the shortening or lengthening of its primary period is slight, at most by a few hours rather than by 12 hrs; in other words, certain schedules may not be acceptable, even though they are forced upon the organism in a drastic fashion, such as R.E.S.T.

Conceivably, certain 24-hr rhythms assume a free-running circadian period in human beings as well as in the studies of Tribukait (1954, 1956) on the mouse, if they are continuously confronted with certain environmental schedules which exceed the plasticity of metabolic adaptation, as long as no other secondary synchronizers, with a more acceptable schedule, are given the chance to become dominant. Much work remains to be done on the adaptability of the daily period, a problem which also has been discussed by Kleitman (1949), Utterback and Ludwig (1949). Behnke (1951) and Brindley (1954). Behnke has justly emphasized the fact that efficiency loss and fatigue may result when daily rhythms are desynchronized from the sleeping and waking cycle. More recently, Lewis and Lobban (1957a,b) investigated 24-hr rhythms in human subjects on long-maintained unusual time routines in two isolated communities in Spitzbergen and, what is of methodologic importance, they examined their data by a modified form of Fourier analysis. While initial adaptation of excretory rhythms in their subjects to a 21-hr routine or to a 27-hr routine was uncommon, such adaptation progressively improved, but was seldom complete, even after six weeks on the new environmental routine. Their subjects carried specially adjusted wrist watches showing 12 hr during 10½ ordinary hr (21-hr time) or showing 12 hr during 13½ ordinary hours (27-hr time). The authors point out that these watches were worn by the subjects to facilitate strict adherence to the experimental routine even when the subjects were away from base, an aim which is likely to have been achieved. On the other hand, the question may be raised as to how easy it may have been for the subjects to compute from one look at the clock (giving experimental time) the corresponding "control" time (24-hr time, BST). If, as would appear, easy arithmetic would have sufficed for the latter purpose, the new time schedule according to which activities were scheduled may have been "compared," occasionally, with time on a 24-hr day basis. The awareness of the corresponding old time (24-hr time), in turn, even if it was subconscious [in the psychologist's terminology: "suppressed" (out of experimental loyalty)], may have conceivably counteracted the effect of activities on the experimental schedule (either 21-hr time or 27-hr time), at least with respect to the phase control of some of the rhythms studied. If this assumption is correct, the degree to which one or the other excretory rhythm adapted to the new routines could have depended upon the dominance over phase control of one or the other time schedule. But whether or not we are dealing in this case with interacting synchronizers, and whether or not the dominant synchronizer varied in prominence and/or kind among the subjects as well, the same investigation by Lewis and Lobban brought to the fore a most important point, namely a dissociation among different daily rhythms on a given unusual routine. Thus the temperature rhythm adapted almost immediately to the experimental routines in most subjects, while for excretory rhythms the reverse held true. Moreover, rhythms in the excretion of water, chloride, and potassium also revealed dissociations, that in potassium excretion being usually out of phase with those in water and chloride. In human subjects living on different routines, a similar dissociation also has been recorded for the rhythms in serum iron and blood eosinophils (Halberg and Howard, 1958). It seems likely, particularly under unusual circumstances, that at the same time and in the same individual, different synchronizers can gain dominance over the phase control of different rhythms.

But is the nervous system involved in more than phase control of rhythms? Can it account for the free-running circadian periods as well, as we record them presumably in the absence of environmental synchronizers? We must accept the circadian period of a rhythm as endogenous rather than exogenous, if we find that it happens to be slightly yet significantly different from 24 hours, if it is maintained as such for prolonged periods and if we can assume that no environmental factor with similar frequency existed. As long as circadian periods in the mammal describe only body activity (Figs. 9 and 10), we might think of a neural oscillator possessing the corresponding natural period. The detection of circadian periods in rectal temperature behavior may lead us to believe that such an oscillator may be located at the site of temperature control. But in the mammal we now have indications for the operation of circadian periods in blood eosinophils (Fig. 8) and epidermal mitoses as well, which may serve to suggest that we are dealing with spontaneous cellular rhythms, comparable to those encountered in unicellulars (Bruce and Pittendrigh, 1957; Hastings and Sweeney, 1957a,b; Hastings et al., 1956; Pittendrigh, 1954; Pittendrigh and Bruce, 1957). But obviously, free-running periods in a given variable must not necessarily result from an "oscillator" located specifically in the underlying function; if this were true, the list of prospective cellular (or other) oscillators may prove to be rather long and the heuristic value of such an approach remains debatable. On the other hand, we should consider the extent to which, under self-determined conditions in the absence of periodic environmental sync signals, maintenance of circadian behavior in mammals may depend upon feedbacks to the central nervous system from periodic sequences of peripheral metabolic events that are loosely locked in phase with each other via specialized hormonal (and autonomic nervous) controls. If the leads and lags in phase of periodic cellular events should play an important role in this connection, they could account for both, our resistance (manifested *inter alia* by efficiency loss) to the assumption of unusual schedules enforced from without and our but slow adaptation to suddenly instituted acceptable changes of the synchronizer. With this in mind we may now turn back to the role played by the central nervous system with respect to aspects other than phase control, and we shall refrain at this time from regarding any one part of the brain as an endogenous master oscillator underlying all circadian rhythms, an entity which has more often been assumed to exist than documented as to what it does.

Already by 1933, Jores (1933, 1940) had ascribed to a hypophyseo-mesencephalic rhythm the daily changes in urinary volume. Mills (1951) more recently referred to the same structures as possibly underlying the habitual rhythms of "sleepiness," temperature, and urine flow. Moreover, in the course of work unrelated to 24-hr periodicity per se, the feeding rhythm was found to be obliterated in mice made obese by hypothalamic lesions or by goldthioglucose poisoning (Anlicker and Mayer, 1956; Skinner, 1957), which latter procedure also damages the hypothalamus (for references see Liebelt and Perry, 1957). A hypothalamic oscillator, or this area as a part of an oscillating circuit not necessarily possessing a free-running period of its own, but "driven" from within (by feedbacks) and "triggered" from without, may well control certain 24-hr rhythms of the body as a whole, such as that in motor activity. The hypothalamus also represents, of course, an added autonomic control of those rhythms that are more intimately dependent upon the endocrines.

Before leaving the hypothalamus, however, we must introduce a rather ill-defined point into our discussion. Somewhere and somehow (neurally?) a "comparison" must be made between the composite phase information from within the body and that from without, COPI and CEPI, respectively. The composite *organismic* phase information (COPI) may be yielded by the mixing, weighting, and combining of information from various feedbacks, psychogenic, neurogenic, hormonal, and metabolic. The composite *environmental* phase information (CEPI), in turn, may schematically be subdivided into the potentials evoked by the sync signals of the physicochemical environment (EPI_p) (light being an important case in point), and into those evoked by other signals, arbitrarily designated as "socioecological" (EPI_s) cf. Aschoff, 1958). Most likely, EPI_s, our social schedule (and our "emotional" response to it) is more critical in determining the phase of bodily rhythms in urbanized human beings, while EPI_p might be more pertinent for humans living in the setting of an isolated farm. But to separate experimentally the effects of EPI_p and EPI_s constitutes no minor undertaking in the case of man. This same task seems more amenable to study in certain experimental animals, even though in the latter EPI_s also has dramatic and often unexpected effects. We may only allude to studies carried out, *inter alios,* by Gangloff and Monier (1956) on the unanesthetized rabbit. The electroencephalographic changes occurring in this animal, when it is confronted with the investigator, probably involve "emotional" components, and these thoroughly studied changes (Gangloff and Monier, 1956) are actually more striking than the corresponding changes evoked by light in itself. Moreover, such "emotional" EPI_s, interfering with EPI_p, involves not only brain waves, with their short periods, but also the 24-hr rhythm in rectal temperature and even the daily sequence of periodic cellular events, such as mitosis (Halberg, in press). Unless we anticipate these varied effects, their contribution via EPI_s to CEPI will remain uncontrolled. It becomes evident that in studying the effect of a change in EPI_p (e.g., in the lighting schedule), we must endeavor to evaluate, for experimental animals, as well as for human beings, possible concomitant changes in EPI_s. It can hardly be overemphasized that ambiguous results obtained in studies of effects of EPI_p can quite easily be brought about by our failure to evaluate inadvertent yet critical changes in EPI_s. At any rate, changes either in EPI_p or in EPI_s (or in both) can alter CEPI.

Accordingly, a physiologic mechanism [a neural phase comparator(s)(?)] is now confronted with a new CEPI and an old COPI. It will compare the two, of course, and if the phase relations of COPI and CEPI are found to be altered, an appropriate message will be sent to various bodily rhythms to speed up or to slow down, as need be. Moreover, the phase comparator will continue to send messages until the rhythms are again in step with the environment, i.e., until the abnormal relations between CEPI and COPI have been corrected.

The medical researcher in viewing the above processes poses, of course, the question of diseases of "synchronization." Psychoses are often defined as illnesses that separate the individual from the realities of the environment. Can some of them result from abnormal phase relations of COPI and CEPI? Can the psychogenic component of the former and/or the latter, arrive at the wrong time, e.g., because of some delay underway? Rigorously analyzed evidence for the possibility that a failure of synchronization, if chronic, can characterize a disease remains to be accumulated, and the question whether the same failure of synchronization may, in addition, underlie disease also awaits study. Defects, e.g., in the transducer or in the "phase comparing," come to mind in this connection. In this connection, also, in the mouse (Halberg, 1954b) and perhaps in human beings as well (Landau and Feldman, 1954), we have an example at least of "transducer-disease" (blinding). Such an alteration of synchronization is not a clinically important aspect of blindness, since sync signals are of more than one modality, and thus the loss of one transducer is eventually compensated by another, as far as the phase of 24-hr rhythms is concerned. The data after blinding are of value, however, since they reveal the occurrence of free-running periods in an illness. The same data also demonstrate a methodologic point of import (Ingle, 1951a). Since in this case, a change in period is not necessarily associated with changes in amplitude or level (Fig. 3, data on individuals), we are here dealing with an alteration which periodicity analysis can describe but the study of gross deviations from a normal range may not detect.

From the undefined physiologic equivalents of a neural "phase comparator" and/or "oscillator" we now turn to their endocrine counterparts, the pituitary and its target glands. "Information" from higher centers is channeled, of course, neurally to the periphery, but in addition, some of it also travels from the hypothalamus to the pituitary (Fortier, 1951; Sayers *et al.,* 1958). We are not certain whether or not in the pituitary messages from above again are compared with hormonal feedbacks from target glands (Sayers *et al.,* 1958), but we can assume that in the case of altered phase relations of CEPI and COPI the pituitary does send appropriate messages to the "generators" of rhythms, until the alteration of phase is corrected (Ingle, 1951b). The "messengers" are the pituitary tropic hormones; the "generators" of rhythms appear to be (at first) the appropriate target glands (see later for qualification); the latter are stimulated by their tropins to speed up or they are slowed down by throttling of tropin secretion until normal phase relations are reestablished. The question may be raised, however, whether the path from the central nervous system via the pituitary is obligatory for the transmission of phase information to the target glands. This need not be the case in all instances (Royce and Sayers, 1958). Of interest in this connection is ample direct evidence as well as indirect evidence (Farrell *et al.,* 1954; Liddle *et al.,* 1955, 1956; Rauschkolb, 1956; Rauschkolb and Farrell, 1956; Thorn, Renold, and Winegrad, 1957; Thorn, Ross, Crabbé, and Hoff, 1957; Zimmermann and Schoenbauer, 1952) of continued aldosterone secretion by the adrenal cortex in the absence of pituitary function, and particularly the clinical work of Müller *et al.* (1958). Whether or not, under such circumstances, aldosterone secretion is periodic, will have to be reinvestigated with more frequent sampling along the 24-hr scale, a problem which remains difficult in view of the exigencies of method.

Two endocrines, the adrenal cortex and the female gonad can safely be regarded as periodic glands par excellence, yet we can think of other endocrine periodicity as well. For the case of the thyroid, the existence of a characteristic period may not be unequivocally established, yet the participation of this gland in the control, e.g., of seasonal periodicity seems fascinating (cf. data of W. H. Brown, 1930). The same gland contributes, of course, to the maintenance of 24-hr rhythms, even though its effect may be exerted indirectly, via classic thyroid-adrenal cortical interrelations. It seems pertinent that periodic endogenous eosinopenia was not detected in thyroid insufficiency (Flink and Halberg, 1952; Halberg and Visscher, 1953a). We shall have to ascertain whether or not this effect of chronic thyroid insufficiency is the result of associated adrenal cortical hypofunction.

Let us now refocus upon the adrenal cortex as the "driver" of a cellular sequence of events. Such driving could result from corticoid effects (not necessarily direct ones) upon one or a few pacemaking reactions. Corticoids may be pacemakers of 24-hr periodic metabolism simply by changing certain conditions of the transport of reactants— by effects exerted, e.g., upon permeability (Hechter, 1957; Szego, 1957). At any rate, in verified states of cortical adrenal insufficiency ("generator" removal) certain 24-hr rhythms [but not all of them (Hamilton *et al.*, 1950; R. B. Howard, 1952)] are gravely altered. Those in motor activity, rectal temperature, and feeding are damped out, and only to these we may perhaps apply the analogy of damped oscillatory circuits. It must be recognized that in the case of these rhythms of the body as a whole, the neural control (and its exogenous triggers, if present) is more direct, as compared with the corticoid control via feedbacks, but the latter control also matters. Does the corticoid effect concern the amplitude of these rhythms (of the body as a whole) more prominently than their phase? The lack of strength (for motor activity) and the lack of appetite, appearing early and consistently in adrenal insufficiency, are both pertinent in this connection, as is also the accompanying hypothermia.

It must further be emphasized that the statistically ascertained evidence involving the adrenal cortex as a control of certain 24-hr rhythms differs from case to case. For the eosinophil rhythm of human beings, the extinction of synchronized rhythm in verified cortical insufficiency has been established (Halberg *et al.*, 1951) and confirmed (Kaine *et al.*, 1955) with sufficiently frequent serially dependent sampling. The eosinophil rhythm in the mouse has been established by a variety of sampling procedures (Brown and Dougherty, 1956; Halberg and Visscher, 1950, 1952; Halberg, Visscher, and Bittner, 1953; Louch *et al.*, 1953; Panzenhagen and Speirs, 1953), but its "obliteration" was examined only in serially independent data (Halberg, Visscher, and Bittner, 1953; Brown and Dougherty, 1956). The data on hepatic phospholipid metabolism in the mouse (Halberg, Barnum, and Vermund, 1953; Halberg *et al.*, 1956; Vermund *et al.*,

1956) and on epidermal mitoses (Halberg, in press) in this species, represent serially independent spotchecks at only two times of day. These were the times of the usual high and low of rhythm in the intact animal, and at these times no significant differences in mean values were found in states of adrenal cortical insufficiency. Such findings may be interpreted *inter alia* as lack of rhythm or as a change in period or phase, since the latter effect also may account for the lack of a significant difference at the clock hours of the usual "high" and "low" of rhythm.

In discussing the degree and the nature of the dependence upon corticoid of basic cellular functions (e.g., mitosis) we must also remember that circadian periods have been recorded under controlled conditions, in the absence of conventional nerves and hormones, in lower forms of life (Hastings and Sweeney, 1957b; references in Bruce and Pittendrigh, 1957; Pittendrigh and Bruce, 1957). In these cases the "generator" of rhythm obviously is in the cell. Moreover, a mammalian tissue has recently been shown to undergo periodic mitoses in culture under controlled conditions (Hupe and Gropp, 1957). Most likely, none of the integrative mammalian functions can be regarded as independent "generators" of metabolic rhythms, even when a secretion such as that of the adrenal is necessary for "maintenance"; instead, the sequential changes of cellular metabolism may constitute the more basic characteristic underlying periodicity in the mammal as well as in the unicellular.

Rather than restricting ourselves to test indirectly hypotheses involving metabolic "clocks" or "generators," it seems desirable to speak of the leads and lags in phase of metabolic events defined in time, when illustrative examples are known and their effects demonstrated (Fig. 15). In adopting this biochemical viewpoint, the different "maintenance" factors, superimposed upon cellular cycles such as specific endocrines, can be regarded as subserving specialized tasks of organismic synchronization. (To the degree to which the cellular cycles can then be regarded as the beneficiaries of synchronization in mechanisms of transport, they are likely to be victims as well as synchronization failure!). Several superficially divergent aspects of the problem of physiologic "synchronization" have already been discussed or documented by Kalmus (1957) and Bünning (1957), or by Ball and Dyke (1957, Pittendrigh (1954), and ourselves (Halberg, Visscher, and Bittner, 1954). But in speaking of "synchronization," we emphasize that herein this term is used to denote functions with equal periods and it does not necessarily imply the occurrence of certain events at identical times: synchronization in the mammal can be regarded as a state in which defined time relations (locked phase relations) with organismically determined phase differences ($\pm$) exist (or can be brought about) among various functions (1) in a given organ, (2) in different tissues, organs, and systems, (3) at various levels of organization, and (4) between functions at one, several, or all of the foregoing levels of integration on one hand and certain environmental factors on the other. To what extent do the various aspects of organismic synchronization (1 to 3 above) depend upon the environmental synchronizer, and can they all be shifted by changing the schedule of the dominant synchronizer? Will these shifts differ as a function of differences in the complexity of phase control? For the system just sketched we may predict that all 24-hr rhythms can eventually be shifted ("pulled") by changing the dominant synchronizer and also that the speed or ease of shifting may be different as a function, e.g., of the "time constants" of the "phase comparators" involved. With these considerations in mind, let us now turn to the effect upon various 24-hr rhythms of changes in the dominant synchronizer. We shall refer particularly to effects of the lighting schedule in the mouse and to those of more complex schedules in human beings. But at this point, the reader interested in models of physiologic rhythms may be directed to reviews (Pittendrigh, 1954; Pittendrigh and Bruce, 1957; Schmitt, to be published).

ENVIRONMENT: THE SYNCHRONIZER

It is particularly with respect to gross motor activity, among other functions of the body as a whole or of certain organ systems, that the effect of light and darkness upon 24-hr rhythms in animals has been most extensively investigated in the past. The broadest approach to the problem was perhaps that carried out in Bykow's laboratories (Bykow, 1953, 1954). O. P. Shcherbakova (1937, 1938, for discussion see Bykow, 1953) investigated species ranging from monkeys, bears, jackals, wild and domestic dogs and dingos to cats, rabbits, guinea pigs, hedgehogs, rats, mice, cocks, and owls, and she collected data that showed the dependence of phase of rhythms investigated upon external factors.

Against that background and after many valuable studies by others (Aschoff, 1958), the pertinent results of Minnesota work were gathered with the following aims in mind: first, to study in one appropriate mammal, the mouse, the degree of generality of those effects brought about by reversing the lighting regimen. Certain physical, chemical, and morphological parameters previously found to be periodic under physiologic conditions by others and/or ourselves were chosen for this purpose from various levels of physiologic organization. A pathological periodicity that in convulsions, long known in the clinic (Beau, 1836; Janz, 1955), for which we had devised, however, an experimental animal model (Halberg, Bittner, Gully, Albrecht, and Brackney, 1955; Halberg, Bittner, and Gully, 1955; Halberg, Halberg, and Bittner, 1955) also was included for study. Second, we were interested in possible differences in the effects of the lighting schedule upon these various rhythms in the mouse. Third, we wanted to see whether effects similar to those obtained in the mouse by changing the timing of the daily alternating light and dark periods also may be obtained by changes in routine in human beings, and to evaluate the statistical significance of these changes on groups of volunteers when feasible. Thus we aimed, finally, at a species comparison, since some of those rhythms studied in mice were chosen for human investigation as well.

Let us now turn to results of an exploration of lighting effects at lower levels of physiologic organization (Halberg, Barnum, Silber, and Bittner, 1958). Again, two schedules of illumination were used: the "regular" schedule provided for light from 6 A.M. to 6 P.M., while the "reversed" schedule provided for light from 6 P.M. to 6 A.M. All the mice in each study were first kept on the regular schedule for a week (for standardization). Thereafter, in the studies of blood glucose (Fig. 19), liver glycogen (Fig. 20), and phospholipid (Fig. 21): (1) the regular schedule was continued for some of the mice and replaced by the reversed schedule for others; (2) either schedule was then maintained unchanged for at least 2 weeks; and (3) the mice on

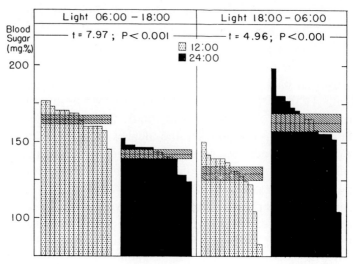

FIG. 19. Shift in phase of blood sugar rhythm after inversion of lighting regimen in mouse. Horizontal lines and shaded areas around them denote ±1 standard error.

both schedules were then killed on the same day, at the same two times which were those of the daily "high" and "low" in a given variable (previously established on a regular schedule of lighting in experiments based upon data from seven groups of mice, killed at 4-hr intervals, during each of two independent 24-hr periods) (Barnum

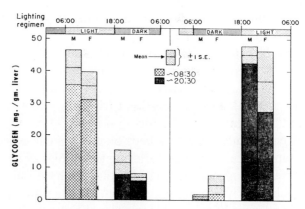

FIG. 20. Shift in phase of liver glycogen rhythm after inversion of lighting regimen in mouse.

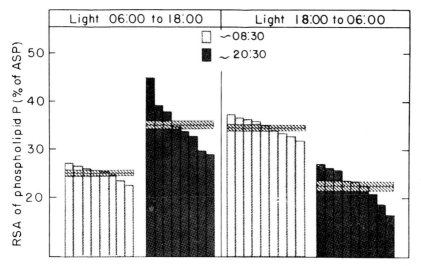

FIG. 21. Shift in phase of microsomal phospholipid rhythm in mouse liver after inversion of lighting regimen.

et al., 1957; Jardetzky *et al.,* 1956). Mitotic activity in pinnal epidermis and hepatic parenchyma (Fig. 22) and hepatic RNA and DNA metabolism (Fig. 23) were studied at two time points, with mice on a reversed schedule for 8 days (hepatic mitoses), 2 weeks (RNA and DNA), and 23 days (pinnal mitoses), respectively. The two series on serum corticosterone (Fig. 24) each describe seven groups of mice killed at 4-hr intervals throughout a 24-hr period; in

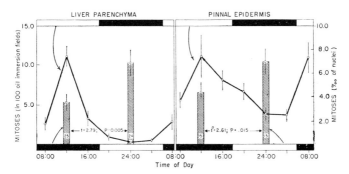

FIG. 22. Shift in phase of mitotic rhythms in liver parenchyma and pinnal epidermis, after inversion of lighting regimen in mouse. (° Based upon $\log_{10}$ transformation of counts.)

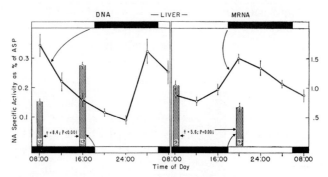

FIG. 23. Shift in phase of rhythms in nucleic acid specific activities in mouse liver after inversion of lighting regimen.

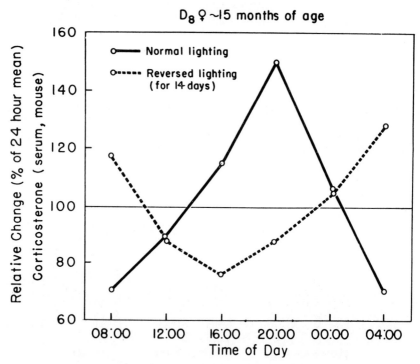

FIG. 24. Shift in phase of serum corticosterone rhythm after inversion of lighting regimen in mouse.

this study, the group on the regular schedule was sampled first. For the remainder of the mice, the reversed schedule was then instituted and maintained for 2 weeks prior to killing. Moreover, for the study of corticosterone, pools of serum were used, by contrast to the rest of the data, all of which describe individual mice.

There was considerable variability in individual values and it also is recognized that with such spot checks (at only two time points, on the reversed schedule) the completeness of inversion of rhythm cannot be ascertained, a consideration which seems particularly pertinent to the data on hepatic mitoses (Figs. 22 and 25). We can conclude, however, for all the functions studied, that an important shift of rhythm had taken place after the shift of lighting schedule. Except for blood corticosterone and some data in Fig. 25 (see below), the day-night differences on both schedules were significant. Blood corticosterone is the only variable for which a statistical test was not

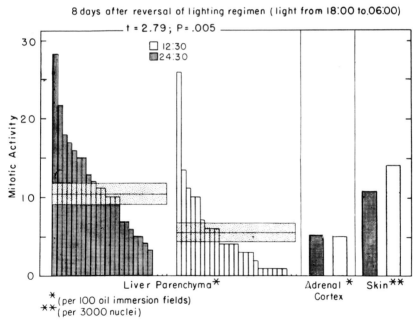

Fɪɢ. 25. Data suggesting unequal shift times for phase changes of mitotic rhythms in different tissues in mouse (see text).

carried out since each point represents one determination made on a pool of serum.

With particular reference to Fig. 25, it is important that the day-night difference in mitotic count of liver parenchyma had changed sign and was statistically significant at 8 days after inversion of lighting, while in the same animals mitoses in pinnal epidermis were as yet not significantly reversed. In other experiments, at 23 days after lighting inversion (Halberg, Bittner, and Smith, 1957), and at 12 days thereafter, the shifted timing of mitoses in pinnal epidermis was clearly apparent. That a shift of mammalian 24-hr rhythms occurs only gradually (rather than abruptly) after the sudden change in lighting regimen has previously been shown elsewhere for rhythms at the level of the body as a whole (Calhoun, 1945; Johnson, 1939) and in our laboratory, with special reference to cellular rhythms (Fig. 25) (Halberg, Bittner, and Smith, 1957; Halberg, Visscher, and Bittner, 1953). Moreover, such shifts of rhythm, by shifts of lighting schedule, are in the mouse the rule rather than the exception as regards 24-hr periodic phenomena at different levels of organization. Other things being comparable, we note, as was predicted, that the shift times of various rhythms need not be the same, even if we are dealing with the same phenomenon, mitosis, in the same inbred stock. If, as is likely, this assumption is correct, it follows that subtle differences among the factors governing mitotic rhythms in various tissues are amenable to analysis, *inter alia,* by explorations of their shift times.

Hastings and Sweeney (1957b) have shown that in the unicellular *Gonyaulax* certain 24-hr rhythms (which persist in constant dim light) can be shifted in their timing by a shift in the regimen of alternating light and darkness. With the lighting conditions used, in *Gonyaulax* the shift is accomplished in 1 day. Brown and Webb (1949) had shown that the same applies to 24-hr periodicity in crabs but with a slightly longer shift time; the shift in crabs takes a few days, and the shift time is a function of illumination. Corresponding data by Johnson and others (Calhoun, 1945; Johnson, 1939) demonstrated that the activity rhythm of rodents also may be shifted, but again, more slowly. Under our conditions, the shift in activity rhythm is completed within 6 to 7 days. With the data of Figs. 19–25, viewed against the background of earlier work (e.g., Snell *et al.,* 1944; Bykow, 1953; Aschoff, 1958), we can conclude for the functions, conditions, and species so far rigorously studied that the failure to shift by manipulation of the lighting regimen the timing of 24-hr rhythms can result from (1) the institution of certain unusual circumstances (e.g., starvation), under which otherwise secondary sync signals (latent or modulating synchronizers, e.g., feeding time) may gain dominance over the phase of rhythm (Halberg, Visscher, and Bittner, 1953), or from (2) a failure to allow for the necessary shift time. To illustrate the latter point, the results of an outstanding investigator of mitotic rhythm may be cited since they may have led to the view that in mammals (Blumenfeld, 1944) by contrast to birds (Riley, 1937) the phase of mitotic rhythm is independent of the lighting schedule. Blumenfeld, in 1944, had not noted an inversion of epidermal mitotic rhythm 2 days after inversion of lighting, and in our laboratory we have confirmed this finding at the 3-day time point after lighting inversion. Under Blumenfeld's (1944) conditions as well as ours (Halberg, Bittner, and Smith, 1957), a 2- or 3-day period of inversed lighting did not suffice to reverse the rhythm in cell division of the mammal studied, even though the identical period may suffice for a similar purpose in lower forms of life.

In viewing these results, we must remember that several rhythms are known to persist in continuous darkness in various animal forms (for reviews see Calhoun, 1945; Halberg, in press; Kleitman, 1949). As regards the mouse, earlier work has dealt mostly with the 24-hr rhythm in body activity (Calhoun, 1945; Johnson, 1939), while more recently it was found in our laboratory and elsewhere that the rhythms in body temperature and in tail blood eosinophils (Halberg, Visscher, and Bittner, 1953; Panzenhagen and Speirs, 1953) also persist after the institution of a regimen of continuous darkness as well as after removal of the eye (for over 1 month postoperative, the effects of the latter procedure are roughly comparable to those of the maintenance in darkness). Results obtained recently in our laboratory further suggest that the same applies to rhythms such as those in mitotic activity. It seems fair to generalize that 24-hr rhythms in the mammal are not necessarily "brought about" by lighting. The effects of the lighting schedule are exerted primarily upon the phase of a given rhythm in relation to the environment and not necessarily upon the "maintenance" of rhythm (see qualifications above).

But quite apart from the effect of illumination, it may also be seen from Figs. 19–25 that the amplitude of the various rhythms is not the same. With reference to carbohydrate metabolism, for example, it may be noted that percentage-wise the daily change in blood glucose is much smaller as compared to that in liver glycogen. In mice feeding *ad libitum,* glycogen practically disappears from the liver once a day; glucose while exhibiting a significant 24-hr periodic change, is present in blood at all times in relatively large amounts. Such information on the periodic behavior of various aspects of metabolism is of obvious interest to students of bioassay. To cite an example, for studies of drug effects upon blood glucose, periodicity analysis seems to offer several advantages; (1) one may compare the effect of the agent tested at high and low levels of liver glycogen, while the blood sugar levels are relatively high and predictable; (2) one can do so without being forced into dealing with starved animals; instead, one works with animals in as physiologic a condition as feasible; and moreover, (3) one can carry out the work whenever one wishes since by an appropriate control of illumination the desired physiologic state can be shifted to any convenient clock hour (cf. also Elfvin *et al.,* 1955; Pitts, 1943). Figure 23 reveals that this last consideration is particularly pertinent for the student of DNA metabolism since the peak in the relative specific activity (RSA) of hepatic DNA in mice kept under usual lighting conditions occurs at about 4 A.M. Likewise, it may be desirable to shift to a more convenient hour the peaks of the RSA of the hepatic RNA or phospholipid, which usually occur at 8 P.M. All this can be done by a shift in lighting regimen. The advantages derived from physiologic work in defined phases of daily cycle may be illustrated by a reference to the effect of pituitary growth hormone upon hepatic mitoses in the immature intact mouse; after hormone administration an increase in mitotic count will be seen consistently in one phase of mitotic rhythm, but not in another (Litman *et al.,* 1958) (Fig. 15). For the study of certain other problems as well (Halberg, Halberg, and Bittner, 1955; Halberg and Stephens, 1958) the selection of the "right time" has proved as important as our decision as to the "right dose." Accordingly, data on synchronized periodicities at various physiologic levels of organization serve two purposes. First, they constitute maps "in time" depicting significant changes in physiologic state. Second, they demonstrate how, in standardized mice, one may obtain certain desired physiologic states at a convenient clock hour, by the manipulation of an easily controlled environmental factor.

In turning to the problem of effects upon phase of 24-hr rhythms in human beings, the "controversial" state of our knowledge has recently been discussed by Pierach (1955) and earlier by Vering (1950). With our results, we shall illustrate merely the feasibility of shifting the phase of certain rhythms in man by a shift in daily routine (including the lighting schedule).

The timing of eosinophil rhythm, in groups of human males or females, is a function of daily routine (Halberg, Engel, Treloar, and Gully, 1953; cf. also R. B. Howard, 1952; Levy and Conge, 1953). Figure 26e,f exhibits the curves for blood eosinophils and rectal temperature of two individuals living on a schedule providing for activity by day and sleep by night. It must be noted that sleep indicates the usual times of rest; on the day of study, however, the subjects were given their isocaloric meals at equidistant intervals (arrows).

The curves in Fig. 26e,f are shown for comparison with (1) those of a subject on a prolonged shifted routine (Fig. 26a) and (2) those of another subject who had two daily periods of sleep for many years, including weekends and holidays. In the latter case (Fig. 26c) there is no significant evidence for a 12-hr rhythm; only once during 24 hr does the eosinophil count overshoot markedly its series mean (100 on the ordinate). Superficially, the temperature rhythm in Fig. 26c reveals two peaks, but again, one of these barely exceeds the series mean.

These results on a schedule interrupted twice a day, consistently for several years, support the inference that the 24-hr eosinophil rhythm of man is not easily made into a 12 hourly rhythm (Halberg, Halberg, and Gully, 1953). The same inference gains support from data obtained during the 12 hourly application of R.E.S.T. for about 2 weeks (Fleeson et al., 1957). It is pertinent, however, that in the monkey, O. P. Shcherbakova reportedly (Bykow, 1953) succeeded in

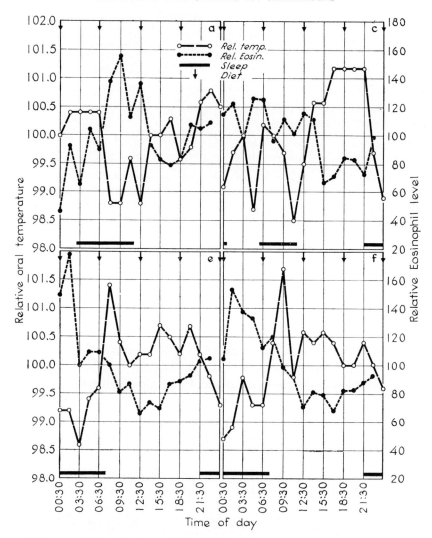

Fig. 26. Daily routine, synchronizer of rhythms in human beings (see text).

bringing about 2 "days" and 2 "nights" during one 24-hr period by illuminating the cage and feeding her animals from 9 A.M. to 3 P.M. and from 7 P.M. to 1 A.M. Under such conditions, she registered two periods of motor activity and two peaks in body temperature and

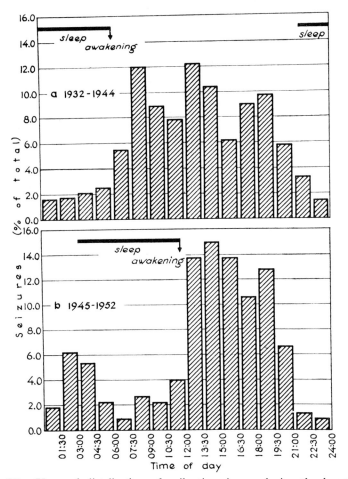

Fig. 27. Unequal distribution of epileptic seizures during the hours of the day, on two schedules, maintained for many years. Same subject, "day-type." Note change in seizure distribution following change in routine. Daily routine may be regarded as the environmental synchronizer of seizure rhythm; the clock hour as such does not matter in determining times of occurrence of seizures.

respiratory rate. We have earlier referred to other aspects of her work that dealt with the successful shift of phase of rhythm by a shift in routine. In commenting on our problem as a whole, Bykow points out that in the monkey ". . . a 'change' of 24-hour periodicity in

Shcherbakova's experiments was achieved with different ease, most easily by changing night to day, with most difficulty by creating 2 'days' and 2 'nights' during 24 hours. In the first case, a complete change of 24-hour periodicity was achieved by 7 to 8 days, in the second on the 14th to 15th day."

The data of Fig. 26a reveal that in man, as well as in the mouse, the timing of rhythms can be shifted within the 24-hr period, by a changed routine, if one adheres to the latter for a sufficient period of time. While Fig. 26a demonstrates shifts of rhythms in blood eosinophils and rectal temperature, Fig. 27 shows the feasibility of shift in at least one type of convulsive periodicity of man (Halberg, Halberg, and Bittner, 1955; Halberg, Halberg, and Gully, 1953).

The question may now be explored whether the shift times of these rhythms are the same. A statistical analysis summary in Table I

TABLE I.   Relation of 24-hr Periodicity in Body Temperature to That in Number of Eosinophils; Correlation Coefficients (r) and Their Significance (P)

Subject	Routine[a]	Period	r	P
A	N	Years	−0.63	0.01
B	N	2 days[b]	−0.04	0.80
C	D & N	Years	−0.69	0.003
D	D & N	2 days[b]	−0.03	0.80
E	D	Years	−0.56	0.025
F	D	Years	−0.53	0.037

[a] D = active by day; N = active by night.
[b] Note lack of correlation during shift in routine.

seems pertinent in this connection. It can be seen that rectal temperature and blood eosinophils show a significant negative correlation (under standardized conditions) on long-maintained routines, whether they involve activity by day or by night. At 2 days following the institution of a shift, however, this correlation is lost. Among other possible explanations, these findings may perhaps be interpreted as indicative of different shift-times with respect to the two rhythms studied.

Figures 28 and 29 show data on two groups of human volunteers obtained in an experiment involving a 90° shift in routine. The

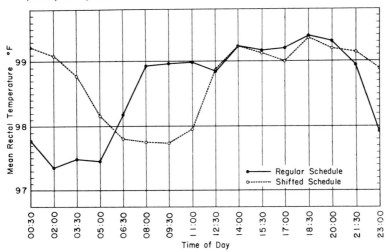

Mean rectal temperatures of groups investigated, during the second month of experiment (12 subjects / group).

FIG. 28.   Shift in phase of temperature rhythm following a 6-hr shift in schedule during the second month after initiation of the shifted schedule. Twelve subjects per group.

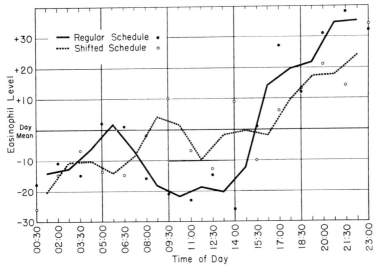

FIG. 29.   Shift in phase of eosinophil rhythm following a 6-hr shift in daily routine during the second month after initiation of the shifted schedule. Twelve subjects per group. Curve smoothed by moving average of two items; relative means for each time and group are drawn on the grid to visualize original data.

subjects on the shifted schedule were up and about until 3:30 A.M. and slept until noon in a room shielded from light and sound. A shift of rhythm (by ~90°) may be seen for this group as compared with that on a regular schedule (to bed at 9:30 P.M.; up at 6 A.M.). Moreover, the shift of temperature rhythm seen early after the institution of a new schedule persists 2 months thereafter (Fig. 28), and the τ of the mean temperature is comparable for the two groups, on the regular and shifted schedules, respectively. Finally, Fig. 29 reveals that the eosinophil rhythm of human beings also may be shifted by changes in routine.

It may be concluded that in man the lighting regimen and/or the daily routine can shift the timing of certain 24-hr rhythms (when this problem is tested under rigorous conditions). Such a conclusion has been statistically ascertained for the data in Fig. 29. Reported cases in which a shift of rhythm in man was not accomplished by a change in routine come to mind in this connection. Underlying the results of such studies we may find, perhaps, the inadvertent maintenance of some synchronizing information on a given "old" schedule and/or the failure to allow for the necessary "shift time." It also is apparent from the data shown herein that the shift can be accomplished by manipulating the daily routine (including the lighting schedule), other things being maintained the same as far as feasible. There are, of course, many environmental factors, which in addition to the lighting schedule, constitute our "routine" and thus govern the timing of rhythms in man. Other factors, such as diet and oxygen ("power supply"), in turn, constitute conditions that are necessary, yet in themselves ordinarily not sufficient for control of the timing of rhythm; e.g., the eosinophil rhythm of human beings maintains its usual timing under conditions of constant environmental temperature and four equidistant-isocaloric meals per day (Halberg and Howard, 1958; R. B. Howard, 1952).

In viewing the problem of phase control by the environment, the synchronizer, we cannot lose sight of those important cellular processes and their humoral controls that are involved in the control of period. From the available evidence it does not seem likely that the environment alone determines the "average" period of circadian rhythms, even though it is undoubtedly the ultimate master of their phase.

Generally speaking, in the case of a system open to the environment, such as the organism, we shall bias our model whether we attribute its basic phenomena *entirely* to factors from without or *entirely* to mechanisms from within—and 24-hr rhythms are a case in point. As has been done in the past, we could classify without further qualification 24-hr changes in physiologic state among conditioned reflexes or among stress reactions, and we may also continue to relate them to known or as yet unknown (cosmic) factors from without; but in so doing we may adopt a biased approach. The demonstration of shifts in phase of rhythm following changes in schedule of known environmental factors, in human beings as well as in mice, may be used, on the one hand, to suggest that the periodic operation of unknown cosmic factors does not have to be invoked (as sometimes is done) in accounting for physiologic rhythms. On the other hand, any factor, terrestrial or cosmic, will be more rigorously studied if effects upon rhythmic variables are evaluated as deviations from the normal period, amplitude, or phase of rhythm, rather than as deviations from an imaginary straight base line. Along similar lines of thought, the complex 24-hr periodic changes of the body as a whole may, perhaps, fruitfully be regarded as physiologic entities in their own right, rather than solely as conditioned reflexes or stress reactions. The importance of dealing with such entities can be demonstrated in studies of the outcome of exposure to noxious agents in defined phases of rhythm.

Phase of Rhythm, a Determinant of Response, Particularly to Noxious Agents

If factors such as genetics, age, sex, and physical environment are kept comparable, the phase of the 24-hour periodic changes in physiologic state can critically determine survival from noxious agents. Cases in point are death, from bacterial toxins (Halberg and Stephens, 1958) or noise-induced convulsions (Halberg, Bittner, Gully, Albrecht, and Brackney, 1955; Halberg, Jacobsen, Bittner, and Wadsworth, 1958; for underlying factors see Halberg, Engel, Halberg, and Gully, 1952, and Harner and Halberg, 1958).

Recent work in this department, with Doctor E. Haus, also shows hours of different resistance to toxic doses of alcohol or ouabain. The factors underlying such periodic changes in susceptibility are not the same from one agent to the next. Tests done at the same time, on groups of comparable animals, exposed under comparable conditions to one or the other noxious agent, predictably show maximal damage from one agent at one time and from the other agent at another.

By the use of such applied periodicity analysis the experimental pathologist may then work at defined peaks or troughs in susceptibility to a given agent. In pathology, certain more vulnerable parts of the body have been described as spots of diminished resistance (*loci minoris resistentiae*). These spots now have their temporal counterpart, the hours of diminished resistance (*horae minoris resistentiae* or *horae variae resistentiae*, since one may wish to emphasize the change in resistance, rather than its drop). In terms of experimental documentation, the "hours" may not compare unfavorably with the "spots." Information on a spectrum of peaks and troughs in susceptibility seems useful as well to bioassayists interested in approaches to their sources of variations, particularly in regard to the vexing problem of interassay variability.

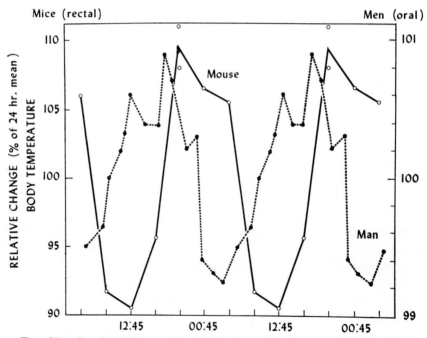

FIG. 30.   Species difference in mode of synchronization of temperature rhythm with environment.

In work with Professor E. Johnson (Division of Biostatistics, University of Minnesota), e.g., a potency ratio of 1 to 4 was obtained for samples from the *same* batch of *E. coli* endotoxin (Difco) tested on separate groups of comparable animals (for an LD_{50}), when assays were made 12 hr apart, at predicted times of low and high susceptibility, respectively. It would be pharmacologically important if certain therapeutic-toxic ratios also change periodically. In such as yet hypothetical cases, one may eventually revise some customary practices of drug administration (at clock hours chosen for convenience only).

Species Difference

Figures 30, 31, and 33 summarize some of our knowledge on the timing of 24-hr rhythms in human beings and mice. Important species differences may first be seen for the rhythms in body temperature

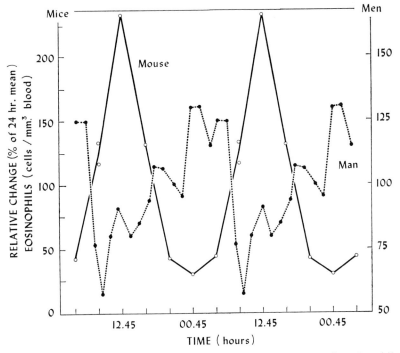

FIG. 31. Species difference in mode of synchronization of eosinophil rhythm with environment.

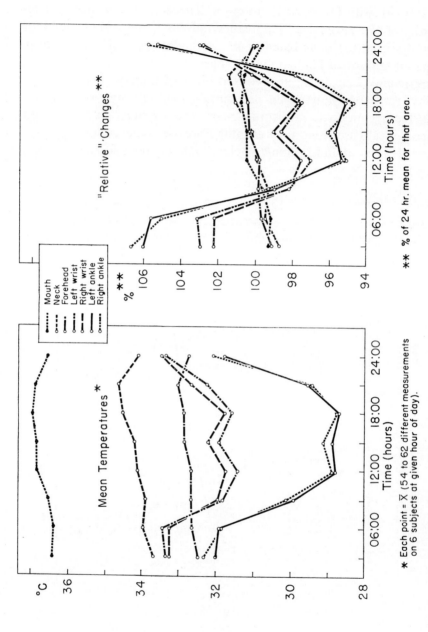

FIG. 32. Twenty-four-hour changes in temperatures of different areas in man (data from Heiser and Cohen, 1933).

* Each point = X̄ (54 to 62 different measurements on 6 subjects at given hour of day).

** % of 24 hr. mean for that area.

and blood eosinophils (Figs. 30, 31). Whether we compare the timing of the ascending phases of rhythms or that of the descending phases, the phase difference between the two species is prominent for either rhythm.

With respect to the temperature graph (Fig. 30), it is pertinent that orally obtained data are shown for man (Halberg *et al.*, 1951), while rectal temperatures are graphed for mice (Halberg, Levy, and Visscher, 1953). This limitation, while real, may contribute only slightly to the species difference in timing, since both temperatures (oral and rectal) approximate the behavior of the core of the body rather than that of its periphery. It is recognized, of course, that very significant differences in the timing of temperature rhythm may be had in the same individual, if, for instance, temperatures are recorded from the mouth and an extremity (Fig. 32).

In Fig. 33 epidermal mitotic counts on mouse pinna are compared with counts made by the late Dr. Zola Cooper (1939) on prepuces removed at circumcisions carried out at various times of day. The comparison cannot be justified by the similarity of absolute counts in

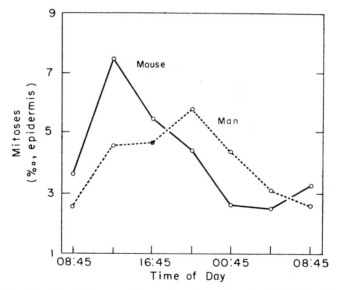

Fig. 33. Species difference in mode of synchronization of epidermal mitotic rhythm with environment.

materials from the two species (see Fig. 33). We err by comparing material from very young infants with that from mice 5 weeks of age. (In view, *inter alia,* of the species difference in life span, the mice are "children" if not "adolescents.") Therefore, the species difference in timing of mitotic rhythm in man and mouse may not be regarded as fully established, but the data are quite suggestive of its existence. Finally, when a curve published by Peterson (1957) for daily oxycorticoid changes in human plasma is compared with data for the mouse obtained by the use of the same method (Kliman and Peterson, 1958), important differences in the phases of these rhythms with respect to local time come clearly to the fore. It can be concluded that an adrenal cycle does characterize man and mice, but the timing of the rhythmic changes associated with this cycle in predominantly diurnal human beings is different from that in the nocturnally active mouse. The species difference in the timing of these rhythms with respect to local time is of interest to the comparative biologist. In the mouse, the cycle has been traced directly to the adrenal gland itself by corticosterone determinations and by mitotic counts (Fig. 14). The associated hormonal changes have been followed in the blood by direct chemical determinations and more simply, but only indirectly, by eosinophil counts done under standardized circumstances. Among the peripheral consequences of the cycle we find 24-hr periodic effects at the intracellular level of organization in the nucleus and in the cytoplasmic metabolism of hepatic phospholipid. While this cycle constitutes a critical mechanism of adaptation to the environment, the endogenous aspects of its periodicity also may deserve emphasis. In comparing the time course of the daily changes in the blood level of hormone with those in motor activity of the body as a whole, we may infer that the adrenal cortex not only reacts to the activities of daily life, as has been amply demonstrated, but what is equally important, the periodicity of the gland underlies our preparation for daily activity as well (Halberg, 1953 and in press). Thus, as long as optimal physiologic conditions prevail, a new sequence of metabolic events is being initiated in the cell once a day, under at least partial corticoid control. Normally, such metabolic arousal occurs *before* the reticular activating system (Bremer, 1935; Ingram *et al.,* 1951; Magoun, 1952), starts us out on our daily activities; in other words, the adrenal cortical and metabolic "arousals" ordinarily precede in time cerebral cortical arousal.

Can the altered phase relations of these "arousals" result in functional impairment? Moreover, if left uncorrected, can such an impairment of synchronization underlie disease? These are interesting clinical problems, but their discussion is beyond the scope of this Symposium. Here we have to note only that, at present, periodicity analysis for clinical purposes represents no more than a potential tool, awaiting rigorous tests of its usefulness. But in more basic fields related to medicine, the method has proved itself in several instances as a workable approach to at least one aspect of the critical problem of physiologic changes with time.

SUMMARY

1. The desirability and feasibility of obtaining quantitative descriptions of physiologic 24-hr periodicity by sample estimates of period and amplitude have been illustrated.

2. Free-running circadian periods (periods that may be slightly but significantly different from 24-hr) have been explored at several levels of physiologic organization in mammals.

3. Several observations of 24-hr rhythms made under conditions standardized for periodicity analysis in the mammal have been disclosed, and several other rhythms earlier described by others have been reexamined under the same conditions. Maps "in time" for 24-hr periodic physiologic changes thus were obtained. Such maps describe a sequential order in time among physiologic events at several levels of organization; they refer to normal and pathologic variables and extend from the organism as a whole to certain aspects of nuclear or cytoplasmic functions.

4. Some factors from within the organism which underlie the normal period of mammalian 24-hr rhythms, such as the adrenal cycle and a metabolic sequence of cellular events are discussed.

5. The effect of factors from without the organism, such as the lighting schedule and/or the daily routine, was then illustrated in the case of man and mouse; a species difference in the timing of rhythms is documented.

6. Problems of physiologic "synchronization" then are depicted. A crude and inadequate scheme of neural, endocrine, and metabolic interactions involved in mammalian 24-hr periodicity is discussed.

7. Twenty-four-hour periodic changes in physiologic state represent an integrative as well as adaptive characteristic of the *organism*, rather than merely "reactions" to factors from without. Some limits to the adaptability of periodic body functions and the critical extent to which the organism's periodicity determines its ability to withstand damage were indicated.

COMMENT

Most of the data presented and discussed herein represent the work of many individuals at the Cambridge State School and Hospital as well as at the University of Minnesota Medical School (see References). They constitute, of course, only a few selected aspects of much broader problems (Aschoff, 1955, 1958; Bliss, 1958; Brown, 1957a,b; Calhoun, 1944; Everett and Sawyer, 1950; Geyer and Keibl, 1953; Haus, 1957; Hechter, 1957; Hendricks, 1956; Isikawa, 1931; Manson-Bahr and Alcock, 1927; Menzel and Othlinghaus, 1948; Mühlemann, 1956; Richter, 1956; Stephens, 1957; Strughold, 1952; Szego, 1957; Tatai and Osada, 1956; Toole *et al.*, 1954; Withrow, this volume).

The electronic analogies in this paper emerged from long discussions with Earl Bakken. They were used (1) in an attempt to predict what the lighting schedule will do with respect to phase of mammalian rhythms, while (2) we endeavored to achieve this prediction in accordance with the available pertinent anatomical and physiologic information. If the analogies are useful in experimental design for the first purpose, the credit is Mr. Bakken's, but if, as is certain, our crude discussion of neural-endocrine-metabolic interactions will be inadequate to achieve the second purpose, only the authors are responsible for interpretations. It would appear, indeed, that physiologic periodicity analysis is a field replete with important data and with stimulating concepts. But it awaits the design and the application of appropriate methods for quantitative estimations of period, amplitude, and phase of rhythms, at different levels of organization in many forms of life. To the extent to which such measurements will become reliably and reproducibly feasible, problems of synchronization and desynchronization among rhythms will become amenable to study. If, as seems likely, such problems revolve around basic aspects of functional integration in time, as well as of environmental adaptation, periodicity analysis may serve as an instrument for functional resolution in time, just as the microscope serves for structural resolution in space.

REFERENCES

Ågren, G. 1935. Die cyclischen Veränderungen im Leberglykogen von Ratten nach Nebennierenexstirpation. *Biochem. Z., 281,* 367–69.

Ågren, G. O. Wilander, and E. Jorpes. 1931. Cyclic changes in the glycogen content of the liver and the muscles of rats and mice. Their bearing upon the sensitivity of the animals to insulin and their influence on the urinary output of nitrogen. *Biochem. J., 25,* 777–85.

Albrecht, P., M. B. Visscher, J. J. Bittner, and F. Halberg. 1956. Daily changes in 5-hydroxytryptamine concentration in mouse brain. *Proc. Soc. Exptl. Biol. Med., 92,* 703–706.

Allen, W. F. 1923. Origin and destination of the secondary visceral fibers in the guinea-pig. *J. Comp. Neurol., 35,* 275–311.

Anlicker, J., and J. Mayer. 1956. An operant conditioning technique for studying fasting patterns in normal and obese mice. *J. Appl. Physiol., 8,* 667–70.

Appel, W., and K. J. Hansen. 1952. Lichteinwirkung, Tagesrhythmik der eosinophilen Leukocyten und Hypophysennebennierenrindensystem. *Deut. Arch. klin. Med., 199,* 530–37.

Aschoff, J. 1951. Die 24-Stundenperiodik der Maus unter konstanten Umweltbedingungen. *Naturwissenschaften, 38,* 506.

———. 1954. Zeitgeber der tierischen Tagesperiodik. *Naturwissenschaften, 41,* 49–56.

———. 1955a. Der Tagesgang der Körpertemperatur beim Menschen. *Klin. Wochschr., 33,* 545–51.

———. 1955b. Exogene und endogene Komponente der 24-Stunden-Periodik bei Tier und Mensch. *Naturwissenschaften, 42,* 569–75.

———. 1958. Tierische Periodik unter dem Einfluss von Zeitgebern. *Z. Tierpsych., 15,* 1–30.

Ball, N. G., and I. J. Dyke. 1957. The effects of decapitation, lack of oxygen, and low temperature on the endogenous 24-hour rhythm in the growth-rate of the *Avena* coleoptile. *J. Exptl. Botany, 8,* 323–38.

Barnum, C. P., C. D. Jardetzky, and F. Halberg. 1957. Nucleic acid synthesis in regenerating liver. *Texas Repts. Biol. Med., 15,* 134–47.

———. 1958. Time relations among metabolic and morphologic 24-hour changes in mouse liver. *Am. J. Physiol., 195,* 301–10.

Beau, M. 1836. Recherches statistiques pour servir à l'histoire de l'epilepsie et de l'hystérie. *Arch. gén. méd.,* Ser. 2, *11,* 328–52.

868 PERIODIC FUNCTIONS IN MAMMALS

Behnke, A. R. 1951. Physical agents and trauma. *Ann. Rev. Med., 2,* 243–72.
Beringer, A. 1950. Über das Glykogen und seinen Einfluss auf den Stoffwechsel der Leber beim Gesunden und Diabetiker. *Deut. med. Wochschr., 75,* 1715–19.
Bliss, C. I. 1958. Periodic regression in biology and climatology. *Conn. Agr. Expt. Sta., Bull. 615,* 1–55.
Blumenfeld, C. M. 1942. Normal and abnormal mitotic activity; comparison of periodic mitotic activity in epidermis, renal cortex, and submaxillary salivary gland of the albino rat. *Arch. Pathol., 33,* 770–76.
———. 1944. Studies on cancer. I. Relationship of function, light and temperature to growth by mitosis. *Arch. Pathol., 38,* 321–25.
Boutwell, R. K., M. K. Brush, and H. P. Rusch. 1948. Some physiological effects associated with chronic caloric restriction. *Am. J. Physiol., 154,* 517–24.
Bremer, F. 1935. Cerveau "isolé" et physiologie du sommeil. *Compt. rend. soc. biol., 118,* 1235–41.
Brindley, G. S. 1954. Intrinsic 24-hour rhythms in human physiology, and their relevance to the planning of working programmes. *RAF Inst. Aviation,* FPRC 871.
Browman, L. G. 1952. Artificial 16-hour day activity rhythms in the white rat. *Am. J. Physiol., 168,* 694–97.
Brown, F. A., Jr. 1957a. Symposium on biological chronometry. *Am. Naturalist, 91,* 129–95.
———. 1957b. The rhythmic nature of life. In *Recent Advances in Invertebrate Physiology,* B. T. Schear, Editor. University of Oregon Publs., Eugene, Oregon. Pp. 287–304.
Brown, F. A., Jr., and H. M. Webb. 1949. Studies of the daily rhythmicity of the fiddler crab, *Uca.* Modifications by light. *Physiol. Zoöl., 22,* 136–48.
Brown, H. E., and T. F. Dougherty. 1956. The diurnal variation of blood leucocytes in normal and adrenalectomized mice. *Endocrinology, 58,* 365–75.
Brown, W. H. 1930. Constitutional variation and susceptibility to disease. In *The Harvey Lectures,* Williams and Wilkins Co., Baltimore, Md. Pp. 106–50.
Bruce, V. G., and C. S. Pittendrigh. 1957. Endogenous rhythms in insects and microorganisms. *Am. Naturalist, 91,* 179–95.
Bruss, R. T., E. Jacobsen, F. Halberg, H. A. Zander, and J. J. Bittner. 1958. Effects of lighting regimen and blinding upon gross motor activity of mice. *Federation Proc., 17,* 21.
Bullough, W. S. 1955. Hormones and mitotic activity. *Vitamins and Hormones, 13,* 261–92.
Bünning, E. 1957. Endogenous diurnal cycles of activity in plants. In *Rhythmic and Synthetic Processes in Growth,* Princeton University Press, Princeton, N. J. Pp. 111–26.
Bykow, K. M. 1953. *Grosshirnrinde und Innere Organe.* VEB Verlag Volk und Gesundheit, Berlin.
Bykow, K. M. 1954. *Studien über periodische Veränderungen physiologischer Funktionen des Organismus.* Akademie-Verlag, Berlin.
Calhoun, J. B. 1944. Twenty-four hour periodicities in the animal kingdom. I. The Invertebrates. *J. Tenn. Acad. Sci., 19,* 179–200.

──────. 1945. Diel activity rhythms of the rodents, *Microtus ochrogaster* and *Sigmodon hispidus hispidus*. *Ecology, 26,* 251–73.

Cannon, W. B. 1929. Organization for physiological homeostasis. *Physiol. Revs., 9,* 399–431.

Chaudhry, A. P. 1956. Certain physiologic and pharmacologic aspects of 24-hour periodicity in mitosis. University of Minnesota Graduate School, Minneapolis, Minn.

Chaudhry, A. P., F. Halberg, and J. J. Bittner. 1956. Mitoses in pinna and interscapular epidermis of mice in relation to physiologic 24-hour periodicity. *Federation Proc., 15,* 34.

Chaudhry, A. P., F. Halberg, C. E. Keenan, R. N. Harner, and J. J. Bittner. 1958. Daily rhythms in rectal temperature and in epithelial mitoses of hamster pinna and pouch. *J. Appl. Physiol., 12,* 221–24.

Cloudsley-Thompson, J. L. 1956. Diurnal rhythms of activity in terrestrial arthropods. *Nature, 178,* 215.

Cole, L. C. 1957. Biological clock in the unicorn. *Science, 125,* 874–76.

Cooper, Z. K. 1939. Mitotic rhythm in human epidermis. *J. Invest. Dermatol., 2,* 289–300.

Deane, H. W. 1944a. A cytological study of the diurnal cycle of the liver of the mouse in relation to storage and secretion. *Anat. Record, 88,* 39–65.

──────. 1944b. A cytological study of storage and secretion in the developing liver of the mouse. *Anat. Record, 88,* 161–73.

Doe, R. P., E. B. Flink, and M. G. Flint. 1954. Correlation of diurnal variations in eosinophils and 17-hydroxycorticosteroids in plasma and urine. *J. Clin. Endocrinol. Metabolism, 14,* 774–75.

Doe, R. P., E. B. Flink, and M. G. Goodsell. 1956. Relationship of diurnal variation in 17-hydroxycorticosteroid levels in blood and urine to eosinophils and electrolyte excretion. *J. Clin. Endocrinol. Metabolism, 16,* 196–206.

Echeverria, G. 1879. De l'épilepsie nocturne. *Ann. méd. psychol.,* Ser. 6, *1,* 177–97.

Ekman, C. A., and Hj. Holmgren. 1947. An investigation of the rhythmic metabolism of the liver with help of radio-active phosphorus. *Acta Med. Scand. (Suppl.), 196,* 63–74.

──────. 1949. The effect of alimentary factors on liver glycogen rhythm in the liver lobule. *Anat. Record, 104,* 189–216.

Elfvin, L. G., T. Petren, and A. Sollberger. 1955. Influence of some endogenous and exogenous factors on diurnal glycogen rhythm in chicken. *Acta Anat., 25,* 286–309.

Euler, U. S., and A. G. Holmquist. 1934. Tagesrhythmik der Adrenalinsecretion und des Kohlehydratstoffwechsels beim Kaninchen und Igel. *Arch. ges. ·Physiol., 234,* 210–24.

Everett, J. W., and C. H. Sawyer. 1950. A 24-hour periodicity in the "LH release apparatus" of female rats, disclosed by barbiturate sedation. *Endocrinology, 47,* 198–218.

Farrell, G. L., E. W. Rauschkolb, P. C. Royce, and H. Hirschmann. 1954. Isolation of desoxycorticosterone from adrenal venous blood of the dog; effect of hypophysectomy and ACTH. *Proc. Soc. Exptl. Biol. Med., 87,* 587–90.

Féré, C. 1888. De la fréquence des accés d'épilepsie suivant les heures. *Compt. rend. soc. biol., 40,* 740–42.

Ferguson, D. J., M. B. Visscher, F. Halberg, and L. M. Levy. 1957. Effects of hypophysectomy on daily temperature variation in C3H mice. *Am. J. Physiol., 190,* 235–38.

Fleeson, W., B. C. Glueck, Jr., and F. Halberg. 1957. Persistence of daily rhythms in eosinophil count and rectal temperature during "regression" induced by intensive electroshock therapy. *Physiologist, 1,* 28.

Flink, E. B., and F. Halberg. 1952. Clinical studies on eosinophil rhythm. *J. Clin. Endocrinol., 12,* 922.

Forsgren, E. 1928. On the relationship between the formation of bile and glycogen in the liver of rabbit. *Scand. Arch. Physiol., 53,* 137–51.

Forsham, P. M., V. Di Raimondo, D. Island, A. P. Rinfred, and R. H. Orr. 1944. Dynamics of adrenal function in man. *Ciba Foundation Colloquia on Endocrinology, 8,* 279–308. J. A. Churchill, Ltd., London.

Fortier, C. 1951. Dual control of adrenocorticotrophin release. *Endocrinology, 49,* 782–88.

French, J. D., M. Verseano, and H. W. Magoun. 1953a. An extralemniscal sensory system in the brain. *Am. Med. Assoc. Arch. Neurol. Psychiat., 69,* 505–18.

———. 1953b. A neural basis of the anesthetic state. *Am. Med. Assoc. Arch. Neurol. Psychiat., 69,* 519–29.

French, J. D., F. K. Von Amerongen, and H. W. Magoun. 1952. An activating system in brain stem of monkey. *Am. Med. Assoc. Arch. Neurol. Psychiat., 68,* 577–90.

Galbraith, J. J., and S. Simpson. 1903. Conditions influencing the diurnal wave in the temperature of the monkey. *J. Physiol., 30,* XX–XXII.

Gangloff, H., and M. Monnier. 1956. Electrographic aspects of an "arousal" or attention reaction induced in the unanesthetized rabbit by the presence of a human being. *Electroencephalog. Clin. Neurophysiol., 8,* 623–29.

Gerritzen, F. 1940. The rhythmic function of the human liver. *Acta Med. Scand. (Suppl.), 108,* 121–31.

Geyer, G., and E. Keibl. 1953. Die Pepsinogenausscheidung im Harn und ihre tagesrhythmischen Schwankungen. *Wiener med. Wochschr., 103,* 748–52.

Glueck, B. C., H. Reiss, and L. E. Bernard. 1957. Regressive electric shock therapy. *Psychiat. Quart., 31,* 117–36.

Griffiths, G. M., and J. T. Fox. 1938. Rhythm in epilepsy. *Lancet, 235,* 409–16.

Gumbel, E. J., J. A. Greenwood, and D. A. Durand. 1953. The circular normal distribution: theory and tables. *J. Am. Statistical Assoc., 48,* 131–52.

Halberg, F. 1946. Medizin. In *Jahrbuch der Internationalen Hochschulwochen des Osterreichischen College.* Igonta Verlag, Salzburg. Pp. 336–51.

———. 1953. Some physiological and clinical aspects of 24-hour periodicity. *J.-Lancet, 73,* 20–32.

———. 1954a. Eosinopenic effects of tryptamines in mice. Synergism of effects of cortisone and serotonin. *Am. J. Physiol., 179,* 309–13.

———. 1954b. Beobachtungen über 24-Stundenperiodik in standardisierter

Versuchsanordnung vor und nach Epinephrektomie and bilateraler optischer Enucleation. *Berichte ges. Physiol., 162,* 354–55.

———. 1955a. Methodological aspects of studies on physiologic rhythms with special reference to the adrenal cycle. *Fifth Intern. Cong. Soc. for Study of Biol. Rhythms,* Stockholm (oral communication).

———. 1955b. Experimentelles zur Physiologie des Nebennierenzyklus. *Acta Med. Scand. (Suppl.), 307,* 117–18.

———. 1957. Young NH-mice for the study of mitoses in intact liver. *Experientia, 13,* 502–503.

———. Physiologic 24-hour periodicity; general and procedural considerations with reference to the adrenal cycle. *Z. Vitamin-, Hormon- und Fermentforsch.* (in press).

Halberg, F., C. P. Barnum, R. Silber, and J. J. Bittner. 1958. 24-hour rhythms at different levels of integration in the mouse and the lighting regimen. *Proc. Soc. Exptl. Biol. Med., 97,* 879–900.

Halberg, F., C. P. Barnum, and H. Vermund. 1953. Hepatic phospholipid metabolism and the adrenal. *J. Clin. Endocrinol. Metabolism, 13,* 871.

Halberg, F., J. J. Bittner, and R. J. Gully. 1955. Twenty-four-hour periodic susceptibility to audiogenic convulsions in several stocks of mice. *Federation Proc., 14,* 67–68.

Halberg, F., J. J. Bittner, R. J. Gully, P. G. Albrecht, and E. L. Brackney. 1955. 24-hour periodicity and audiogenic convulsions in I mice of various ages. *Proc. Soc. Exptl. Biol. Med., 88,* 169–73.

Halberg, F., J. J. Bittner, and D. Smith. 1957. Belichtungswechsel und 24-Stundenperiodik von Mitosen im Hautepithel der Maus. *Z. Vitamin-, Hormon- und Fermentforsch., 9,* 69–73.

Halberg, F., R. Engel, E. Halberg, and R. J. Gully. 1952. Diurnal variations in amount of electroencephalographic paroxysmal discharge and diurnal eosinophil rhythm of epileptics on days with clinical seizure. *Federation Proc., 11,* 62.

Halberg, F., R. Engel, A. E. Treloar, and R. J. Gully. 1953. Endogenous eosinopenia in institutionalized patients with mental deficiency. *Am. Med. Assoc. Arch. Neurol. Psychiat., 69,* 462–69.

Halberg, F., M. J. Frantz, and J. J. Bittner. 1957. Phase difference between 24-hour rhythms in cortical adrenal mitoses and blood eosinophils in the mouse. *Anat. Record, 129,* 349–56.

Halberg, F., L. A. French, and R. J. Gully. 1958. 24-hour rhythms in rectal temperature and blood eosinophils after hemidecortication in human subjects. *J. Appl. Physiol., 12,* 381–84.

Halberg, F., E. Halberg, and J. J. Bittner. 1955. Daily periodicity of convulsions in man and in mice. *Fifth Intern. Cong. Soc. for Study of Biol. Rhythms,* Stockholm (oral communication).

Halberg, F., E. Halberg, and R. J. Gully. 1953. Effects of modifications of the daily routine in healthy subjects and in patients with convulsive disorder. *Epilepsia,* Ser. 3, *2,* 150.

Halberg, F., and R. B. Howard. 1958. 24-hour periodicity and experimental medicine: examples and interpretations. *Postgraduate Medicine, 24,* 349–58.

Halberg, F., E. Jacobsen, G. Wadsworth and J. J. Bittner. 1958. Audiogenic abnormality spectra, 24-hour periodicity, and lighting. *Science, 128,* 657–58.

Halberg, F., and I. H. Kaiser. 1954. Lack of physiologic eosinophil rhythm during advanced pregnancy of a patient with Addison's disease. *Acta Endocrinol., 16,* 227-32.

Halberg, F., L. Levy, and M. B. Visscher. 1953. Relation of 24-hour rhythm in body temperature to lighting conditions and to the adrenal. *Federation Proc., 12,* 59.

Halberg, F., R. E. Peterson, and R. H. Silber. 1959. Phase relations of 24-hour periodicities in blood corticosterone, mitoses in cortical adrenal parenchyma, and total body activity. *Endocrinology, 64,* 222–30.

Halberg, F., and A. N. Stephens. 1958. 24-hour periodicity in mortality of C mice from *E. coli* lipopolysaccharide. *Federation Proc., 17,* 439.

Halberg, F., and R. A. Ulstrom. 1952. Morning changes in number of circulating eosinophils in infants. *Proc. Soc. Exptl. Biol. Med., 80,* 747–48.

Halberg, F., H. Vermund, E. Halberg, and C. P. Barnum. 1956. Adrenal hormones and phospholipid metabolism in liver cytoplasm of adrenalectomized mice. *Endocrinology, 59,* 364–68.

Halberg, F., and M. B. Visscher. 1950. Regular diurnal physiological variation in eosinophil levels in five stocks of mice. *Proc. Soc. Exptl. Biol. Med., 75,* 846–47.

———. 1952. A difference between the effects of dietary calorie restriction on the estrous cycle and on the 24-hour adrenal cortical cycle in rodents. *Endocrinology, 51,* 329–35.

———. 1953a. Zum Eosinophilentest. In *Probleme des Hypophysen-Nebennierenrindensystems.* Springer-Verlag, Berlin. Pp. 155–62.

———. 1953b. The dependence of an adrenal cycle in the mouse upon lighting. *XIX Intern. Physiol. Cong.,* Thérien Frères Limitée-Montreal. Pp. 428–29.

———. 1954a. Some physiologic effects of lighting. *Proc. First Intern. Photobiol. Congr., Amsterdam.* H. Veenman & Zonen, Wageningen. Pp. 396–98.

———. 1954b. Temperature rhythms in blind mice. *Federation Proc., 13,* 65.

Halberg, F., M. B. Visscher, and J. J. Bittner. 1953. Eosinophil rhythm in mice: range of occurrence, effects of illumination, feeding and adrenalectomy. *Am. J. Physiol., 174,* 109–22.

———. 1954. Relation of visual factors to eosinophil rhythm in mice. *Am. J. Physiol., 179,* 229–35.

Halberg, F., M. B. Visscher, E. B. Flink, K. Berge, and F. Bock. 1951. Diurnal rhythmic changes in blood eosinophil levels in health and in certain diseases. *J.-Lancet, 71,* 312–19.

Halberg, F., H. A. Zander, M. W. Houglum, and H. R. Mühlemann. 1954. Daily variations in tissue mitoses, blood eosinophils and rectal temperatures of rats. *Am. J. Physiol., 177,* 361–66.

Hamar, N. 1940. Über Tagesschwankungen des Glucoseresorptionsvermögens des Dünndarms. *Arch. ges. Physiol., 244,* 164–70.

Hamilton, L. D., C. J. Gubler, G. E. Cartwright, and M. M. Wintrobe. 1950. Diurnal variation in the plasma iron level of man. *Proc. Soc. Exptl. Biol. Med., 75,* 65–68.

Harner, R. N. and F. Halberg. 1958. Electrocorticographic differences in D_8 mice at times of daily high and low susceptibility to audiogenic convulsions. *Physiologist, 1,* 34–35.

Hastings, J. W., and B. M. Sweeney. 1957a. The luminescent reaction in extracts of the marine dinoflagellate, *Gonyaulax polyedra. J. Cellular Comp. Physiol., 49,* 209–25.

――――. 1957b. On the mechanism of temperature independence in a biological clock. *Proc. Natl. Acad. Sci. U. S., 43,* 804–10.

Hastings, J. W., M. Wiesner, J. Owens, and B. Sweeney. 1956. The rhythm of luminescence in a marine dinoflagellate. *Anat. Record, 125,* 611.

Haus, E. 1957. Besonderheiten der Nebennierenrindenfunktion bei primär chronischer Polyarthritis und M. Bechterew. *Z. Rheumaforsch., 16,* 400–11.

Hechter, O. 1957. Reflections about hormone action and implications for the cancer problem. *Cancer Research, 17,* 512–19.

Heiser, F., and L. H. Cohen. 1933. Diurnal variations of skin temperature. *J. Ind. Hyg., 15,* 243–54.

Hendricks, S. B. 1956. Control of growth and reproduction by light and darkness. *Am. Scientist, 44,* 229–47.

Higgins, G. M., J. Berkson, and E. Flock. 1932. The diurnal cycle in the liver. 1. Periodicity of the cycle with analysis of chemical constituents involved. *Am. J. Physiol., 102,* 673–82.

――――. 1933. The diurnal cycle in the liver. 2. Food, a factor in its determination. *Am. J. Physiol., 105,* 177–86.

Hobbs, G. E., E. S. Goddard, and J. A. F. Stevenson. 1954. The diurnal cycle in blood eosinophils and body temperature. *Can. Med. Assoc. J., 70,* 533–36.

Holmgren, H. 1931. Beitrag zur Kenntnis der Leberfunktion. *Z. mikroskop.-anat. Forsch., 24,* 632–42.

――――. 1941. Beitrag zur Kenntnis des Leberrhythmus bei im Dunkel geborenen und aufgezogenen Tieren. *Z. ges. exptl. Med., 109,* 315–32.

Holmquist, A. G. 1931. Beitraege zur Kenntnis der 24-stuendigen Rhythmik der Leber. *Z. mikroskop.-anat. Forsch., 25,* 30–43.

Hornsey, S., and A. Howard. 1956. Autoradiograph studies with mouse Ehrlich ascites tumor. *Ann. N. Y. Acad. Sci., 63,* 915–28.

Howard, A. 1956. Influence of radiation on DNA metabolism. In *Ciba Foundation Symposium on Ionizing Radiations and Cell Metabolism.* Little, Brown, Boston. Pp. 196-211.

Howard, A., and S. R. Pelc. 1953. Synthesis of desoxyribonucleic acid in normal and irradiated cells and its relation to chromosome breakage. *Heredity (Suppl.), 6,* 261–73.

Howard, R. B. 1952. Studies on the metabolism of iron. Ph.D. thesis, University of Minnesota Graduate School, Minneapolis, Minn.

Hupe, K., and A. Gropp. 1957. Über den zeitlichen Verlauf der Mitoseaktivität in Gewebekulturen. *Z. Zellforsch., 46,* 67–70.

Ingle, D. J. 1951a. Parameters of metabolic problems. *Recent Progr. in Hormone Research, 6,* 159–94.

――――. 1951b. The functional interrelationship of the anterior pituitary and the adrenal cortex. *Ann. Internal Med., 35,* 652–72.

Ingram, W. R., J. R. Knott, M. D. Wheatley, and T. D. Summers. 1951. Physiological relationships between hypothalamus and cerebral cortex. *Electroencephalog. and Clin. Neurophysiol., 3,* 37–58.

Isikawa, T. 1931. Studies on the influence of day and night shift system upon the physiological functions of labourers. Institute for Science of Labour, Report No. 3, Kurashiki, Japan.

Janz, D. 1955. Anfallsbild und Verlaufsform epileptischer Erkankungen. *Nervenartz, 26,* 20–28.

Jardetzky, C. D., C. P. Barnum, and F. Halberg. 1956. Physiologic 24-hour periodicity in nucleic acid metabolism and mitosis of immature growing liver. *Am. J. Physiol., 187,* 608.

Johnson, M. S. 1939. Effect of continuous light on periodic spontaneous activity of white-footed mice (*Peromyscus*). *J. Exptl. Zool., 82,* 315–28.

Jores, A. 1933. Die Urineinschränkung in der Nacht. *Deut. Arch. klin. Med., 175,* 244–53.

———. 1940. Rhythmusstudien am hypophysektomierten Tier. *Acta Med. Scand.* (Suppl.), *108,* 114–20.

Kaine, H. D., H. S. Seltzer, and J. W. Conn. 1955. Mechanisms of diurnal eosinophil rhythm in man. *J. Lab. Clin. Med., 45,* 247–52.

Kalmus, H. 1953. Repetition, Autonomy and Synchronization in the Living World. *Acta Med. Scand. (Suppl.), 278,* 19–25.

———. 1957. Space and time in animal life. *Proc. Intern. Soc. Biol. Rhythm,* Semmering (oral communication).

Kendall, M. G. 1948. *The Advanced Theory of Statistics,* Vol. II. Charles Griffin & Co., Ltd., London. Pp. 363–439.

Kleitman, N. 1949. Biological rhythms and cycles. *Physiol. Revs., 29,* 1–30.

———. 1952. Sleep. *Sci. American, 187,* 34–38.

Kleitman, N., and E. Kleitman. 1953. Effect of non-twenty-four-hour routines of living on oral temperature and heart rate. *J. Appl. Physiol., 6,* 283–91.

Kliman, B., and R. E. Peterson. 1958. Isotope derivative assay of aldosterone in biological extracts. *Federation Proc., 17,* 255.

Koehler, F., F. K. Okano, L. R. Elveback, F. Halberg, and J. J. Bittner. 1956. Periodograms for the study of physiologic daily periodicity in mice and in man. *Exptl. Med. Surg., 14,* 5–30.

Laidlaw, J. C., D. Jenkins, W. J. Reddy, and T. Jakobson. 1954. The diurnal variation in adrenocortical secretion. *J. Clin. Invest., 33,* 950.

Landau, J., and S. Feldman. 1954. Diminished endogenous morning eosinopenia in blind subjects. *Acta Endocrinol., 15,* 53–60.

Langdon-Down, M., and W. R. Brain. 1929. Time of day in relation to convulsions in epilepsy. *Lancet, 216* (1): 1029–32.

Lehman, E. L. 1950. Notes on the Theory of Estimation. Associated Students' Store, Univ. Calif., Berkeley. Chap. II, pp. 1–20.

Lehmann, G. and H. Michaelis. 1943. Adrenalin und Arbeit. IV. Mitteilung, Adrenalin und Leistungsfaehigkeit. *Arbeitsphysiol., 12,* 305–12.

Leuret, M. 1843. Recherches sur l'épilepsie. *Arch. gén. méd.,* Ser. 4, *2,* 32–50.

Levy, F. M., and G. Conge. 1953. Action de la lumiére sur l'éosinophilie sanguine çhez l'homme. *Compt. rend. soc. biol., 147,* 586–89.

Lewis, P. R., and M. C. Lobban. 1954. Persistence of a 24-hour pattern of diuresis in human subjects living on a 22-hr day. *J. Physiol., 125,* 34–35.

————. 1957a. The effects of prolonged periods of life on abnormal time routines upon excretory rhythms in human subjects. *Quart. J. Exptl. Physiol., 42,* 356–71.

————. 1957b. Dissociation of diurnal rhythms in human subjects living on abnormal time routines. *Quart. J. Exptl. Physiol., 42,* 371–86.

Liddle, G. W., F. C. Bartter, L. F. Duncan, Jr., J. K. Barber, and C. Delea. 1955. Mechanisms regulating aldosterone production in man. *J. Clin. Invest., 34,* 949–50.

Liddle, G. W., L. E. Duncan, and F. C. Bartter. 1956. Dual mechanism regulating adrenocortical function in man. *Am. J. Med., 21,* 380–86.

Liebelt, R. A., and J. H. Perry. 1957. Hypothalamic lesions associated with goldthioglucose-induced obesity. *Proc. Soc. Exptl. Biol. Med., 95,* 774–77.

Litman, T., F. Halberg, S. Ellis, and J. J. Bittner. 1958. Pituitary growth hormone and mitoses in immature mouse liver. *Endocrinology, 62,* 361–65.

Louch, C., R. K. Meyer, and J. T. Emlen. 1953. Effect of stress on diurnal fluctuations in eosinophils of the laboratory mouse. *Proc. Soc. Exptl. Biol. Med., 82,* 668–71.

Magoun, H. W. 1952. The ascending reticular activating system. *Proc. Assoc. Research Nervous Mental Disease, 30,* 480–92.

Manson-Bahr, P. H., and A. Alcock. 1927. *The Life and Work of Sir Patrick Manson.* Cassel and Co., London.

Menzel, W., and I. Othlinghaus. 1948. Inversion des Blutzuckertagesrhythmus durch Percorten. *Deut. med. Wochschr., 73,* 326–29.

Migeon, C. J., F. H. Tyler, J. P. Mahoney, A. A. Florentin, H. Castle, E. L. Bliss, and L. T. Samuels. 1956. The diurnal variation of plasma levels and urinary excretion of 17-hydroxycorticosteroids in normal subjects, night workers and blind subjects. *J. Clin. Endocrinol. Metabolism, 16,* 622–33.

Mills, J. N. 1951. Diurnal rhythm in urine flow. *J. Physiol., 113,* 528–36.

Möllerström, J. 1940. Der Einfluss der Erkenntnisse des Leberrhythmus auf unsere Anschauungen über Diabetestherapie. *Acta Med. Scand. (Suppl.), 108,* 156–65.

Mühlemann, H. R. 1956. Periodische Phänomene in der Stomatologie. *Deut. zahnärztl. Z., 11,* 977–83.

Mühlemann, H. R., T. M. Marthaler, and P. Loustalot. 1955. Daily variations in mitotic activity of adrenal cortex, thyroid and oral epithelium of the rat. *Proc. Soc. Exptl. Biol. Med., 90,* 467–68.

Müller, A. F., E. L. Manning, and A. M. Riondel. 1958. Diurnal variation of aldosterone related to position and activity in normal subjects and patients with pituitary insufficiency. In *Aldosterone,* A. F. Müller and C. M. O'Connor, Editors. Little, Brown & Company, Boston.

Müller, M., and H. Giersberg. 1957. Über den Einfluss der inneren Sekretion auf die tagesperiodische Aktivität der weissen Maus. *Z. vergleich. Physiol., 40,* 454–72.

Nothdurft, H. 1951. Zur 24-Stunden-Periodik am Beispiel der Mausmotilität, Frequenzabweichungen und anschliessende Auflösung der natürlichen Rhythmik bei ausreichender Konstanthaltung der Umwelt. *Naturwissenschaften, 38,* 436.

O'Leary, J. L., and L. A. Coben. 1958. The reticular core. *Physiol. Revs., 38,* 243–71.

Page, I. H. 1958. Serotonin (5-hydroxytryptamine); the last four years. *Physiol. Revs., 38*, 277–335.

Panzenhagen, H., and R. Speirs. 1953. Effect of horse serum, adrenal hormones, and histamine on the number of eosinophils in the blood and peritoneal fluid of mice. *Blood, 8,* 536–44.

Parzen, E. 1957a. On consistent estimates of the spectrum of a stationary time series. *Ann. Math. Stat., 28,* 329–48.

———. 1957b. On choosing an estimate of the spectral density function of a stationary time series. *Ann. Math. Stat., 28,* 921–32.

Peter, K. 1940. Die indirekte Teilung der Zelle in ihren Beziehungen zu Tätigkeit, Differenzierung und Wachstum. *Z. Zellforsch., 30,* 721–50.

Peterson, R. E. 1957. Plasma corticosterone and hydrocortisone levels in man. *J. Clin. Endocrinol. Metabolism, 17,* 1150–57.

Petren, T. 1939. Die 24-Stunden-Rhythmik des Leberglykogens bei *Cavia cobaya* nebst Studien ueber die Einwirkung der "chronischen" Muskelarbeit auf diese Rhythmik. *Morphol. Jahresber., 83,* 256–76.

Pierach, A. 1955. Nachtarbeit und Schichtwechsel beim gesunden und kranken Menschen. *Acta Med. Scand. (Suppl.), 307,* 159–66.

Pincus, G. 1943. A diurnal rhythm in the excretion of urinary ketosteroids by young men. *J. Clin. Endocrinol., 3,* 195–99.

Pincus, G., L. P. Romanoff, and J. Carlo. 1948. A diurnal rhythm in the excretion of neutral reducing lipids by man and its relation to the 17-ketosteroid rhythm. *J. Clin. Endocrinol., 8,* 221–26.

Pittendrigh, C. S. 1954. On temperature independence in the clock system controlling emergence time in *Drosophila. Proc. Natl. Acad. Sci. U. S., 40,* 1018–29.

Pittendrigh, C. S., and V. G. Bruce. 1957. An oscillator model for biological clocks. In *Symposium, Society for the Study of Development and Growth.* Princeton University Press, Princeton, N. J.

Pitts, G. C. 1943. A diurnal rhythm in the blood sugar of the white rat. *Am. J. Physiol., 139,* 109–16.

Ramey, E. R., and M. S. Goldstein. 1957. The adrenal cortex and the sympathetic nervous system. *Physiol. Revs., 37,* 155–95.

Rashevsky, N. 1955. Is the concept of an organism as a machine a useful one? *Sci. Monthly, 80,* 32–35.

Rauschkolb, E. W. 1956. Decreased aldosterone secretion in decapitated dogs. *J. Clin. Endocrinol., 16,* 915–16.

Rauschkolb, E. W., and G. L. Farrell. 1956. Evidence for diencephalic regulation of aldosterone secretion. *Endocrinology, 59,* 526–30.

Richter, C. P. 1956. Experimental production in rats of abnormal cycles in behavior and metabolism. *Trans. Soc. Biol. Psychiat., 11,* 43–45.

Riley, G. M. 1937. Experimental studies on spermatogenesis in the house sparrow, *Passer domesticus (Linnaeus). Anat. Record, 67,* 327–51.

Royce, P. C., and G. Sayers. 1958. Extrapituitary interaction between Pitressin and ACTH. *Proc. Soc. Exptl. Biol. Med., 98,* 70–74.

Russell, G. V. 1957. The brainstem reticular formation. *Texas Repts. Biol. Med., 15,* 332–37.

Sayers, G. 1950. The adrenal cortex and homeostasis. *Physiol. Revs., 30,* 241–320.

Sayers, G., E. S. Redgate, and P. C. Royce. 1958. Hypothalamus, adenohypophysis and adrenal cortex. *Ann. Rev. Physiol., 20,* 243–74.

Schmitt, O. Biophysical models of physiologic rhythms. Animal Orientation. Conference Biological Rhythms, Woods Hole, 1957. (To be published.)

Selye, H. 1953. Stress. *Explorations, 1,* 57.

———. 1954. On the nature of disease. *Texas Repts. Biol. Med., 12,* 390.

–———. 1956. What is stress? *Metabolism, 5,* 525–30.

Shcherbakova, O. P. 1937. Studies on the diurnal periodicity of physiological processes in higher mammals. I. Communication. The normal diurnal periodicity of physiological processes. *Bull. de Biol. Med. Exp., 4,* 327–29.

———. 1938. Contributions to the study of diurnal and seasonal periodicity of physiological processes in higher vertebrates; II Communication. *Bull. biol. méd. exptl. U.R.S.S., 5,* 159–62.

Sjoegren, B., T. Nordenskjoeld, H. Holmgren, and J. Möllerström. 1938. Beitrag zur Kenntnis der Leberrhythmik. *Arch. ges. Physiol. Pflüger's, 240,* 427–48.

Skinner, B. F. 1957. The experimental analysis of behavior. *Am. Scientist, 45,* 343–71.

Snell, G. D., K. P. Hummel, and W. H. Abelmann. 1944. A technique for the artificial insemination of mice. *Anat. Record, 90,* 243–53.

Sollberger, A. 1954. A study of biological variation. *Acta Anat., 22,* 127–43.

———. 1955a. Statistical aspects of diurnal biorhythm. *Acta Anat., 22,* 97–127.

———. 1955b. Diurnal changes in biological variability. *Acta Anat., 23,* 259–287.

Starzl, T. E., C. W. Taylor, and H. W. Magoun, 1951. Collateral afferent excitation of reticular formation of brain stem. *J. Neurophysiol., 14,* 479–96.

Stauder, K. H. 1948. Anfall, Schlaf, Periodizitaet. *Nervenarzt, 19,* 107–19.

Stephens, G. C. 1957. Twenty-four cycles in marine organisms. *Am. Naturalist, 91,* 135–51.

Strughold, H. 1952. Physiological day-night cycle in global fights. *J. Aviation Med. 23,* 464–73.

Szego, C. M. 1957. Primary mechanisms of hormonal action on target cells. In *Physiological Triggers,* T. H. Bulloch, Editor American Physiological Society, Washington, D. C. Pp. 152–62.

Tatai, K., and Y. Osada. 1956. Dynamics of Eosinophils. Igaku Shoin Ltd., Tokio-Osaka.

Taylor, J. H., and R. D. McMaster. 1954. Autoradiographic and microphotometric studies of desoxyribose nucleic acid during microgametogenesis in *Lilium longiflorum. Chromosoma, 6,* 489–521.

Thorn, G. W., A. E. Renold, and A. I. Winegrad. 1957. Some effects of adrenal cortical steroids on intermediary metabolism. *Brit. Med. J., 2,* 1009–17.

Thorn, G. W., E. J. Ross, J. Crabbé, and W. V. Hoff. 1957. Studies on aldosterone secretion in man. *Brit. Med. J., 2,* 955–66.

Toole, E. H., H. A. Borthwick, S. B. Hendricks, and V. K. Toole. 1954. Physiological studies on the effects of light and temperature on seed germination. *Proc. Intern. Seed Testing Assoc., 18,* 267–76.

Tribukait, B. 1954. Aktivitätsperiodik der Maus im künstlich verkürtzen Tag. *Naturwissenschaften, 41,* 92–93.

———. 1956. Die Aktivitätsperiodik der weissen Maus im Kunsttag von 16–29 Stunden Länge. *Z. vergleich. Physiol., 38,* 479–90.

Tyler, F., C. Migeon, A. A. Florentin, and L. T. Samuels. 1954. The diurnal variation of 17-hydroxycorticosteroid levels in plasma. *J. Clin. Endocrinol. Metabolism, 14,* 774.

Utterback, R., and G. Ludwig. 1949. A comparative study of schedules for standing watches aboard submarines, based on body temperature cycles. NM004 003 (1), Naval Medical Research Inst., Bethesda, Md.

Vering, F. 1950. Einfluss der Tag- und Nachtschicht auf den Arbeiter. *Wien. med. Wochschr., 100,* 652–55.

Vermund, H., F. Halberg, C. P. Barnum, G. W. Nash, and J. J. Bittner. 1956. Physiologic 24-hour periodicity and hepatic phospholipid metabolism in relation to the mouse adrenal cortex. *Am. J. Physiol., 186,* 414–18.

Wadsworth, G. L., F. Halberg, P. Albrecht, and G. Skaff. 1957. Peak urinary excretion of 5-hydroxyindoleacetic acid following arousal in human beings. *Physiologist, 1,* 86.

Zander, H. A., J. Waerhaug, and F. Halberg. 1954. Effect of hypophysectomy upon cyclic mitotic activity in the retromolar mucosa of rats. *J. Clin. Endocrinol. Metabolism, 14,* 829.

Zimmermann, B., and M. M. Schoenbauer. 1952. Studies on the control of salt-regulating adrenal hormones. In *Surgical Forum 1951,* American College of Surgeons, W. B. Saunders Co., Philadelphia and London. Pp. 547–51.